TEACHER'S MANUAL

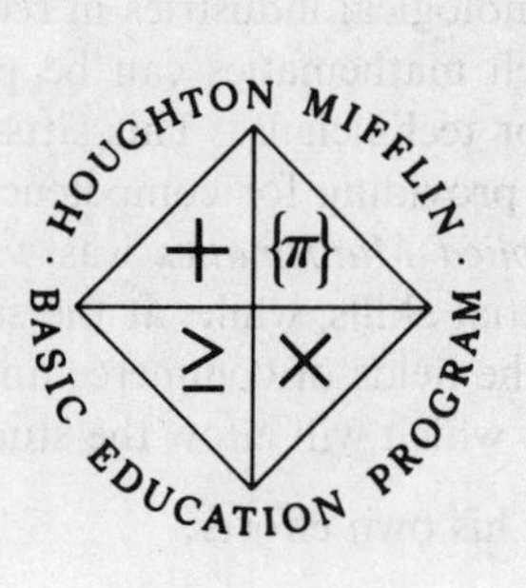

MATHEMATICS

We are pleased to present *Modern Applied Mathematics*, a textbook in the Houghton Mifflin Basic Education Program.

Modern Applied Mathematics was developed to provide for those students who require a background of the essentials of mathematics for use in vocational or consumer situations. The authors of this textbook believe that students learn best when they are actively involved in what they are learning and are aware of its relevance. In demonstrating that belief, the authors have written a textbook which utilizes familiar examples of applied mathematics and directed experimentation by the student as integral components in the instruction. This approach makes the book particularly well-suited for use by students with non-academic interests. In general, *Modern Applied Mathematics* will provide students with the firm background needed for jobs in business and industry, as well as for everyday use.

Modern Applied Mathematics represents a full-year course in arithmetic, informal geometry, formulas, and trigonometry. Every facet of the book has been used successfully in the classroom. The authors are experienced teachers in the field of applied mathematics, and the editorial adviser, Albert E. Meder, is nationally known for his involvement in the various proposals for changes in the mathematics curriculum.

TEACHER'S MANUAL AND ANNOTATIONS

Basic Philosophy

The rapid growth of technological industries in recent years has broadened the range of endeavors to which mathematics can be properly applied and has increased the opportunities for technicians. This situation dramatically underlines the growing importance of providing for competence in the use of basic mathematical skills. *Modern Applied Mathematics* was written to provide the student with practice in those essential skills, while, at the same time, illustrating the importance of those skills in the fields of commerce and industry. Every effort has been made to create a book which will allow the student to:

1. find success through his own efforts;
2. progress at his own rate of speed; and
3. gain experience of typical everyday needs.

Modern Applied Mathematics is based on the universally accepted principle that a student learns best when he is actively engaged in what he is studying. Accordingly, the authors have attempted to strike a balance between discussion and discovery by augmenting the formal discussion of topics with experimentation by the student. Interest is sustained by keeping discussions brief and relatively nontechnical, and by explaining difficult concepts by means of examples rather than formal definitions. Variety in both the instructional and exercise material provides the necessary diversity of interests required by students with short spans of attention.

Throughout the book the authors have tried to present those concepts from arithmetic, geometry, trigonometry and formula solving in which the more complex applications of mathematics are rooted. Mastery of these skills will give the student the necessary background for work in more specialized areas.

Features of the Textbook

Modern Applied Mathematics was written for the specific purpose of maintaining and extending the student's mathematical skills through the study of many of the common applications of mathematics. To fulfill that purpose, the textbook has been written and designed to include the following features:

1. Emphasis is placed on the functional role of mathematics as a problem-solving tool in business and industry.

2. The use of technical terms and symbols to clarify discussions is kept to a minimum. Explanations are briefly stated in simple, crisp language supported by appropriate illustrative examples.

3. An abundance of carefully selected exercises, graded A or B, in order of increasing difficulty, provides for individual student differences.

4. Numerous activities are included as a motivating way to reinforce and extend the understanding of concepts through experimentation.

5. Self-Analysis Tests provide for periodic self-evaluation of the understanding of important ideas.

6. Optional sections, including several dealing with flow charts, may be used as enrichment material or as challenging projects for individual work by the abler students.

7. Chapter Summaries and Chapter Tests serve as a built-in evaluation program. A Glossary showing the pages on which important terms are introduced is also provided.

8. Maintaining Your Skills sections at the end of each chapter provide for students needing additional practice of basic computational skills.

9. Chapters are divided according to major topics, indicated by a heading preceded by a small colored square. Further subdivision of chapters into sections with numbered sideheads allows for easy identification and reference.

10. Every chapter opens with one or more eye-catching photographs which illustrate varied applications of mathematics in industrial and commercial settings. A concise explanation relates the photographs to the topics discussed in the chapter.

11. Clearly stated objectives preface each chapter to give positive direction to the student's investigation of the topics to be studied.

12. The functional use of color calls attention to significant terms, ideas, and rules. Clear and open typography gives pages an uncluttered, inviting appearance.

13. Numerous diagrams in discussion and exercise sections are an integral part of the instructional material.

14. Teaching aids to supplement this Teacher's Edition include a complete Solution Key and Progress Tests.

Suggestions for Teaching

The best way to use any particular textbook varies from teacher to teacher and from student to student. Therefore, any printed suggestions such as these cannot be expected to fit all situations. Nevertheless, the general comments here and the annotations on the text pages will serve to clarify the authors' point of view.

The material in *Modern Applied Mathematics* is arranged so that students have to concentrate on only one basic idea at a time. The division of each chapter into brief sections and subsections enables the teacher to plan the course to fit the needs and abilities of the class.

Teachers are urged to evaluate students essentially on the basis of their success in solving problems rather than on their ability to verbalize definitions, rules, and procedures.

Discuss with the students how to make effective use of the organization of the textbook. For example, call their attention to the Chapter Summaries and discuss possible ways of using them. As the course proceeds, show students how to locate topics and terms in the Contents, the Glossary, and the Index.

By emphasizing the importance of self-reliance and a questioning attitude, you will be developing your students' mathematical maturity.

USES OF THE EXERCISE MATERIAL

Exercises in this book are grouped into categories labeled "A" and "B" in order of increasing difficulty. Not all exercise sets contain "B" exercises, although many do. This organization will assist the teacher in making assignments at varying levels of difficulty. All students should be able to do the "A" exercises; "B" exercises are somewhat more challenging. In assigning exercises, teachers should consider, among other things, the following factors:

1. Exercises are usually closely related to the examples given in the discussion portion of the text. Those students who experience difficulty in solving a particular exercise should be encouraged to review the examples given in the text for assistance.

2. Some sets of exercises will require more time than others; therefore, it is suggested that the teacher preview each set of exercises before assigning homework. (That preview may be made easier with the complete Solution Key at hand.) Most exercise sections contain sufficient exercises to permit the teacher to use some for classroom demonstration, while reserving others for homework. Some teachers may choose to dispense with homework and to require all exercises to be done in class, either orally or as deskwork, depending on the nature and degree of difficulty of the exercises.

3. Care should be taken not to overload students with the assignments. A few exercises carefully done are generally of more benefit to the student than a greater number done hastily.

Answers to all exercises and problems are printed at the back of this Teacher's Edition; complete solutions for these are given in the separate Solution Key.

USES OF THE ACTIVITIES

This book contains numerous activity sections to provide the students with a "hands-on" experience of mathematics in applied situations. Some of the activities described in the textbook require the use of special materials and measuring instruments. Others require only a pencil, straightedge, compass, and paper. In most instances, however, the list of materials is given only as a suggestion. The teacher may wish to augment the materials needed or make appropriate substitutions for them as needs arise. It is suggested that the teacher make a thorough preview of each activity to ensure the effective use of classroom time in carrying out the experiment. The Assignment Guide at the end of this Manual gives advance notice to the teacher of upcoming experiments. A reading assignment for the students on the details of the experiment is also strongly recommended. The activities can be carried out either on a group or individual basis.

USES OF THE TESTS

Evaluation and testing material in this book falls in two categories:

1. Self-Analysis Tests; and
2. Chapter Summaries, Chapter Tests, and the Glossary.

Self-Analysis Tests appearing regularly throughout the text permit the student to test his own understanding of the material he has been studying. A time factor is suggested for the completion of each test as a means of evaluating both accuracy and speed. Answers to the Self-Analysis Tests are bound at the back of the text, beginning on page 407. Encourage the student to check his own answers and, in the event of errors, to refer to the discussions in the text for clarification. The teacher may find the Self-Analysis Tests adaptable for supplying programmed instruction for certain students.

Chapter Tests are designed to give a more comprehensive evaluation of the student's understanding of the topics presented in each chapter. Chapter Tests should be announced in advance to allow ample time for review. The Chapter Summary is well-suited for this purpose. The Glossary (pages 395–400) provides a convenient reference of important terms and fundamental principles of the mathematics being studied, and indicates the page on which they are introduced.

USES OF OPTIONAL MATERIAL

Also included in the text are a number of discussions, activities, and exercises designated as optional. This material is intended to allow for individual differences in ability. Optional activities, for example, can be used for independent study by abler students. Flow charts appear in the text in several places, and add a contemporary touch to the overall presentation. For further details on the use and application of flow charts as instructional tools, refer to page 6, **1–6**(1) of this Manual. A detailed outline showing the suggested usage of optional materials for an enriched curriculum is given in the Assignment Guide at the end of this Manual.

DETAILED COMMENTS ON THE TEXT

Chapter 1 Arithmetic Review

This chapter reviews the basic arithmetic operations involving whole numbers and common and decimal fractions needed to solve problems of applied mathematics. Many commonplace instances of applied mathematics, such as templates and invoices, are used to give the student concrete examples for practice in calculating. Flowcharting is introduced as an interesting aid in carrying out certain arithmetic operations. The "divide and average" method for determining square roots is introduced as an alternative to the traditional arithmetic procedure.

1–1 (1) The Self-Analysis Tests are designed to be used as self-evaluation tests, serving to point out to the student his strengths and weaknesses in understanding the material presented. A time factor is recommended in order to encourage speed in computations. Because much of Chapter 1 is a review of the basic operations of arithmetic, several of the Self-Analysis Tests precede the formal presentation of the material found in the tests. This arrangement is designed to allow those students who exhibit competence in one phase of the review to advance to later sections in the chapter. Beginning with Chapter 2 and continuing throughout the remaining chapters, the Self-Analysis Tests will always follow the formal discussion of the material being tested.

(2) The Exercises and Problems in this book are grouped into categories labeled "A" and "B." All students should be able to do the "A" exercises. "B" exercises are somewhat more challenging. Students who have successfully completed the "A" exercises should be encouraged to try the "B" exercises.

(3) Some students may recognize the associative and commutative properties of addition being used here. Wherever possible the authors have refrained from introducing technical mathematical terminology, feeling that, for the purposes of applied mathematics, practice in calculating should take precedence over analyzing the properties of a number system.

1–5 The authors have tried to eliminate much of the confusion surrounding the order of operations in an arithmetic expression lacking the usual symbols of inclusion. Notice that the exercises in this section ask only that the grouping symbols be inserted in the appropriate locations in order to establish the truth of the arithmetic statement. In the Exercises throughout the book care has been taken to delineate clearly for the student the elements to be grouped within a given expression.

1–6 (1) Students often enjoy flowcharting familiar processes such as the procedure used in starting a car or in buying merchandise. The teacher will find that many of the Activities and constructions treated later in the book can be readily adapted to flowcharting in order to facilitate the student's understanding. Making an odometer (page 54) and bisecting a line segment (page 256) are two examples suitable for flowcharting.

(2) The shapes used in the flow charts in this book are commonly employed. However, there is no general agreement as to what shape should be used for a particular operation. What matters is that the flow chart should be consistent in using the particular shapes to indicate particular kinds of operations.

1–8 Challenge Problems are located at several places in the book, and may be used profitably by students of varied abilities. Because their solutions entail a combination of arithmetic operations, they can serve as a review for those students who have encountered little difficulty in handling the material thus far. To accommodate students who have experienced difficulty with the material, the teacher can assign problems from this set which require using arithmetic operations related to the student's weaknesses.

1–11 Students often experience difficulty in determining whether a fraction is in lowest terms. Suggest that the student ask himself whether there is a number which is a factor of (that is, can be divided into) both the numerator and denominator. Have him use this number to form a fraction according to the Principle of 1, and follow the procedure shown in Example 2. Have the student test the resulting fraction as often as needed until no number can be found which is a factor of both the numerator and the denominator. With practice the student learns to choose progressively larger common factors, and eventually the greatest common factor.

1–13 The authors have purposefully avoided introducing the concept of cancellation in discussing the multiplication and division of fractions. The number of mathematical heresies propagated in the name of this "short cut" seems to militate against its inclusion in the text here. Students will appreciate knowing that the rules for operation with fractions in the panels on pages 27 and 28 are adequate for all purposes, and need no further qualifications placed upon them.

1–18 The authors prefer the "divide and average" method for determining square roots over the technique frequently taught in arithmetic for these reasons: First, it is a self-correcting procedure. Even though a numerical error may produce a relatively poor estimate for the square root of the given number, the effect of the error is dissipated after several repetitions of the method. Second, unlike the traditional method, which uses operations largely foreign to the student (pairing of digits, doubling of trial roots, and so on), the present method uses only the addition and division of decimals.

Chapter 2 Measurement

This chapter familiarizes the student with many of the common devices and methods used in measuring distance, area, volume, weight, time, and temperature. In addition, it will introduce the student to several less familiar kinds of measurements, such as those which record the amount of gas or electricity used in a certain period of time. Included in the chapter are ten Activities designed to acquaint the student with the instruments, methods, and difficulties involved in making accurate measurements.

In covering the material in this chapter, we suggest that the teacher try to stress the following facts about measurement:

1. Measurement is essentially the process of comparing a given magnitude (distance, area, volume, and so on) with an appropriate standard unit of measure. See especially the treatment of area measurement (pages 65–67) and of angle measurement (pages 77–79).

2. Most standard units of measure (the yard, the meter, the degree, and so on) originated either from convenience or from convention. This arbitrary nature of standard units is hinted at in the Activity on weight. See especially Exercise 8, page 77.

3. Measurement is always approximate. The results of the Activities on the stopwatch, the revolution counter, and the temperature scales (pages 87–89) will help the student verify this fact.

4. The accuracy of a measurement is jointly dependent upon, among other things, the type of measuring device being used and the thing being measured. The student should be brought to realize that, for example, a micrometer is more accurate than an odometer in measuring extremely small dimensions, whereas an odometer is more precise than a micrometer in measuring large distances.

2–1 (1) An Activity is designed to let the student learn by doing. Each of the ten Activities in this chapter is self-contained, to give the teacher flexibility in fixing the order of their presentation. The teacher may wish to organize the class into small groups and rotate the work on each experiment among the groups. A master chart may be helpful in recording each student's progress in handling the experiments. Encourage the students to work at their own rates of speed and to confer with one another in checking the results of their experiments. Because of the large number of manipulative devices needed for these Activities, we suggest careful pre-planning to ensure effective use of the time allowed for these experiments.
(2) To subtract C, place the compass at the end of B and measure back in the opposite direction.

The student will usually conclude that addition of line segments involves extension in the same direction, while subtraction requires extension in both directions. The teacher can profitably use this observation to strengthen the student's understanding of the inverse operations of addition and subtraction. Refer to Exercises 16–22, page 5, for some arithmetic counterparts of the Exercises here.

2–7 The authors have chosen to introduce the measurement of area through the use of the square unit. It is their belief that the student handles area problems more satisfactorily when asked to deal with the general case using the unit area, leaving aside for the moment any consideration of the dimensions of the unit or of the necessity of converting from one unit to another. The emphasis here is on understanding the concept of determining the area of a figure, which is essentially a process of comparison. Later, when this process is sufficiently clear to the student, he will be required to enunciate the specific dimensions involved and carry out certain specified conversions (Chapter 6). The same thinking applies to the treatment of volume in Section 2–9 of this chapter.

The teacher can provide additional help for students having difficulty in working with area by making area patterns from cardboard like those shown in the Exercises on pages 66–67.

2–14 Students may offer a variety of explanations to account for differences in the results, such as irregularities in the wood, inexperience in using the stopwatch, and so on. Reasonable explanations of the discrepancies are acceptable; highly technical reasons are not expected. It is more important that the students become aware of the inevitability of error in the process of measuring, and the consequences of this fact.

Chapter 3 Geometric Figures

This chapter acquaints the student with the basic figures of plane and solid geometry, and prepares for a fuller treatment of them in subsequent chapters. The study of their properties is informal, rather than deductive, and utilizes the discovery approach to facilitate understanding. The intent is to provide the necessary background for those whose work will require an understanding of geometric figures and relationships. Included in the chapter are several Activities in which the student will make models of prisms, pyramids, and other polyhedrons as a means of investigating the properties of these solids. The chapter also contains a thorough treatment of the formulas for determining the measure of certain angles associated with the circle.

3–1 Students frequently experience difficulty in conceptualizing pure geometric forms. The teacher can assist the student in reaching an intuitive idea of each geometric figure by referring to familiar, physical objects having properties approximately similar to those of the geometric figure. The abler students will appreciate the difference between an object and its geometric form. It is unnecessary, however, to dwell upon theoretical aspects of the subject.

3–2 (1) You may wish to point out to the student that acute angles and obtuse angles, contrary to right angles, can exhibit a considerable range in their measures.

(2) Point out to the students that three or more angles are not called complementary even though the sum of their measures is 90°. This is also true in the case of supplementary angles. The definitions specify *two* angles.

3–4 The teacher may wish to suggest the following as an alternative method for determining the sum of the measures of the angles of a triangle.

1. On light cardboard draw a triangle and label the angles A, B, and C in their interiors.
2. Using scissors, cut out the triangle and then cut off each angle from the triangle.
3. Position the three angles so that they share a common point P as vertex, and their common sides lie flat, as in the diagram below.

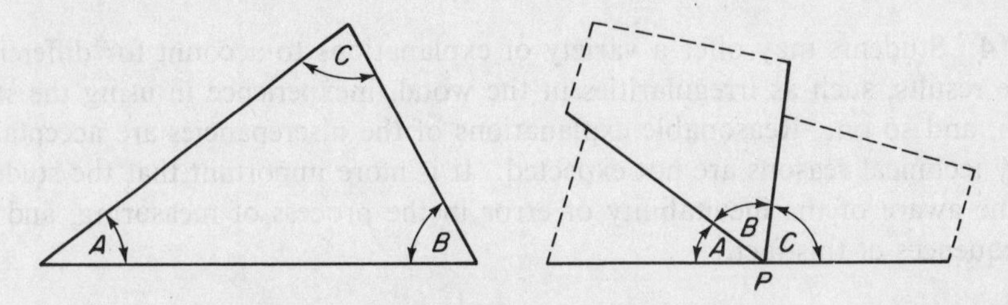

4. If you place your protractor over the angles so that its center is at P, the outside edges of the angles should coincide with the straight edge of the protractor, indicating that the sum of the measures of angles A, B, and C is 180°.

The teacher may wish to refer the student to page 108, Exercise 4 to review the meaning of a straight angle. As always, encourage those students whose protractors and angles do not align to analyze the possible causes of inaccuracy in their work.

3–6 The study of three-dimensional geometric figures is always more complicated when they are represented on a two-dimensional printed page. Accordingly, the authors have attempted in the next two sections to remove this obstacle to the student's understanding by having the student make actual models of the more common types of solid figures. Care should be exercised in the labeling of the different parts of these solids. Some students may wish to use other media in constructing these solids, such as wood, polystyrene, plastic, and so on. An interesting class project to complement the present study of polyhedrons is to construct a mobile using the models made by the students as weights.

3–8 (1) The students can demonstrate this definition by using a pencil with a piece of string tied to it. Point out that this simple device is commonly used by carpenters, gardeners, and others for drawing circles and arcs of sizeable radius.

(2) Students need to be made aware of the distinction between "the degree measure of an arc" and "the length of an arc." You can use the figure on page 133 to illustrate three arcs that have the same degree measure but unequal lengths. Emphasize that the *degree measure* of an arc does not depend upon the radius of the circle, whereas the *length* of an arc does. Thus, $m\widehat{AB} = m\widehat{CD} = m\widehat{EF}$, but length of $\widehat{EF}$ > length of $\widehat{CD}$ > length of $\widehat{AB}$.

3–9 Challenge the students to find a diameter of a circle with an unmarked carpenter's square, using what they know about the measure of an inscribed angle. To do so, set the square so that point P of the square lies on the circle. Mark intersection points R and S. Draw $\overline{RS}$. $\overline{RS}$ is the diameter since $\angle RPS$ is an inscribed right angle. The problem can be extended to finding the center of the circle. In this case, the student must draw two diameters. Their intersection is the center.

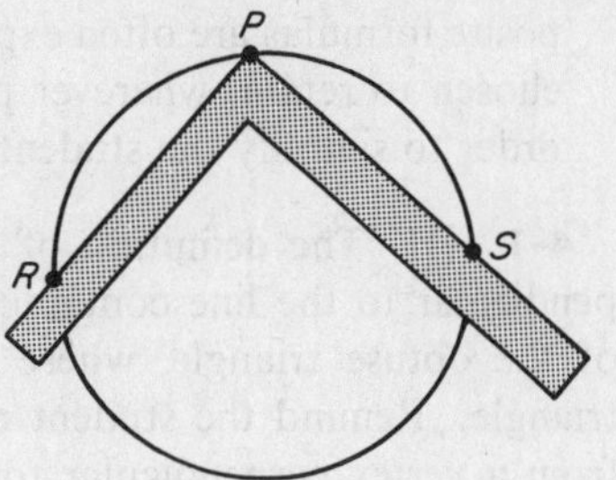

3–10 Point out that a diameter (or a radius) drawn to the point of tangency forms a right angle with the tangent.

3–12 The right circular cylinder is often referred to as a *cylinder of revolution;* the right circular cone is sometimes called a *cone of revolution*. Demonstrating with string and cardboard why these figures are so called can prove to be an interesting method for strengthening the students' ability to visualize three-dimensional figures. Students may wish to cut out other geometric shapes, rotate them in the manner above, and describe what they see.

Chapter 4 Geometric Formulas

Chapter 4 extends the discussion of the plane and solid figures from the previous chapter to cover many useful formulas related to them. The formulas for the perimeter and area of simple plane figures are given, as well as the area and volume formulas for the more common solid figures. Like Chapter 3, the purpose is to furnish the background necessary for understanding relationships among the geometric figures commonly put to industrial and household uses.

Much of the bewilderment and frustration which students regularly experience in working with formulas—especially formulas from geometry—can be eliminated by reminding the student of two important facts about formulas.

1. The terms used in describing a particular formula, as well as the symbols used to represent those terms, vary in meaning from formula to formula. Thus, for example, the word *base* used in describing the area of a triangle does not convey the same meaning as the word *base* used in describing the volume of a triangular prism. Accordingly, the variable b does not denote the same quantity as the variable B. Generally, lower case letters are used to refer to linear measure, while capital letters are used to refer to area or volume measure.
2. Many formulas are aggregates of simpler, more familiar terms. For instance, the formula for the total area of a right circular cone, $\pi rl + \pi r^2$, is composed of two terms, each of which is recognizable by itself. The student will learn that πrl represents the lateral area of the cone, while πr^2, of course, is the familiar

formula for the area of the circular base. The total area is, logically, the sum of these two quantities, as the formula clearly indicates. Although such composite formulas are often expressed in shorter, factored forms, the authors have chosen to retain, wherever possible, the expanded forms of these formulas in order to simplify the student's task of interpreting them.

4–1 (1) The definition of the altitude of a triangle uses the wording "perpendicular to the line containing the opposite side" in order to cover the case of the obtuse triangle, where two of the three altitudes must fall outside the triangle. Remind the student not to refer to the altitude as the "segment drawn from a vertex perpendicular to the opposite side," without, at least, adding the qualification "extended, if necessary."

(2) Students often find it difficult to accept the truth of this statement, especially in the case of an obtuse triangle and an acute triangle whose bases and altitudes are equal in measure, as in the figures below.

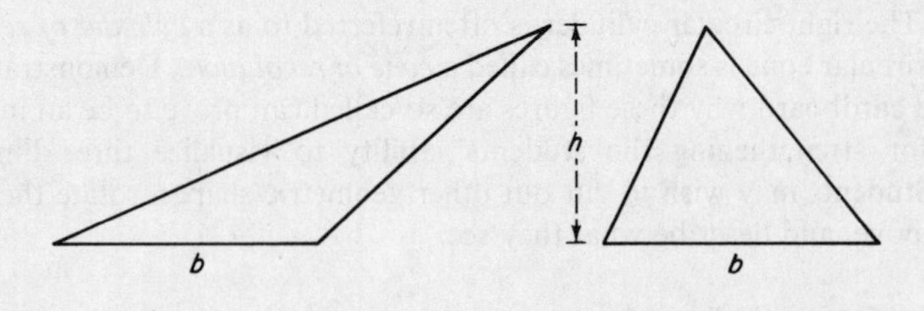

The use of a geoboard, if available, can be extremely helpful in demonstrating the truth of this formula.

4–2 (1) Emphasize that the altitude of a rectangle is one of the sides; thus, taking the product of the length of the two sides is a valid procedure for finding the area. Caution the student, however, against trying to apply this same method in attempting to find the area of a parallelogram or rhombus. See especially Exercise 5, page 159 for a good illustration of this distinction.

(2) This formula can be readily developed from the area formula for a triangle by drawing a diagonal in each of the figures on page 158. The result will show two triangles, each having an area equal to $\frac{1}{2}bh$. Thus, the area of each quadrilateral here will equal twice that of the triangles it contains, or $A = 2 \times \frac{1}{2}bh = bh$.

The division of polygons into a number of triangles as a means of determining the area of the polygon is a commonplace technique. Exercises 6 and 7, page 166, are good examples of the use of this method.

4–9 A cardboard model of a cylinder can be a useful device in discussing lateral area. As shown in the figure on page 180, when the cylinder is cut along a vertical line and laid flat, its lateral area becomes a rectangle whose base is equal to the circumference of the base of the cylinder ($2\pi r$) and whose altitude is equal to that of the cylinder (h). The area of the rectangle is determined by taking their product, $2\pi rh$.

Determining the lateral area (or total area) of a solid figure by reducing it to a plane figure or combination of plane figures is a method which many students find intriguing. The teacher may wish to have the students pursue this approach in analyzing other solid geometric figures such as prisms and cones, or in designing patterns for familiar objects such as containers and funnels.

Chapter 5 Formulas from Industry

In this chapter the student is introduced to many specialized, industrial formulas, particularly those related to the construction trade and the automobile industry. Each formula is presented directly, rather than derived, so that the student can focus his attention solely on using the formulas in several important applications. Also included in the chapter is a discussion of estimation, accompanied by a number of exercises and activities, to give the student practice in using this valuable skill.

5–1 (1) Point out to the students that the prices of lumber are generally based on the following thicknesses: 1″, $1\frac{1}{4}$″, $1\frac{1}{2}$″, $1\frac{3}{4}$″, 2″, 3″, and in even inches (4″, 6″, 8″ and so on). Since lumber is measured before it is seasoned and planed, finished boards are actually smaller than the dimensions indicated. For example, 4-inch boards actually measure $3\frac{5}{8}$ inches wide. In the exercises accompanying this section, consider the dimensions given to be the "rough" sizes so that calculating for board feet can be done directly with these dimensions.

(2) The teacher may wish to supplement these exercises by having the students determine the number of board feet in samples of scrap lumber. As mentioned in the previous note, the dimensions for the width and thickness are likely to involve fractions. Calculating for board feet using these dimensions can serve as a good review of the multiplication of fractions. The result of these calculations, however, should be referred to as the *actual* board feet. As an alternative method the students can solve for the *indicated* board feet. In this case the students would round off dimensions to the next greater size (see Note **5–1**(1)). For example, lumber that is $\frac{3}{4}$″ thick is considered to be 1″ thick, lumber that is $1\frac{1}{8}$″ thick is considered to be $1\frac{1}{4}$″ thick, lumber that is $2\frac{1}{2}$″ thick is considered to be 3″ thick, and so on.

5–4 Some students may be puzzled by this definition of work since it does not seem to relate to their everyday experience of work. Point out that in addition to the common meanings of work as exertion, a job, and so on, there is also the more technical meaning of work as the product of force and distance. In keeping with this definition of work as a product, remind the student that if either of the two factors—force or distance—is zero, the amount of work done is zero (recall the multiplicative property of zero on page 8). Thus, for example, a man who pushes against a large boulder, but fails to move it, has done no work.

5–5 Some students may find these formulas for horsepower somewhat remote. Having the student determine his own horsepower output during an everyday activity, such as climbing a flight of stairs, can be an interesting way to make this concept more familiar. If, for example, a student who weighs 150 pounds climbs a stairway 22-feet high in 15 seconds, the amount of horsepower expended in this activity can be calculated by reference to the formula on page 205. Thus,

$$\text{ft.-lb./sec.} = \frac{150 \times 22}{15} = 220$$

$$\text{hp} = \frac{220}{550} = \frac{4}{10}$$

The teacher may wish to carry out such an experiment in class, both to aid the students' understanding of horsepower, and to review the methods used in taking the different types of measurements involved in this experiment (distance, weight, and time).

5–7 Automotive literature showing the specifications of certain engines and other power train components is generally available upon request from automobile dealers. Such material can be used to supplement the discussion and exercises related to the topics covered in the next three sections.

5–8 In overhauling an engine it is a common practice to rebore the cylinders to a slightly larger diameter and equip the engine with oversize pistons. (An increase of $\frac{1}{8}''$ to the bore is generally a safe maximum.) The engine displacement is thereby increased. An interesting extension to the exercises given on page 210 consists in determining the increase in the cubic-inch displacement after a slight overbore. Thus, in the case of Exercise 1, if the bore were enlarged by $\frac{1}{8}''$ from 4.125″ to 4.250″, the engine displacement would be increased from approximately 401 cubic inches to about 426 cubic inches, for a gain of about 25 cubic inches. For students showing competence in this work, suggest lengthening the strokes given in Exercises 1–4. (An increase of $\frac{1}{4}''$ is usually a safe maximum when lengthening the stroke.)

5–12 A bicycle wheel mechanism like that shown on page 133 can be helpful in demonstrating the relationships between pulley sizes and pulley speeds. Attach a cardboard "snapper" to a spoke of the rear wheel, as was done in making the odometer (pages 54–55). Rotate the pedal mechanism slowly for a given number of times, say, 50 revolutions. At the same time count the number of snaps made by the rear wheel. (Do *not* allow the wheel to rotate freely.) Find the ratio of the number of snaps to the number of revolutions made by the pedal. Measure the diameter of the pedal gear and the diameter of the wheel gear, and find their ratio. Compare the two ratios. The ratios should be sufficiently close to substantiate the pulley formula, $DS = ds$. (Note. There is no need to consider a time factor in this experiment since both the pedal and the rear wheel are rotated for the same length of time.) Following the experiment, a discussion of the possible sources of error can be profitable.

Chapter 6 Systems of Measurement

Prior to this chapter, calculations involving measurement had dimensions given in the same units. In applied mathematics, it is often necessary to convert given information into related units in order to make comparisons and to perform calculations. In this chapter, the common units of measure used in the United States are reviewed, and the metric system, which may be a new concept to many students, is introduced. Although students are expected to remember the most common of the conversion relations, they are encouraged to place greatest emphasis on actually converting measures within and between each of the two systems.

6–1 Students should already be familiar with many conversions within the United States System of Measurement. Those relations which are used frequently will become memorized automatically. The student should be allowed, however, to refer to tables as necessary.

6–5 (1) The metric system was developed by French scientists and became the legal measurement system of France in 1799. Although it is not the customary system used in the United States, it is used quite extensively in many branches of science. Since the system is based on powers of 10, calculations (and conversions) are greatly simplified. Take this opportunity to review multiplication and division by 10 and its multiples. Referring to the gas and electric meters from Chapter 2 might be a helpful tool for this review. Throughout the remainder of this chapter you may wish to make comparisons between the two systems and discuss some of the advantages of each.

(2) Students should become familiar with the dimensions of these most commonly used metric units. A pertinent activity would be the construction of a meter stick calibrated in centimeters, and perhaps, millimeters. This will help the student develop a feeling for the actual length of each of these units.

6–6 A yard is *defined* to be 0.9144 meters; consequently, dividing by 36 *defines* 1 inch to be 0.0254 meters (since 0.9144 is divisible by 36). Dividing 1 by 0.0254 yields the *approximation* that 1 meter equals 39.37 inches. However, this approximate equivalence and those given in subsequent tables are accurate enough for most applications.

6–7 You may wish to discuss the advantages of converting areas within the metric system compared to converting within the United States system. For instance, it is easier to convert from square millimeters to square centimeters than from square inches to square feet.

6–10 (1) The distinction between mass and weight is more properly the concern of physics. The purpose in introducing it here, as suggested in the note on page 245, is to enable the student to make comparisons between units of weight in the United States System and units of mass in the metric system. Students generally have an intuitive understanding of the difference between weight and mass, and having them discuss their understanding of these concepts could be profitable. Do not expect, however, highly technical accounts of these terms.

(2) The students may be interested in knowing that the metric system relates its unit of mass (1 gram) to a unit volume (1 cc.) of water at a certain temperature and pressure. Since students often find it difficult to comprehend the dimensions of these unfamiliar units, it would be most helpful to obtain a balance and a set of weights from the science department so that they can determine the weight of several objects in metric units. Since "gram" and "kilogram" sound heavier than they actually are, students tend to underestimate the weight of an object when expressed in these units.

Chapter 7 Geometric Constructions

Geometric constructions involve the use of a compass and a straightedge only. Although a ruler may be used as a straightedge, it should be used solely to draw lines and not to measure distance.

Students generally are quite interested in constructions and are easily encouraged to try doing them on their own. Basic constructions in this chapter should probably be illustrated on the board or an overhead projector, if available; however, the student should learn to follow the construction directions given in the text. It might be helpful to discuss some of the problems that commonly occur in doing constructions; for example, in bisecting a line segment (page 256), discuss what happens when the radius is not greater than half the length of $\overline{AB}$.

7–3 (1) Encourage the student to keep his pencil sharp and his compass tight enough to prevent it from slipping and changing the radius. You may wish to discuss how these, and other factors, influence the accuracy of a construction.

(2) Labelling all points helps to avoid confusion. Students sometimes have difficulty with this step.

7–5 In this case, line *n* is the reference line. Both the given angle and the angle to be constructed lie "below" *n*. If the angle is constructed "above" *n*, the lines will not be parallel, but instead will intersect.

7–6 Varying the *length* of the equal units on ray $\overrightarrow{AN}$ does not affect this construction. The *number* of equal units marked off on ray $\overrightarrow{AN}$ determines the number of parts into which the given line segment is divided.

7–8 To avoid confusion in a construction like this, where *three* altitudes are to be drawn, the student should complete the construction of each altitude before starting the next one.

7–9 Step 2 locates the midpoints of each of the sides of $\triangle ABC$. Suggest that the student might prefer to locate one midpoint and draw the median before proceeding to the next. Overlapping construction marks may cause some confusion.

7–12 For students interested in pursuing the construction of the ellipse, the following exercise might be suggested.

Draw an ellipse with the foci 3″ apart and the string loop $5\frac{1}{2}$″ across (when taut).

a. Move each thumbtack $\frac{1}{4}$″ outward on the major axis and draw another ellipse. Continue this process two more times.

1. What happens to the shape of the ellipse each time the tacks are moved outward?
2. What figure would you draw if the tacks were put $5\frac{1}{2}$″ apart?

b. Reset the thumbtacks at their original positions. Draw the ellipse. Move each thumbtack $\frac{1}{4}$″ inward along the major axis and draw another ellipse. Continue this process two more times.

1. What changes do you notice in the shape of the ellipse now?
2. What figure would you get if both tacks were put at the intersection point of the major and minor axes?

Chapter 8 Ratio and Proportion

This chapter acquaints the student with a number of important uses of ratio and proportion. The student will learn about various types of levers and see how the concepts of ratio and proportion are involved in the operation of these devices. Similar triangles and polygons are introduced as examples of common geometric shapes which depend on proportion for their very definition. Scale drawings are presented as another familiar area in which proportions are used extensively. Throughout the chapter emphasis should be placed on strengthening the student's understanding of ratio and developing his ability to solve for the unknown term of a proportion.

8–1 For Exercise 6, point out that the answer should properly be expressed as $\frac{6}{1}$ and not simply 6. For exercises involving decimals, like Exercise 9, suggest that the students multiply the numerator and denominator by the appropriate multiple of 10 (see page 36) to obtain a ratio containing only whole numbers, and then simplify. Thus, $\frac{2.1}{.3} \times \frac{10}{10} = \frac{21}{3} = \frac{7}{1}$.

8–5 **(1)** Similar triangles always have the two properties listed on page 295. However, it is sufficient to show that one of the two conditions is satisfied in order to establish that the two triangles are similar, since each property necessarily follows from the other. The students should remember these important properties in the work which follows.

(2) If two angles of one triangle are equal to two angles of another triangle, the third angles of each triangle must also be equal since the sum of the angles of any triangle is 180° (page 115).

8–7 Ask the students to name examples of objects whose extremely large or small dimensions must be represented by scale drawings. Also remind the student that, although a scale may be 1″ to 6′, for example, the ratio is 1:72, since both terms of a ratio must be expressed in the same unit.

Chapter 9 Percentage

Chapter 9 extends the discussion of ratio and proportion from the previous chapter to consider the special case of ratios having 100 as denominator, namely, percents. The early portion of the chapter is devoted to reviewing equivalences among percents, ratios (expressed as common fractions), and decimal fractions. The student will also investigate two common applications of percentage in the field of consumer mathematics—calculating interest and fixing discounts.

9–4 The distinction between *interest* and *rate of interest* is often overlooked in conversation. You may wish to point out to the student that interest is always a sum of money, while rate of interest is usually expressed as a certain percent. By referring to the formula for interest (page 330) it can be seen that interest, I, is the product of three factors, one of which, r, is the rate of interest.

9–5 Since many banks and savings institutions use computers to calculate interest payments, you may find the flow chart below an interesting means of adding authenticity to the discussion of compound interest. The students will find this flow chart especially helpful in completing the Exercises on page 329. References to "row" and "column" are for the Compound Interest Table on page 328.

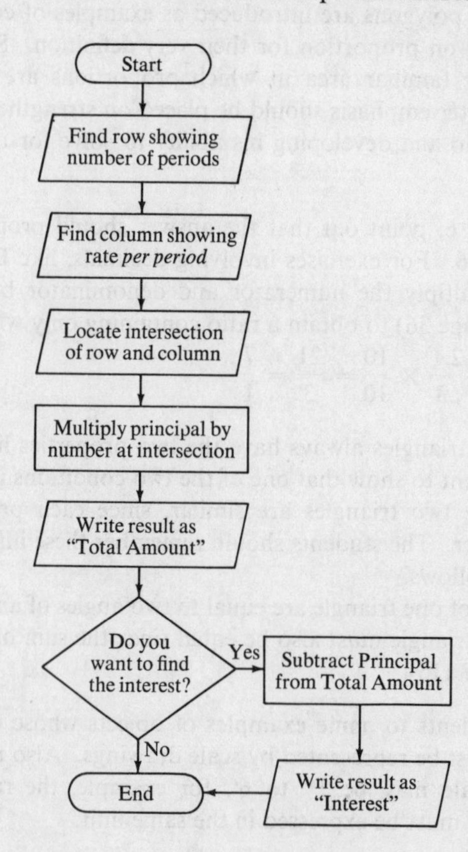

9–6 The accelerated trend toward installment purchasing and the recent proliferation of unified credit cards combine to make this topic especially timely. The enactment of the "Truth-in-Lending Bill" calls attention to the necessity of understanding fully the details of all credit charges and loan finance rates. For the full particulars on the background and stipulations of the law, consult the pamphlet entitled "Regulation Z," available from the United States Treasury Department.

9–7 As in the case of problems involving interest, the distinction between *discount* and *discount rate* is frequently passed over. Emphasize that the discount represents a certain sum of money saved on a purchase, whereas the discount rate simply indicates the percent by which the marked price has been reduced. The teacher may wish to remind the students that a discount rate expressed as a fraction, such as "$\frac{1}{3}$ off," can be readily converted to its decimal equivalent by division (recall page 318). For the more difficult fractions, refer the student to the Table of Equivalents on page 320.

Chapter 10 Right Triangles and Trigonometry

This chapter introduces the Rule of Pythagoras, an important mathematical tool in studying the properties of right triangles. Special emphasis is placed on learning the relationships among the lengths of the sides of 30°–60° right triangles and isosceles right triangles. The basic trigonometric ratios for the right triangle are defined and used to determine the measure of unknown sides and angles of the triangle. Among the various applications of trigonometry which the students will consider in this chapter are those related to such fields as surveying, carpentry, and navigation.

10–1 **(1)** The Rule of Pythagoras can be stated either in terms of area (page 342) or in terms of numbers (page 343). Although both statements imply the same thing, the second one is more commonly used since it involves only numbers. Remind the students that this property is true for right triangles only.

(2) Students who can apply this property of equations need only to remember the formula $c^2 = a^2 + b^2$ since the others follow from it. Some students will probably find it easier to follow this property of subtraction by using a numerical example. For instance, in Example 2 on page 344, an alternative method of solving would be:

$$\begin{aligned} c^2 &= a^2 + b^2 \\ 5^2 &= a^2 + 4^2 \\ 25 &= a^2 + 16 \\ 9 &= a^2 \text{ (or } a^2 = 9) \\ a &= \sqrt{9} \\ a &= 3 \end{aligned}$$

10–2 Although students may find this activity difficult, they should see that the relationship between AC and BC is independent of the length of the sides of the equilateral triangle. Point out that the second property mentioned in the box on page 351 follows from the first, since a 30°–60° right triangle is "half" of an equilateral triangle.

10–4 The definitions of the ratios in terms of *side opposite*, *side adjacent*, and *hypotenuse* are the same for both acute angles ($\angle A$ and $\angle B$) of a right triangle. Some students may find this type of definition easier since it avoids the problem of identifying which side is a and which is b when given a triangle whose sides and angles are not labeled by letters (see Example 1 on page 359). Also compare this table with one giving the ratios for $\angle B$ $\left(\sin B = \frac{b}{c},\ \cos B = \frac{a}{c},\ \tan B = \frac{b}{a}\right)$ to show an advantage of the definitions in descriptive terms. Some students may be interested in the other possible ratios; they are defined as follows:

$$\text{cotangent of angle } A = \frac{\text{side adjacent}}{\text{side opposite}} = \frac{b}{a} \quad \text{or} \quad \cot A = \frac{b}{a}$$

$$\text{secant of angle } A = \frac{\text{hypotenuse}}{\text{side opposite}} = \frac{c}{b} \quad \text{or} \quad \sec A = \frac{c}{b}$$

$$\text{cosecant of angle } A = \frac{\text{hypotenuse}}{\text{side opposite}} = \frac{c}{a} \quad \text{or} \quad \csc A = \frac{c}{a}$$

Note that these three ratios are the reciprocals of the ratios tangent, cosine, and sine, respectively.

10–6 Some students may prefer to substitute values into the basic formula before solving for the desired value. Thus,

$$\sin A = \frac{a}{c}$$

$$\sin 30^\circ = \frac{10}{c}$$

$$c = \frac{10}{\sin 30^\circ}$$

$$c = \frac{10}{.5000}$$

$$c = 20 \text{ in.}$$

Solving the problem by using this formula or by the one used in Example 1 will clearly yield the same result. Emphasis, however, should be placed on the ability to recognize the correct trigonometric *ratio* involved in solving a given problem.

10–7 The authors have chosen to avoid the subject of interpolation (a method for estimating the value of a ratio between two others in the table). Accordingly, students should round off values to the nearest entry in the table.

This table is arranged so that headings at the top are used with angles in the left-hand column and those at the bottom are used with angles in the right-hand column. Students may need some help in using this type of table. The heading at the bottom of the fourth column is *cotangent* (see TM p. 20, **10–4**); it has been omitted since the student will not be using it.

Chapter 11 Statistical Tables and Graphs

The operation of many businesses requires that information be available in a form that allows for quick and accurate interpretation. This chapter describes several widely used methods for organizing and presenting data — statistical tables and graphs. Statistical tables use sets of numbers to present large amounts of information in a compact form. Graphs, on the other hand, use a pictorial approach to show data at a glance. The relative magnitudes of data are quite evident in graphs. Among the types of graphs which the student will study are pictographs, bar graphs, broken-line graphs, and circle graphs.

11–3 Caution students about possible distortions of bar graphs. For example, failure to start the scale of a bar graph at zero produces a misleading picture, as indicated by the adjoining graph. A casual look might suggest that the average life expectancy for men at birth in the U. S. A. is less than half that in the Netherlands, while the difference shown is only 4 years of life. Jagged lines should be drawn on the scale and the bars whenever the values on the scale are interrupted.

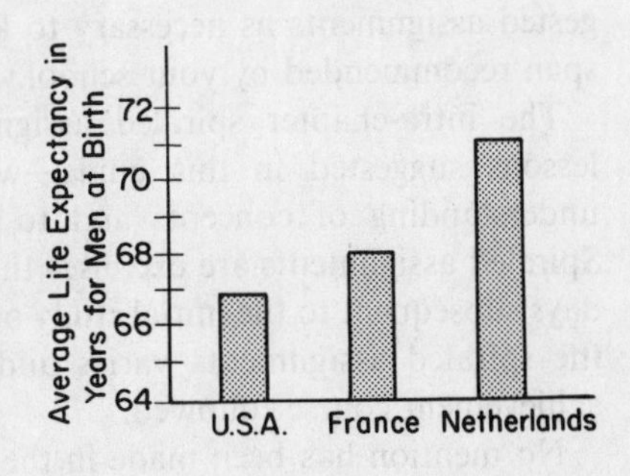

Time Schedule and Assignment Guide

The following Time Schedule and Assignment Guide can be of help to you in planning either an average or an enriched course. The 170 assignments include provision for testing student achievement at the end of each chapter. Ten days are available in a 180-day year for scheduling a one-week review period roughly at mid-year and again at the end of the year. The number of days allotted to each chapter and to review periods may be varied according to the needs of students, the time available, and the requirements of the course of study.

SUGGESTED 180-DAY TIME SCHEDULE (INCLUDING TESTING)

Chapter	1	2	3	4	5	*	6	7	8	9	10	11	*
Average Course	21	23	18	16	16	5	13	18	13	10	13	9	5

*Days allowed for review, and so on.

As it stands, the Assignment Guide covers all sections of the book. The pace and suggested assignments are such as to produce a course of about average difficulty. The level of difficulty can be raised, and the course enriched, by assigning, not necessarily more problems, but more chosen from the "B" parts of the exercise sets. The level may, of course, be lowered by assigning fewer problems. In any case, the daily assignments are to be considered as suggestions only and should be modified as necessary. We suggest that a close check be kept on the amount of time that the students spend on their homework, and that you try to adapt the suggested assignments as necessary to keep the homework demands within the time span recommended by your school.

The intra-chapter spiraled assignments—an important feature of the daily lessons suggested in this guide—will contribute significantly to the student's understanding of concepts and to the improvement or maintenance of skills. Spiraled assignments are exercises that are assigned at spaced intervals on various days subsequent to the initial study of the topic. The type of problems presented in the spiraled assignments varies and is dependent upon the particular level-of-achievement course followed.

No mention has been made in the Assignment Guide of the Maintaining Your Skills sections appearing at the end of each chapter. These sections can be used at the discretion of the teacher either to supplement the daily assignments or to provide additional practice following the completion of the chapter. A separate booklet of Progress Tests is available to assist you further.

Daily assignments are arranged as follows:

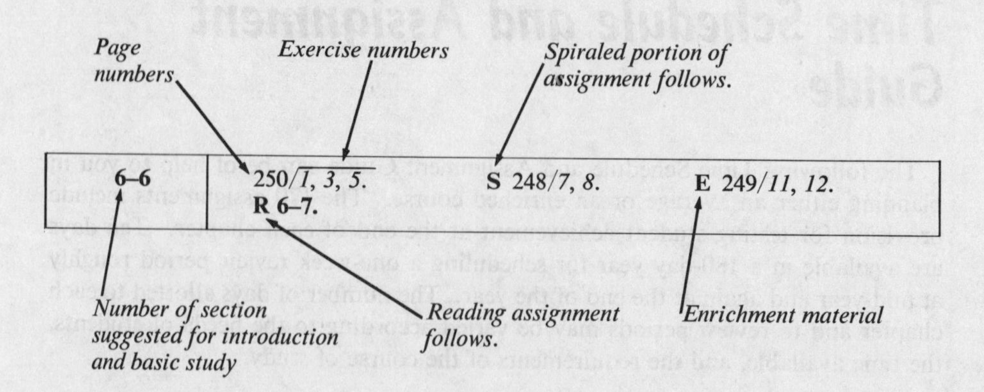

LESSON	SECTION	ASSIGNMENT		
1	**1–1, 1–2**	2/*Test I;* 4 (*top*)/*1–15 odd;* 4 (*foot*)/*2–12 even.*		
2	**1–2**	7/*1–5.*	**S** 4 (*top*)/*2–10 even;* 4 (*foot*)/*1–13 odd.*	
3	**1–3**	9/*2–24 even, 25–29.*	**S** 4–5/*14–20.*	
4	**1–4, 1–5**	10 (*top*)/*1–9;* 10 (*foot*)/*1–8.*	**S** 9/*1–17 odd.*	
5	**1–5**	11/*Test II.*		
6	**1–1—1–6**		**S** 4/*12, 14;* 5/*21, 22;* 9/*19, 21, 23;* 10 (*top*)/*10–12;* 10 (*foot*)/*9, 10.*	**E** 13/*1–6.*
7	**1–7**	14/*Test III;* 15/*1–7.*	**S** 9/*30–33.*	
8	**1–8**	16–18/*1–3.*	**S** 15/*8.*	**E** 19/*4.*
9	**1–9, 1–10**	21/*1–8;* 22/*1–6.*	**S** 15/*9.*	**E** 20/*1–4.*
10	**1–11**	23/*Test IV;* 24/*1–6, 10–16.*	**S** 21/*9, 10;* 22/*7–9.*	**E** 20/*5–8.*
11	**1–12**	25/*1–8.*	**S** 24/*7–9, 17–19.*	**E** 20/*9, 10.*
12	**1–12**	25/*Test V;* 26/*1–19 odd.*	**S** 25/*9, 10.*	**E** 25/*11–15.*
13	**1–13, 1–14**	27–28/*1–10;* 29/*1–18.*	**S** 26/*2–14 even.*	**E** 29/*23–25.*
14	**1–14**	31–32/*1–4.*	**S** 26/*16, 18, 20;* 28/*11;* 29/*19, 20.*	**E** 29/*26–28.*
15	**1–15**	34/*1–6.*	**S** 28/*12;* 29/*21, 22;* 33/*5.*	
16	**1–16**	35/*1–8.*	**S** 34/*7, 8.*	
17	**1–17**	38/*1–20.*	**S** 35/*9, 10.*	**E** 38/*25–27.*
18	**1–17**	38–39/*Test VI.*	**S** 38/*21, 22.*	**E** 38/*28–30.*
19	**1–18**	43/*1–8, 11–14, 17–20.*	**S** 38/*23, 24.*	**E** 44/*22–26.*
20	**1–18**	44/*Test VII.* *Announce chapter test.*	**S** 43/*9, 10, 15, 16, 21.*	**E** 44/*27–31.*
21	**1–1—1–18**	*Administer chapter test.* **R 2–1.**		
22	**2–1**	*Discuss test.* 52/*Activity;* 53/*1–4.*		

LESSON	SECTION	ASSIGNMENT		
23	**2–1**	53–54/*Activity;* 54/*1–10.* **R 2–2.**		
24	**2–2**	54–55/*Activity;* 55/*1–5.*		
25	**2–3**	57/*1–8.*		
26	**2–4**	58/*Test I;* 60–61/*1–14, 19, 20.*		
27	**2–5**	62/*Activity.*		
28	**2–6**	64/*1–4.*		
29	**2–7**	66–67/*1–10.*		
30	**2–8**	69/*1–10.*		**E** 69–70/*13–15.*
31	**2–9**	72–73/*1–6.* **R 2–10.**		
32	**2–10**	73–75/*Test II;* 75–76/*Activity*; 76–77/*1–8.*		
33	**2–11**	78–79/*1–5.*		
34	**2–12**	80–81/*1–4, 6–9.*		
35	**2–1—2–12**	85/*Test III.* **R 2–14.**	**S** 53/*5;* 57/*9, 10;* 61/*15, 16;* 69/*11, 12;* 79/*6.*	**E** 81–84/*Activity;* 84–85/*1–5.*
36	**2–14**	86/*Activity.*		**E** 86/*12.*
37	**2–14**	87/*Activity.* **R 2–16.**		**E** 87–88/*Activity.*
38	**2–16**	88–89/*Activity;* 89/*1–3.*		
39	**2–17**	91–93/*1–9.*		
40	**2–17**	94–96/*1–9.*		
41	**2–17**	96–97/*Test IV. Selected enrichment material.*		
42	**2–1—2–17**	*Selected enrichment material.*		
43	**2–1—2–17**	*Announce chapter test.*	**S** 57/*11, 12;* 61/*17, 18;* 65/*5;* 67/*11, 12;* 79/*7;* 81/*5, 10;* 93/*10;* 96/*10.*	
44	**2–1—2–17**	*Administer chapter test.* **R 3–1.**		
45	**3–1**	*Discuss test.* 106/*1–8.*		
46	**3–2**	108–109/*1–6, 8.*	**S** 106/*9, 10.*	**E** 109/*10, 11.*
47	**3–3**	112–113/*2–14 even.*	**S** 109/*7, 9.*	**E** 109/*12, 13.*

LESSON	SECTION	ASSIGNMENT		
48	**3–4**	115/*Activity;* 115–116/*1–7.*	**S** 112/*1–11 odd.*	
49	**3–4**	116–117/*Activity;* 118–119/*1–8.*	**S** 112/*13.*	
50	**3–5**	120 *Test I;* 122/*1–10.*		
51	**3–5**	122–123/*Activity;* 123/*2–5.*	**S** 119/*9–11.*	
52	**3–6**	125/*1–6.* **R 3–7.**		
53	**3–7**	126–127/*Activity;* 127/*1–3.*		**E** 128/*4.*
54	**3–7**	128–129/*Activity.*		
55	**3–8**	129–130/*Test II;* 133/*1–6.*		
56	**3–9**	135/*1–4;* 137/*1, 2.*		
57	**3–10**	138–139/*Test III;* 140/*1–5.*	**S** 136/*5.*	**E** 137/*3.*
58	**3–11**	144/*1–4.*	**S** 140–141/*6, 7.*	**E** 138/*4.*
59	**3–11**	145–146/*Test IV.*		**E** 144/*5, 6.*
60	**3–12**	148/*1–5.*		
61	**3–12**	148/*Test V. Announce chapter test.*		
62	**3–1—3–12**	*Administer chapter test.* **R 4–1.**		
63	**4–1**	*Discuss test.* 156–157/*1–8.*		
64	**4–2**	159–160/*1–7.*	**S** 157/*9.*	**E** 158/*10–13.*
65	**4–3**	161–162/*1–8.*	**S** 160/*8.*	**E** 160/*9.*
66	**4–4**	164/*1–6.*	**S** 162/*9.*	**E** 160/*10;* 164–165/*1–3.*
67	**4–4**	167–168/*Test I.*	**S** 164/*7.*	**E** 165–166/*4–7.*
68	**4–5**	170–171/*1–5, 7, 8.*		
69	**4–6**	173/*1–3.*	**S** 170/*6;* 171/*9.*	**E** 171/*10.*
70	**4–7**	174/*1–3;* 176/*1–3.*	**S** 173/*4.*	**E** 171/*11;* 173/*5.*
71	**4–8**	178/*1–4.*	**S** 176/*4.*	**E** 173/*6;* 175/*4, 5.*
72	**4–8**	179–180/*Test II.*		**E** 176/*5, 6.*
73	**4–9**	181/*1, 2;* 182/*1, 2.*		**E** 178/*5, 6.*

LESSON	SECTION	ASSIGNMENT		
74	**4–10**	183/*1, 2.*		**E** 181/*3–5;* 182/*3.*
75	**4–11**	186/*1–4.*		**E** 181/*6;* 182/*4;* 183/*3.*
76	**4–12**	187/*1–3.*	**S** 186/*5.*	**E** 184/*4, 5.*
77	**4–12**	187–189/*Test III. Announce chapter test.*		**E** 187/*4.*
78	**4–1—4–12**	*Administer chapter test.* **R 5–1.**		
79	**5–1**	*Discuss test.* 196/*1–5.*		**E** 197/*6.*
80	**5–2**	199/*1–6.*		**E** 197/*7;* 200/*8.*
81	**5–2**	201/*Activity.*	**S** 200/*7.*	**E** 200/*9, 10.*
82	**5–3**	202/*1–6.*		
83	**5–4**	202–203/*Test I;* 203–204/*1–4;* 204/*1–3.*	**S** 202/*7.*	
84	**5–5**	205/*1–3.*	**S** 204 (*top*)/*5, 6;* 204 (*foot*)/*4.*	
85	**5–6**	206/*1–4.*	**S** 205/*4.*	**E** 206/*5, 6.*
86	**5–7**	207/*Test II;* 209/*1–3.*		
87	**5–8**	210/*1–3.*	**S** 209/*4, 5.*	
88	**5–9**	211/*1–3.*	**S** 210/*4.*	
89	**5–10**	211–212/*Test III;* 213/*1–4;* 214/*1–3.*		**E** 211/*4.*
90	**5–11**	215/*1–4.*	**S** 213/*5;* 214/*4.*	**E** 211/*5.*
91	**5–12**	216/*Test IV;* 217/*1–3.*	**S** 214/*5;* 215/*5.*	
92	**5–12**	219/*1–4.*	**S** 217/*4.*	
93	**5–12**	219/*Test V. Announce chapter test.*		
94	**5–1—5–12**	*Administer chapter test.* **R 6–1.**		
95	**6–1**	*Discuss test.* 226–227/*1–7, 9.*		
96	**6–2**	229/*1–4.*	**S** 227/*8, 10.*	**E** 229/*6–8.*
97	**6–3**	230/*Test I;* 232–233/*1–4.*	**S** 229/*5.*	**E** 229/*9;* 233/*6.*
98	**6–4**	235/*1–8.*	**S** 233/*5.*	**E** 230/*10;* 233/*7.*
99	**6–5**	235/*Test II;* 237/*2–16 even.*		**E** 235/*9, 10.*

LESSON	SECTION	ASSIGNMENT
100	**6–6**	239/*1–13 odd.* **S** 237/*1–11 odd.* **E** 239/*14–16.*
101	**6–7**	241/*1–8;* 242/*1–3.* **S** 237/*13, 15;* 239/*2–8 even.* **E** 239/*17, 18.*
102	**6–8**	243/*1–4.* **S** 239/*10, 12;* 241/*9, 10;* 242/*4.* **E** 240/*19, 20.*
103	**6–9**	245/*1–4.* **S** 242/*5;* 243/*5.*
104	**6–10**	246/*1–7.* **S** 245/*5.*
105	**6–11**	247/*Test III;* 248–249/*1–8.* **E** 247/*8, 9.*
106	**6–11**	249/*Test IV.* **S** 249/*9, 10.* *Announce chapter test.*
107	**6–1—6–11**	*Administer chapter test.* **R 7–1, 7–2.**
108	**7–1, 7–2**	*Discuss test.* 257/*1–4;* 259/*1–2.*
109	**7–3**	261/*1–4.* **S** 259/*3.*
110	**7–4**	262–263/*1–3.* **S** 261/*5.*
111	**7–5**	264/*1, 2.* **S** 263/*4, 5.*
112	**7–6**	266/*1–3.* **S** 264/*3.*
113	**7–6**	266/*Test I.*
114	**7–7**	269/*1–5.*
115	**7–8**	270/*1, 2.* **S** 269/*6.*
116	**7–9**	271/*1–4.*
117	**7–9**	272/*Activity;* 272/*1–4.* **R 7–10, 7–11.**
118	**7–10, 7–11**	273/*1, 2;* 275/*1.*
119	**7–11**	275/*2, 3.* **E** 275/*4, 5.*
120	**7–11**	275/*Activity;* 275/*1, 2.* **R 7–12.**
121	**7–12**	277/*1–4.*
122	**7–12**	278/*Test II.* **E** 277/*5, 6.*
123	**7–12**	278/*Activity;* 279/*1–4.* **E** 279–280/*5–8.*
124	**7–12**	280–281/*Activity;* 281/*1, 2.* *Announce chapter test.*
125	**7–1—7–12**	*Administer chapter test.* **R 8–1.**

LESSON	SECTION	ASSIGNMENT		
126	**8–1**	*Discuss test*. 286–287/*1–8*, *10*.		
127	**8–2**	288/*1–4*.	**S** 286–287/*9*, *11*.	**E** 288/*6*.
128	**8–3**	290/*1–8*.	**S** 287/*12;* 288/*5*.	**E** 288/*7*.
129	**8–4**	293/*1–5 odd*.	**S** 290/*9*.	**E** 290/*11*, *12*.
130	**8–4**	293/*2–6 even*. **R 8–5.**	**S** 290/*10*.	**E** 290/*13–15*.
131	**8–5**	293–294/*Test I;* 294–295/*Activity;* 295–296/*1*, *2*.		
132	**8–5**	296/*Activity;* 297–298/*1–4*.		
133	**8–6**	300–301/*1–5*.	**S** 298/*5*.	**E** 298/*6*.
134	**8–6**	301–303/*Test II*.		**E** 298/*7*.
135	**8–7**	304–306/*1–10*.		
136	**8–8**	307–310/*1–13 odd*.	**S** 306/*11–18*.	
137	**8–8**	310–311/*Test III*. *Announce chapter test*.	**S** 307–310/*2–12 even*.	
138	**8–1—8–8**	*Administer chapter test*. **R 9–1.**		
139	**9–1**	319/*1–31*.		
140	**9–2**	321/*Test I*.	**S** 323/*1–13 odd*.	**E** 323/*14–17*.
141	**9–3**	324/*1–4*.	**S** 323/*2–8 even*.	**E** 323/*18–20;* 324/*5*, *6*.
142	**9–4**	326/*1–5*.	**S** 323/*10*, *12*.	**E** 324/*7*, *8;* 326/*6–8*.
143	**9–5**	326/*Test II*.	**S** 329/*1–8*.	**E** 326/*9*, *10*.
144	**9–6**	331/*1–4*.	**S** 329/*9*, *10*.	**E** 329/*11–13*.
145	**9–7**	333/*1–4*.	**S** 331/*5*.	**E** 329/*14*, *15;* 331/*6*.
146	**9–8**	334/*1*.		**E** 333/*5*, *6*.
147	**9–8**	336/*Test III*. *Announce chapter test*.		**E** 335/*2*.
148	**9–1—9–8**	*Administer chapter test*. **R 10–1.**		
149	**10–1**	*Discuss test*. 345/*1–7*.		
150	**10–2**	348–349/*Activity;* 349/*1–4*.	**S** 345/*8*.	**E** 346/*10–12*.

LESSON	SECTION	ASSIGNMENT		
151	**10–2**	350/*Test I;* 351/*Activity;* 352/*1–3.*	**S** 349/*5.*	**E** 347/*13*, *14.*
152	**10–3**	354–355/*1–3.*	**S** 352/*4.*	**E** 356/*6.*
153	**10–3**	356–357/*Test II.*	**S** 345/*9;* 352/*5;* 355/*4*, *5.*	**E** 356/*7.*
154	**10–4**	360/*1*, *3.*		
155	**10–4**	360/*2*, *4.*		
156	**10–5**	364/*1–17 odd.*	**S** 360/*5.*	
157	**10–5**	364/*2–18 even.*		
158	**10–6**	365/*Test III;* 367/*1–7.*	**S** 364/*19*, *20.*	
159	**10–7**	370/*1–4.*	**S** 367–368/*8*, *9.*	**E** 371/*5.*
160	**10–7**	371/*Test IV.* *Announce chapter test.*	**S** 368/*10.*	**E** 371/*6.*
161	**10–1—10–7**	*Administer chapter test.* **R 11–1.**		
162	**11–1**	*Discuss test.* 379/*1–6.*		
163	**11–2**	379–380/*1–9.*		**E** 380/*10.*
164	**11–3**	380–381/*Test I;* 383–384/*1–10.*		
165	**11–3**	384/*Activity;* 384/*1–5.*		
166	**11–4**	386–387/*1–10.*		
167	**11–4**	387–389/*Test II.*		
168	**11–5**	390/*1–12.*		
169	**11–5**	391/*Test III. Announce chapter test.*		
170	**11–1—11–5**	*Administer chapter test.*		

MODERN APPLIED MATHEMATICS

The following pages are an annotated copy of the student textbook. Annotations are printed in color. References to the Teacher's Manual bound at the front of this Teacher's Edition are indicated by the symbol TM. Answers to all Exercises, Tests, and Reviews are bound at the back of this book.

MODERN APPLIED

MATHEMATICS

MARVIN GOLD
ROBERT E. CARLBERG

EDITORIAL ADVISER
ALBERT E. MEDER, JR.

HOUGHTON MIFFLIN COMPANY · BOSTON

NEW YORK • ATLANTA • GENEVA, ILLINOIS • DALLAS • PALO ALTO

The authors bring to the field of applied mathematics their experience in the teaching of industrial and vocational mathematics.

ABOUT THE AUTHORS

Marvin Gold, Counselor, Oxford Junior High School, Anaheim Union High School District, Anaheim, California. Mr. Gold was Mathematics Consultant for the Industrial Occupations Program, Orange County, California. He served as co-chairman of the research and writing team that developed a curriculum guide in applied mathematics for the Orange County Superintendent of Schools.

Robert E. Carlberg, Oxford Junior High School, Anaheim Union High School District, Anaheim, California, and formerly Industrial Arts Department Chairman, Kennedy High School, Anaheim.

Editorial Adviser

Albert E. Meder, Jr., Dean and Vice Provost and Professor of Mathematics, Emeritus, Rutgers University, the State University of New Jersey. Dr. Meder was Executive Director of the Commission on Mathematics of the College Entrance Examination Board, and has been an advisory member of SMSG.

Library of Congress Catalog Card Number 79-128710

CONTENTS

Major subdivisions of the chapter with headings printed in color.

This glossary gives a convenient listing of definitions of technical terms used in the book.

Answers to the Self-Analysis Tests provide for self-evaluation by the student.

PICTURE CREDITS

x	Courtesy of the College of Engineering, University of Arizona
5	Courtesy of Precision Valve Corporation
11	Courtesy of Burroughs Corporation
15	Courtesy of International Business Machines
48	Courtesy of National Aeronautics and Space Administration
102	Gordon N. Converse/Christian Science Monitor
125	Wide World Photos
154	United Press International
194	(*top*) Courtesy of General Motors Guide Lamp Division (*bottom*) Courtesy of Home Center, Chicago
207	Courtesy of Tennessee Valley Authority
215	Courtesy of Pan American Airlines
224	(*top*) Courtesy of Blaw-Knox Foundry and Mill Machinery, Inc. (*bottom*) Courtesy of Ford Motor Company, Product Planning and Design Staff
254	Courtesy of M.I.T. School of Architecture
284	Courtesy of Charles H. Brewer, Jr., New Haven
316	Peter W. Main/Christian Science Monitor
340	Courtesy of Elgin Junior College/Elgin Daily Courier-News
376	Wide World Photos

This book will help you prepare for positions like those advertised.

1 Arithmetic Review

← Each chapter is introduced by an intriguing picture.

Each chapter is prefaced by clearly defined objectives to help the student chart his progress in learning the subject matter.

OBJECTIVES

1. To review basic concepts and methods of computation.
2. To improve speed and skill in computation.
3. To use the "principle of 1" in working with fractions.
4. To learn the meaning of exponents and square roots.
5. To learn a method for finding square root.

Each chapter opens with a statement placing the material to be studied in the broad context of its applications.

In this chapter you will review some of the basic ideas of mathematics and improve your skill in computation. Simple arithmetic is an everyday part of any job, no matter how technical. This chapter shows some of the uses of arithmetic and opens the door to many more applications which you will find throughout this book.

Reference to the Teacher's Manual bound at the front of this book.

These headings indicate the main divisions of each chapter.

■ Whole Numbers

Throughout this book you will be given Self-Analysis Tests to help you test your own understanding and speed. Here is the first one.

TM p. 6 , 1-1(1)

Self-Analysis Tests appearing throughout the book allow the student to test his understanding of the material.

SELF-ANALYSIS TEST I

Time: 5 minutes

Solve for the value of N that makes the sentence true.

1. $2 + (3 + 7) = N$

2. $2(4 + 8) = N$

3. $(7 + 6) + (5 + 3) = N$

4. $(2)(3)(4) = N$

5. $7 - (2 + 3) = N$

6. $42 + 27 + 5 = N$

7. $38 - (2 + 17) = N$

8. $100 - 2(2 + 3) = N$

9. $2[2 + 2(2)] = N$

10. $(7)(6)(5) = N$

11. $N + 7 = 9$

12. $(16 - 8) - 5 = N$

Find the missing numbers.

13. $(?)(2) = 22$

14. $(?) - 2(5) = 49$

15. $(?)(5 + 2) = 42$

16. $(2 \times 5) + 2 = (?)$

17. $(7)(6)(?) = 210$

18. $28 - 5 + 2 = (?)$

19. $(?)(2 + 18) = 60$

20. $(127 + 137) - (2 + 3) = (?)$

If you made any errors, you should study pages 3–9 and then try the test again. (See Answers at end of book.)

The following pages will give you an opportunity to review fundamental operations with whole numbers — addition, subtraction, multiplication, and division.

The side heads indicate chapter number and section number.

1–1 Addition

Can you add this column of figures quickly and accurately? If not, perhaps you are having trouble with the basic addition facts.

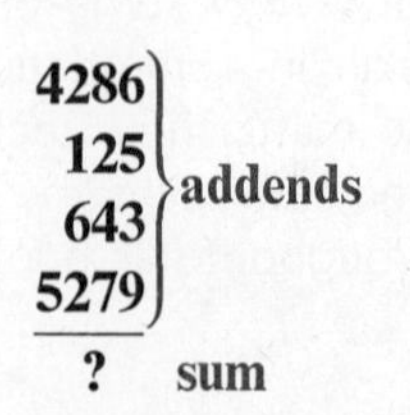

The answers to Self-Analysis Tests follow directly after the Index in the student's book as well as in this one. Answers to all other exercises are bound at the back of this Teacher's Edition. A complete Solution Key for all tests and exercises is available.

A-B grouping of Exercises and
blems offers one means of
viding for individual differences.
also TM p. 6, 1-1(2).

EXERCISE

Copy and complete this addition chart.

A

+	0	1	2	3	4	5	6	7	8	9
0	0	1	2	3	4	5	6			
1	1	2	3	4						
2	2	3								
3	3									
4	4									
5										
6										
7										
8										
9										

If you are unsure of any of these combinations, make your own personal list. Practice in your spare time.

Note that 0 added to any number gives the number itself. "0" is called the **identity element for addition.**

You can sometimes shorten your work by noticing special combinations. In the following example, **parentheses ( )** are used to group the numbers to be added (the addends).

Note the use of color for emphasis.

$$\begin{aligned} & 9 + 4 + 6 + 9 + 2 \\ = {} & 9 + (4 + 6) + 9 + 2 \\ = {} & (9 + 9 + 2) + (4 + 6) \\ = {} & 20 + 10 = 30 \end{aligned}$$

Emphasize that where grouping symbols are present, the student should simplify the expressions within them first. See also TM p. 6 , 1-1(3).

In vertical form,

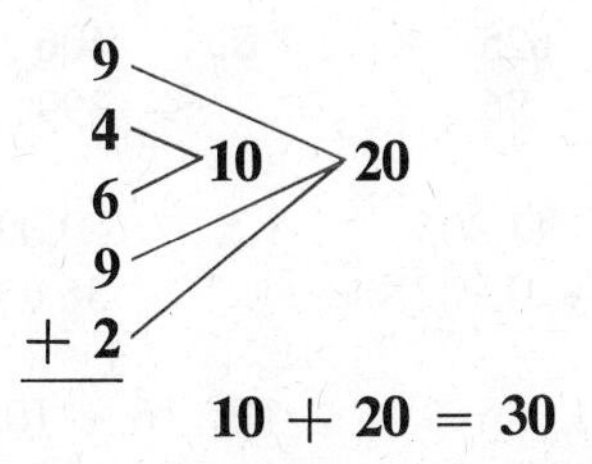

$10 + 20 = 30$

EXERCISES

Add. Check each answer by adding in the opposite direction.

A

1. $\begin{array}{r} 92 \\ +\ 14 \\ \hline \end{array}$ **2.** $\begin{array}{r} 27 \\ +\ 35 \\ \hline \end{array}$ **3.** $\begin{array}{r} 12 \\ +\ 67 \\ \hline \end{array}$ **4.** $\begin{array}{r} 37 \\ +\ 24 \\ \hline \end{array}$ **5.** $\begin{array}{r} 59 \\ +\ 83 \\ \hline \end{array}$

6. $\begin{array}{r} 426 \\ +\ 375 \\ \hline \end{array}$ **7.** $\begin{array}{r} 195 \\ +\ 568 \\ \hline \end{array}$ **8.** $\begin{array}{r} 964 \\ 285 \\ +\ 316 \\ \hline \end{array}$ **9.** $\begin{array}{r} 688 \\ 49 \\ +\ 256 \\ \hline \end{array}$ **10.** $\begin{array}{r} 5684 \\ 29 \\ +\ 385 \\ \hline \end{array}$

11. $\begin{array}{r} 469 \\ 874 \\ 56 \\ 569 \\ +\ 822 \\ \hline \end{array}$ **12.** $\begin{array}{r} 468 \\ 642 \\ 591 \\ 342 \\ +\ 798 \\ \hline \end{array}$ **13.** $\begin{array}{r} 26 \\ 429 \\ 314 \\ 277 \\ +\ 146 \\ \hline \end{array}$ **14.** $\begin{array}{r} 6897 \\ 4621 \\ 3589 \\ 268 \\ 121 \\ +\ 15 \\ \hline \end{array}$ **15.** $\begin{array}{r} 268 \\ 439 \\ 862 \\ 521 \\ +\ 266 \\ \hline \end{array}$

1–2 Subtraction

Addition is useful in checking the accuracy of a subtraction result. For example,

$$\begin{array}{r} \mathbf{230} \\ -\ \mathbf{142} \\ \hline \mathbf{88} \end{array} \qquad \begin{array}{r} \textit{Check} \\ \mathbf{142} \\ +\ \mathbf{88} \\ \hline \mathbf{230} \end{array}$$

For a student showing a weakness in subtraction recommend making a subtraction chart.

EXERCISES

Subtract. Check by addition.

A

1. $\begin{array}{r} 92 \\ -\ 14 \\ \hline \end{array}$ **2.** $\begin{array}{r} 27 \\ -\ 18 \\ \hline \end{array}$ **3.** $\begin{array}{r} 53 \\ -\ 38 \\ \hline \end{array}$ **4.** $\begin{array}{r} 87 \\ -\ 69 \\ \hline \end{array}$ **5.** $\begin{array}{r} 76 \\ -\ 29 \\ \hline \end{array}$

6. $\begin{array}{r} 438 \\ -\ 209 \\ \hline \end{array}$ **7.** $\begin{array}{r} 625 \\ -\ 96 \\ \hline \end{array}$ **8.** $\begin{array}{r} 406 \\ -\ 399 \\ \hline \end{array}$ **9.** $\begin{array}{r} 837 \\ -\ 292 \\ \hline \end{array}$

10. $\begin{array}{r} 1548 \\ -\ 929 \\ \hline \end{array}$ **11.** $\begin{array}{r} 11{,}405 \\ -\ 3{,}962 \\ \hline \end{array}$ **12.** $\begin{array}{r} 50{,}000 \\ -\ 36{,}666 \\ \hline \end{array}$ **13.** $\begin{array}{r} 20{,}605 \\ -\ 19{,}637 \\ \hline \end{array}$

14. $(16 + 6) - 4$ **15.** $16 + (6 - 4)$

Exercises 14-15, 19-20, and 21-22 show how the use of grouping symbols can affect the value of an expression.

16. $(17 - 3) + 95 + 5$

17. $16 + 4 + 11 - 9$

18. $17 - 6 + 3 + 4$

19. $7 - (2 + 4)$

20. $(7 - 2) + 4$

21. $(127 + 3) - (13 + 7)$

22. $(127 + 3 - 13) + 7$

Frequent reference to actual objects stimulates interest in the uses of applied mathematics.

Template Problems

A template is a pattern used as a guide in making something accurately. The templates pictured in this book are usually reduced in size because of page limitations.

EXAMPLE 1 Graphically illustrated Examples help the student understand concepts and operations.

Find the distance between A and F.

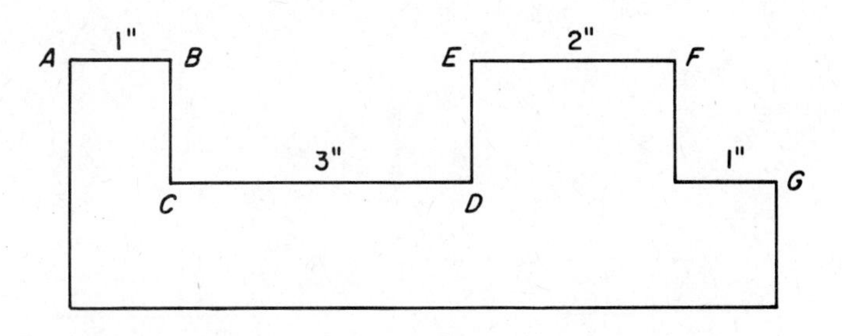

Solution. $AB = 1''$, $CD = 3''$, $EF = 2''$.
$1'' + 3'' + 2'' = 6''$. That is, the distance between A and F is **6 inches.**

This is the first of many references to the basic figures of geometry.

The diagram at the right will help you recall the use of two terms used in connection with a circle.

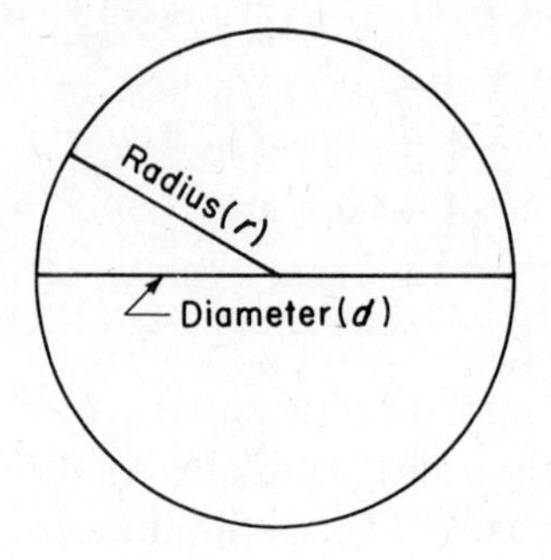

EXAMPLE 2

Find the distance X.

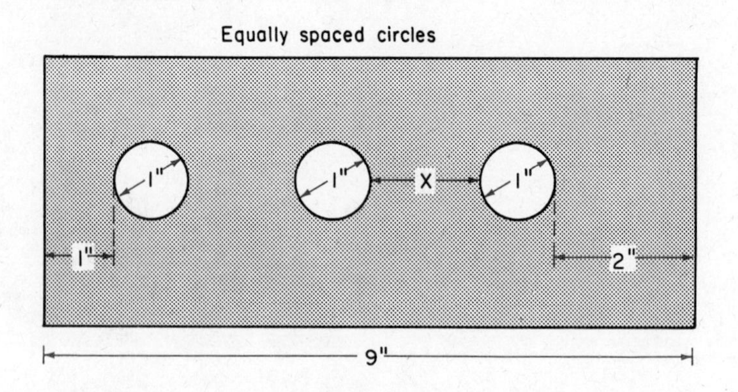

Solution. Each circle is 1″ in diameter.

$$2 \times X = 9'' - (1'' + 1'' + 1'' + 1'' + 2'')$$
$$= 9'' - 6'' = 3''$$
$$X = 3'' \div 2 = \mathbf{1\tfrac{1}{2}''}$$

EXERCISES

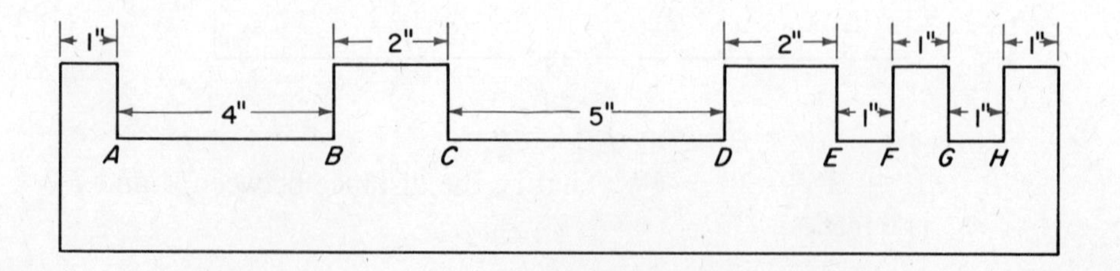

For Exercises 1–3, use the diagram at the foot of page 6.

A

1. What is the distance from A to D?
2. What is the distance from C to G?
3. What is the distance from D to H?

4. Find the distance X in the drawing below.

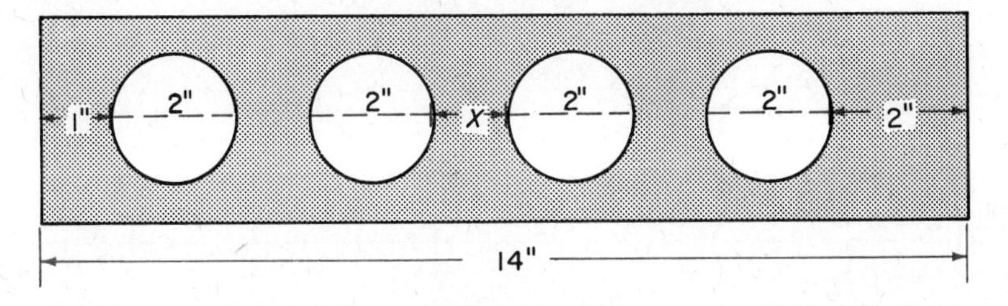

5. Find the distance Y.

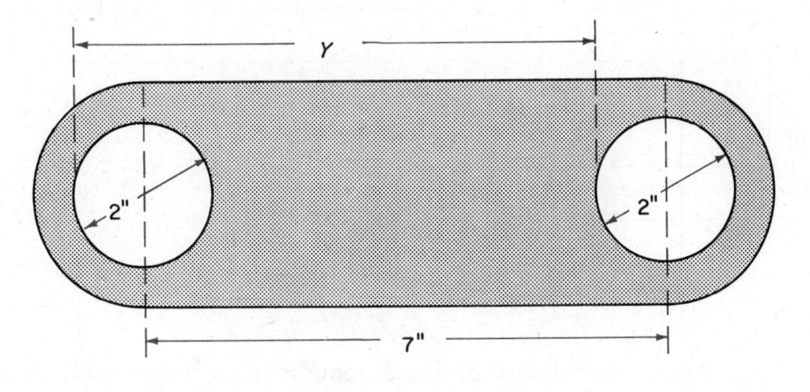

1–3 Multiplication

Can you multiply 43 by 65 without difficulty? Keeping the numerals in straight columns will help your accuracy. You may also need to review the multiplication facts.

Stress this.

$$\begin{array}{rl} 43 & \text{factor} \\ \times\ 65 & \text{factor} \\ \hline 215 & \\ 258 & \\ \hline 2795 & \text{product} \end{array}$$

EXERCISE

Copy and complete this table.

A

×	0	1	2	3	4	5	6	7	8	9	10	11	12
0	0	0	0	0	0	0	0	0	0	0			
1	0	1	2	3	4	5	6	7	8				
2	0	2	4	6	8								
3	0	3	6	9									
4	0	4											
5	0	5											
6	0	6											
7	0	7											
8	0												
9	0												
10													
11													
12													

Students tend to doubt the truth of this multiplication fact.

If you are unsure of any of these combinations, make your own personal list and practice as necessary.

Note that any number multiplied by 1 gives the number itself: $1 \times 2 = 2$; $1 \times 237 = 237$. "1" is called the **identity element for multiplication.**

When 0 is one of the factors, the product is always zero; $2 \times 0 = 0$; $2{,}317{,}462 \times 0 = 0$.

Sometimes you will see a raised dot instead of the sign ×. Thus,

$$\mathbf{4 \cdot 3} \text{ means } \mathbf{4 \times 3}$$

If we used parentheses, we could omit the sign altogether.

$$\mathbf{(4)(3)} \text{ means } \mathbf{4 \times 3},$$
$$\mathbf{3(2 + 4)} \text{ means } \mathbf{(3) \times (2 + 4)}.$$

Be sure the student is familiar with each symbol denoting multiplication. These symbols are used interchangeably throughout the book.

EXERCISES

Find the products. Check by interchanging the factors.

A

1. 34×2	**7.** 71×5	**13.** 56×38	**19.** 28×63
2. 38×7	**8.** 84×8	**14.** 34×52	**20.** 75×18
3. 84×6	**9.** 29×3	**15.** 67×34	**21.** 28×79
4. 55×3	**10.** 47×6	**16.** 88×35	**22.** 389×97
5. 98×7	**11.** 69×3	**17.** 73×24	**23.** 466×28
6. 14×8	**12.** 79×5	**18.** 42×89	**24.** 928×37

Solve for the value of N that makes the sentence true.

25. $6 \cdot 29 = N$
26. $2 + (3 + 6) = N$
27. $2(3 + 6) = N$
28. $(41)(309) = N$
29. $3 \cdot (16 - 1) = N$
30. $4(16 + 17 - 2) = N$
31. $317 \cdot 2 \cdot 0 = N$
32. $(31)(60)(415) = N$
33. $110 - 2(2 + 3) = N$

1–4 Division

The example at the right will help you to review the division process. Perhaps you need to practice some of the more difficult combinations, such as $63 \div 9$. To do so, use the multiplication table you made for page 8. The products in the table may be thought of as the dividends.

Having the student show all the steps will lessen the likelihood of errors.

```
               36   quotient
divisor 24)865   dividend
               72
               145
               144
                 1  remainder
```

$36\frac{1}{24}$ **answer**

To check your work in division, recall that

(Divisor $\times$ Quotient) + Remainder = Dividend

EXERCISES

Divide. Check your work.

A

1. $5\overline{)625}$	**4.** $4\overline{)296}$	**7.** $9\overline{)387}$	**10.** $13\overline{)692}$
2. $3\overline{)153}$	**5.** $6\overline{)462}$	**8.** $26\overline{)546}$	**11.** $37\overline{)518}$
3. $7\overline{)168}$	**6.** $2\overline{)394}$	**9.** $91\overline{)1020}$	**12.** $59\overline{)5020}$

1–5 Signs of Grouping TM p. 6 , 1-5

What is the meaning of $4 \times 10 + 2$? Is it $40 + 2 = 42$ or is it $4 \times 12 = 48$? To avoid confusion, always use parentheses or brackets to make your meaning clear.

In $4 \times 10 + 2$, if you mean the result to be 42, write $(4 \times 10) + 2$. But if you mean 48, then write $4 \times (10 + 2)$, or $4(10 + 2)$.

EXAMPLE 1

a. $2 + (3 \times 5)$ means $2 + 15$.
b. $(2 + 3) \times 5$ means 5×5.

EXAMPLE 2

Use the signs $+, -, \times, \div$, and parentheses to make true statements from the following:

a. 8 8 8 = 9

Solution. $(8 \div 8) + 8$
$1 + 8$
$9 = 9$

b. 8 8 8 = 8

Solution. $(8 \times 8) \div 8$
$64 \div 8$
$8 = 8$

EXERCISES

Use the signs $+, -, \times, \div$ and parentheses to make these into true statements. (Some have more than one solution.)

A

1. 5 4 2 = 22	**6.** 5 4 2 = 3
2. 5 4 2 = 18	**7.** 5 4 2 = 30
3. 5 4 2 = 10	**8.** 5 4 2 = 13
4. 5 4 2 = 2	**9.** 5 4 2 = 40
5. 5 4 2 = 11	**10.** 5 4 2 = 7

SELF-ANALYSIS TEST II

Time: 20 minutes

Find the value for each $\square$ or ( ) to make the statement true.

1. $7 + 8 + 9 = \square$

2. $15 + 4 + 2 - 11 = \square$

3. $77 - 17 + 4 = \square$

4. $23 - 5 - 4 = \square$

5. $5 \times 7 = \square$

6. $8(7) = \square$

7. $5 + (5 \times 7) = \square$

8. $4(5) + 2 = \square$

9. $37 + 7(9) = \square$

10. $25(4) - 8(7) = \square$

11. $\begin{array}{r} 36 \\ \times\ 4 \\ \hline \square \end{array}$

12. $\begin{array}{r} 87 \\ \times\ 6 \\ \hline \square \end{array}$

13. $\begin{array}{r} 75 \\ \times\ 29 \\ \hline \square \end{array}$

14. $\begin{array}{r} 932 \\ \times\ 18 \\ \hline \square \end{array}$

15. $440 \div 5 = \square$

16. $487 \div 12 = \square$

17. $9(\ ) = 27$

18. $7(\ ) = 63$

19. $17(\ ) = 3791$

Use signs of addition, subtraction, multiplication, or division where necessary to make the statement true; use parentheses or brackets to help group the numbers.

20. 2 5 7 = 37

21. 3 9 4 = 31

22. 7 6 3 = 9

23. 24 3 2 = 30

24. 72 8 3 = 6

25. 2 8 3 = 10

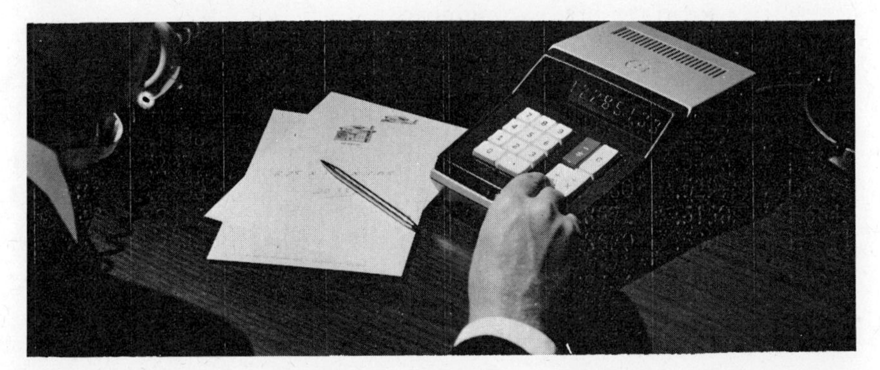

Flow charts add an interesting and contemporary flavor to the study of arithmetic operations.

1–6 Flow Charts (Optional)
See also TM p. 6, 1-6(1).

Diagrams called flow charts are often used to picture the steps in a problem to be solved by an electronic computer. Here is an easy flow chart you can use for an addition problem.

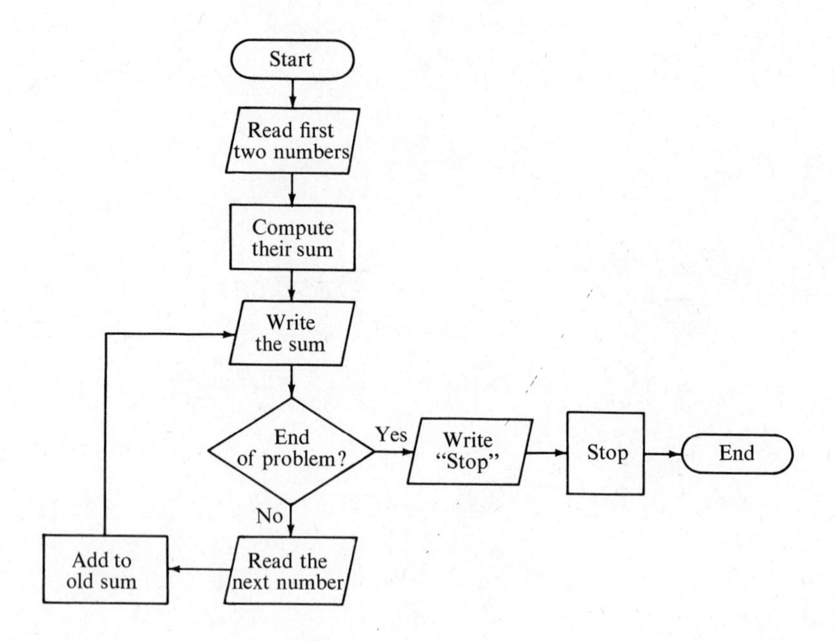

EXAMPLE

4
2
7

Solution. Using the flow chart above,

1. Read the first two numbers.	4, 2
2. Compute their sum.	$4 + 2$
3. Write the sum.	6
4. Is this the end of the problem?	No
5. Follow the "no" arrow. Read the next number.	7
6. Add to the old sum.	$6 + 7$
7. Write the sum.	13
8. Is this the end of the problem?	Yes

Notice that the boxes have special shapes according to their meanings.

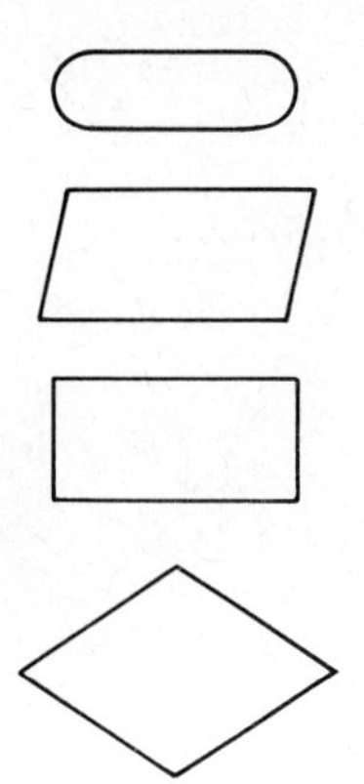

Begin or end. TM p. 7 , 1-6(2)

Describe a number or message to be read or written.

Describe computations to be done.

Ask a "yes" or "no" question.

EXERCISES

Follow the Flow Chart for Addition in solving the exercises below.

B

1.	3.	5.
11	91	2,047
7	73	3,269
5	50	47,707
9	121	101,203
	1234	

2.	4.	6.
27	374	427
101	576	18,915
35	224	3,062
4	1111	56
		398

Applications

1-7 Money Numbers

Everyone needs to be able to handle money numbers accurately. At home there are various bills to be checked — the telephone bill, the light bill, and so on. At work you may be asked to check larger amounts, or you may some day have your own business. No good businessman tolerates errors, because they may cost him money.

Try yourself on the test on the next page.

SELF-ANALYSIS TEST III
Time: 10 minutes

Add.

1.
```
 $2.37
  5.78
  3.35
$
```

2.
```
 $2.76
  4.38
  6.24
  5.73
$
```

3.
```
$ 4.46
   .26
 27.14
   .86
  8.29
$
```

Find the products and total them. (Do not write in your book.)

4. 2 × $1.20 = ______
4 × .50 = ______
3 × .75 = ______
Total = $ ______

5. 7 × $ .05 = ______
8 × .25 = ______
9 × .30 = ______
11 × 1.05 = ______
13 × .13 = ______
Total = $ ______

Addition and subtraction of money numbers are easy if you keep the decimal points in line. See what happens if you do not. Stress this.

Incorrect

```
$ 7.98
 30.05
 2.98
$67.83
```

Correct

```
$ 7.98
 30.05
  2.98
$41.01
```

Bookkeepers use a line in place of the decimal point. You can do this too if it helps you.

7	98
30	05
2	98

In multiplying a number like $5.95 by 3, be sure to point off the cents.

3 × $5.95 = $17.85

Division is just as easy if you keep the points in line.

```
    $ 5.95
3)$17.85
```

EXERCISES

Add.

A

1. $ .27
 .79
 .05

2. $1.25
 2.75
 1.25

3. $ 4.40
 19.95
 6.98
 1.02

4. $1.15 + $11.75 + $39.99 = ?

5. $125.00 + $87.98 + $3.33 = ?

Find the products and total them.

6. 2 × $1.50 = ?
7 × $1.20 = ?
9 × $1.80 = ?
Total = $?

7. 6 × $1.75 = ?
7 × $ .85 = ?
8 × $1.09 = ?
9 × $ .37 = ?
Total = $?

8. If a dozen golf balls cost $14.76, **(a)** how much does one cost; **(b)** how much would you pay for 5 balls; **(c)** how much would 5 doz. cost?

9. A golf bag cost $25.46, golf shoes $22.75, golf shirt $6.95, golf hat $4.98, and a golf set $187.00. What is their total cost?

1–8 Invoices

An **invoice** is an itemized bill. If you were working in the Purchasing Department of a corporation, you might need to check the accuracy of invoices. A computing machine may be used in the following work if available.

The use of typical business forms arouses interest in common business mathematics.

EXERCISES

Some of the following invoices contain errors. See if you can find them, and then make the necessary corrections.

A 1.

AMERICAN RADIO STORE
1916 Center Street
Jamestown, N.Y. 14701

No. 42351
Date: 7/21/

Sold to: John Dover
10 Main Street
Fredonia, N.Y. 14063

Cash	
Charge	✓

Quantity	Item	Each	Total
12	6AG7 Tube	2.13	25.56
18	12CV4	1.76	33.68
15	7G453 Switch	1.24	18.60
36	4A7GV Condenser	.29	11.44
9	MS4351 6" Speaker	3.86	34.74
24	MC 4562 Coil	.79	19.96
		Total	151.00

2.

Acme Food Company
453 S. Dock Street
San Diego, California 92101

No. 7943
Date: 8/26/--

Sold to: Seaside Hamburgers
105 Coast Road
Oceanside, California 92054

Cash ☐ **Charge** ☑

Quantity	Item	Unit	Price/Unit	Total
500	Ground Round	lb.	.53	265.00
350	Weiners	lb.	.49	174.50
100	Cheese, sliced	lb.	.59	59.00
360	Hamburger buns	doz.	.33	128.00
240	Weiner buns	doz.	.34	81.60
45	Pickles, dill	gal.	.63	28.55
980	Potatoes	lb.	.11	108.00
60	Mustard	qt.	.84	50.40

Total 898.55

3.

GoCar Auto Parts, Inc.
1313 Center Street
Middletown, Michigan 48060

Date 8/8/--
No. 23561

Sold to: U.S. Trucking Co.
1443 Addison Road
Flint, Mich. 48502

Cash X
Charge

Part No.	Part	Quantity	Each	Total
GC-135	Headlamp door	2	3.64	7.28
GC-1620B	Molding	1	2.11	2.11
GC-1307B	Sealed beam	2	2.40	4.40
GC-1307A	Sealed beam	2	2.40	4.80
GC-1308	Headlamp Door	2	3.64	6.28
GC-8200G	Side Grille	1	19.09	19.09
GC-8201G	Side Grille	1	19.09	19.90
GC-1667A	Molding	3	2.78	7.34
GC-674PL	Parking Lens	2	.64	1.28
GC-73PD4	Parking Lamp	2	3.00	3.00
GC-1756B	Bumper Bar	1	85.27	85.27
			Total	159.78

B 4.

All American Automotive Engine Rebuilding Co.
2345 E. 67th Street
Elgin, Illinois 60120

Bill to: • Edward Perkins
• 177 River Road
• Rockford, Illinois 61101

Invoice No. 44107
Date: 11/25/--

	Quan.	Description	Part No.	Cost	Total
1	8	Piston ring set	B5-6148C	2.52	20.16
2	8	Piston	EA-6237V	5.64	45.12
3	8	Piston pin	EA-6135B	.85	6.80
4	8	Connecting rod	B5-6200A	7.20	57.60
5	16	Pin bushing	EA-6206A	.28	4.48
6	8	Rod bearing set	EA-6211G	.80	6.40
7	4	Main bearing set	B9-6333S	1.35	5.40
8	2	Motor mount	EA-6734M	2.45	4.90
9	8	Exhaust valve	EA-3546E	1.32	10.56
10	8	Intake valve	EA-3547I	1.13	9.04
11	32	Valve retainer	EA-6543R	.16	5.12
12	16	Rocker arm	EA-5436A	1.43	22.88
13	16	Valve spring	EA-6547S	.77	12.32
14	8	Pushrod (intake)	EA-4532I	.68	5.44
15	8	Pushrod (exhaust)	EA-4325E	.73	5.84
16	4	Camshaft bearing	EA-6261B	1.24	4.96
17	16	Flywheel bolt	EA-6543F	.17	2.72
18	48	Head bolt	EA-6223C	.19	9.12
19					
20					
				Total	238.86

Challenge Problems are another means of allowing for individual differences. See also TM p. 7 , 1-8.

CHALLENGE PROBLEMS

B

1. What is the product of 13 and the next consecutive number?
2. A truck driver earned $35.00 a day. How much would he earn in one year if he worked 250 days?
3. To build a room addition, two carpenters worked eight hours per day for 10 days; 2 electricians worked 6 hr. one day and 2 hr. another day; 2 roofers worked 8 hr. one day; 2 cement men worked 5 hr. per day for two days; and 2 tilemen worked 6 hr. per day for one day. How many working hours were necessary to build the room addition?
4. A farmer wishes to paint the outside of his barn. How many gallons of paint should he buy if a gallon of paint covers 700 sq. ft. and the approximate outside area is 4900 sq. ft.?
5. A machine shop buys 750 lb. of $\frac{1}{8}$ in. diameter steel; 1156 lb. of 3 in. diameter steel; 5750 lb. of flat stock rectangular shape, 1 in. by 2 in.; 200 lb., $\frac{1}{8}$ in. by 2 ft.; 350 lb., $\frac{1}{2}$ in. square. What is the total number of pounds purchased?
6. If the quotient of two numbers is 5, and the larger is 35, what is the smaller number?
7. Several students want to purchase jointly a surfboard at $27 and a tent at $37. If each one pays $16, how many students bought these articles?
8. A customer purchases 13 gal. of gas at 35¢ per gallon, 5 qt. of oil at 60¢ per quart, and a new tire for $24.75. What is his total bill?
9. A cabinetmaker uses 12 board feet (bd. ft.) of birch at 72¢ per board foot, and 6 bd. ft. of ash at 51¢ per board foot. How much did the wood cost?
10. If the sum of two addends is 45, and one addend is 12, then the other addend is what number?

A clear understanding of fractions is essential to the study of ratio and proportion later.

■ Fractions

1–9 Meaning of Fractions

Do you remember the words we use with fractions?

$$\frac{3}{4} \begin{matrix} \leftarrow \textbf{numerator} \\ \leftarrow \textbf{denominator} \end{matrix}$$

When the numerator is less than the denominator, the fraction is called a **proper fraction.** If the numerator is equal to or greater than the denominator, the fraction is called an **improper fraction.** An improper fraction is usually written as a whole number and a proper fraction, such as $\frac{5}{4} = 1\frac{1}{4}$. $1\frac{1}{4}$ is a **mixed number.**

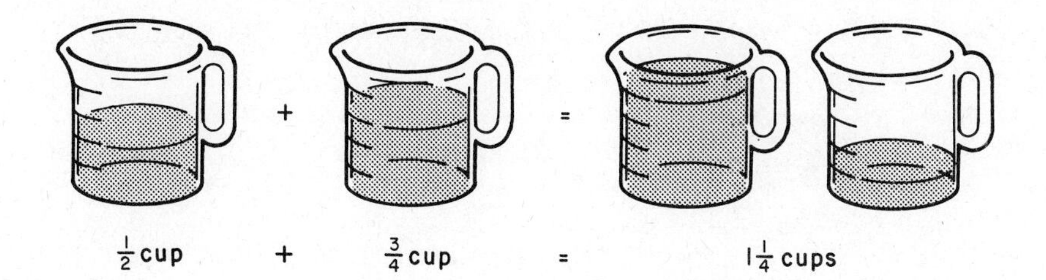

The line shown is divided into 16ths, and **equivalent fractions** are placed one under the other. Your ruler probably is divided into 16ths of an inch.

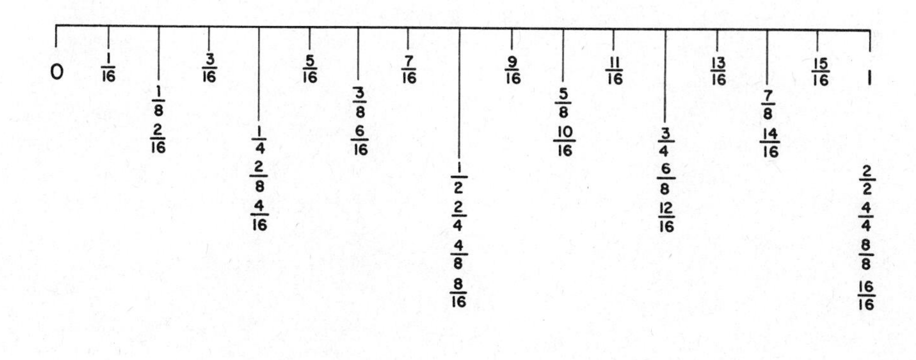

A fuller treatment of equivalence will be found in Chapter 6 in the study of units of measurement.

EXERCISES

Use your ruler or the diagram to help you with these exercises.

A

1. $\frac{1}{2} = \frac{?}{4} = \frac{?}{8}$ **3.** $\frac{1}{4} = \frac{?}{16}$ **5.** $\frac{5}{?} = \frac{10}{16}$

2. $\frac{12}{16} = \frac{?}{4}$ **4.** $1 = \frac{?}{2} = \frac{?}{4} = \frac{?}{16}$ **6.** $\frac{4}{?} = \frac{1}{4}$

7. $\frac{1}{4} + \frac{1}{4} = \frac{?}{4} = \frac{?}{2}$ **9.** $\frac{7}{16} - \frac{3}{16} = \frac{?}{16} = \frac{?}{4}$

8. $\frac{1}{8} + \frac{2}{8} = \frac{?}{8}$ **10.** $\frac{1}{2} + \frac{1}{4} = \frac{?}{4} + \frac{1}{4} = \frac{?}{4}$

1–10 Addition and Subtraction — Like Denominators

Exercises 7, 8, and 9 above suggest the following rule.

Panels are used to emphasize important rules of operation.

> To add fractions with like denominators, add the numerators and use the same denominator.
> To subtract fractions with like denominators, subtract the numerators and use the same denominator.

EXAMPLE

Add $\frac{3}{5}$ and $\frac{1}{5}$.

Solution. $\frac{3}{5}$ and $\frac{1}{5}$ have like denominators.
Therefore $\frac{3}{5} + \frac{1}{5} = \frac{4}{5}$.

EXERCISES

Add or subtract.

A

1. $\frac{1}{8} + \frac{2}{8}$ **4.** $\frac{1}{7} + \frac{3}{7}$ **7.** $\frac{2}{11} + \frac{4}{11}$

2. $\frac{1}{9} + \frac{4}{9}$ **5.** $\frac{7}{15} - \frac{3}{15}$ **8.** $\frac{5}{9} + \frac{2}{9}$

3. $\frac{2}{13} + \frac{4}{13}$ **6.** $\frac{6}{8} - \frac{1}{8}$ **9.** $\frac{1}{15} + \frac{7}{15}$

1–11 Equivalent Fractions

In Exercise 10 on page 21 we changed $\frac{1}{2}$ to the equivalent fraction $\frac{2}{4}$ before adding ($\frac{1}{2} + \frac{1}{4} = \frac{2}{4} + \frac{1}{4} = \frac{3}{4}$). To add or subtract fractions whose denominators are not alike, we need to know how to find equivalent fractions.

Recall that any number multiplied by 1 gives the number itself. Likewise, any number divided by 1 gives the number itself. For example,

$$3 \times 1 = 3 \qquad \frac{4}{5} \times 1 = \frac{4}{5} \qquad 2 \div 1 = 2 \qquad \frac{1}{2} \div 1 = \frac{1}{2}$$

This is sometimes called the **Principle of 1.**

But 1 has many forms: $\frac{2}{2}, \frac{4}{4}, \frac{5}{5}, \frac{100}{100}$, and so on. We may use *any* form of 1 as its equivalent. For example,

Be certain that students understand this.

The imposition of the 1 over the fraction calls attention to the Principle of 1.

$$\frac{1}{2} \times 1 = \frac{1}{2}$$
$$\frac{1}{2} \times \frac{2}{2} = \frac{2}{4}$$

$\frac{1}{2}$ and $\frac{2}{4}$ are equivalent fractions.

Thus we have the following rule for finding equivalent fractions.

1. The numerator and denominator of any fraction may be multiplied by the same number (except zero) without changing the value of the fraction.
2. The numerator and denominator of any fraction may be divided by the same number (except zero) without changing the value of the fraction.

Be certain the student understands why multiplication and division by zero is not an allowable procedure. Refer to page 8.

SELF-ANALYSIS TEST IV

Time: 10 minutes

Write in the simplest form.

1. $\frac{8}{10}$ **2.** $\frac{9}{45}$ **3.** $\frac{15}{30}$ **4.** $\frac{26}{78}$ **5.** $\frac{32}{48}$

Add the following fractions. Express answers in simplest form.

6. $\frac{2}{5} + \frac{1}{5} = ?$

7. $\frac{1}{15} + \frac{4}{15} = ?$

8. $\frac{1}{6} + \frac{5}{12} = ?$

9. $\frac{1}{8} + \frac{3}{4} = ?$

10. $\frac{1}{2} + \frac{1}{4} + \frac{3}{8} = ?$

EXAMPLE 1

Express $\frac{1}{2}$ and $\frac{1}{5}$ as fractions with the same denominator.

Solution. We choose 2×5, or 10, as the new denominator.

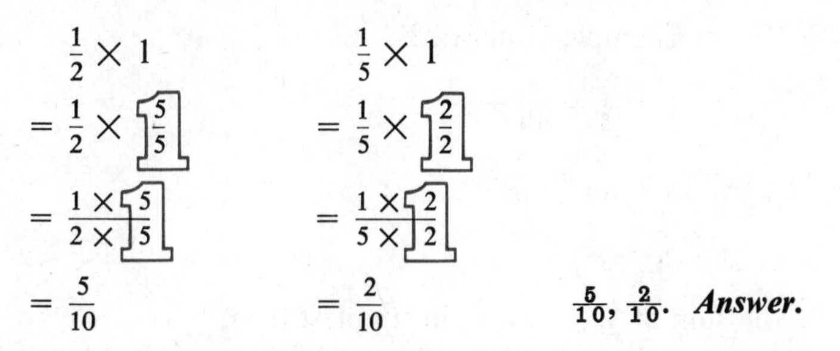

$$\frac{1}{2} \times 1 = \frac{1}{2} \times \frac{5}{5} = \frac{1 \times 5}{2 \times 5} = \frac{5}{10} \qquad \frac{1}{5} \times 1 = \frac{1}{5} \times \frac{2}{2} = \frac{1 \times 2}{5 \times 2} = \frac{2}{10}$$

$\frac{5}{10}, \frac{2}{10}$. ***Answer.***

The Principle of 1 also enables us to write fractions in simplest form, or to *reduce them to lowest terms.*

EXAMPLE 2 TM p. 7 , 1-11

Write $\frac{4}{16}$ in simplest form.

$$\frac{4}{16} \div 1 = \frac{4}{16} \div \boxed{\frac{4}{4}} = \frac{4 \div \boxed{4}}{16 \div \boxed{4}} = \mathbf{\frac{1}{4}}$$

EXERCISES

Express as equivalent fractions having like denominators.

A

1. $\frac{1}{3}, \frac{1}{6}$
2. $\frac{1}{3}, \frac{1}{2}$
3. $\frac{1}{12}, \frac{1}{4}$
4. $\frac{3}{4}, \frac{1}{2}$
5. $\frac{1}{16}, \frac{3}{8}$
6. $\frac{1}{4}, \frac{3}{8}$
7. $\frac{1}{2}, \frac{1}{4}, \frac{1}{8}$
8. $\frac{1}{16}, \frac{3}{8}, \frac{1}{2}$
9. $\frac{1}{10}, \frac{1}{5}, \frac{1}{2}$

Write in simplest form.

10. $\frac{4}{6}$
11. $\frac{10}{15}$
12. $\frac{5}{10}$
13. $\frac{27}{36}$
14. $\frac{20}{24}$
15. $\frac{14}{21}$
16. $\frac{16}{18}$
17. $\frac{26}{39}$
18. $\frac{8}{48}$
19. $\frac{15}{20}$

1–12 Addition and Subtraction — Unlike Denominators

We can now solve problems such as the following.

EXAMPLE 1

Add $\frac{1}{2}$ and $\frac{1}{5}$.

Solution. From Example 1, page 23,

$$\frac{1}{2} + \frac{1}{5} = \frac{5}{10} + \frac{2}{10}$$

Then $\frac{5}{10} + \frac{2}{10} = \mathbf{\frac{7}{10}}$

EXAMPLE 2

Write the sum of $\frac{1}{3}$, $\frac{1}{4}$, and $\frac{1}{12}$ in simplest form.

Solution. Because 12 is divisible by both 3 and 4, we choose 12 as the new denominator.

$$\frac{1}{3} = \frac{1}{3} \times 1 \qquad \frac{1}{4} = \frac{1}{4} \times 1$$
$$= \frac{1}{3} \times \boxed{\frac{4}{4}} \qquad = \frac{1}{4} \times \boxed{\frac{3}{3}}$$
$$= \frac{4}{12} \qquad = \frac{3}{12}$$

Therefore $\frac{1}{3} + \frac{1}{4} + \frac{1}{12}$

$$= \frac{4}{12} + \frac{3}{12} + \frac{1}{12}$$
$$= \frac{8}{12}$$

Change $\frac{8}{12}$ to simplest form:

$$\frac{8}{12} \div 1 = \frac{8}{12} \div \boxed{\frac{4}{4}} = \frac{8 \div 4}{12 \div 4} = \frac{2}{3}$$

EXERCISES

Express the results in simplest form.

A

1. $\frac{1}{4} + \frac{3}{4} + \frac{5}{4}$
2. $\frac{3}{4} + \frac{1}{2}$
3. $\frac{1}{3} + \frac{1}{5}$
4. $\frac{2}{3} + \frac{1}{6}$
5. $\frac{1}{7} + \frac{2}{3}$
6. $\frac{3}{16} + \frac{1}{8}$
7. $\frac{3}{4} + \frac{13}{16}$
8. $\frac{3}{32} + \frac{7}{64}$
9. $\frac{5}{4} - \frac{7}{16}$
10. $\frac{2}{11} + \frac{1}{13}$

B

11. $\frac{1}{7} + \frac{3}{7} + \frac{6}{7}$
12. $\frac{1}{2} + \frac{1}{3} + \frac{1}{4}$
13. $\frac{2}{3} + \frac{3}{8} + \frac{4}{5}$
14. $\frac{3}{8} + \frac{1}{4} - \frac{2}{5}$
15. $\frac{3}{8} + \frac{1}{8} + \frac{1}{16}$

SELF-ANALYSIS TEST V

Time: 10 minutes

1. $\frac{3}{5} = \frac{?}{20}$
2. $\frac{4}{5} = \frac{?}{60}$
3. $\frac{3}{8} = \frac{?}{24}$
4. $\frac{3}{4} = \frac{?}{12}$
5. $\frac{1}{4} = \frac{?}{40}$
6. $\frac{1}{2} - \frac{1}{3} = \square$
7. $\frac{1}{8} + \frac{1}{4} = \square$
8. $\frac{1}{7} + \frac{1}{14} = \square$
9. $\frac{3}{7} + \frac{5}{6} = \square$
10. $\frac{7}{20} + \frac{1}{4} + \frac{3}{5} = \square$

Lowest Common Denominator

Up to now we have found a common denominator to solve each problem, but in many instances it was not the *lowest*, or least, common denominator (LCD). Thus 24 can be taken as a common denominator for the fractions $\frac{2}{3}$, $\frac{1}{6}$, and $\frac{1}{12}$, which are equivalent to $\frac{16}{24}$, $\frac{4}{24}$, and $\frac{2}{24}$ respectively. But 12, which is less, could have been used: $\frac{8}{12}$, $\frac{2}{12}$, and $\frac{1}{12}$ respectively.

An easy way to find the LCD is to write multiples of the largest denominator. The smallest such multiple which is exactly divisible by the other denominators will be the LCD.

EXAMPLE 1

Emphasize that using the LCD keeps computations on a simpler level and lessens the chance of error.

Find the least common denominator of $\frac{1}{2}$, $\frac{1}{4}$, $\frac{1}{5}$.

Solution. The multiples of 5 are 5, 10, 15, 20, 25, 30, 35, ... The smallest multiple which is exactly divisible by both 2 *and* 4 is 20. Thus, **20 is the LCD.**

Finding the multiples of odd denominators is usually a good starting point.

EXAMPLE 2

What is the least common denominator of $\frac{1}{3}$, $\frac{1}{7}$, $\frac{1}{6}$?

Solution. The multiples of 7 are 7, 14, 21, 28, 35, 42, 49, ... The smallest multiple divisible by both 3 and 6 is 42. Thus, **42 is the LCD.**

EXERCISES

Find the least common denominator for the fractions below.

A

1. $\frac{1}{2}, \frac{1}{3}, \frac{1}{4}$

2. $\frac{1}{2}, \frac{1}{3}, \frac{1}{8}$

3. $\frac{1}{6}, \frac{1}{8}, \frac{1}{3}$

4. $\frac{1}{3}, \frac{1}{4}, \frac{1}{8}$

5. $\frac{1}{4}, \frac{1}{8}, \frac{1}{5}$

6. $\frac{1}{16}, \frac{1}{8}, \frac{1}{3}$

7. $\frac{1}{12}, \frac{1}{10}, \frac{1}{5}$

8. $\frac{1}{2}, \frac{1}{4}, \frac{1}{5}$

9. $\frac{1}{3}, \frac{1}{4}, \frac{1}{9}$

10. $\frac{1}{7}, \frac{1}{3}, \frac{1}{14}$

11–20. Add the fractions in each of Exercises 1–10. Express answers in lowest terms.

1–13 Multiplication of Fractions

See TM p. 7 , 1-13 on cancellation.

You know that

$$\frac{5}{4} \times 1 = \frac{5}{4} \times \frac{2}{2} = \frac{5 \times 2}{4 \times 2}$$

It should seem reasonable then to write

$$\frac{5}{4} \times \frac{1}{2} = \frac{5 \times 1}{4 \times 2} = \frac{5}{8}$$

Or,

$$\frac{3}{4} \times \frac{7}{8} = \frac{3 \times 7}{4 \times 8} = \frac{21}{32}$$

Would you agree with this rule?

> To multiply two fractions, multiply the numerators to give the new numerator, and multiply the denominators to give the new denominator.

To multiply a fraction by a whole number, you may follow this method:

$$3 \times \frac{5}{16} = \frac{3}{1} \times \frac{5}{16} = \frac{15}{16}$$

Actually, we have simply multiplied the numerator 5 by the whole number 3.

EXAMPLES

1. $\frac{2}{3} \times \frac{4}{7} = \frac{2 \times 4}{3 \times 7} = \frac{8}{21}$
2. $\frac{3}{4} \times \frac{5}{7} = \frac{15}{28}$
3. $\frac{14}{23} \times \frac{2}{5} = \frac{14 \times 2}{23 \times 5} = \frac{28}{115}$
4. $\frac{5}{6} \times 5 = \frac{5 \times 5}{6 \times 1} = \frac{25}{6} = 4\frac{1}{6}$

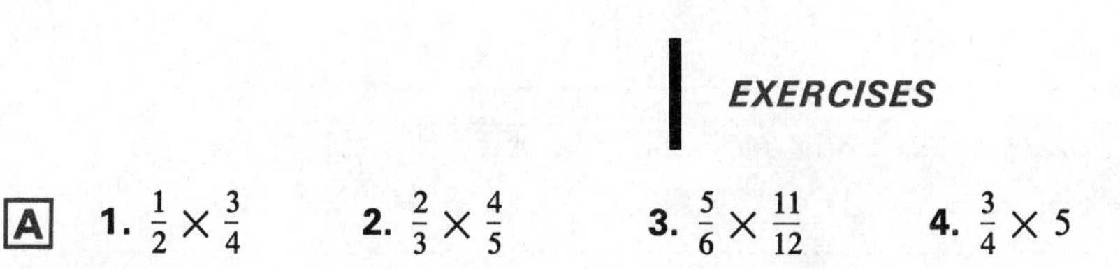

EXERCISES

A **1.** $\frac{1}{2} \times \frac{3}{4}$ **2.** $\frac{2}{3} \times \frac{4}{5}$ **3.** $\frac{5}{6} \times \frac{11}{12}$ **4.** $\frac{3}{4} \times 5$

5. $\frac{3}{5} \times \frac{6}{7}$ 7. $\frac{5}{6} \times \frac{13}{14}$ 9. $\frac{2}{9} \times \frac{2}{3}$ 11. $\frac{9}{16} \times 72$

6. $\frac{2}{3} \times \frac{5}{7}$ 8. $\frac{1}{5} \times \frac{6}{7}$ 10. $\frac{3}{8} \times \frac{11}{12}$ 12. $\frac{3}{4} \times \frac{7}{8} \times \frac{5}{16}$

1–14 Division of Fractions

You probably remember the rule for dividing one fraction by another, "invert and multiply," but do you remember which one to invert and why?

Suppose the problem is the following one.

$$\frac{3}{5} \div \frac{2}{3}$$

Our problem is to write this expression as a single fraction. If we write it in the following form, we can find a method to simplify it.

$$\frac{\frac{3}{5}}{\frac{2}{3}}$$

Certain students may recognize this as a "complex fraction."

It is now a fraction, made up of two fractions. We may use the Principle of 1 and multiply both numerator and denominator by the same non-zero number to get a simpler form. Look at the following work and notice the form of "1" we choose and the result we obtain.

$$\frac{\frac{3}{5}}{\frac{2}{3}} \times \frac{\frac{3}{2}}{\frac{3}{2}} = \frac{\frac{3}{5} \times \frac{3}{2}}{\frac{2}{3} \times \frac{3}{2}}$$

$$= \frac{\frac{3}{5} \times \frac{3}{2}}{1}$$

$$= \frac{3}{5} \times \frac{3}{2} = \frac{9}{10}$$

In this case, where the denominator was $\frac{2}{3}$, we multiplied both numerator and denominator by the **reciprocal** of $\frac{2}{3}$, namely, $\frac{3}{2}$. We would choose such a number each time because the product of a number multiplied by its reciprocal is always 1. This is why we can use the following rule:

> To divide by a fraction, multiply by the reciprocal of the divisor.

EXAMPLE

$\frac{2}{7} \div \frac{3}{4}$

Solution 1. $\frac{2}{7} \div \frac{3}{4} = \frac{\frac{2}{7}}{\frac{3}{4}} = \frac{\frac{2}{7}}{\frac{3}{4}} \times \frac{\frac{4}{3}}{\frac{4}{3}} = \frac{\frac{2}{7} \times \frac{4}{3}}{\frac{3}{4} \times \frac{4}{3}}$

$= \frac{\frac{2}{7} \times \frac{4}{3}}{1}$

$= \frac{2}{7} \times \frac{4}{3} = \mathbf{\frac{8}{21}}$

Solution 2. $\frac{2}{7} \div \frac{3}{4} = \frac{2}{7} \times \frac{4}{3} = \mathbf{\frac{8}{21}}$

EXERCISES

Name the reciprocal.

A

1. $\frac{1}{3}$ **3.** 3 **5.** $\frac{3}{8}$ **7.** 100 **9.** $\frac{3}{4}$

2. $\frac{2}{3}$ **4.** $\frac{1}{2}$ **6.** $\frac{6}{5}$ **8.** $\frac{1}{10}$ **10.** $\frac{4}{3}$

Divide. Leave all answers in simplest form.

11. $\frac{3}{4} \div \frac{2}{3}$ **14.** $\frac{7}{16} \div \frac{1}{2}$ **17.** $\frac{5}{8} \div \frac{3}{16}$ **20.** $\frac{1}{8} \div \frac{2}{3}$

12. $\frac{1}{6} \div \frac{7}{8}$ **15.** $\frac{3}{8} \div \frac{3}{5}$ **18.** $\frac{3}{16} \div \frac{9}{32}$ **21.** $\frac{4}{5} \div \frac{6}{7}$

13. $\frac{2}{5} \div \frac{1}{4}$ **16.** $\frac{3}{10} \div \frac{9}{20}$ **19.** $\frac{1}{2} \div 100$ **22.** $4 \div \frac{3}{4}$

Optional. Use the flow chart for these problems.

B

23. $6\frac{1}{4} \div 2$

24. $4\frac{1}{2} \div 3\frac{7}{8}$

25. $16 \div \frac{3}{4}$

26. $16\frac{1}{2} \div \frac{1}{2}$

27. $\frac{1}{32} \div \frac{1}{4}$

28. $\frac{3}{16} \div \frac{3}{8}$

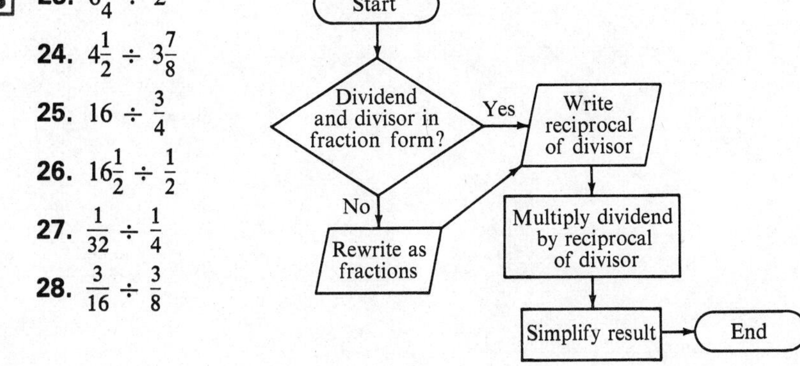

Template Problems involving Fractions

EXAMPLE 1

Find X, assuming the holes are evenly spaced.

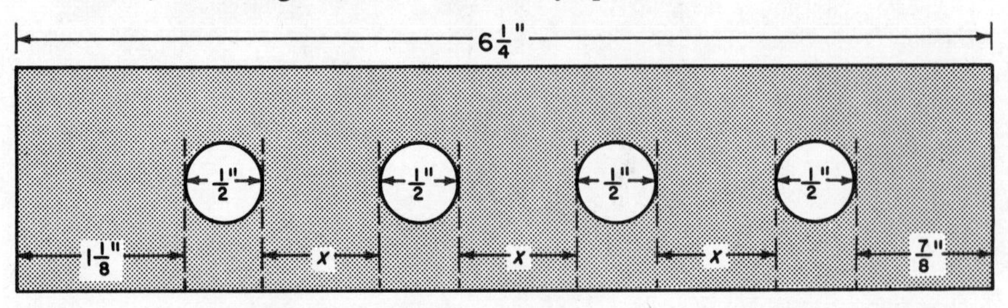

Solution. Total length *minus* length of ends

$$= 6\tfrac{1}{4}'' - (1\tfrac{1}{8}'' + \tfrac{7}{8}'')$$

$$= 6\tfrac{1}{4}'' - 2''$$

$$= 4\tfrac{1}{4}'' \text{ (total width of holes and distance between them)}$$

Total width of holes

$$= \tfrac{1}{2}'' + \tfrac{1}{2}'' + \tfrac{1}{2}'' + \tfrac{1}{2}'' = 2''$$

$$3X = 4\tfrac{1}{4}'' - 2'' = 2\tfrac{1}{4}''$$

$$X = 2\tfrac{1}{4}'' \div 3 = \tfrac{9}{4} \times \tfrac{1}{3} = \tfrac{3}{4}''.$$

EXAMPLE 2

Find the distance X.

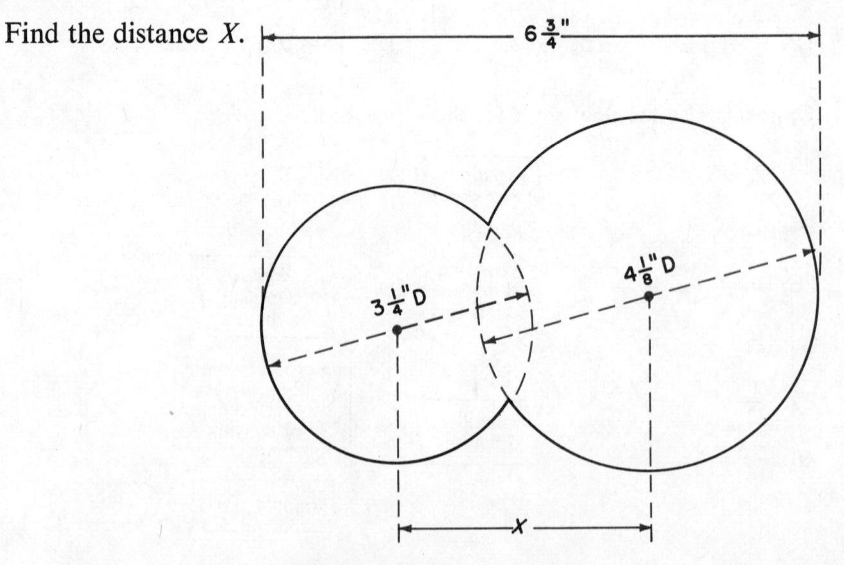

Solution.
$$X = 6\frac{3}{4} - \frac{1}{2}(3\frac{1}{4}) - \frac{1}{2}(4\frac{1}{8})$$
$$= 6\frac{3}{4} - \frac{1}{2}(\frac{13}{4}) - \frac{1}{2}(\frac{33}{8})$$
$$= \frac{27}{4} - \frac{13}{8} - \frac{33}{16}$$
$$= \frac{108}{16} - \frac{26}{16} - \frac{33}{16}$$
$$= \frac{49}{16}$$
$$= \mathbf{3\frac{1}{16}\ (in.)}$$

EXERCISES

A

1. Find distance X.

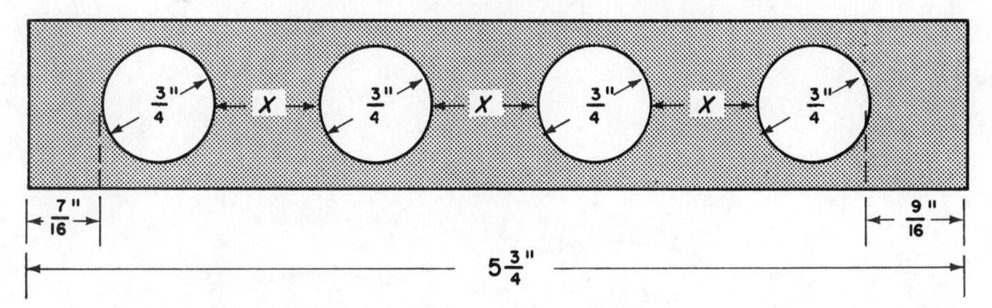

2. Find distance Y.

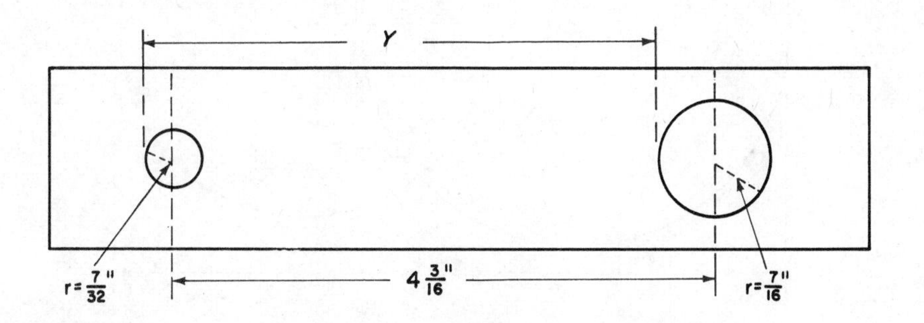

3. Find distance X.

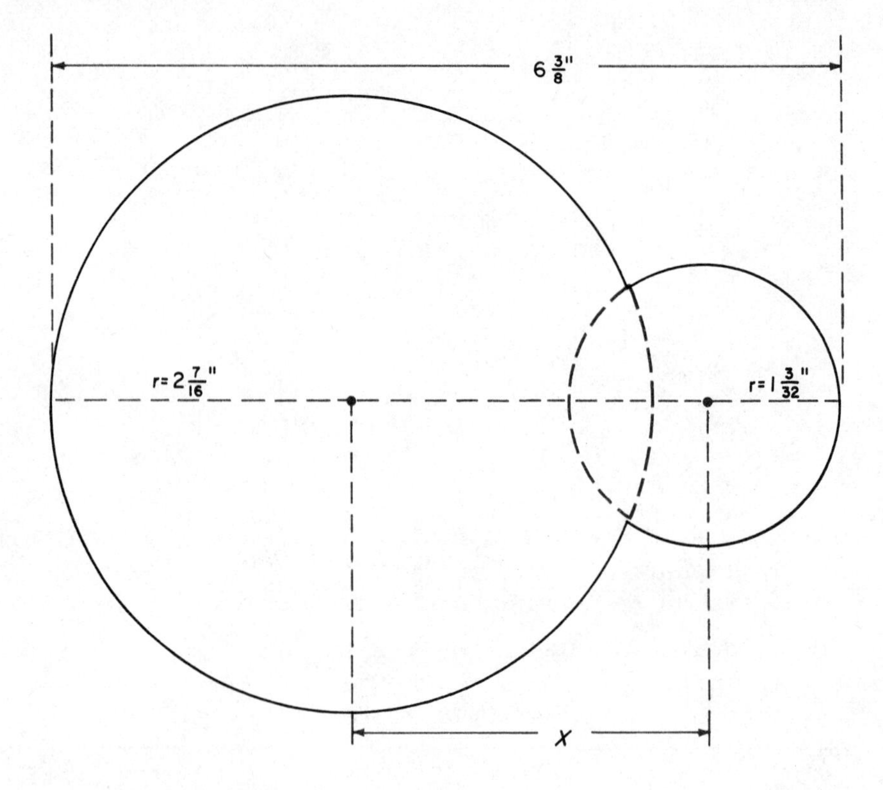

4. Find distance Y.

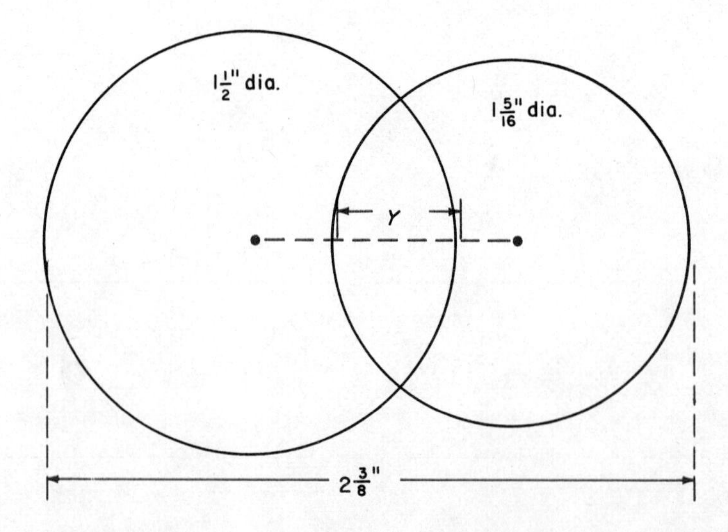

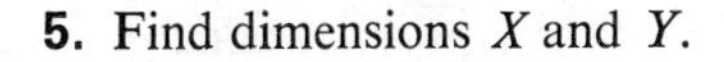

5. Find dimensions X and Y.

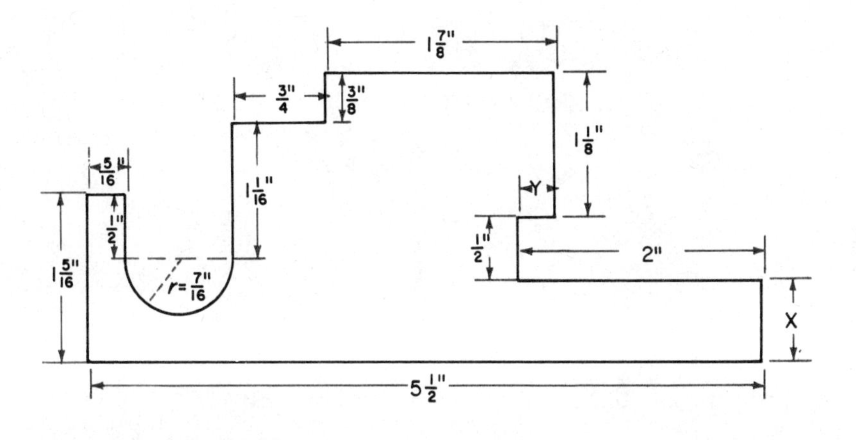

A firm grasp of decimal fractions will prove helpful in studying the metric system and percentages later in the book.

■ Decimal Fractions

1–15 Properties; Addition and Subtraction

Decimal fractions are simply special fractions. They are fractions with denominators of 10, 100, 1000, and so on. We write them without the denominators by using the "decimal point." Thus,

$$\frac{1}{10} = 0.1, \quad \frac{1}{2} = \frac{5}{10} = 0.5, \quad \frac{3}{100} = 0.03$$

Just as places to the left of the decimal point have place value, so do places to the right of the decimal point.

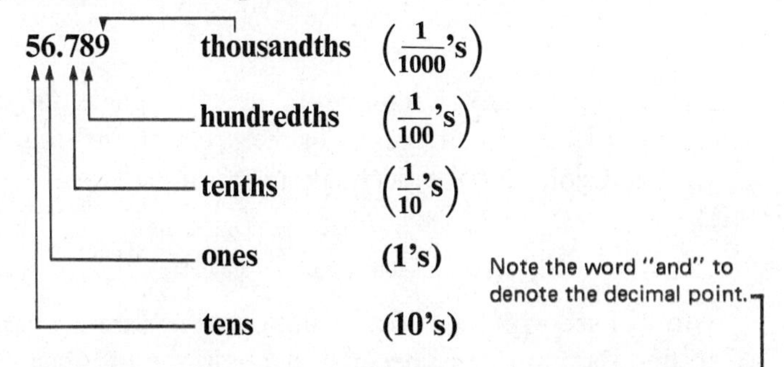

Note the word "and" to denote the decimal point.

When reading a decimal, use the name of the last place to the right; for example, 56.789 is read "56 and 789 thousandths." Sometimes in business we read this as "5, 6, point, 7, 8, 9."

When you add or subtract decimals, you must be careful to add columns of the same value, such as tenths and tenths, just as you must be careful to add columns of the same value with whole numbers. This

Stress this.

is why, when we add columns with decimal fractions, we are careful to have the decimal points in line.

This		Not this!	
	34.6		34.6
	2.65		2.65
	381.74		381.74

EXERCISES

Copy and simplify.

A

1. $2.5 + 16.3 + 14.2$
2. $6.0 + 0.6 + 26.6 + 16.5$
3. $535.5 + 27.1 + 9.9 + 28.8$
4. $\$15.27 + \$75.55 + \$18.98$
5. $\$15.25 - \$1.36$
6. 2.07 in. − 1.323 in.
7. 14.5 mi. − 9.6 mi.
8. $(3.2 + 4.2 + 7.5) - 5.5$

1–16 Multiplication of Decimals

Do you remember how to multiply decimals? You probably remember *how*, but do you know *why* you locate the decimal point in the answer the way you do?

$$\begin{array}{r} .13 \\ \times\ .2 \\ \hline .026 \end{array}$$

You count the total number of decimal places in both factors and "point off" that many places in the product, moving from right to left.

If you consider the decimals in fractional form and then multiply,

$$\frac{13}{100} \times \frac{2}{10} = \frac{26}{1000} = .026,$$

you will see why we add the number of decimal places in each factor to find the number of decimal places in the product.

The number of decimal places in a product is the sum of the number of decimal places in the factors.

EXAMPLES

1.
```
   .245 ← 3 places
 × 1.6  ← 1 place
  1470
  245
 .3920  ← 4 places
```

Caution students to retain this "necessary" zero in counting decimal places to locate the decimal point.

2.
```
   2.31 ← 2 places
 × .014 ← 3 places
    924
   231
 .03234 ← 5 places
```

Notice that we had to insert a 0 in order to locate the decimal point.

EXERCISES

A

1. $3.68 \times 2.5 = ?$
2. $265.1 \times .13 = ?$
3. $13.4 \times 5.8 = ?$
4. $62.34 \times 9.1 = ?$
5. $2.63 \times 4.25 = ?$
6. $.1875 \times .3125 = ?$
7. $2.375 \times .0625 = ?$
8. $.750 \times .1875 = ?$
9. $.4375 \times .125 = ?$
10. $.250 \times .625 = ?$

1–17 Division involving Decimals

Do you remember how to divide a decimal by a whole number? It is easy if you keep the decimal points in line.

EXAMPLE 1

$6.25 \div 5$

Solution.
```
    .
 5)6.25
```
Place the point for the quotient just above the one in the dividend.

```
  1.25
 5)6.25
```
Then divide as for whole numbers.

EXAMPLE 2

$3 \div 8$

Solution. Think of 3 as 3., and add zeros after the decimal point. (You can add as many zeros after the decimal point as you wish.)

```
   .375
 8)3.000
```

Notice that the division in Example 2 is what is needed to express $\frac{3}{8}$ as a decimal, because $\frac{3}{8} = 3 \div 8$.

Sometimes the division gives only an approximate equivalent. For example, to change $\frac{1}{3}$ to a decimal, we write

$$3\overline{)1.0000}^{\,.3333\ldots}$$ (The . . . means "and so on.")

We can then give the result as a *rounded* number. The result to the nearest thousandth is .333.

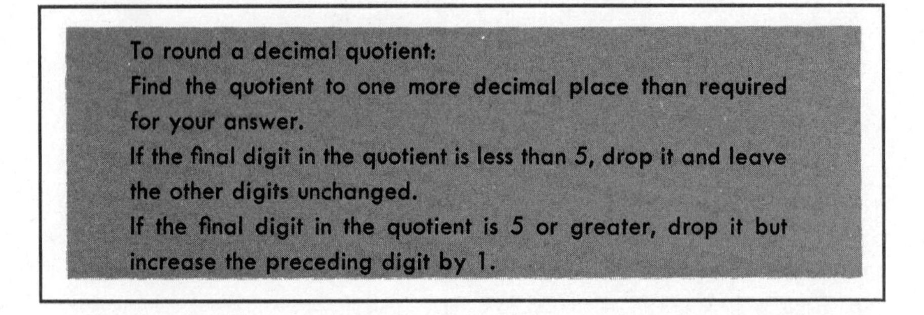
To round a decimal quotient:
Find the quotient to one more decimal place than required for your answer.
If the final digit in the quotient is less than 5, drop it and leave the other digits unchanged.
If the final digit in the quotient is 5 or greater, drop it but increase the preceding digit by 1.

EXAMPLES

3. .377 rounded to two places is .38
4. .5223 rounded to three places is .522
5. .745 rounded to two places is .75

Suppose you have the problem $.75 \div .25$; you can express it as $\frac{.75}{.25}$. The problem becomes a simple one if we think as follows:

$$\frac{.75}{.25} \times \boxed{\frac{100}{100}} = \frac{75}{25} = 3$$

EXAMPLE 6

$.3 \div .12 = ?$

Solution. $.3 \div .12 = \dfrac{.3}{.12}$

$$\frac{.3 \times 100}{.12 \times 100} = \frac{30}{12}$$

$$\begin{array}{r} 2.5 \\ 12\overline{)30.0} \\ 24 \\ \hline 6\,0 \\ 6\,0 \\ \hline \end{array}$$ **Answer**

There is no need to write out all these steps once you are sure of the process.

Certain fractions occur so often that it is convenient to know their decimal equivalents. People who work with such fractions usually have a table of fractions and decimal equivalents similar to the following.

Tables are presented within the text for convenient reference to the material being discussed.

FRACTIONS AND DECIMAL EQUIVALENTS

		1/64	.015625			33/64	.515625
	1/32		.03125		17/32		.53125
		3/64	.046875			35/64	.546875
	1/16		.0625		9/16		.5625
		5/64	.078125			37/64	.578125
	3/32		.09375		19/32		.59375
		7/64	.109375			39/64	.609375
1/8			.125	5/8			.625
		9/64	.140625			41/64	.640625
	5/32		.15625		21/32		.65625
		11/64	.171875			43/64	.671875
	3/16		.1875		11/16		.6875
		13/64	.203125			45/64	.703125
	7/32		.21875		23/32		.71875
		15/64	.234375			47/64	.734375
1/4			.25	3/4			.75
		17/64	.265625			49/64	.765625
	9/32		.28125		25/32		.78125
		19/64	.296875			51/64	.796875
	5/16		.3125		13/16		.8125
		21/64	.328125			53/64	.828125
	11/32		.34375		27/32		.84375
		23/64	.359375			55/64	.859375
3/8			.375	7/8			.875
		25/64	.390625			57/64	.890625
	13/32		.40625		29/32		.90625
		27/64	.421875			59/64	.921875
	7/16		.4375		15/16		.9375
		29/64	.453125			61/64	.953125
	15/32		.46875		31/32		.96875
		31/64	.484375			63/64	.984375
1/2			.5	1			1.

EXERCISES

Use the table on page 37 to state the decimal equivalents.

A

1. $\frac{3}{8}$ **3.** $\frac{1}{4}$ **5.** $\frac{1}{16}$ **7.** $\frac{3}{32}$ **9.** $\frac{1}{64}$

2. $\frac{5}{8}$ **4.** $\frac{3}{4}$ **6.** $\frac{5}{16}$ **8.** $\frac{7}{8}$ **10.** $\frac{3}{16}$

Round these decimals to one less decimal place than given.

11. .625 **13.** 5.2333 . . . **15.** 1.866 . . . **17.** .4062

12. .375 **14.** 12.66 . . . **16.** 3.141 . . . **18.** 1.1406

Find the quotients. Round decimal results to hundredths.

19. $1.187 \div 4$ **21.** $.0625 \div 2.5$ **23.** $28.62 \div 4.18$

20. $.828125 \div 5$ **22.** $523.6 \div .04$ **24.** $17.55 \div .83$

B

25. $\frac{.1875}{.0625}$ **27.** $\frac{.4375}{.65625}$ **29.** $\frac{8.667}{3.8}$

26. $\frac{.28125}{.3125}$ **28.** $\frac{1.375}{.1875}$ **30.** $\frac{.421875}{.5625}$

SELF-ANALYSIS TEST VI

Time: 20 minutes

Multiply.

1. $\frac{1}{4} \times \frac{1}{4} = ?$

2. $\frac{1}{8} \times \frac{1}{8} = ?$

3. $\frac{1}{2} \times \frac{1}{4} = ?$

4. $\frac{1}{16} \times \frac{1}{4} = ?$

5. $\frac{1}{8} \times \frac{1}{24} = ?$

6. $.75 \times .25 = ?$

7. $.75 \times .125 = ?$

8. $.375 \times .25 = ?$

9. $.25 \times .50 = ?$

10. $.125 \times 3.125 = ?$

Divide.

11. $\frac{\frac{1}{4}}{\frac{2}{4}} = ?$ **12.** $\frac{\frac{1}{4}}{\frac{1}{8}} = ?$ **13.** $\frac{\frac{5}{16}}{\frac{3}{32}} = ?$ **14.** $\frac{\frac{3}{8}}{\frac{7}{32}} = ?$

15. $\dfrac{\frac{3}{16}}{\frac{5}{32}} = ?$

16. $\dfrac{.25}{.50} = ?$

17. $\dfrac{.375}{.125} = ?$

18. $\dfrac{.625}{.750} = ?$

19. $\dfrac{.1875}{.0625} = ?$

20. $\dfrac{.4375}{.125} = ?$

1–18 Exponents and Square Roots

Exponents are often used in formulas where a repeated multiplication occurs. The area of a square is given by the product of the lengths of two sides.

Point out that the exponent indicates the number of times the given number is to be used as a factor.

$$A = s \times s, \text{ or } s^2$$

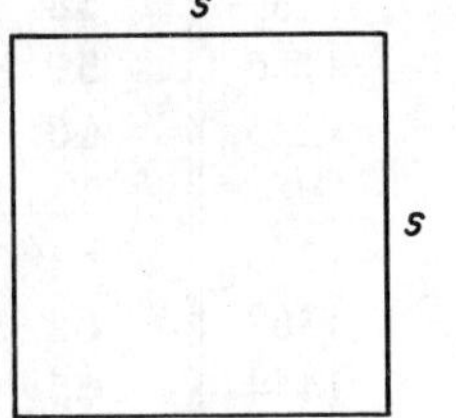

If the side s is 3 in. long, we have

$$A = 3 \times 3, \text{ or } 3^2$$

$$A = 9 \text{ (sq. in.)}$$

The table on page 40 gives the squares of whole numbers up to 100. If you are careful, you can use it with decimals too. (Recall the rule on page 34.)

EXAMPLES

1. $37^2 = 1369$ 2. $23^2 = 23 \times 23 = 529$ 3. $1.1^2 = 1.21$

Now suppose we know the product of *two* equal factors and want to know what the factors are. For example, we may know that the area of a square is 64 square feet. To find the length of a side of this square, we find the square root of 64, which is 8. The side of the square is 8 feet.

$\sqrt{64}$ **means "the square root of 64"**

Do you see that the table of squares can be used to find certain square roots? We also show a table of square roots on page 41 which will be helpful in later work with formulas.

SQUARES OF WHOLE NUMBERS FROM 1 TO 100

Number	*Square*	*Number*	*Square*	*Number*	*Square*	*Number*	*Square*
1	1	**26**	676	**51**	2601	**76**	5776
2	4	**27**	729	**52**	2704	**77**	5929
3	9	**28**	784	**53**	2809	**78**	6084
4	16	**29**	841	**54**	2916	**79**	6241
5	25	**30**	900	**55**	3025	**80**	6400
6	36	**31**	961	**56**	3136	**81**	6561
7	49	**32**	1024	**57**	3249	**82**	6724
8	64	**33**	1089	**58**	3364	**83**	6889
9	81	**34**	1156	**59**	3481	**84**	7056
10	100	**35**	1225	**60**	3600	**85**	7225
11	121	**36**	1296	**61**	3721	**86**	7396
12	144	**37**	1369	**62**	3844	**87**	7569
13	169	**38**	1444	**63**	3969	**88**	7744
14	196	**39**	1521	**64**	4096	**89**	7921
15	225	**40**	1600	**65**	4225	**90**	8100
16	256	**41**	1681	**66**	4356	**91**	8281
17	289	**42**	1764	**67**	4489	**92**	8464
18	324	**43**	1849	**68**	4624	**93**	8649
19	361	**44**	1936	**69**	4761	**94**	8836
20	400	**45**	2025	**70**	4900	**95**	9025
21	441	**46**	2116	**71**	5041	**96**	9216
22	484	**47**	2209	**72**	5184	**97**	9409
23	529	**48**	2304	**73**	5329	**98**	9604
24	576	**49**	2401	**74**	5476	**99**	9801
25	625	**50**	2500	**75**	5625	**100**	10,000

SQUARE ROOTS OF WHOLE NUMBERS FROM 1 TO 100

Number	Square Root	Number	Square Root	Number	Square Root	Number	Square Root
1	1.000	**26**	5.099	**51**	7.141	**76**	8.718
2	1.414	**27**	5.196	**52**	7.211	**77**	8.775
3	1.732	**28**	5.292	**53**	7.280	**78**	8.832
4	2.000	**29**	5.385	**54**	7.348	**79**	8.888
5	2.236	**30**	5.477	**55**	7.416	**80**	8.944
6	2.449	**31**	5.568	**56**	7.483	**81**	9.000
7	2.646	**32**	5.657	**57**	7.550	**82**	9.055
8	2.828	**33**	5.745	**58**	7.616	**83**	9.110
9	3.000	**34**	5.831	**59**	7.681	**84**	9.165
10	3.162	**35**	5.916	**60**	7.746	**85**	9.220
11	3.317	**36**	6.000	**61**	7.810	**86**	9.274
12	3.464	**37**	6.083	**62**	7.874	**87**	9.327
13	3.606	**38**	6.164	**63**	7.937	**88**	9.381
14	3.742	**39**	6.245	**64**	8.000	**89**	9.434
15	3.873	**40**	6.325	**65**	8.062	**90**	9.487
16	4.000	**41**	6.403	**66**	8.124	**91**	9.539
17	4.123	**42**	6.481	**67**	8.185	**92**	9.592
18	4.243	**43**	6.557	**68**	8.246	**93**	9.644
19	4.359	**44**	6.633	**69**	8.307	**94**	9.695
20	4.472	**45**	6.708	**70**	8.367	**95**	9.747
21	4.583	**46**	6.782	**71**	8.426	**96**	9.798
22	4.690	**47**	6.856	**72**	8.485	**97**	9.849
23	4.796	**48**	6.928	**73**	8.544	**98**	9.899
24	4.899	**49**	7.000	**74**	8.602	**99**	9.950
25	5.000	**50**	7.071	**75**	8.660	**100**	10.000

Not all square roots can be found from these tables.

The following method is a way of finding the square root of a number. This is an easy method to remember and easy to use. It is called the "divide and average" method.

EXAMPLE 4 TM p. 7 , 1-18

Find the approximate value for $\sqrt{3}$.

Solution. Since $1^2 = 1$ and $2^2 = 4$, we know the value is between 1 and 2. Suppose we guess somewhere between 1 and 2, say 1.5. We divide the number whose root we are finding by our "guess"; that is, we divide 3 by 1.5.

```
      2.
1.5)3.00
    30
```

Next, take the average of 1.5 and 2.

$$\frac{1.5 + 2}{2} = 1.75$$

Now this value, 1.75, is closer to $\sqrt{3}$ than our first guess, 1.5, since

$$(1.75)^2 = 3.0625$$

while

$$(1.5)^2 = 2.25$$

If we repeat the process again, we can get an even better approximation. That is, we divide 3 by 1.75.

```
         1.714     Do not round the quotient.
1.75)3.000
     1 75
     1 250
     1 225
        250
        175
         750
```

Again we take the average of the divisor and the quotient.

$$\frac{1.75 + 1.714}{2} = \mathbf{1.732}$$

This value, 1.732, is a better approximation than the last one, 1.75. If necessary we could repeat the process and obtain a closer approximation. In this case $3 \div 1.732$ gives 1.7321. The average of 1.732 and 1.7321 is 1.73205, so that the answer is correct to three places. Compare this result with the table on page 41.

EXAMPLE 5

Find the approximate value for $\sqrt{145}$, correct to two decimal places.

Solution. Since 145 is close to 12^2, or 144, we try 12 as our first guess.

Divide:

$$\begin{array}{r} 12.08 \\ 12\overline{)145.00} \\ \underline{144} \\ 1\,00 \end{array}$$

Average: $\dfrac{12 + 12.08}{2} = 12.04$

Divide:

$$\begin{array}{r} 12.043 \\ 12.04\overline{)145.00} \\ \underline{120\,4} \\ 24\,60 \\ \underline{24\,08} \\ 5200 \\ \underline{4816} \\ 3840 \\ \underline{3612} \end{array}$$

Average: $\dfrac{12.04 + 12.043}{2} = 12.042$

Then $\sqrt{145} = \mathbf{12.04}$, approximately.

EXERCISES

Find the value of each of the following.

A

1. 6^2 **3.** 12^2 **5.** 45^2 **7.** 4.1^2 **9.** 3.5^2

2. 8^2 **4.** 61^2 **6.** 125^2 **8.** 1.2^2 **10.** 80^2

Find the square roots.

11. $\sqrt{4}$ **13.** $\sqrt{49}$ **15.** $\sqrt{64}$

12. $\sqrt{81}$ **14.** $\sqrt{144}$ **16.** $\sqrt{225}$

Find an approximation to the square roots correct to two decimal places.

17. $\sqrt{148}$ **18.** $\sqrt{29}$ **19.** $\sqrt{30}$ **20.** $\sqrt{250}$ **21.** $\sqrt{3649}$

Find the value of each of the following.

B **22.** 4^3 $(4 \times 4 \times 4)$

23. 2^3

24. 8^3

25. 5^3

26. 10^3

27. 6.25^2

28. 1.5^2

29. 3.14^2

30. 2^4

31. 4^4

SELF-ANALYSIS TEST VII

Time: 20 minutes

Find the value of each. Carry out square roots to two decimal places.

1. 9^2

2. 16^2

3. 23^2

4. 6^3

5. 3^4

6. $\sqrt{121}$

7. $\sqrt{576}$

8. $\sqrt{289}$

9. $\sqrt{132}$

10. $\sqrt{429}$

The main topics of each chapter are summarized for easy review.

CHAPTER SUMMARY

1. The identity element for addition is "0." (Any number plus 0 gives the number itself.)

2. The identity element for multiplication is "1." (Any number multiplied by 1 gives the number itself.)

3. An important fact is

$$(\text{Divisor} \times \text{Quotient}) + \text{Remainder} = \text{Dividend}.$$

4. The grouping symbols ( ) and [ ] are often used to make the meaning of an expression clear.

5. To add (or subtract) fractions with like denominators, add (or subtract) the numerators and use the same denominator.

6. To add (or subtract) fractions with unlike denominators, use the "Principle of 1" to change them to equivalent fractions having the same denominator.

7. To multiply two fractions, multiply the numerators to give the new numerator, and multiply the denominators to give the new denominator.

8. To divide two fractions, multiply by the reciprocal of the divisor.

9. The number of decimal places in a product is the sum of the number of decimal places in the factors.

10. To round a decimal quotient,
  a. Find the quotient to one more decimal place than required for the answer.
  b. If the last quotient figure is less than 5, leave the preceding figure unchanged.
  If the last quotient figure is equal to or greater than 5, increase the preceding figure by 1.

11. An exponent is used to provide a short way of writing a repeated multiplication.

12. An easy and quick method of finding a square root is the "divide and average" method.

CHAPTER TEST

Each Chapter Test provides a thorough evaluation of the student's understanding of the material.

Solve for the value that makes the sentence true.

1. $2 + 7 + 9 = ?$

2. $24 - (7 + 3) = ?$

3. $7 \times 6 = ?$

4. $8(9) = ?$

5. $35 + 8(7) = ?$

6. $2(?) + 13 = 23$

7. $4(?) - 3 = 25$

8. $15(?) = 105$

9. $(127 + 157) - (30 + 4) = ?$

10. $5[7 + 2(6)] = ?$

Use the signs of addition, subtraction, multiplication, or division where necessary to make the statement true. Use parentheses where necessary.

11. 8   8   8 = 8

12. 7   6   3 = 25

13. 4   11   3 = 41

14. 81   9   3 = 12

15. 27   3   9 = 9

Add.

16. $7.45
.45
1.10

17. $2.75
3.50
1.25
6.50

18. $9.37
4.22
2.95

19. $30.55
.45
4.50
8.27
2.35

20.
7 × $ .15 = ?
9 × .08 = ?
11 × .13 = ?
17 × 1.30 = ?
Total = ?

Complete to make each sentence true.

21. $\frac{3}{8} \times \frac{?}{?} = \frac{24}{64}$

22. $\frac{1}{16} \times \frac{?}{?} = \frac{5}{80}$

23. $\frac{4}{5} = \frac{?}{25}$

24. $\frac{1}{4} + \frac{1}{4} + \frac{1}{2} = ?$

25. $\frac{1}{6} + \frac{1}{6} + \frac{2}{3} = ?$

Find the value of the following.

26. $\frac{1}{2} + \frac{1}{16} = ?$

27. $7\frac{7}{8} + 1\frac{1}{8} + 4\frac{3}{4} = ?$

28. $1\frac{5}{16} + 8\frac{1}{4} - 5\frac{1}{8} = ?$

Multiply.

29. $\frac{3}{8} \times \frac{3}{5} = ?$

30. $\frac{3}{16} \times \frac{1}{2} = ?$

31. $\frac{3}{11} \times \frac{1}{6} \times \frac{5}{8} = ?$

32. $.75 \times .25 = ?$

Divide.

33. $\dfrac{\frac{3}{16}}{\frac{1}{2}}$ **34.** $\dfrac{\frac{3}{4}}{\frac{5}{32}}$ **35.** $\dfrac{.625}{.250}$

36. Find X in the drawing.

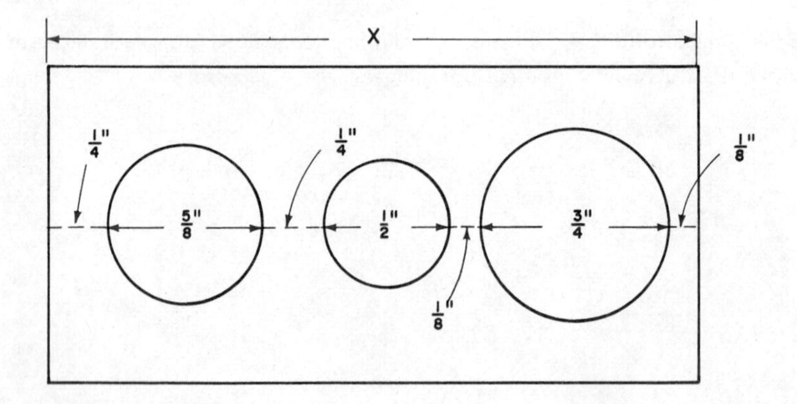

37. $\sqrt{450} = ?$

MAINTAINING YOUR SKILLS

Skill maintenance pages provide additional exercises for students exhibiting weaknesses in computational skills.

Add.

1. 79 + 27

2. 35 + 29 + 47

3. 129 + 425 + 624 + 937

4. 546 + 9342 + 29 + 764

5. 10,027 + 6,343 + 79 + 249

6. 792 + 9403 + 1624 + 87

Subtract.

7. 790 − 345

8. 827 − 649

9. 1453 − 319

10. 4173 − 986

11. 9763 − 8496

12. 52,304 − 36,729

Multiply.

13. 75 × 24

14. 14 × 19

15. 137 × 23

16. 372 × 45

17. 519 × 123

18. 789 × 345

Divide.

19. $5\overline{)110}$

20. $7\overline{)1645}$

21. $11\overline{)132}$

22. $25\overline{)425}$

23. $12\overline{)192}$

24. $20\overline{)6040}$

Moon crater and thin section of moon rock (enlarged). Our system of measures is adaptable to both large and small distances.

Measurement

OBJECTIVES

1. To learn the meaning of measurement.
2. To learn about several measuring instruments.
3. To learn the meaning of indirect measurement.
4. To learn about different types of measurement, such as length, area, volume, weight, time, and temperature.

As you probably know, man once used parts of the human body as units of measurement. These units varied so much that in time agreements were reached to standardize them. Among the units dating from these early times are the foot and the yard, by which we still measure distance.

Linear Measuring Devices

2–1 Rulers and Tapes

Point out that different measuring devices are designed to meet specific needs.

The diagrams show several different types of rulers or tapes used to measure distances. It takes practice to use any instrument skillfully.

Steel rule with easily read scale

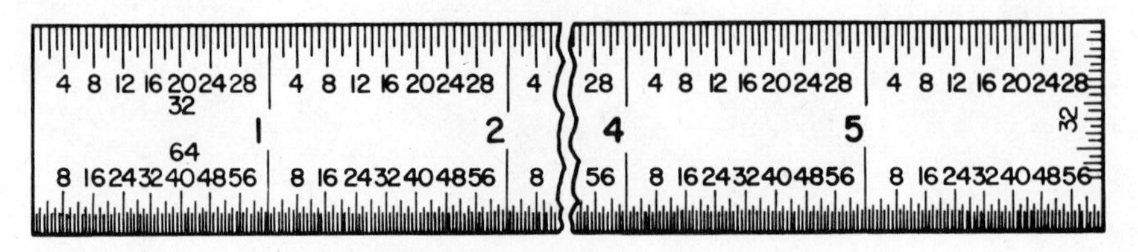

A 2-foot, 4-fold rule, often used in shop work

A 6-foot, zigzag extension rule, useful especially for carpenters

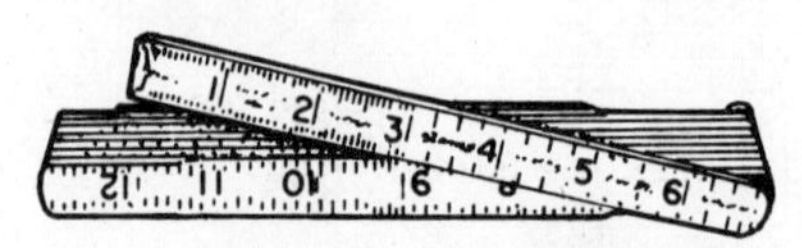

A flexible steel-tape ruler

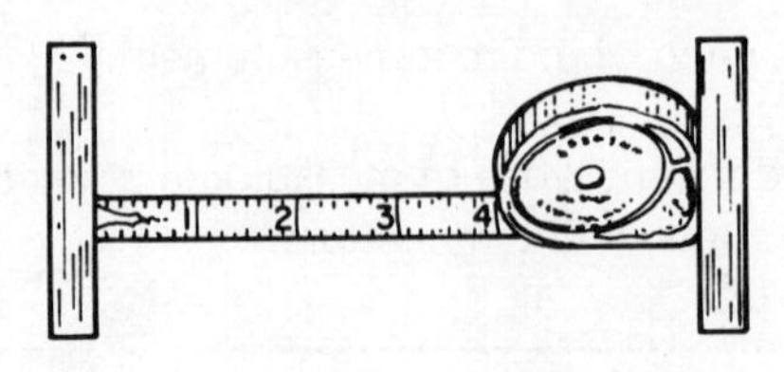

Scale used by mechanical engineers

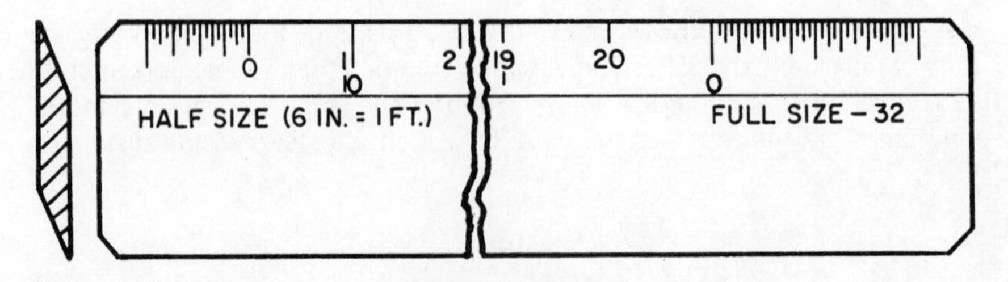

Scale used by architects

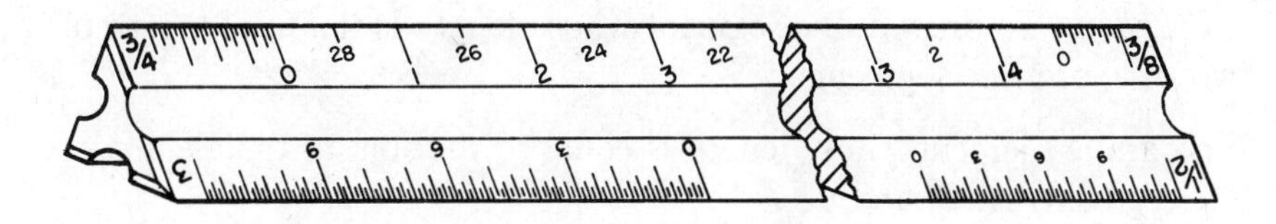

Scale used by civil engineers

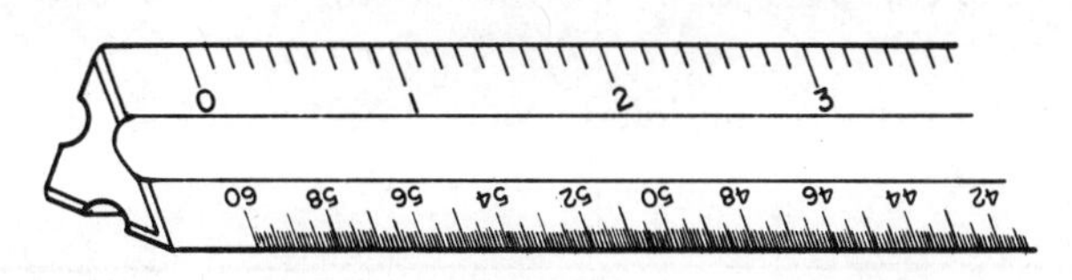

In some of the exercises which follow you will have a chance to use a ruler. You will also need a compass.

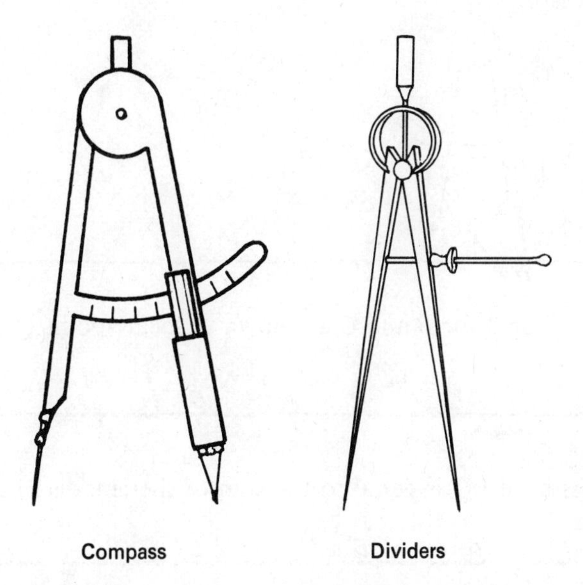

Compass Dividers

A compass has a pencil or pen at one point and is used in drawing circles. Dividers have simply two sharp points; they are useful in checking a length against a scale.

Activities are used throughout the book to promote learning through discovery. See also TM p. 8, 2-1(1).

Compass and straightedge constructions will be treated in detail in Chapter 7.

ACTIVITY: ***Adding line segments with a compass.***

Problem: To draw a line segment whose length is the total length of two or more line segments.

Find a line segment whose length is equal to the sum of the lengths of line segments *A*, *B*, and *C*.

Plan: Use the compass to lay off the lengths of *A*, *B*, and *C* end to end.

1. Using a ruler, draw a line *l* and locate any point *P*.

l

P

2. Set the sharp point of your compass on one end of segment *A*, and open the compass until the pencil touches the other end of the segment.
3. Being careful not to change this distance, lay off the length of segment *A* on line *l*, using *P* as a starting point. (See diagram below.)

4. Repeat Step 3 for *B* and *C* as shown to locate point *Q*.

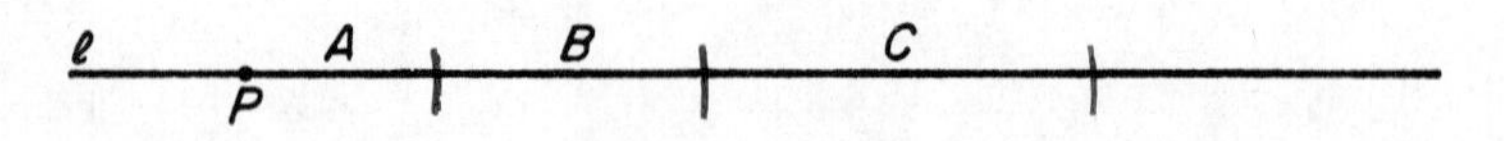

5. The distance *PQ* is equal to the sum of the lengths of *A*, *B*, and *C*.

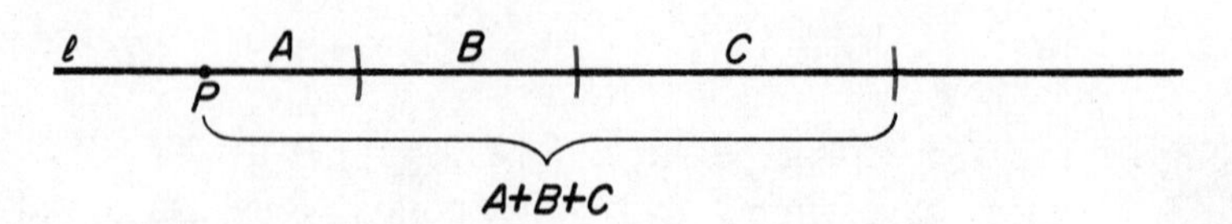

EXERCISES

Draw a line segment equal to the sum indicated.

A

1. A + B + C

2. A + B + C

3. A + B + C

4. A + B − C

5. A + B − C

TM p. 8 , 2-1(2)

ACTIVITY: *Constructing a ruler.*

1 inch

Problem: To construct a 6-inch ruler given the length of one inch.

Plan: Lay off the inch length six times, and by folding locate subdivisions of the inch.

1. Draw a line on heavy paper or cardboard and, using your compass, lay off the 1-inch length six times in succession.
2. On another piece of paper lay off the 1-inch length along a straight edge.
3. Fold the 1-inch line segment so its endpoints meet, to locate its midpoint.
4. Mark off the $\frac{1}{2}$-inch segments on your ruler (Step 1) using the distance determined in Step 3.
5. Repeat Step 3, using the $\frac{1}{2}$-inch length to determine a $\frac{1}{4}$-inch length.
6. Lay this distance on your ruler, and mark off $\frac{1}{4}$-inch divisions.
7. Label the endpoints of each one-inch segment on the ruler.
8. Cut your ruler along the line to give two 6-inch rulers.

EXAMPLE

a. Use the ruler you made to measure this length.

b. Check by using a standard ruler.

(Solution on next page.)

Solution. **a.** The reading on the ruler you made is between 2 and $2\frac{1}{4}$ inches.

b. Standard ruler reads $2\frac{1}{16}$ inches.

Emphasize that the accuracy of a measurement is related to the degree of refinement of the measuring device. See also TM p. 8

EXERCISES

a. Use the ruler you made to measure these lengths to the nearest $\frac{1}{4}$ inch.
b. Use a standard ruler to measure these lengths to the nearest $\frac{1}{16}$ inch.
Compare the two results.

2–2 The Odometer

Tell students that the syllable in heavy black type is to be stressed in pronunciation.

An **odometer** (ō-**dom**-e-ter) is an instrument used to measure distance. In an automobile the odometer is usually mounted on the face of the speedometer dial. It tells the total number of miles the car has been driven.

You can make an odometer and find distances not easily measured by a steel tape.

ACTIVITY: *Making an odometer.*

Problem: To construct and calibrate a simple odometer.
(Note. To calibrate is to mark an instrument for measuring according to some unit of measurement.)

Materials: $\frac{3}{4}'' \times 2'' \times 4'$ piece of wood, a wheel, a 4″ bolt, 2 nuts, 2 washers, a $2'' \times 2''$ plastic card.

Plan: Mount a wheel on a handle and calibrate it.

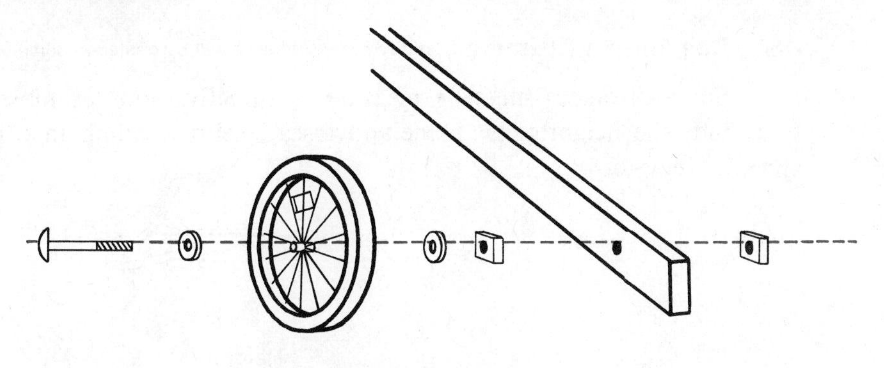

Exploded view of odometer

1. Drill a hole for the axle in the piece of wood.
2. Bolt the wheel on the wooden handle, using the materials shown in the exploded view above. After tightening, check to see that the wheel rotates freely on its axle.
3. Attach a plastic card to the wheel so that it "snaps" each time it passes the handle.
4. Calibrate the odometer by the following method: Put a mark on the rim of the wheel and carefully place this mark on a chalk point on the floor. Slowly roll the wheel along the floor until the mark is again on the floor. Mark this point, and measure the distance between the two points on the floor with a tape. This distance is the distance covered in one revolution of the wheel. Repeat this process several times and record on the handle the measurement that seems most nearly correct, as

1 revolution = __?__ inches.

To improve the accuracy of the odometer, position the wheel so that the card "snaps" immediately upon starting.

EXERCISES

Use your odometer to measure the following distances. Then check your measurements with a steel tape.

A

1. Diagonal of classroom floor.
2. Width of classroom.
3. Distance around schoolroom.
4. Distance from home plate to first base.
5. Distance from home plate to pitcher's mound.

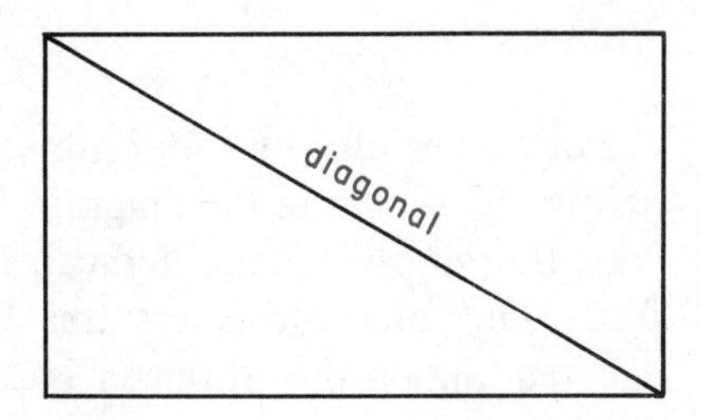

2–3 Reading an Altimeter

Indirect measurement will be treated in detail in Chapter 10.

Some distances must be measured indirectly. For example, a pilot finds the height of his plane above sea level by reading an altimeter (ăl-**tĭm**-e-ter).

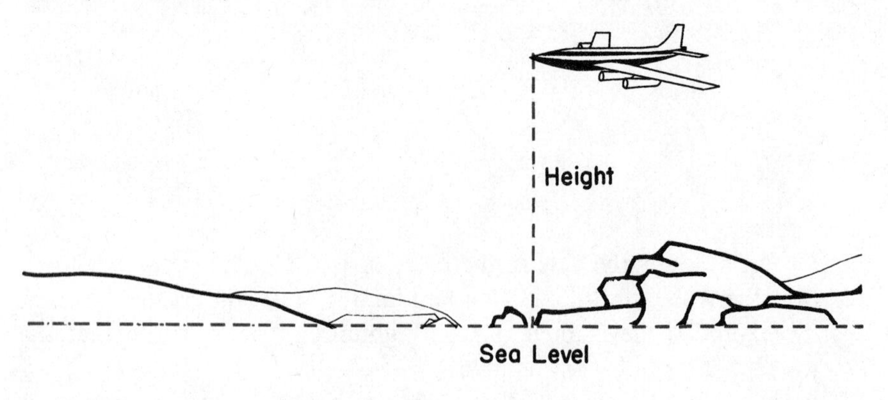

This is a diagram of an altimeter. The shorter hand indicates the number of thousands of feet. The longer hand indicates the number of hundreds of feet.

1. The shorter hand points between which two numbers?
   The shorter hand indicates thousands.
   The height recorded is between 4000 and 5000 feet.
2. The longer hand points to how many spaces beyond 8?
   This hand indicates hundreds.
   The hand indicates the number 820.
3. How high is the airplane?
   $4000 + 820 = 4820$ (feet)
   4820 feet is the altitude of the plane, its distance above sea level.

For higher altitudes an altimeter must have three arrows, as shown in the diagram at the right. In this case the shortest hand indicates ten thousands of feet. On some altimeters this third arrow is red. The reading on this altimeter is 25,850 feet.

EXERCISES

Give the height in feet of an airplane whose altimeter has the following readings. (Note: Red arrow indicates ten thousands of feet.)

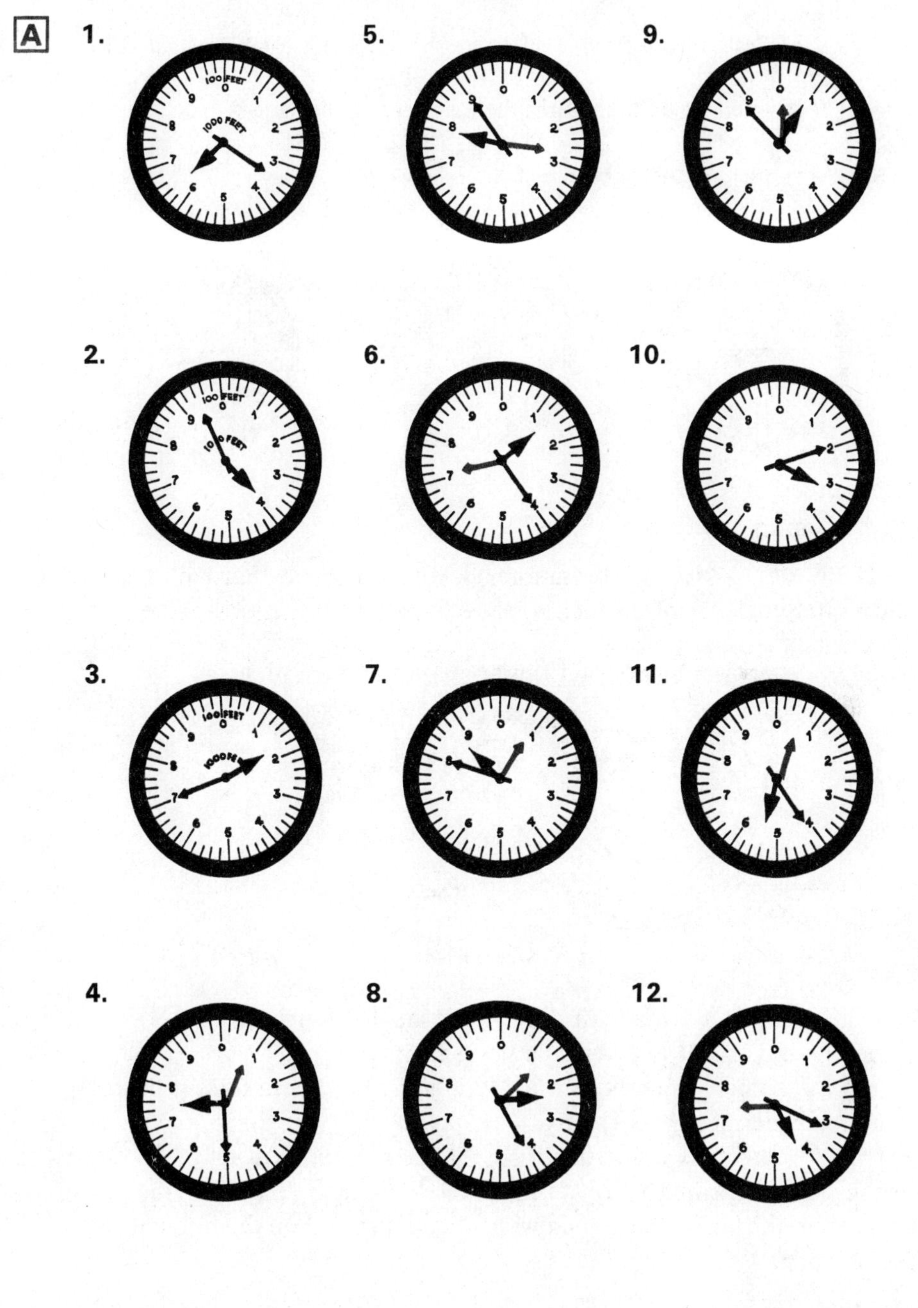

SELF-ANALYSIS TEST I

Time: 5 minutes

1. The compass can be used to reproduce a line segment or to __?__ several segments together.
2. A __?__ is a tool used to determine the distance of lines by comparing them to a scale.
3. An __?__ is a device used to measure distances not easily measured by a ruler or steel tape.
4. The instrument that measures the height of an airplane is called an __?__.

Give the reading in feet for each of the following.

5. **6.** **7.**

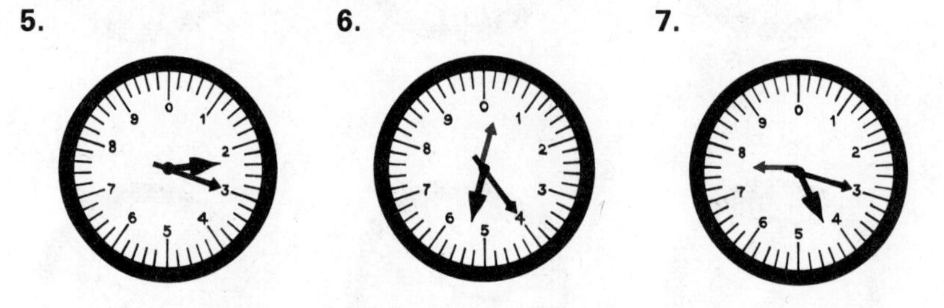

2–4 Using a Micrometer

A **micrometer** (mī-**krŏm**-e-ter) is an instrument that will measure accurately to $\frac{1}{1000}$ of an inch, or even smaller dimensions.

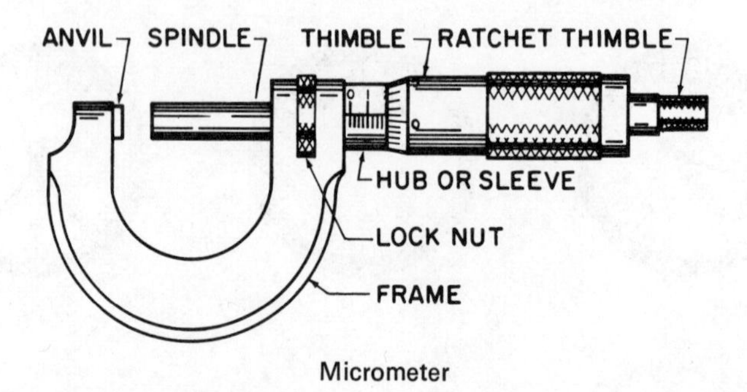

Micrometer

Micrometers are made in different forms for different kinds of uses. The one illustrated is a very common form.

To use a micrometer accurately, you must be able to hold it properly and read the settings correctly.

A micrometer is constructed so that one revolution of the thimble changes the opening $\frac{1}{40}$ of an inch, or 0.025 inch. Each of the small spaces on the hub is 0.025 inch wide. Each numeral on the hub indicates 0.100 inch.

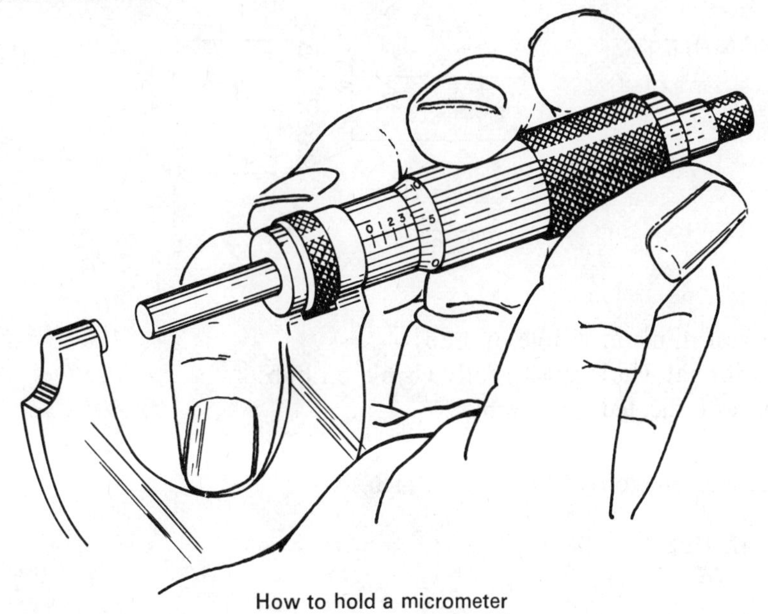

How to hold a micrometer

There are 25 divisions on the thimble. Each division equals $\frac{1}{25}$ of one revolution, or 0.001 inch. ($\frac{1}{25} \times \frac{1}{40} = \frac{1}{1000} = 0.001$)

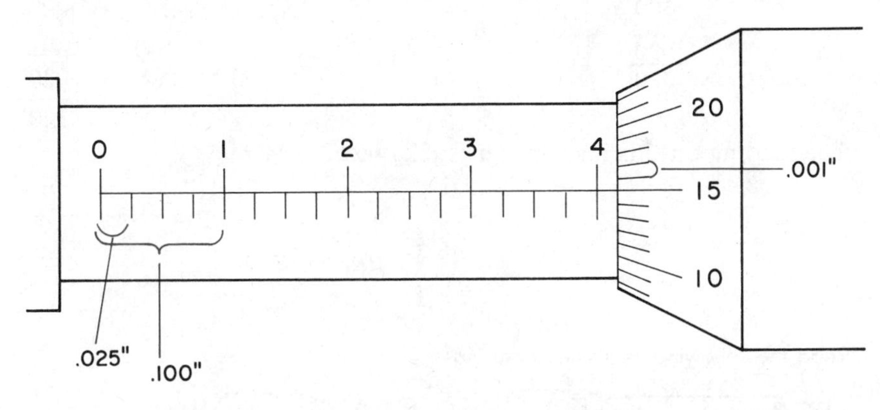

To read the setting on a micrometer, you need to make three observations:

a. The largest numeral visible on the hub.
b. The number of additional spaces visible on the hub.
c. The number of spaces indicated on the thimble.

You then convert these to decimal parts of an inch and find their sum.

EXAMPLE 1

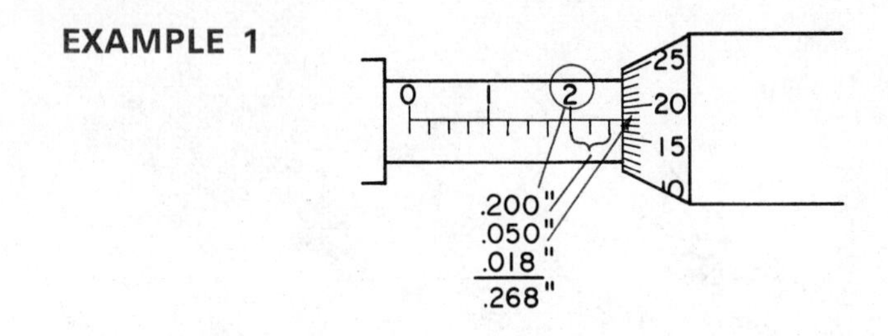

Largest numeral visible on hub: 2	2 × .100″ = .200″
Additional whole spaces fully visible on hub: 2	2 × .025″ = .050″
Spaces indicated on thimble: 18	18 × .001″ = .018″
	Sum = .268″

Stress "whole."

The micrometer reading is **.268 inch.**

EXAMPLE 2

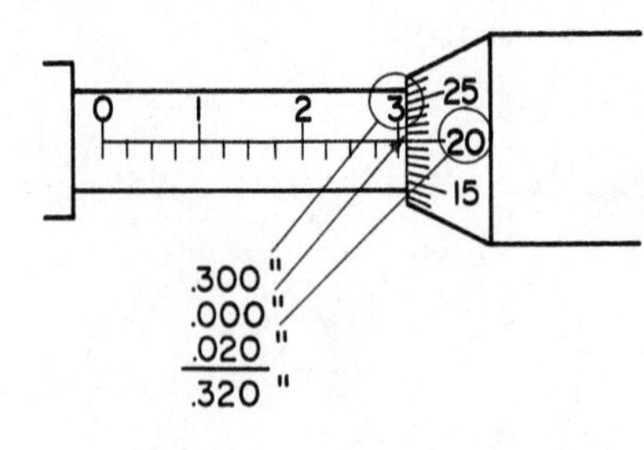

3 × .100″ = .300″

No additional spaces visible on hub = .000″

20 × .001″ = .020″

.320″

The reading on this micrometer is **.320 inch.**

EXERCISES

Read the following micrometer settings.

A

1. 0 1 2 3 4 5 6 7 — 5, 0, 20

2. 0 1 2 — 5, 0

3. 0 1 2 3 4 5 6 — 10, 5, 0

4. 0 — 0, 20

5. 0 1 2 3 4 5 6 7 — 5, 0

6. 0 1 2 — 15, 10

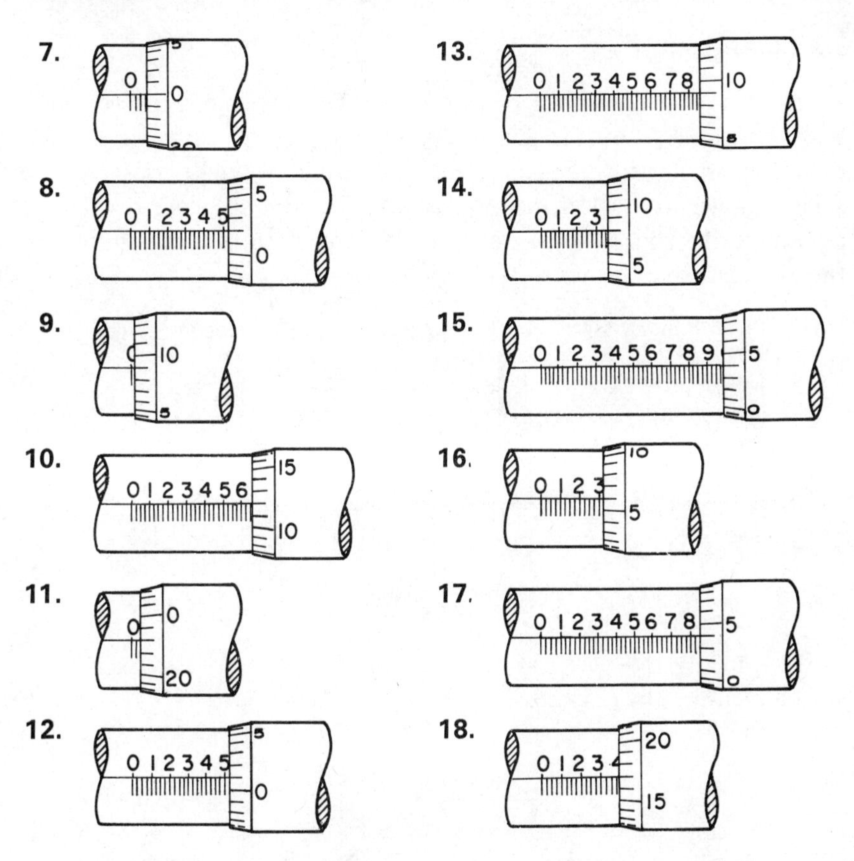

19. Set the micrometer to the following sizes and have the settings checked by your instructor or another student.

.001″	.772″	.533½″ ←
.007″	.881″	.657¼″ ←
.339″	.942″	.352½″ ←
.578″		

The student must approximate these fractional spaces on the thimble.

20. Obtain several pieces of wire, sheet metal, and other objects from your instructor and measure them with the micrometer. Prepare a table like the following:

Object	Measurement

2–5 Gauges

Non-adjustable measuring devices like those here are often referred to as static gauges.

There are many other devices for checking fine measurements; they are usually known as gauges. A feeler gauge, for example, consists of several small wires, or metal leaves, of different thicknesses. To use such a gauge, you select the appropriate size and compare it with the opening to be checked. One common use for such gauges is in setting the gap on a spark plug.

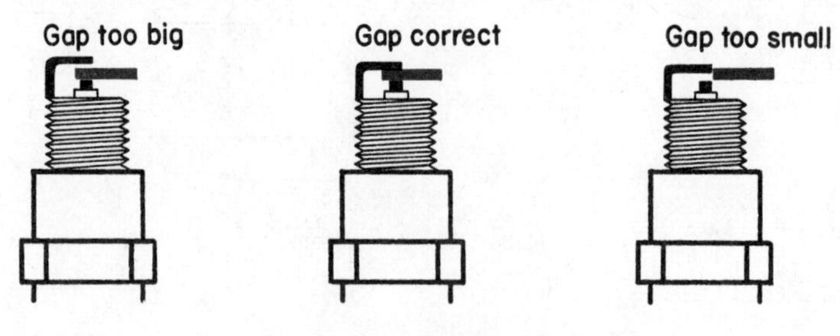

Testing the Gap on a Spark Plug

Sheet metal and wire gauges are similar in operation. You use a slot to measure the thickness of the wire or sheet metal.

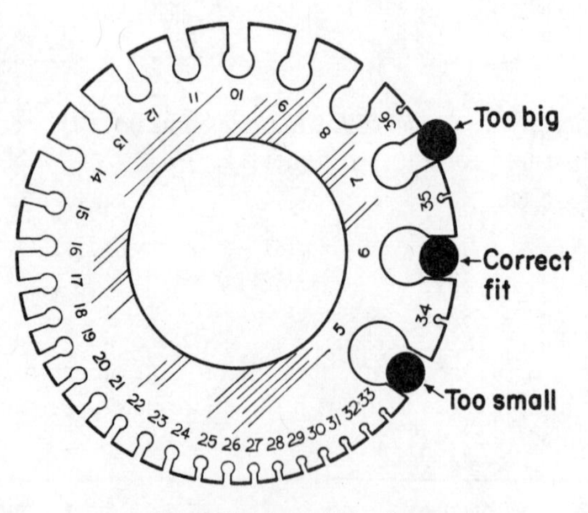

Sheet Metal and Wire Gauge

ACTIVITY: *Use of gauges.*

Problem: To determine the gap on a spark plug.

Plan: Use a feeler gauge to measure the gap on a spark plug. Obtain several spark plugs from your teacher and determine the gap of each, as shown in the diagram at the top of page 63.

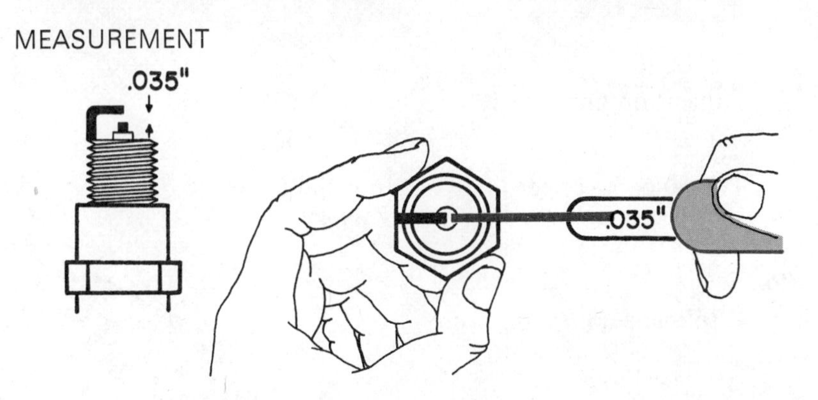

2–6 Tolerance and Dimension Limits

Stress this. See also TM p. 8 .

Measurement is always approximate. In manufacturing an item, it is impossible to make it exactly the desired size. For this reason drawings often show how much of an error can be tolerated. The drawing below shows an article which should be 2″ long, but any size between 1.99″ and 2.01″ will be acceptable.

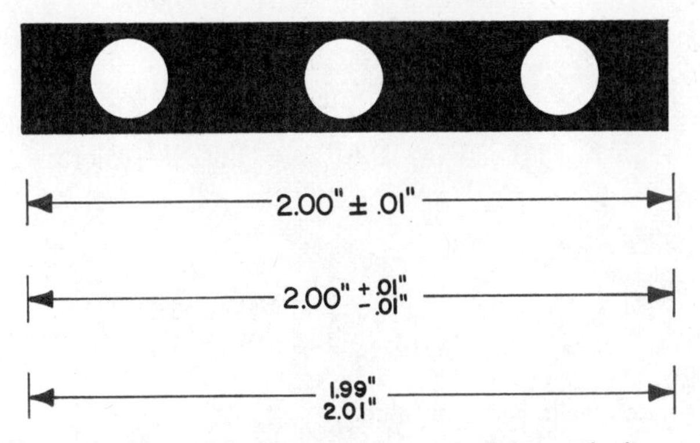

Three different ways of indicating the possible variation are shown. Each of the three shows that the article must not vary more than .01″ from the desired length of 2″.

The term **tolerance** is used to mean the difference between the largest and smallest acceptable dimensions. These maximum and minimum dimensions are called **dimension limits.**

Sometimes called "oversize" and "undersize," respectively.

EXAMPLE 1

Find the dimension limits and tolerance in the drawing below.

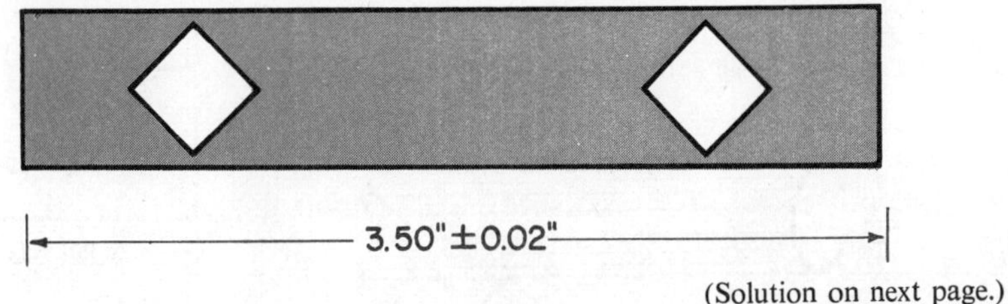

(Solution on next page.)

Solution. Dimension limits: $3.50'' + .02'' = \mathbf{3.52''}$
$3.50'' - .02'' = \mathbf{3.48''}$

Tolerance = upper limit − lower limit
$= 3.52'' - 3.48'' = \mathbf{0.04''}$

EXAMPLE 2

Find the tolerance of a pin, if its diameter should be $\frac{5}{8}'' \pm 0.010''$.

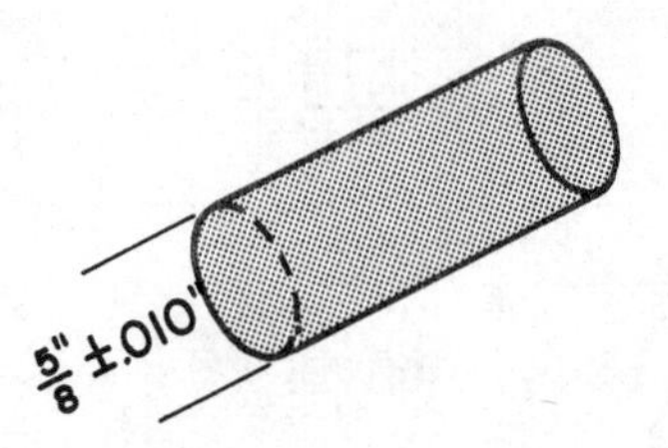

Solution. 1. Convert $\frac{5}{8}''$ to its decimal equivalent. $\frac{5}{8}'' = 0.625''$

2. Find the dimension limits: $0.625'' \pm 0.010''$

$$0.625'' + 0.010'' = 0.635''$$
$$0.625'' - 0.010'' = 0.615''$$

3. Tolerance is equal to the difference of the largest and smallest acceptable dimensions.

$$0.635'' - 0.615'' = \mathbf{0.020''} \text{ (tolerance)}$$

EXERCISES

Find the dimension limits and tolerance.

A

1. $1.750'' \pm .006''$

2. $3.500'' \begin{smallmatrix} + .007'' \\ - .004'' \end{smallmatrix}$

3. A shaft $2\frac{1}{2}''$ in diameter has a tolerance of .002″. What are its limits?

4. What is the tolerance of the spacer shown?

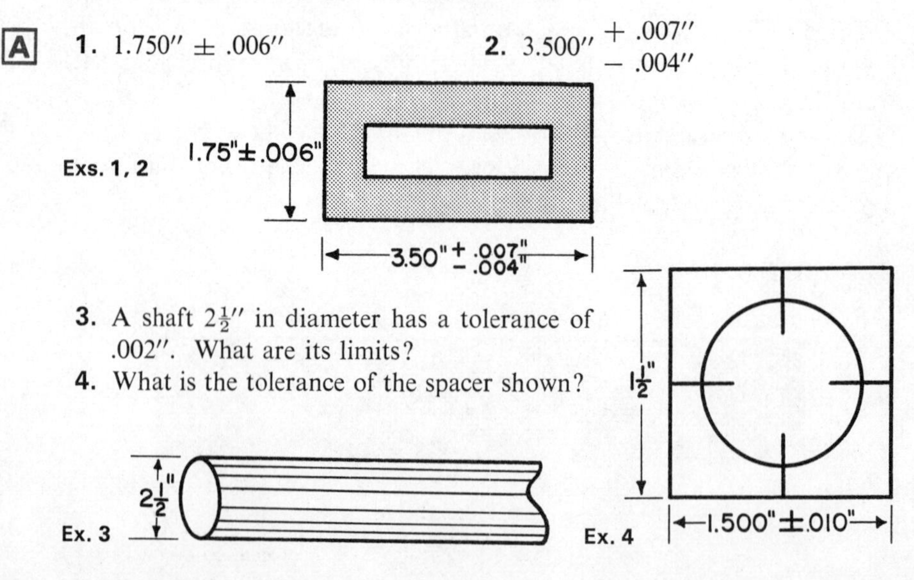

5. Find the dimension limits and tolerance of both diameters of the pilot shaft pictured.

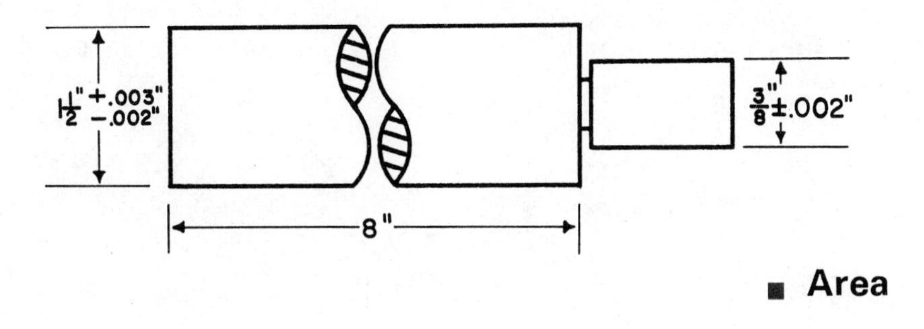

■ Area

2–7 Measuring Area TM p. 8 , 2-7

The area of any plane (flat) figure is the number of square units of measure it contains. We may choose any convenient square unit for our unit of measure and find how many times it is contained in the region to be measured. The total number of square units is called the area of the region or figure.

This represents 1 square unit.

How many of the square units will fit into this figure?

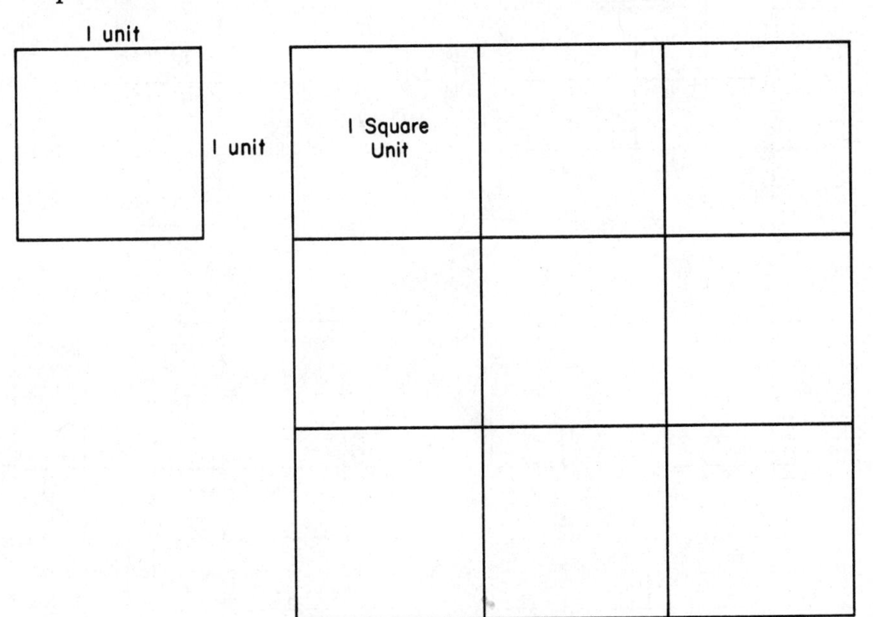

There are 9 square units in the figure. If the unit of length were the inch, the answer would be 9 square inches. If the unit had been the foot, the answer would have been 9 square feet.

EXERCISES

Use the small square as the basic unit to find the area of each of the figures below.

A  **1.**

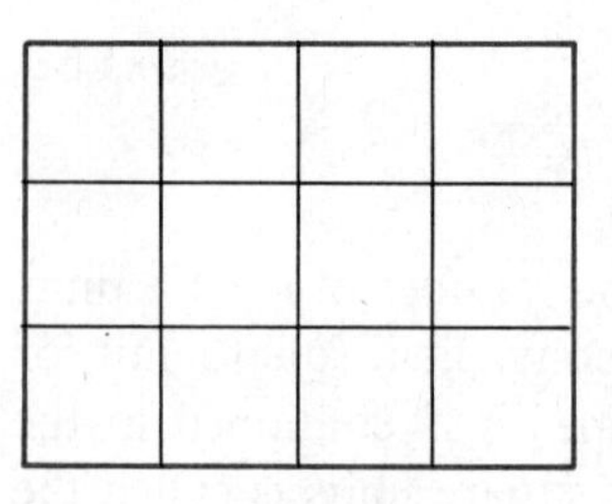

2.

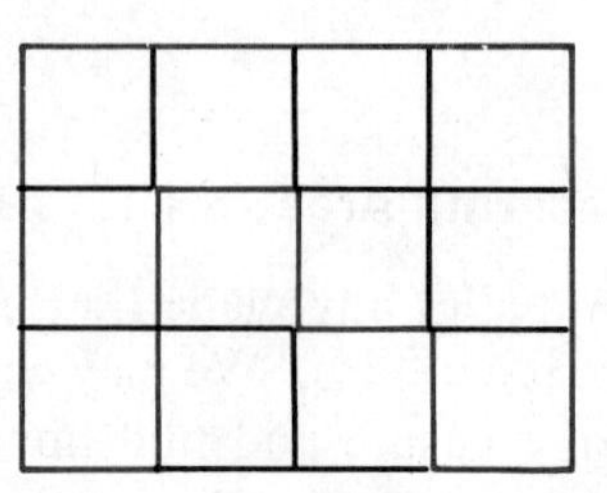

3.

4.

 **5.**

6.

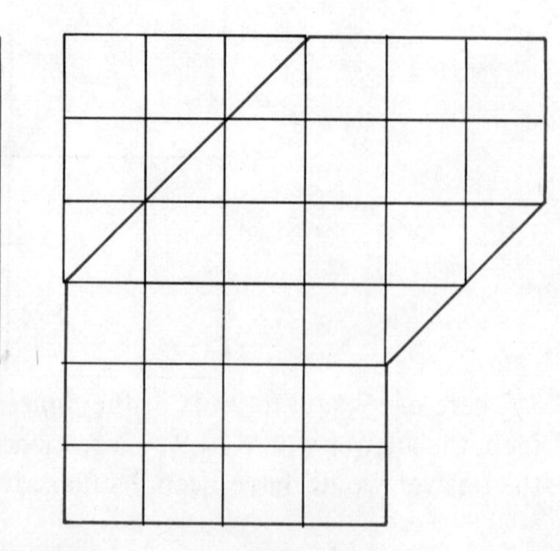

7.

8.

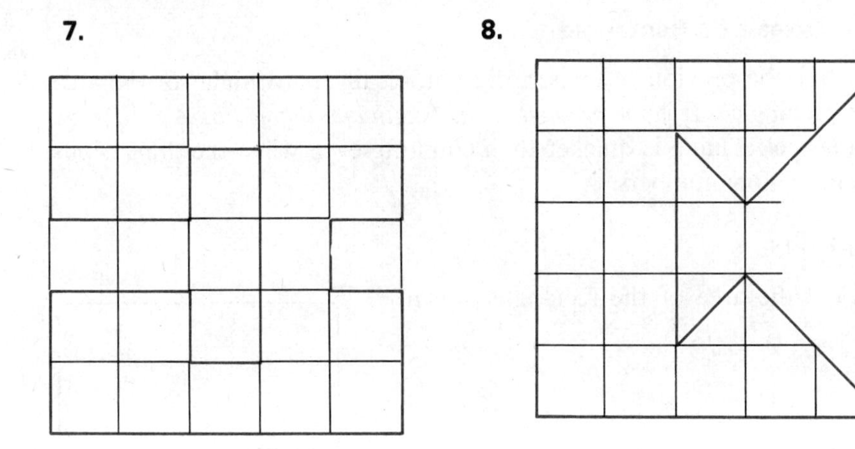

9.

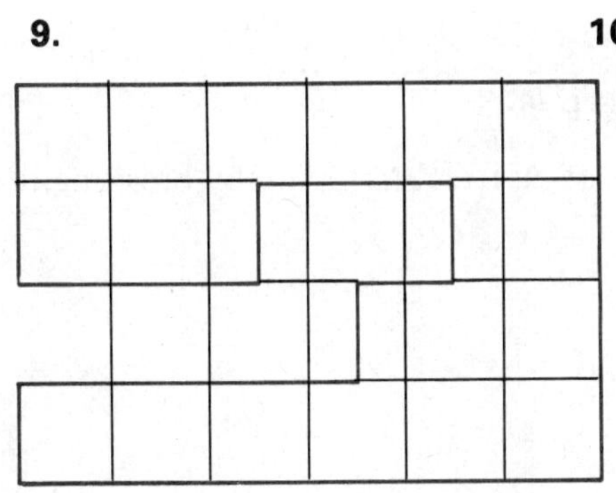

10.

11.

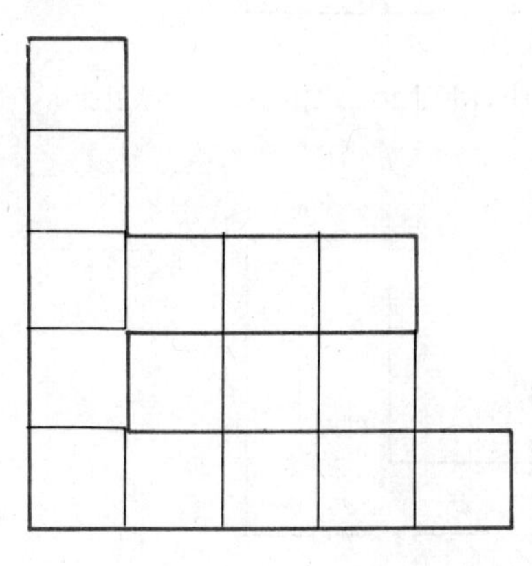

12.

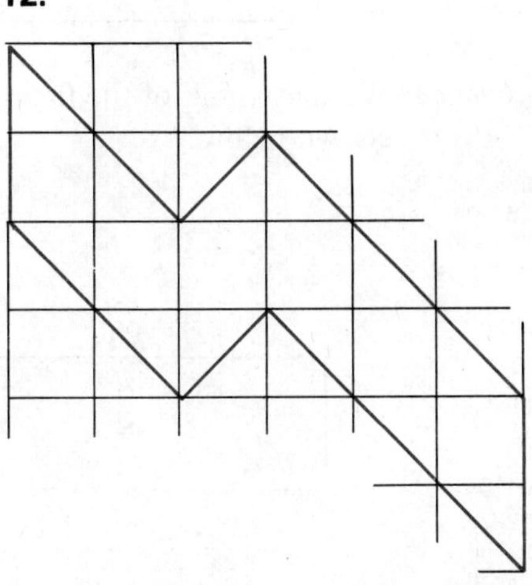

2–8 Area of a Rectangle

In the previous exercises, did you recall the formula for the area of a rectangle? It is *the product of the length and the width;* $A = l \times w$. Using the formula is quicker than counting even when the dimensions are not whole numbers.

EXAMPLE 1

Find the area of the rectangle shown.

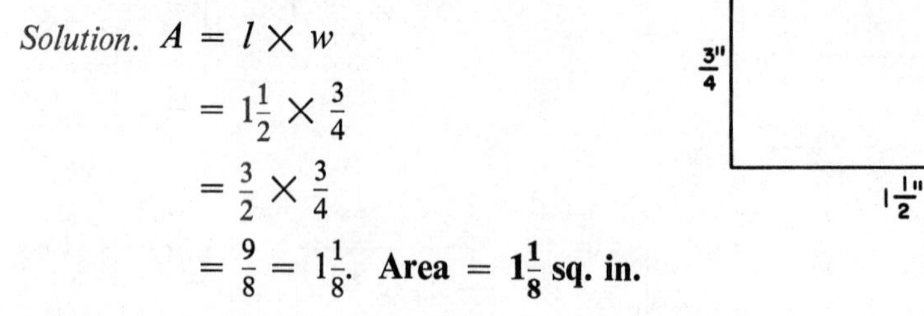

Solution. $A = l \times w$

$= 1\frac{1}{2} \times \frac{3}{4}$

$= \frac{3}{2} \times \frac{3}{4}$

$= \frac{9}{8} = 1\frac{1}{8}$. **Area = $1\frac{1}{8}$ sq. in.**

Sometimes you can find the area of an irregular figure by breaking it into simple shapes.

EXAMPLE 2

Find the area of the figure shown.

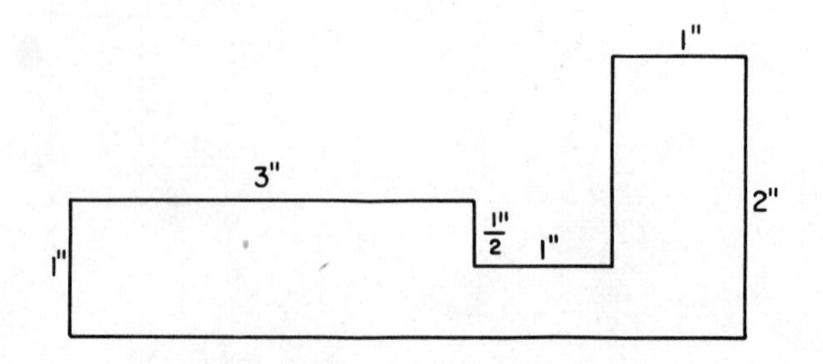

Solution. We may think of the figure as divided into three rectangles as shown below.

Challenge the students to find alternative ways of dividing the figure into rectangles.

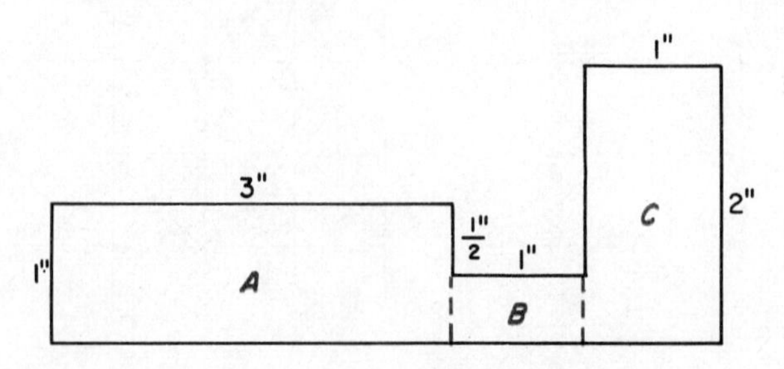

The areas of the rectangles A, B, and C are easily computed and are

$$A = 3 \text{ sq. in.}$$

$$B = \frac{1}{2} \text{ sq. in.}$$

$$C = 2 \text{ sq. in.}$$

Thus the total area is $\mathbf{5\frac{1}{2}}$ **sq. in.**

EXERCISES

Copy and complete this chart by finding the area of the following rectangles. (Remember: Area = length × width.)

	Length	Width	Area
A 1.	2″	1″	?
2.	2″	$1\frac{1}{2}$″	?
3.	$1\frac{1}{2}$″	$1\frac{1}{2}$″	?
4.	$2\frac{1}{2}$″	$\frac{3}{4}$″	?
5.	$4\frac{1}{2}$″	$1\frac{1}{4}$″	?
6.	$\frac{3}{4}$″	$\frac{1}{2}$″	?
7.	$5\frac{1}{4}$″	$\frac{1}{2}$″	?
8.	$2\frac{1}{2}$″	$\frac{1}{4}$″	?
9.	$2\frac{1}{4}$″	$1\frac{3}{8}$″	?
10.	$2\frac{7}{8}$″	$2\frac{5}{8}$″	?

Find the areas of these cross sections.

11.

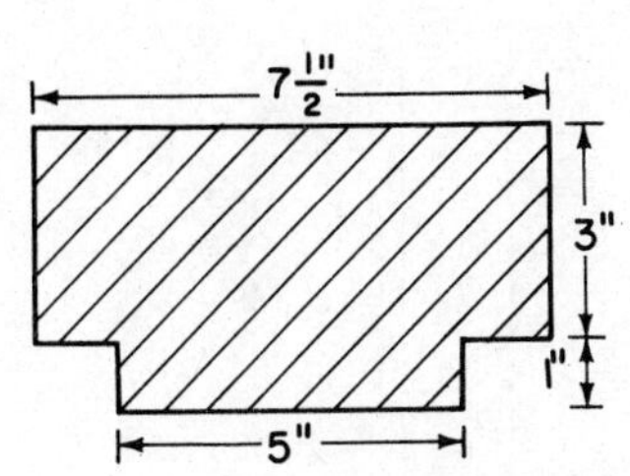

12.

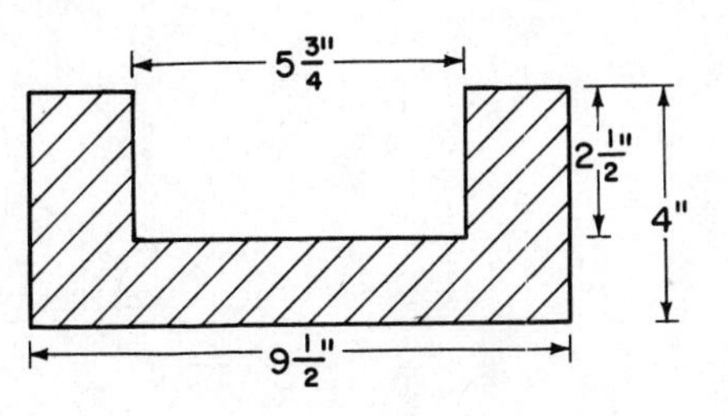

13. Determine the area of your classroom in square inches and square feet.

14. Can you determine a method to convert square inches to square feet?
15. If you were to change square feet to square inches, would the number be larger or smaller? This information can help you determine whether to multiply or divide, when converting from one unit to another.

A fuller treatment of converting units of measurement occurs in Chapter 6.

Volume and Weight

2–9 Measuring Volume

See remarks on units of measure in TM p. 8 , 2-7.

Volume is the amount of space occupied by an object, measured in standard units of measure. The standard unit of volume is a cube one unit of length on each side. The number of cubic units contained in a solid is called the volume. The volume of this solid is 12 cubic units.

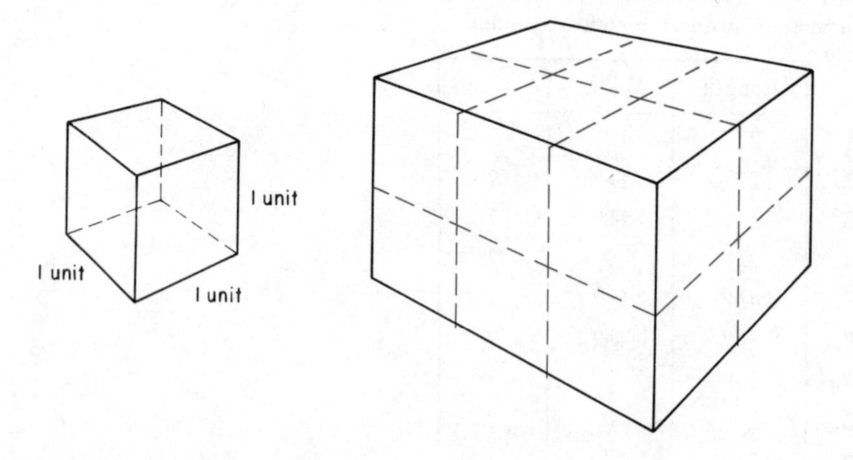

Both of the geometric solids below contain the same amount of volume, one cubic inch, even though their dimensions vary.

This can be graphically demonstrated by using 1/2" cubes to assemble each figure.

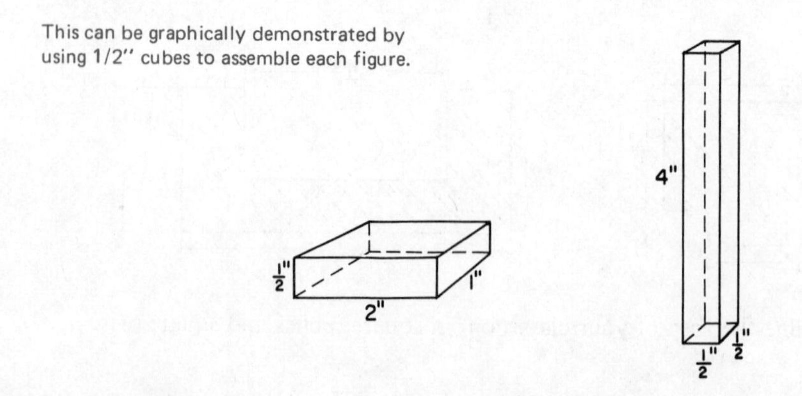

EXAMPLES

In the figures below, estimate the number of cubic units in each.

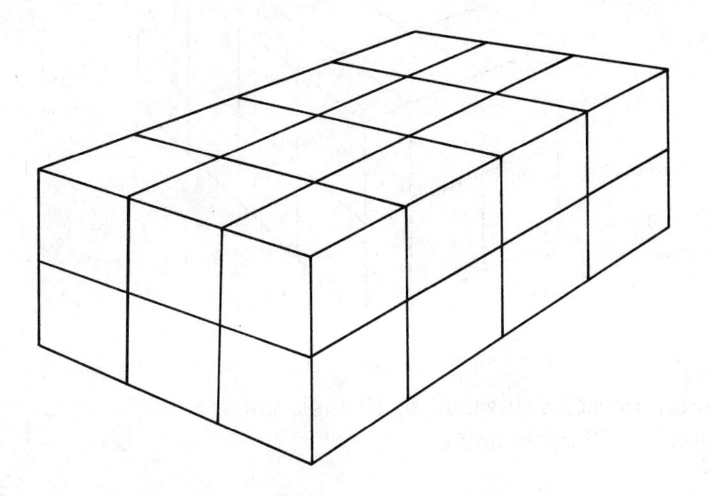

Two layers of 12 cubic units. Volume = 24 cubic units.

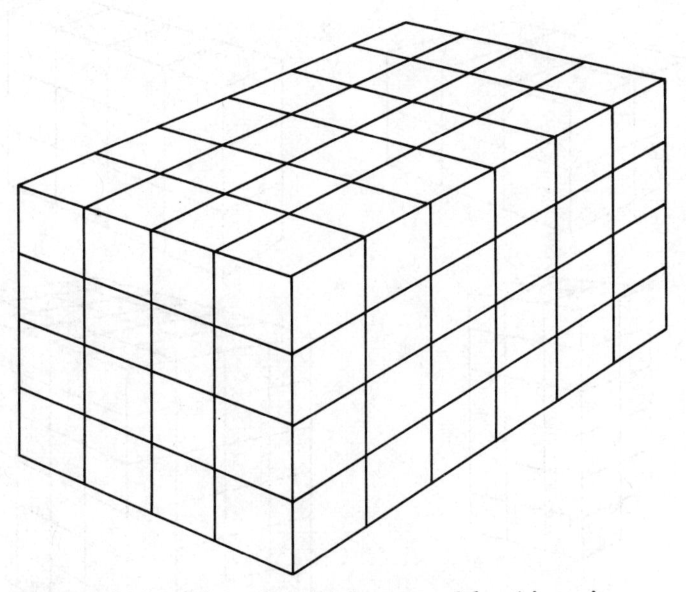

Four layers of 24 cubic units. Volume = 96 cubic units.

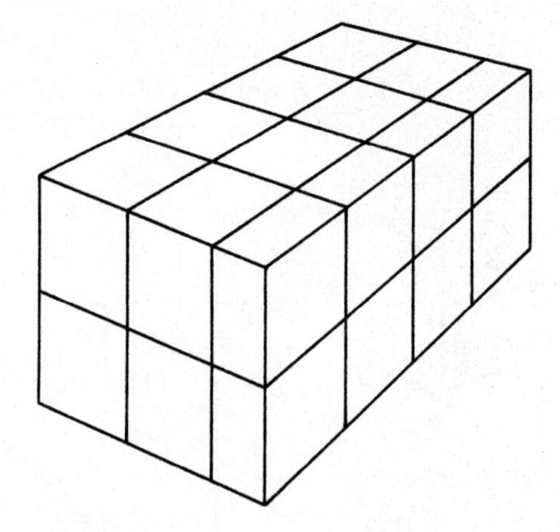

Two layers each equivalent to 10 cubic units.
Volume = 20 cubic units.

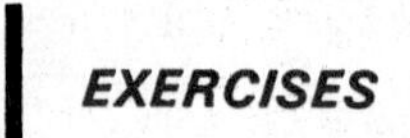

EXERCISES

Estimate the number of cubic units in each solid. Record the data in a chart like the one shown on the facing page.

A 1.

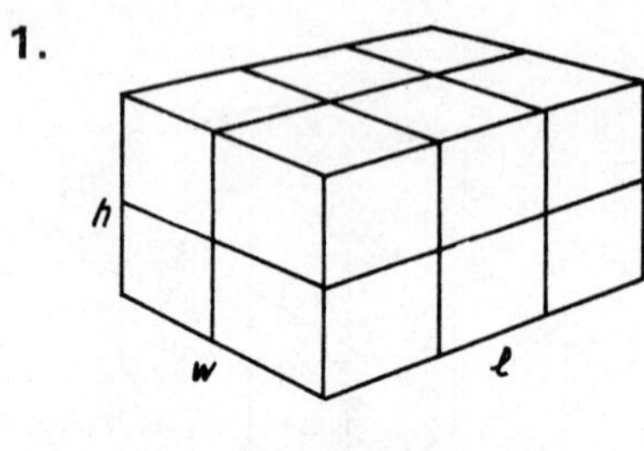

2.

3.

4.

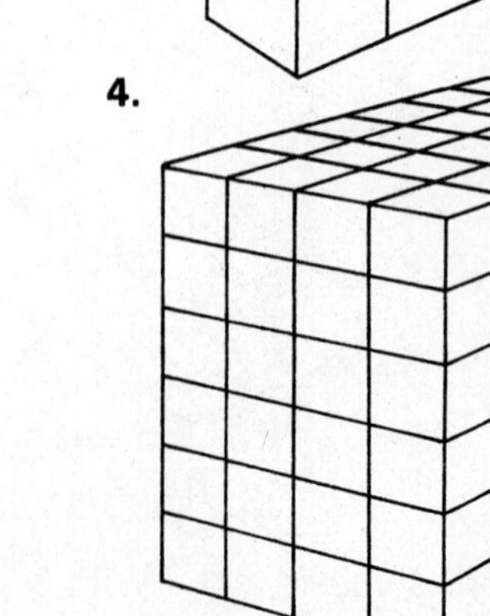

5.

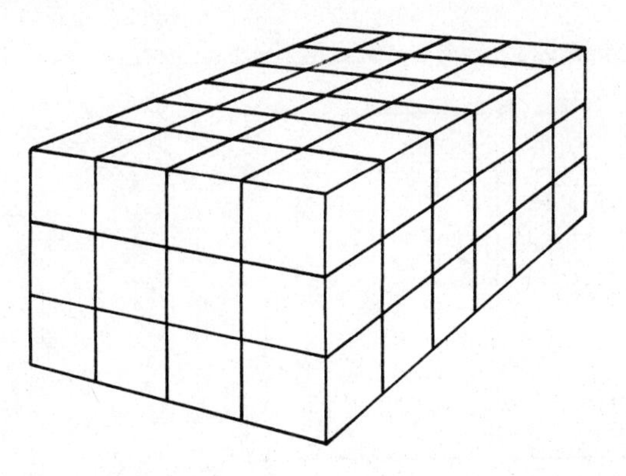

	length = l	width = w	height = h	volume = V
1.				
2.				
3.				
4.				
5.				

6. Look at the data in your chart. Do you see any relationships between length, width, height, and volume? The relationship is one you have used before:

$$V = l \times w \times h$$

Find the volume of these solids.

a. $l = 5$, $w = 24$, $h = 9$
b. $l = 23$, $w = 52$, $h = 12$

SELF-ANALYSIS TEST II

Time: 10 minutes

1. Use a standard ruler to measure the lengths shown. What is their combined length?

   ____

   ____

   ____

2. An odometer is used for measuring ? (distance or volume).
3. An instrument used to measure the height of an airplane above sea level is called an ? .
4. The surface of a plane or flat object is measured in ? .
5. The space occupied by an object is measured in ? .

6. Estimate the area, using the square unit shown.

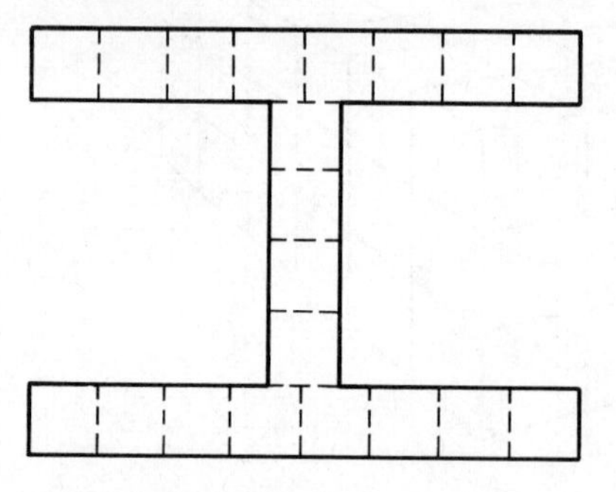

7. Estimate the area, using the square unit shown.

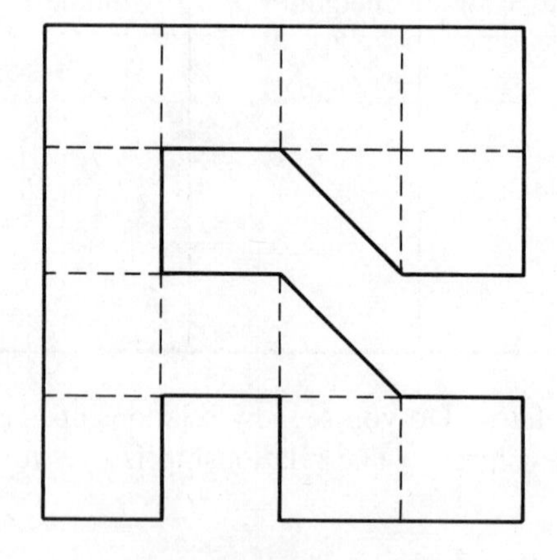

8. Find the volumes of the rectangular solids shown.

a. **b.**

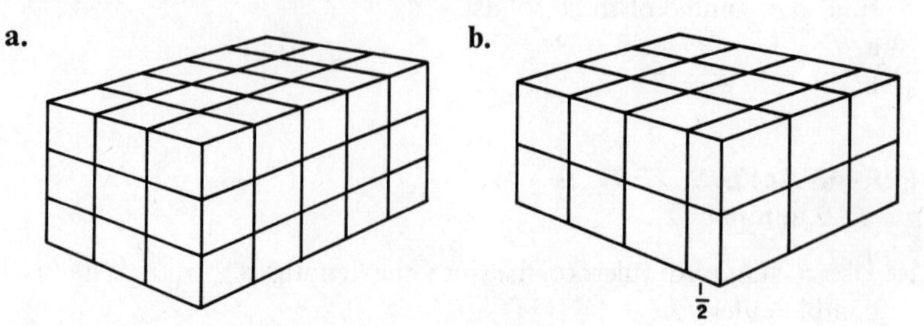

Read the micrometer settings shown.

9.

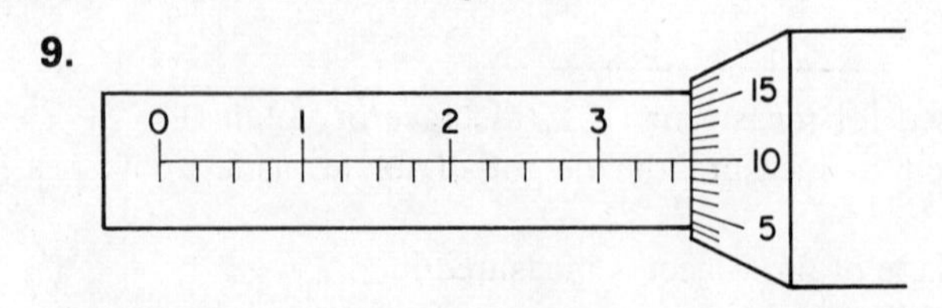

10.

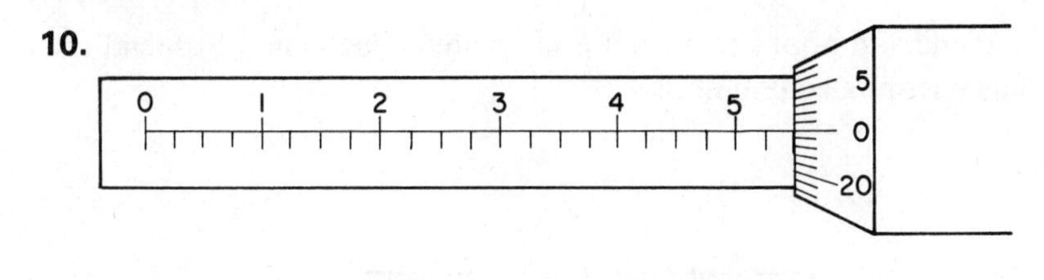

11.

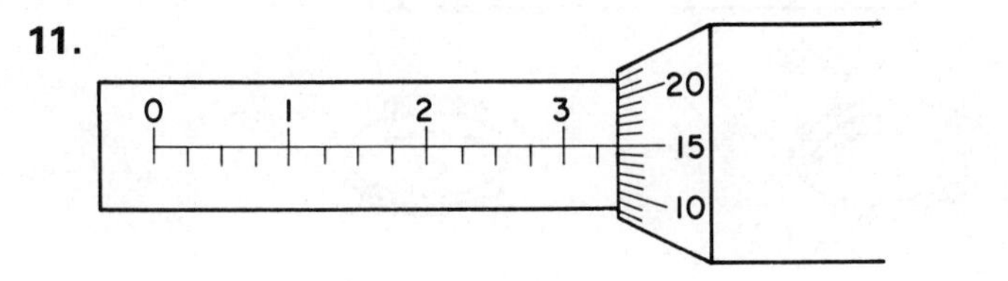

12. Find the dimension limits and tolerance in this drawing.

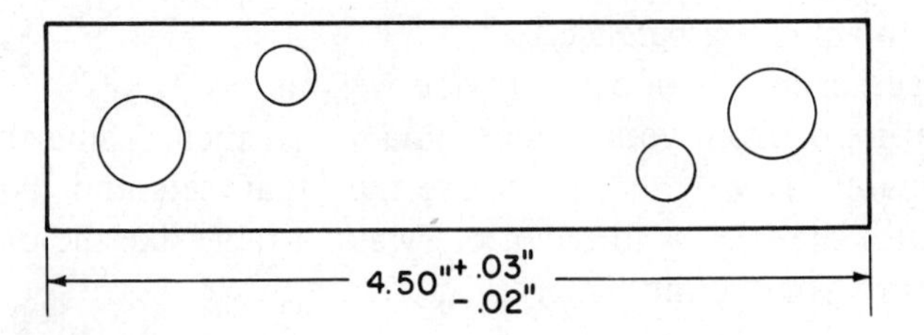

2–10 Weight

We weigh objects with some standard unit of weight, such as the pound. Standard units of weight are established by the National Bureau of Standards. Point out that standard units are often the result of agreements. See TM p. 8 .

ACTIVITY: ***Investigation of weight.***

Purpose: To build and use a balance.

Materials: 36″ × 1″ × 1″ stick; 6 wire hooks; 2 pie plates; twine; 4d nails.

Plan:

1. Drill a hole in the center of the stick and two others at equal distances from the center near the ends.

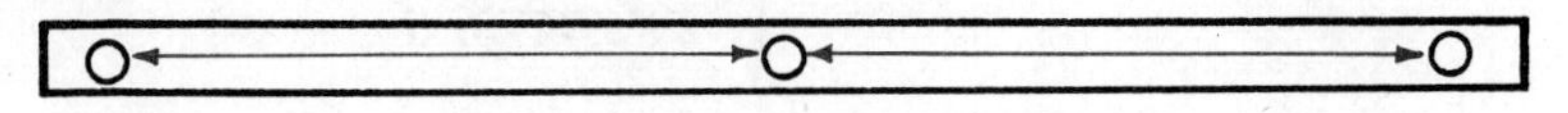

2. Drill three holes, evenly spaced, around the edge of each pie plate.

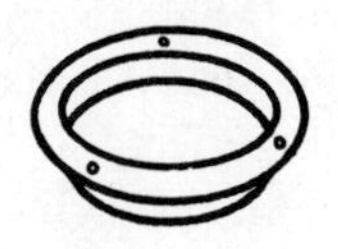

(cont. on next page.)

3. Use twine and hooks to mount a pie plate at each end. Suspend the balance from a ceiling hook.

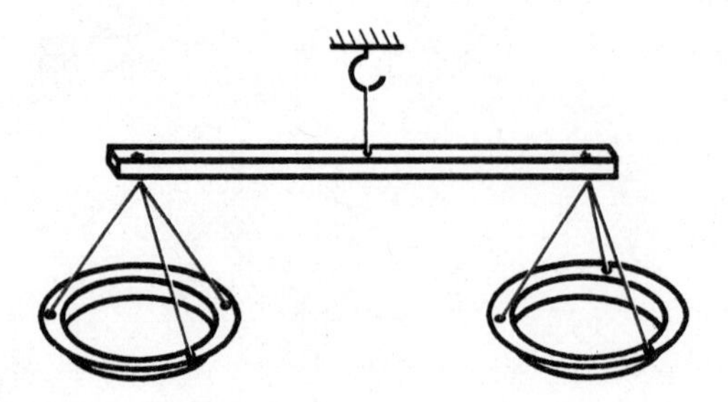

(Note: It may be necessary, because of inaccuracy in workmanship or materials, to tape some light cardboard to the bottom of one of the pie plates to achieve a balance.)

4. Tape nails together in sets of 5 to provide weights.
5. Obtain several items from your teacher and weigh them, using the nails you prepared as weights. First use the 5-nail sets and then single nails, until the stick is in balance. Make a table like the one below and record your results. Emphasize that the results will be expressed in terms of "units."

	A	*B*	*C*
Object	No. of 5-nail sets	No. of single nails	Weight of $(A + B)$
SAMPLE. A pencil	1	1	$1\frac{1}{5}$ units

EXERCISES

A

1. Did all students record the same weight for each object?
2. Why do you think this happened? Give reasons for your answers.
3. Is there some way that your balance might be made more accurate?
4. How accurate do you think that it could be built?
5. Could any balance ever be perfect?
6. Why did you reach that decision? Give reasons.

7. What would happen if you used different units of weight? Would the numbers you recorded be the same?
8. Try another run of the experiment. Weigh the same items, but use different weights as your standard. Point out the flexibility in choosing a standard unit of measure.

Angle Measurement

2–11 The Protractor

Formulas for finding the measure of certain angles are given in Chapter 3.

Angles are measured in much the same way as are distance, area, and volume. That is, we compare the angle to be measured with a standard unit angle. The number of times the unit angle is contained in the angle is called the *measure* of the angle.

One way of thinking about an angle is to consider it the result of rotating a line segment about one of its endpoints. The amount of rotation is related to the size of the angle. For measurement, we take $\frac{1}{360}$ of one complete revolution as the unit angle, and we call it an angle of *one degree* (1°).

This means that a rotation of one quarter of a complete revolution gives an angle of 90°, since $\frac{1}{4} \times 360 = 90$.

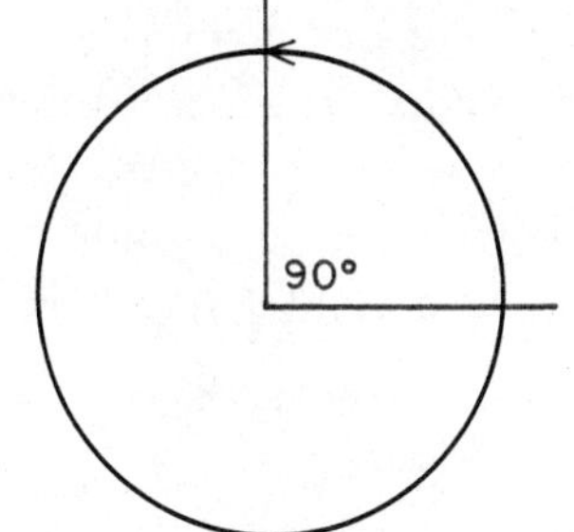

Angles are measured by using a device called a **protractor.**

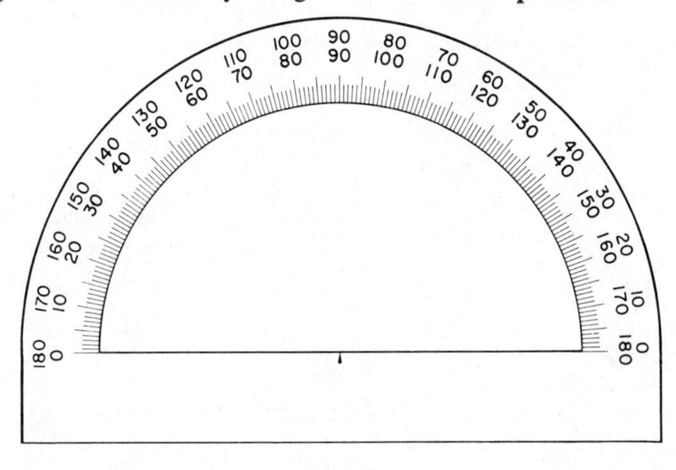

A Protractor

To measure an angle, place the protractor on the angle as shown below. $\angle AOB$ measures 42°.

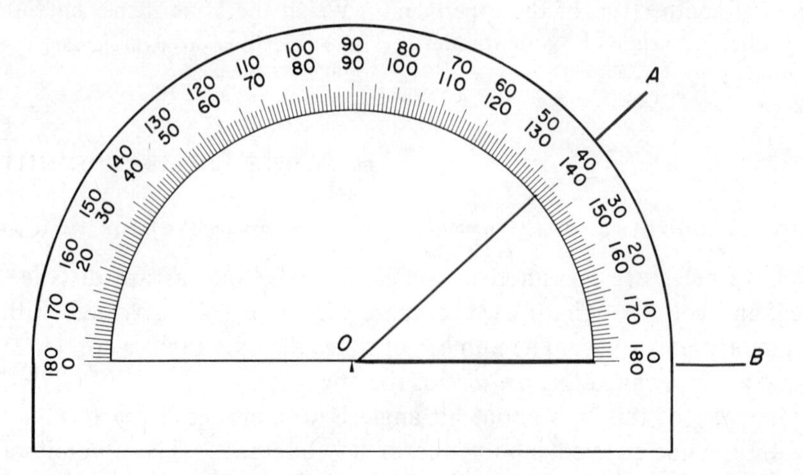

The protractor is placed with the center at the vertex of the angle. If the zero point is placed on one side of the angle (whichever is most convenient), the size of the angle is read at the point where the other side of the angle cuts the edge of the protractor.

Protractors are often numbered with two scales, one from each end. You must always make sure you read the correct scale. Always use the scale whose zero point is on a side of the angle.

Stress this.

EXERCISES

Use your protractor to measure the angles shown below.

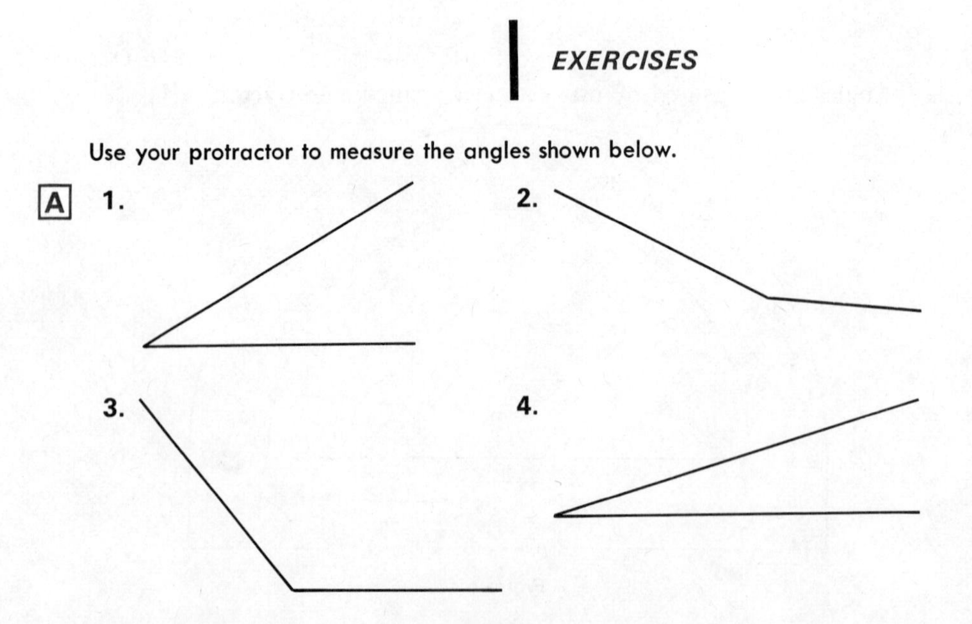

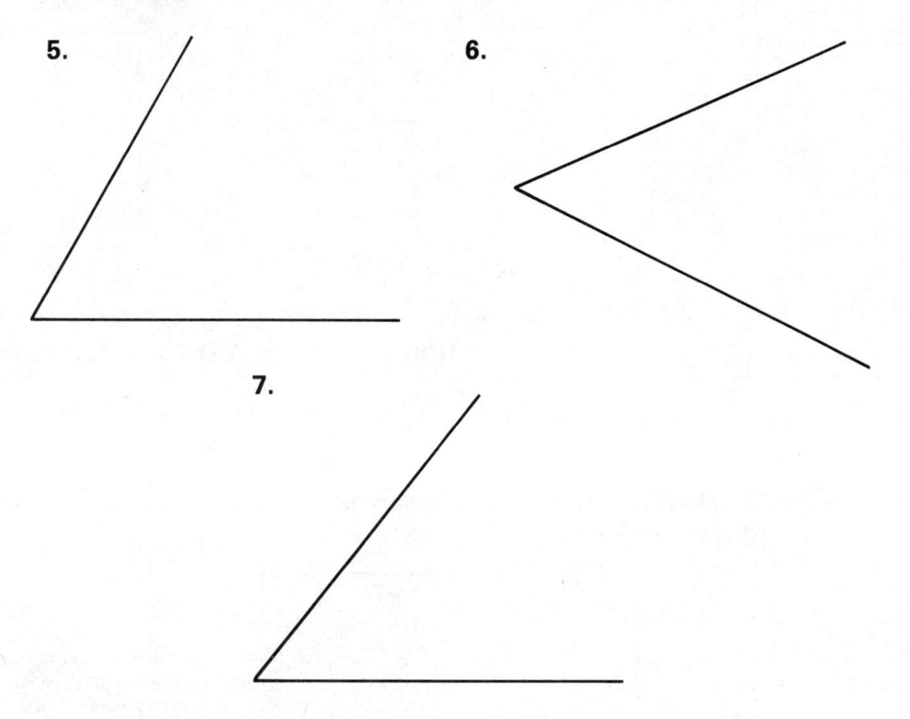

2–12 Degrees, Minutes, Seconds

For very accurate work, each degree is subdivided into 60 minutes, and each minute is subdivided into 60 seconds.

$$\mathbf{1° = 60'} \quad \text{or} \quad \textbf{1 degree = 60 minutes}$$
$$\mathbf{1' = 60''} \qquad\qquad \textbf{1 minute = 60 seconds}$$

In adding or subtracting the measures of angles, we use the following method of working in columns, converting to more convenient units where necessary.

EXAMPLES

Addition.

1. $27° \, 30' \, 20''$
$+ \; 18° \, 20'$

Solution.

°	′	″
27	30	20
18	20	
45	50	20

or **45° 50′ 20″**

2. $20° 50'$ $+ 35° 55'$

Solution.

°	′
20	50
35	55
55	105

or **55° 105′**

Since $105' = 60' + 45' = 1° 45'$, we may write $55° 105'$ in the simpler form **56° 45′**.

Subtraction.

3. $15° 34' 54''$ $- 10° 11' 30''$

Solution.

°	′	″
15	34	54
10	11	30
5	23	24

or **5° 23′ 24″**

Point out the use of the equivalences on page 79 in simplifying and expanding expressions of angle measure.

4. $34° 27'$ $- 23° 45'$

Solution.

°	′
34	27
23	45

We rewrite $34° 27'$ as $33° + 1° + 27'$ or $33° 87'$; then the problem becomes

°	′
33	87
23	45
10	42

or **10° 42′**

EXERCISES

In Exercises 1–5, add.

A

1. $39° 43'$ / $23° 13'$

2. $27° 36' 27''$ / $19° 19'$

3. $24° 32' 24''$ / $32° 23' 35''$

4. 36° 24′ 36″
31° 20′ 32″

5. 45° 43′ 37″
27° 29′ 28″

Subtract.

6. 37° 43′
23° 19′

7. 45° 24′ 46″
23° 13′ 23″

8. 36° 24′
17° 36′

9. 43° 31″
14° 22′ 27″

10. 34° 22′ 33″
16° 29′ 45″

2–13 A Vertical Protractor (Optional)

Many times it is necessary to measure angles in a vertical direction instead of on a horizontal surface. One device for measuring such angles is shown below. It is called a **transit.** A transit is a very accurate instrument which consists of a telescope for sighting an object and scales for measuring angles in both the vertical and horizontal directions.

You can easily make a simple device for measuring angles in the vertical direction, and with a little practice, be able to use it quite accurately.

ACTIVITY: ***Making a vertical protractor.***

Purpose: To construct a simple vertical protractor.

Materials: Protractor, cardboard, string, weight, soda straw, cellophane tape.

Plan: To mount a protractor so that it can be read in a vertical position.

1. Mount the protractor on a piece of cardboard as shown.

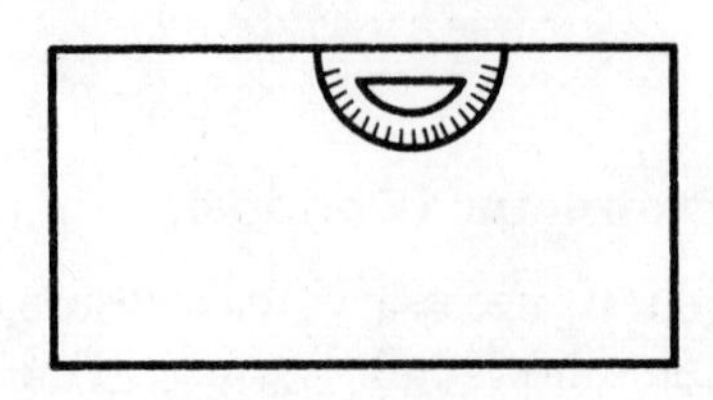

2. Make a small hole at the center point of the protractor and attach a piece of black thread or light-weight string.

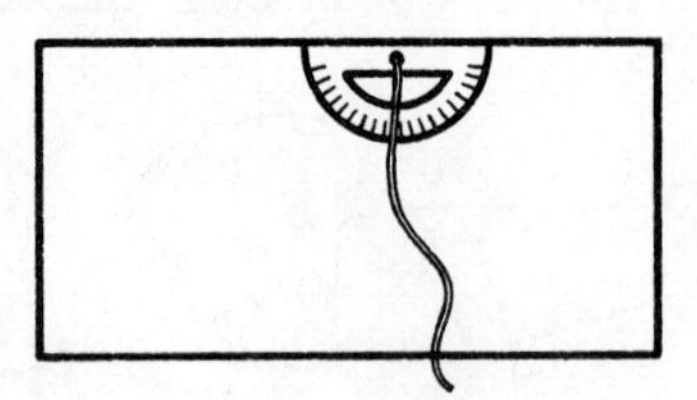

3. Attach a weight (such as a nut or bolt) to the end of the string.

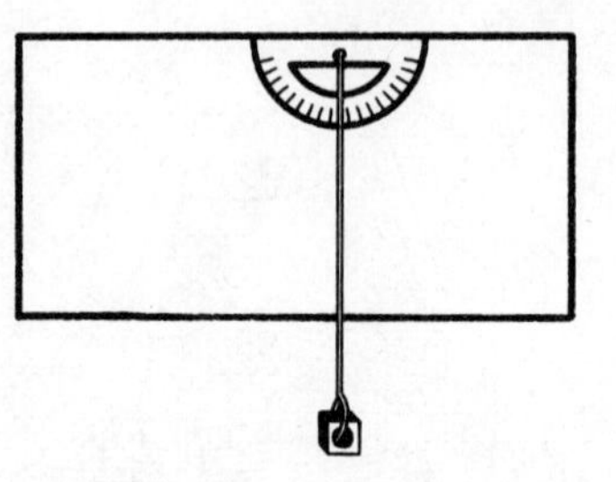

4. Draw lines from the center of the protractor every 10 degrees.

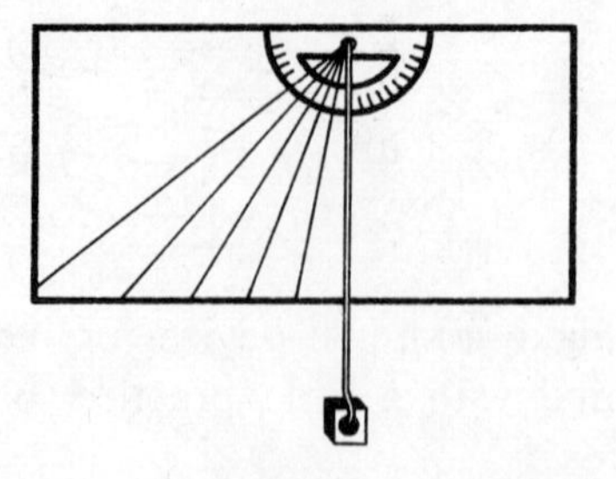

5. Mount a soda straw with tape to the upper edge of the cardboard.

Use: Sight through the straw at an object and read or have someone else read the angle shown on the protractor by the thread. The angle shown on the protractor is equal in measure to the angle from the horizontal to your line of sight. To obtain its measure, subtract the reading where the string crosses the protractor from 90. Practice taking readings until you can obtain consistent results.

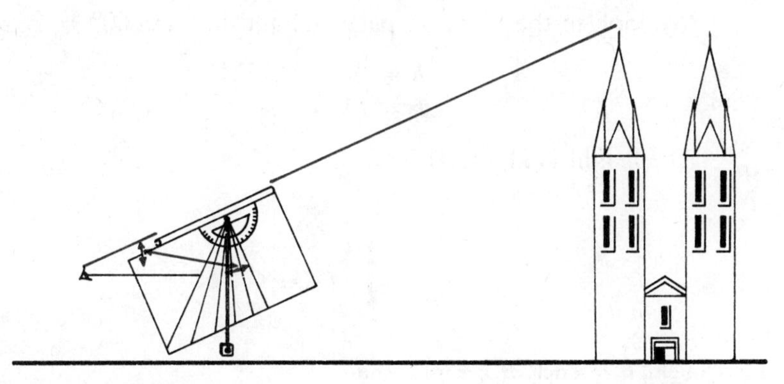

Later in this book you will study trigonometry. There you will find that in a triangle like the one shown, the length $\overline{BC}$ (height) divided by the length $\overline{AC}$ (distance) has been computed for all angles and is available in table form. This number is called the tangent of angle A (written tan A). We can use such a table and our vertical protractor to find the height of buildings, poles, and so on. Obtaining measurements in this way is an example of measuring *indirectly*.

The teacher may wish to postpone treating the remaining material and exercises in this section until Chapter 10.

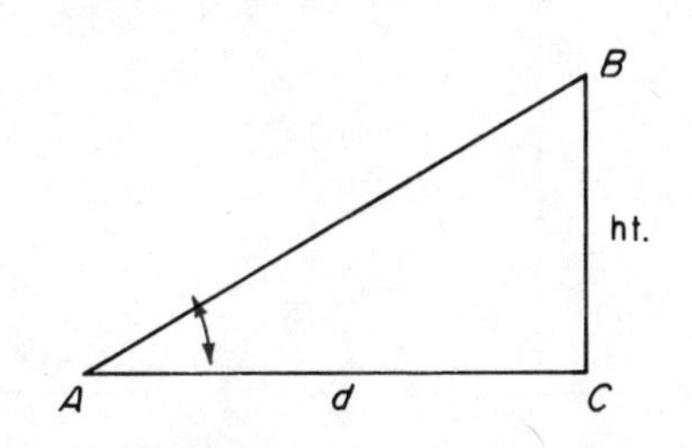

EXAMPLE

Find h, if an angle of 60° is observed at a distance of 30 feet from the building.

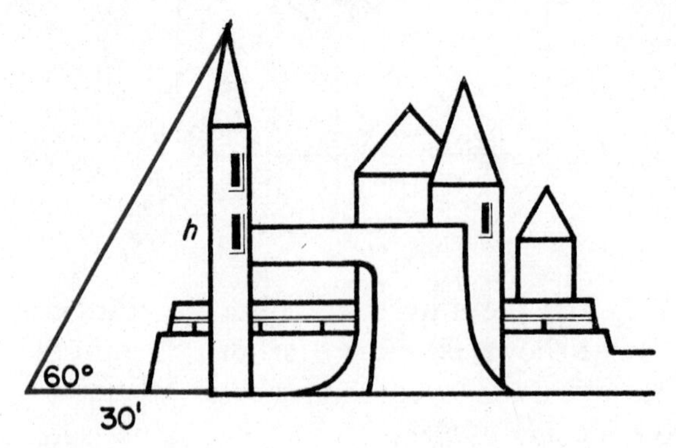

Solution. $\tan 60° = \frac{h}{30}$ or $h = 30 \times \tan 60°$

We look in the table on page 363 and find $\tan 60° = 1.7321$.

$$h = 30 \times 1.7321$$
$$h = 51.963$$

The height is about **52 feet.**

EXERCISES

Find the height, *h*, in each of the following.

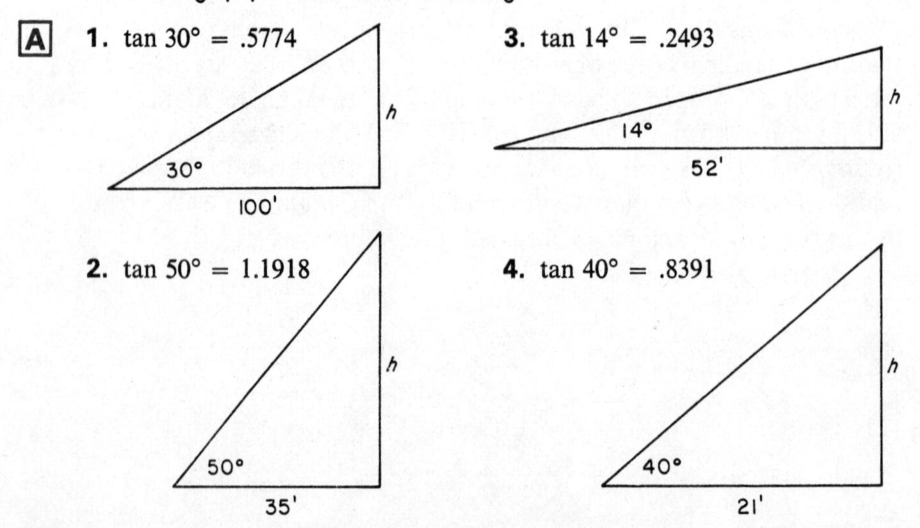

B 5. Find the height of several tall objects (building, flagpole, and so on) suggested by your teacher. Use a steel tape to measure the distance, d, and your vertical protractor to find the angle A. Then use the formula

$$h = d \times \tan A$$

and the table on page 363.

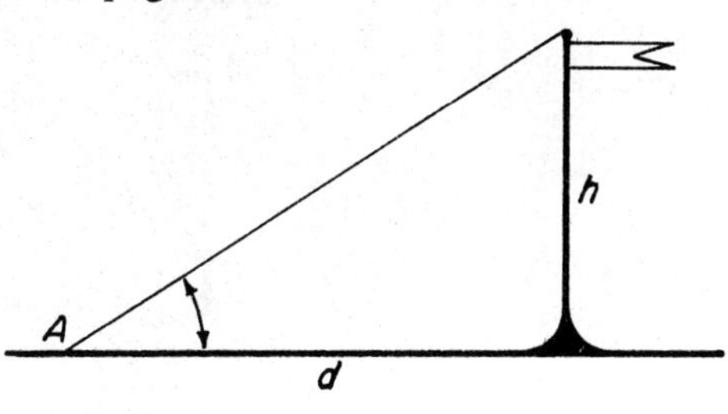

SELF-ANALYSIS TEST III

Time: 10 minutes

1. An instrument used to measure degrees is called a __?__.
2. One quarter of a complete revolution gives an angle of __?__.
3. Degrees are subdivided into __?__ and __?__.
4. Standard units of weight are established and maintained by the __?__.

Measure with a protractor.

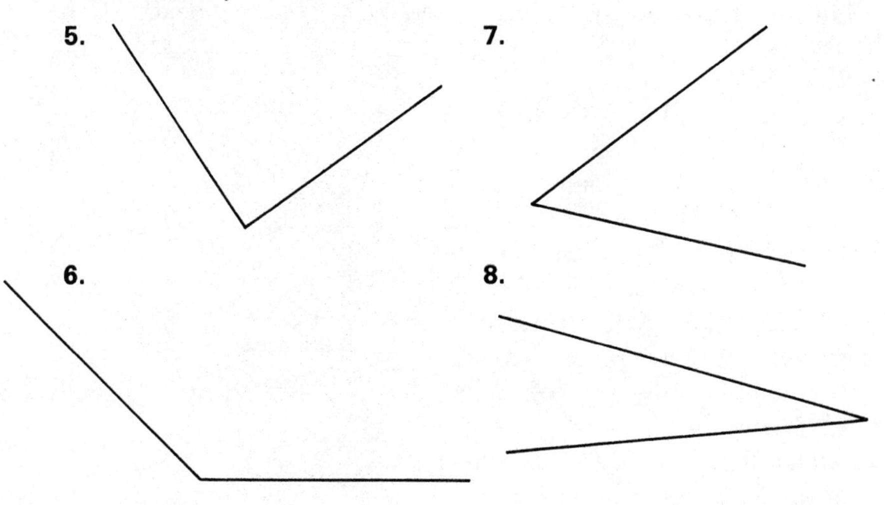

9. Add: $40° \, 27' \, 20''$
   $\underline{30° \, 20' \, 45''}$

10. Add: $35° \, 37' \, 42''$
    $\underline{25° \, 26' \, 37''}$

11. Subtract: $47° \quad 31''$
    $\underline{24° \, 43' \, 35''}$

12. (Optional) Find h if tan 60° is 1.732.

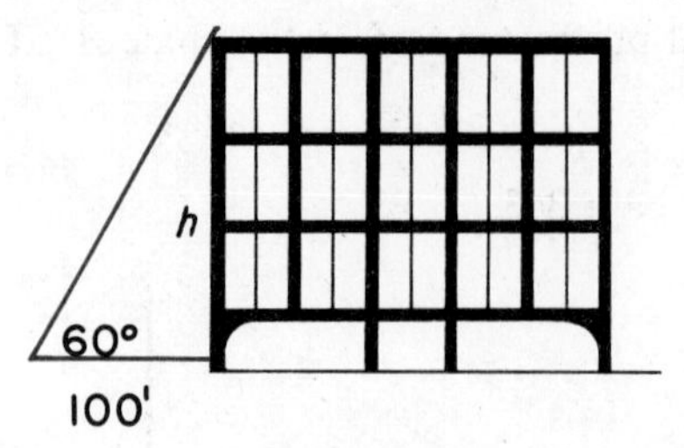

■ Other Measures

2–14 Time

Many instruments are used to measure time. One of the earliest devices was the **sundial,** which measured time by the movement of the sun's shadow. You can easily make a sundial.

ACTIVITY: *Making a sundial.*

Purpose: To develop a method to determine time by the sun.

Materials: Plywood, ruler, protractor, compass (directional), $\frac{3}{4}''$ wire brads.

Plan:

1. Cut the base to approximately 12″ × 12″ dimensions.
2. Cut a rectangular piece of plywood with a base of 6″, and measure with a protractor an angle equal to the latitude of your city. (Consult an atlas to get your latitude.) Cut along this line to form a right triangle. This triangle is the "gnomon" (**no**-mun) of your sundial.
3. Attach the gnomon to the center of the base with $\frac{3}{4}''$ brads.
4. Face the gnomon to North, with the directional compass.
5. Every hour measure the location of the shadow of the sun on the base. (You will probably notice that they are not equal divisions.)

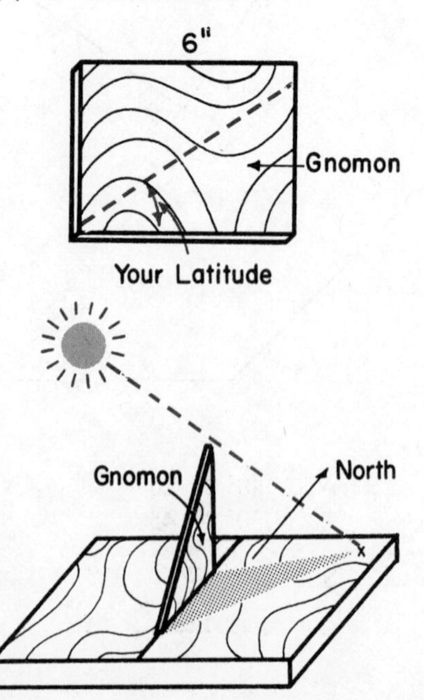

Another way of measuring time is by the use of a **stopwatch.** Most stopwatches are accurate to $\frac{1}{10}$ of a second.

ACTIVITY: *Use of a stopwatch.*

Purpose: To take several readings with a stopwatch and calculate their average.

Materials: Large ball bearing, golf ball, or billiard ball; aluminum or wood V molding approximately 6 feet long; stopwatch.

Plan: To roll a ball down an inclined plane and measure the time required to cover a specific distance.

1. Place V strip on long table at an angle as shown.
2. Mark a spot near each end of the V strip.
3. Place the ball on the top mark; release it and start the stopwatch at the same time.
4. Stop the watch when the ball reaches the bottom mark. Do this several times and calculate the average time the ball takes to cover the distance. Compare your results with those of other students. What reasons can you give to explain any differences in the results?

TM p. 9 , 2-14

2–15 Revolution Counter [Optional]

A revolution counter is a device with a counter which records the number of revolutions when the tip is held against a rotating object. By letting the counter run for one minute you can determine the revolutions per minute (rpm).

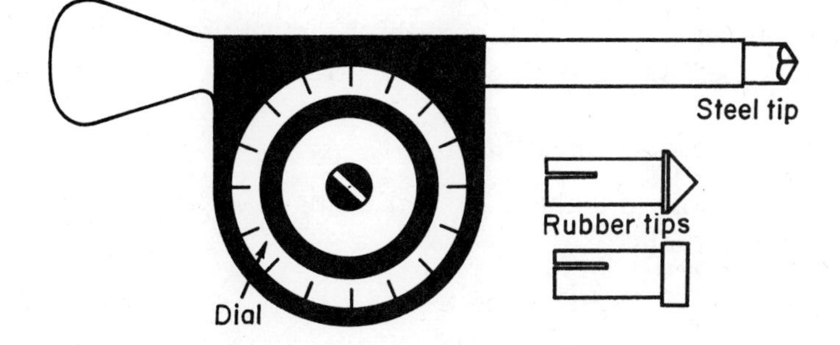

ACTIVITY: *Use of a revolution counter.*

Purpose: To take several readings with a revolution counter and calculate the average.

Materials: Stopwatch, revolution counter, electric grinder.

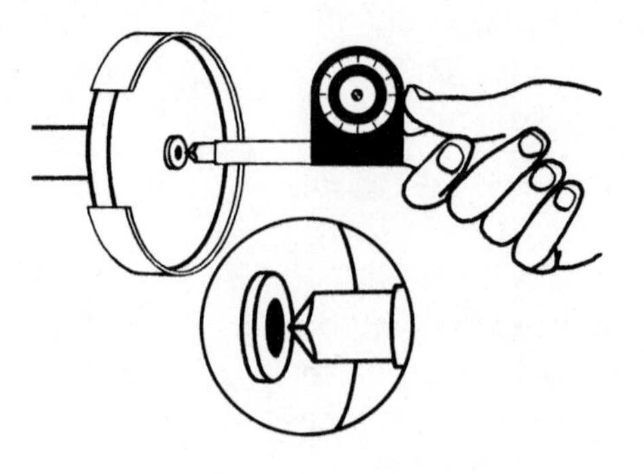

An understanding of rpm will be useful in working with several formulas in Chapter 5.

Plan:

1. Start the grinder and wait until the wheel reaches normal speed.
2. Place the tip of the revolution counter into the center-drilled hole in the end of the shaft. At the same time, start the stopwatch.
3. When a minute has elapsed, pull the revolution counter away from the shaft.
4. Read the dial on the revolution counter. This will tell you how many times the wheel revolves per minute.
5. Repeat several more times to establish accuracy. Take the average of three readings and record in a chart like this one.

Trial	1	2	3	4	Average
Rev./min.					rpm

What reasons can you give to explain any differences in the results?

2–16 Temperature Scales

Two different scales are used to measure temperature. You are familiar with the Fahrenheit scale. You may not have seen the centigrade (Celsius) scale, but it is used throughout Europe. In the United States it is used generally in scientific work.

ACTIVITY: *Reading temperature.*

Problem: To read Fahrenheit and centigrade thermometers under the same conditions.

Materials: Fahrenheit and centigrade thermometers, heating device, ice cubes, glass beaker (200 ml.).

Plan:

1. Place tap water in the beaker and take readings of both thermometers. Make a chart like the one shown.
2. Add ice to the beaker, and take 4 readings, while adding ice. Allow water to reach maximum coolness. Record this temperature as the approximate freezing point.
3. Discard water, and refill the beaker with tap water.
4. Heat gradually and take 4 additional readings as water heats. Record the maximum reading as the boiling point.

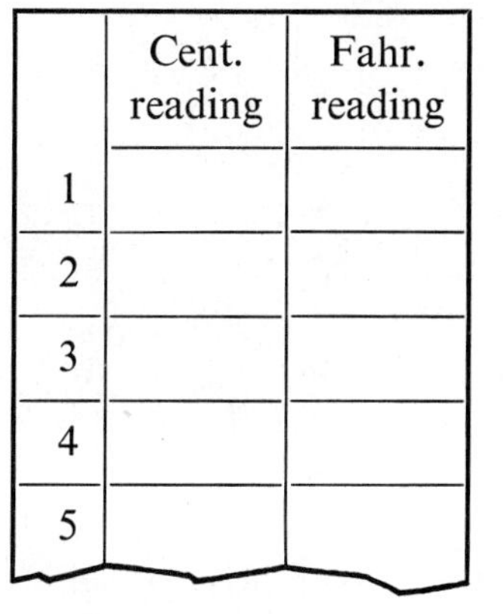

	Cent. reading	Fahr. reading
1		
2		
3		
4		
5		

Suggest taking readings at one-minute intervals.

EXERCISES

A

1. At what temperature reading centigrade and Fahrenheit does water boil?

2. At what temperature reading centigrade and Fahrenheit does water freeze?

3. The relationship between the two temperature scales is given by

$$F = \frac{9}{5}C + 32.$$

Remind student to multiply first, then add.

Do the readings on your chart agree with this formula? If not, why do you think they disagree?

2–17 Electric and Gas Meters

The amount of electricity or gas we use in our homes is measured by a special kind of meter. Although they work differently, the dials look much the same and are read in the same way. Each consists of several dials, usually four.

The kilowatt-hour is the standard unit for measuring domestic and commercial usage of electricity.

A. *Electric Meters*

Electric meters in our homes usually have four dials, as:

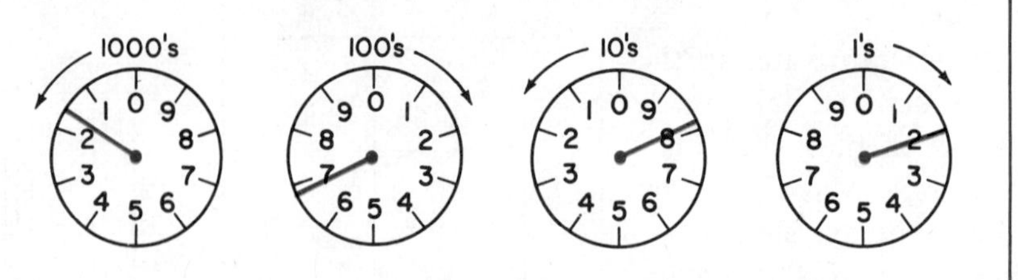

The dial to the right shows kilowatt-hours; the next one to the left shows tens of kilowatt-hours; the next one to the left shows hundreds of kilowatt-hours; and the one to the extreme left shows thousands of kilowatt-hours. The pointers rotate in opposite directions and are so geared that the pointer on the right will make one complete revolution while the one next to it on the left makes $\frac{1}{10}$ of a revolution.

To read the dials, observe the position of the pointer with respect to the numerals within the circle. Set the figures down in order as they appear on the meter, beginning with the dial to the extreme left. When a pointer is between two figures, use the smaller one as a part of the reading.

Important

The meter above reads 1682 KWH.

To obtain the kilowatt-hours (KWH) used during a certain period of time, it is necessary to subtract the previous reading from the present reading. The difference will be the number of kilowatt-hours used between the two readings.

The following month the meter on this page showed this reading:

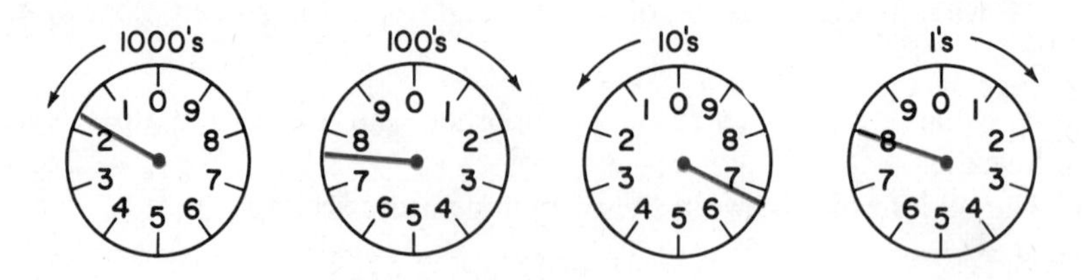

This reading is 1768 KWH.

To find the number of KWH used in the period of time between the readings:

Kilowatt-hours	
Present reading	1768 KWH
minus Previous reading	−1682 KWH
	86 KWH used

The rates charged in a certain city are:

Encourage students to use their local rates in reworking this example.

$1.00 for the first 16 KWH,
3.5¢ per KWH for the next 34 KWH,
3.0¢ per KWH for the next 100 KWH,
and 2.5¢ per KWH for the excess KWH.

KWH		
86		
− 16 →	Cost of first 16 KWH =	$1.00
70		
− 34 →	Cost of 34 KWH @ .035 =	1.19
36 →	Cost of 36 KWH @ .03 =	1.08
	Total =	$3.27

EXERCISES

Read the electric meters.

A

1.

2.

3.

4.

5.

6.

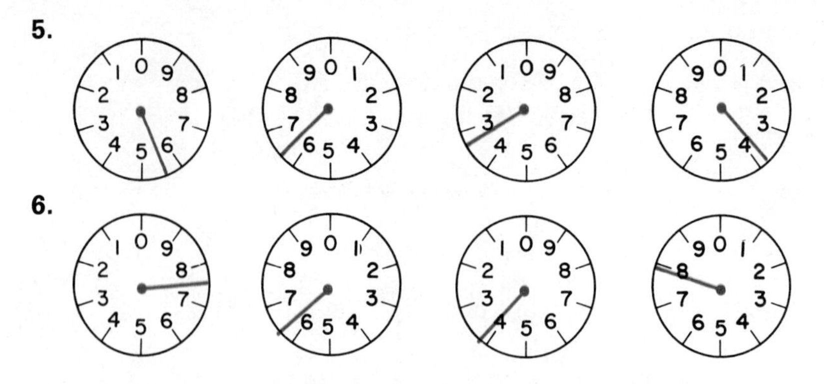

In Exercises 7 and 8, read the meters and compute the charges, using the rates given on page 91.

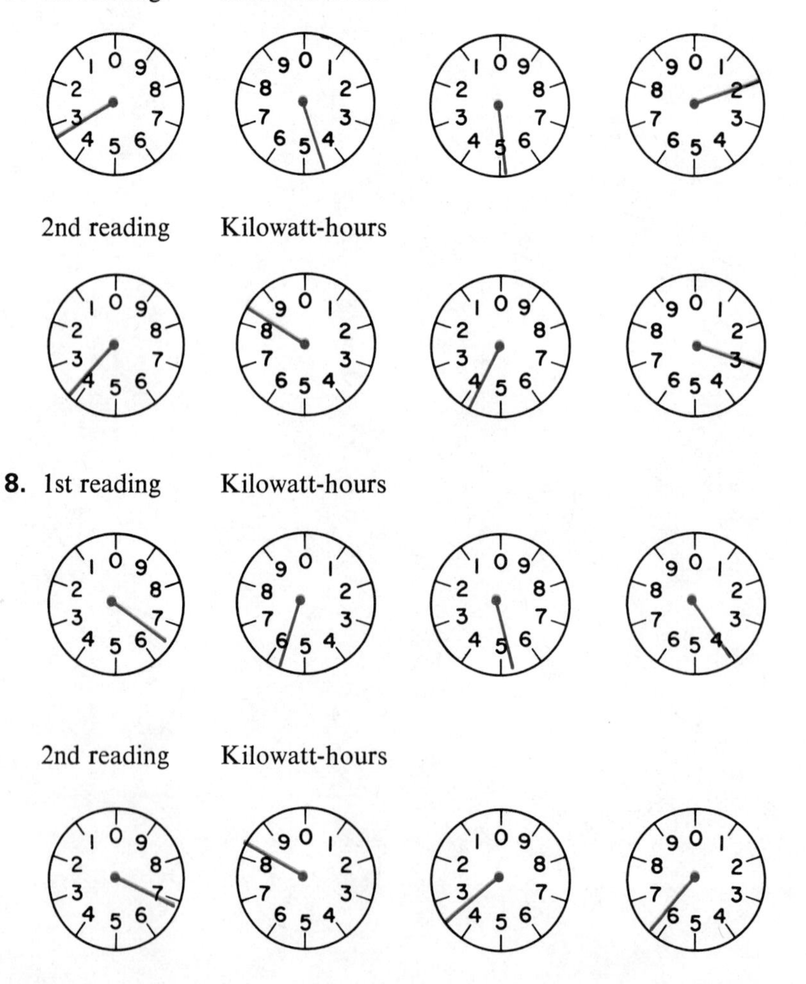

Check the following bills to see if they are correct, using the rates on page 91.

	From	To	Meter readings Present	Previous	KWH used	Amount due
9.	Jan 18	Feb 17	8496	8392	104	\$3.89
10.	Feb 18	Mar 17	8588	8496	92	\$3.52

B. *Gas Meters*

Gas meters look like those illustrated below. The four upper dials are used in reading the meter; the lower dial is used for test purposes only. The dial at the right measures hundreds of cubic feet and the pointer must go around once to produce 1000 cubic feet. The illustrations show how the meter looked on January 27 and on February 27, the days on which it was read by the gas company meter reader.

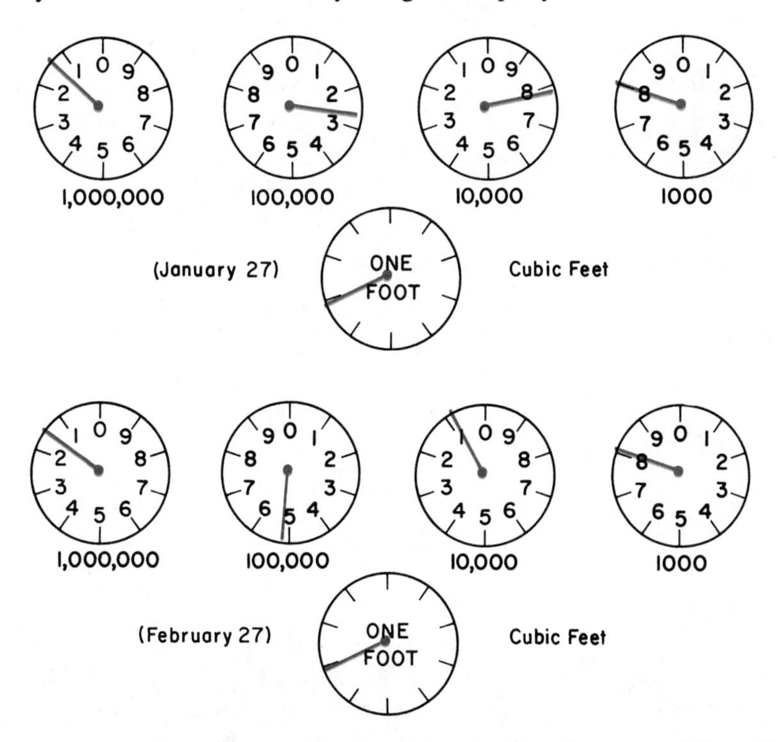

To read the meter on January 27, begin with the dial at the left, which shows the pointer between "1" and "2." Always use the smaller number. Continue reading to the right, each dial in turn. This meter reads 1278, which means 1278 hundred cubic feet and is expressed as:

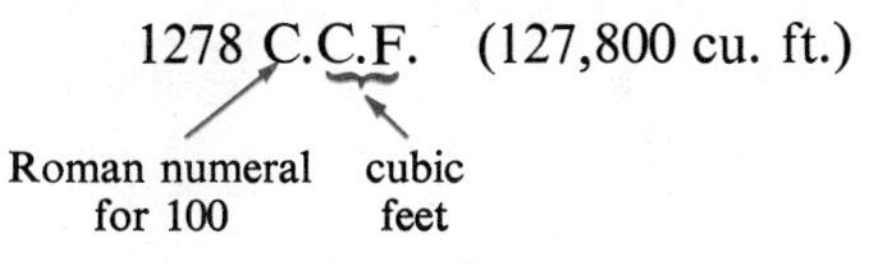

1. What did the meter read on February 27? 1 from first dial, 5 from second dial, 0 from the third dial, and 8 from the fourth. (**1508**)
2. How would you find out how much gas was used from Jan. 27 to Feb. 27? (Subtract reading on Jan. 27 from reading on Feb. 27.)
3. How much gas was used? (1508 − 1278 = **230**)

The rate charged by the gas company is:

First 1000 cubic feet or fraction thereof is $1.50.
Next 99,000 cubic feet, five cents per 100 cubic feet.
All over 100,000 cubic feet, two and eight-tenths cents per 100 cubic feet.

The bill sent to Mr. George's home for the gas used from January 27 to February 27 was as follows:

Present	Previous	C.C.F.	Amount
1508	1278	230	$12.50

This bill was computed as follows:

Have the students rework this example using their local rates.

230 C.C.F. = 23,000 cu. ft.	
First 1000 cu. ft.	$ 1.50
Next 22,000 cu. ft. @ $.05 per hundred	11.00
Total amt.	$12.50

EXERCISES

Read the gas meters.

A **1.**

2.

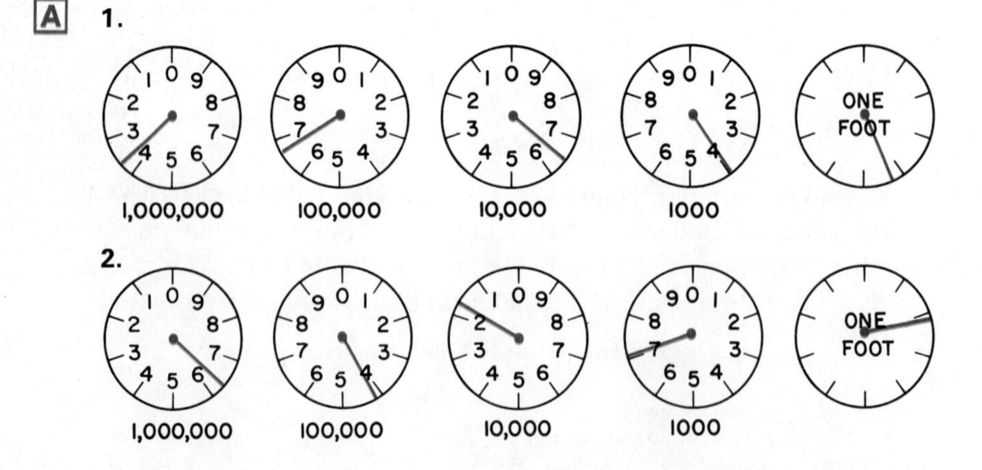

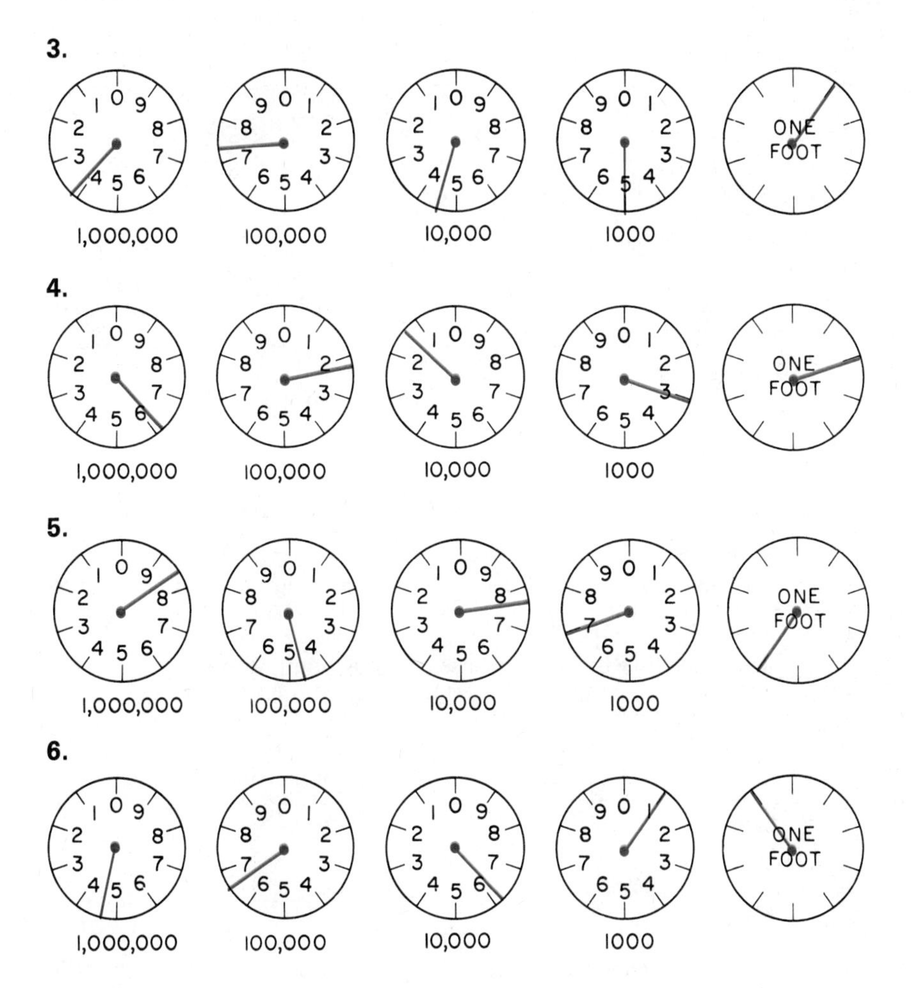

In Exercises 7 and 8, read the meters and compute the charges, using the rates given on page 94.

7. Jan 27

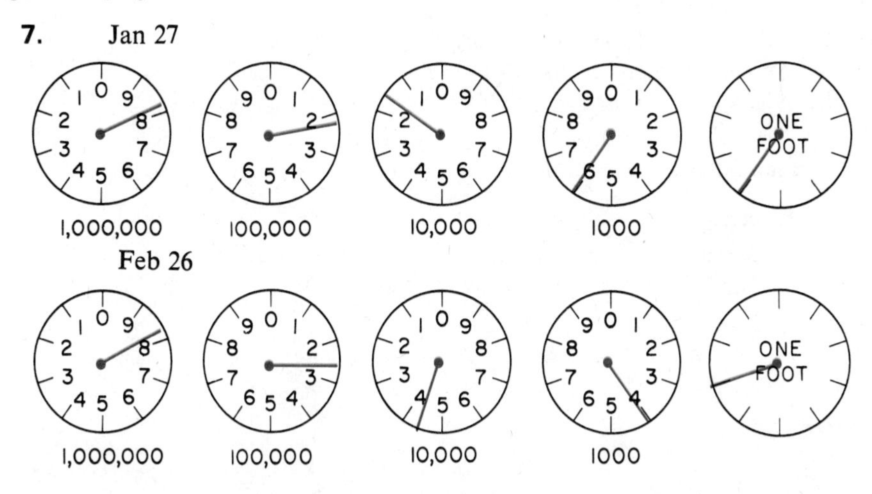

8.

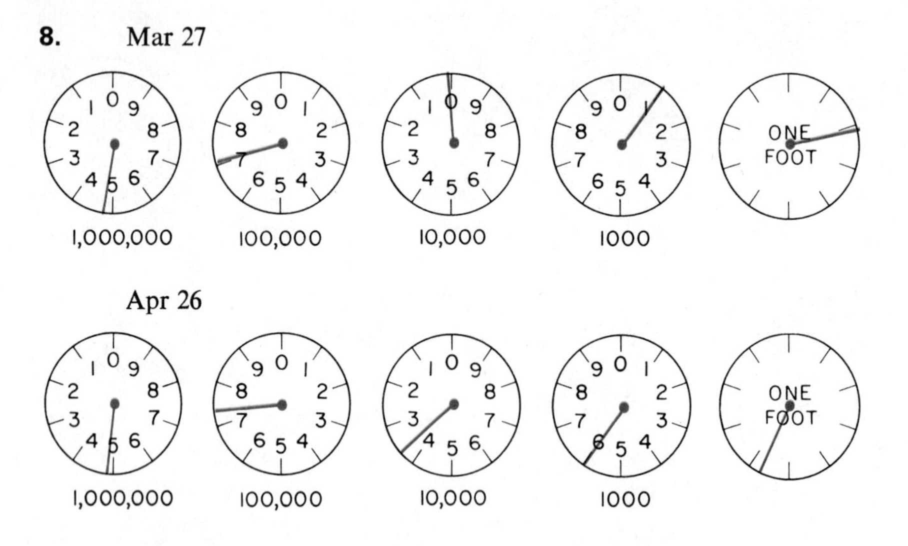

Check the following bills to see if they are correct, using the rates on page 94.

9.

Jan 27 Reading	Dec 28 Reading	C.C.F. used	Amount due
1643	1365	278	$15.90

10.

May 26 Reading	Apr 25 Reading	C.C.F. used	Amount due
2701	2543	158	$8.90

SELF-ANALYSIS TEST IV

Time: 10 minutes

1. An instrument which uses the sun and a gnomon to tell time is called a __?__.
2. An instrument used to measure the number of revolutions per minute of a wheel is called a __?__.
3. An instrument used to measure temperature is called a __?__.
4. An electric meter measures in __?__ hours.
5. A gas meter is read in __?__ feet.

Read the following meters:

6. Electric

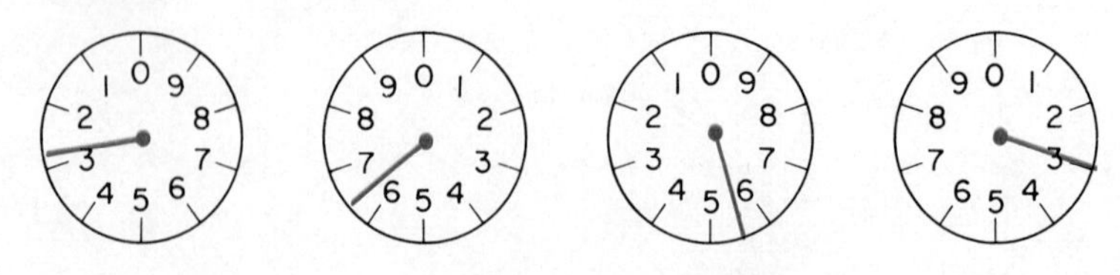

7. Electric

8. Gas

9. Gas

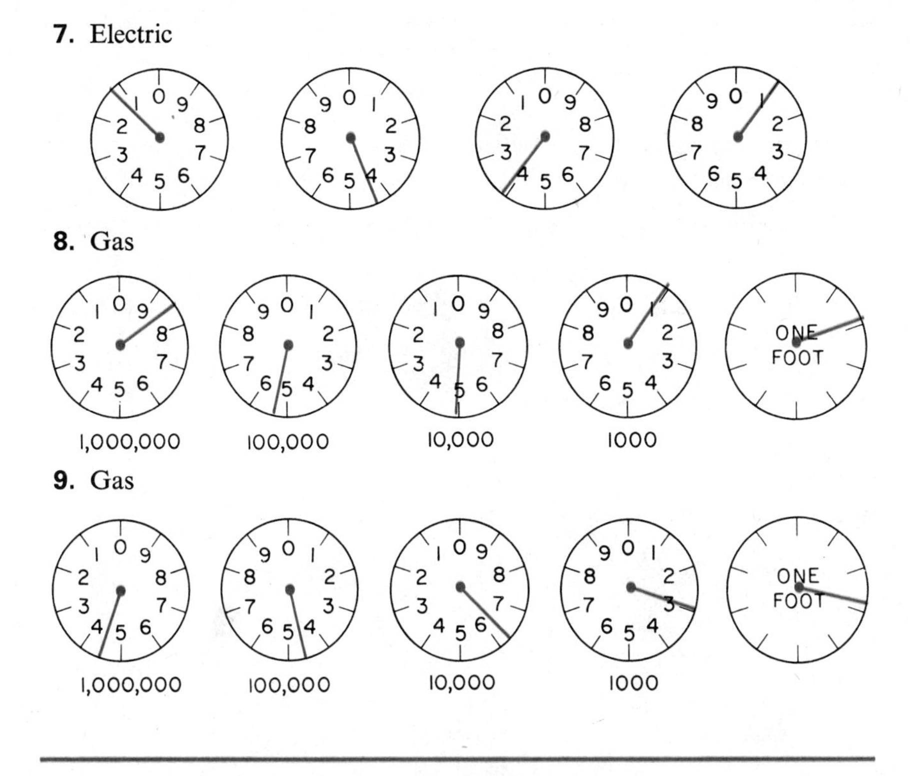

CHAPTER SUMMARY

1. Linear distance is measured with rulers, odometers, altimeters, micrometers, and gauges.
2. Area is measured in terms of a standard unit of area, the square unit.
3. Volume is measured in terms of a standard unit of volume, the cubic unit.
4. Angles are measured in terms of a standard angle, the degree, which is $\frac{1}{360}$ of a complete revolution.
5. The tolerance of a measurement is the difference between the largest and smallest acceptable dimensions.
6. Gauges are devices for making fine measurements.
7. Electric meters are used to measure the amount of electricity used, in terms of kilowatt-hours.
8. Gas meters are used to measure the volume of gas used, in cubic feet.
9. Fahrenheit and centigrade temperatures are related by the formula $F = \frac{9}{5}C + 32$.

CHAPTER TEST

Answer *True* or *False* for statements 1–5. If the answer is *False*, rewrite the statement to make it true.

1. A micrometer is an instrument that measures accurately to $\frac{1}{1000}$ of an inch.
2. A mechanic adjusting a spark plug will use a transit to check the gap.
3. Angles are measured by comparing them with a basic unit angle.
4. Volume is measured in square units.
5. An odometer tells how fast a car is moving.

What altitude is shown on the altimeter?

6. 

7. 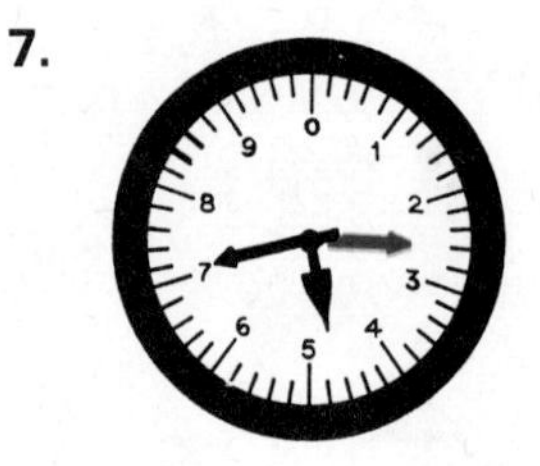

What is the micrometer reading?

8. 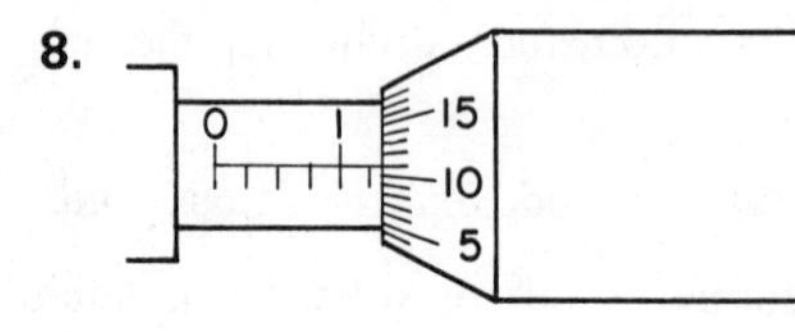

9. 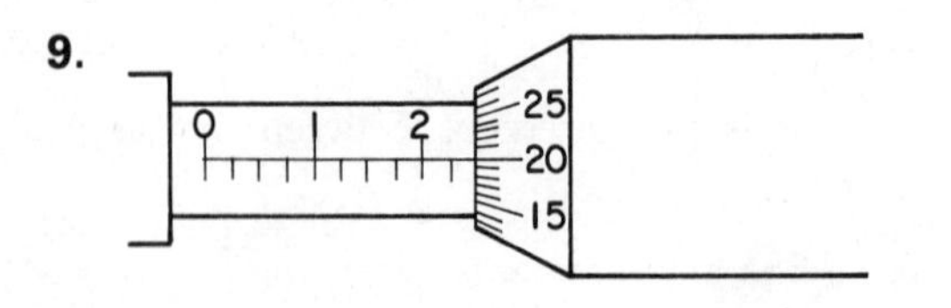

10. 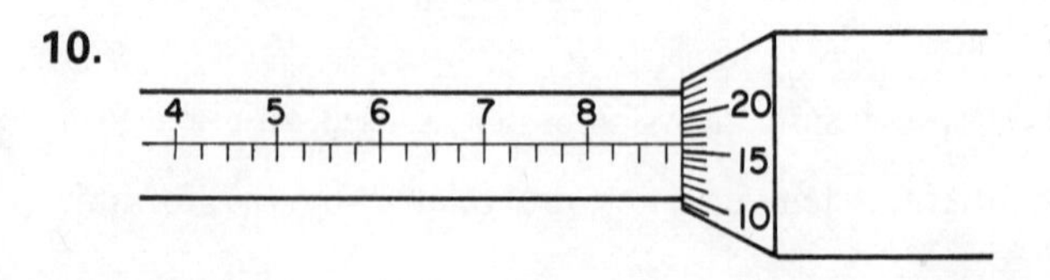

11. Find the tolerance of a pin if its diameter should be $\frac{3}{8}''$ $\pm$ .008″.

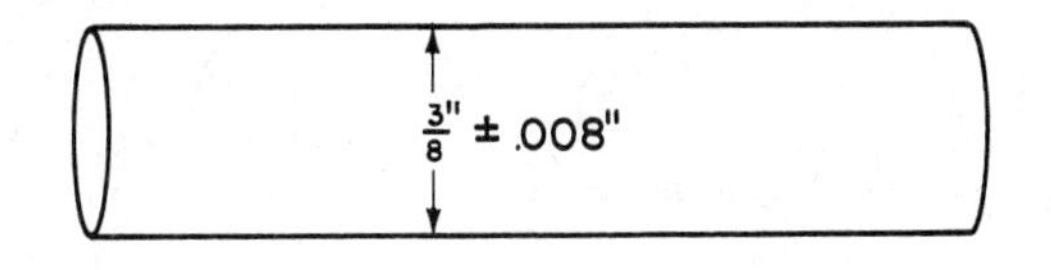

12. A shaft $1\frac{1}{2}''$ in diameter has a tolerance of .002″. What are its limits?

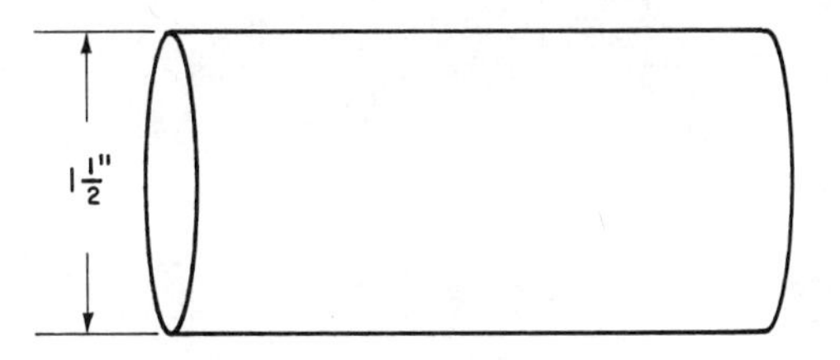

13. Using the square unit shown as the basic unit, find number of square units in the figure below it.

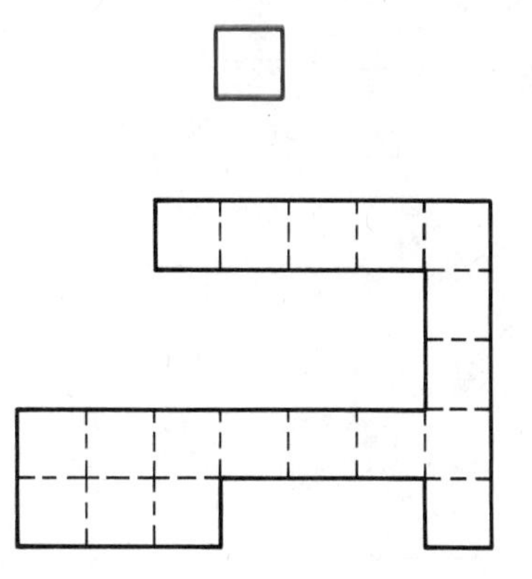

14. Find the volume of the figure below.

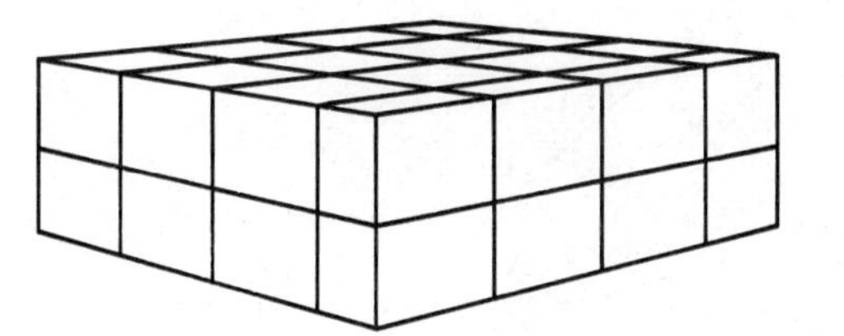

15. 1st reading

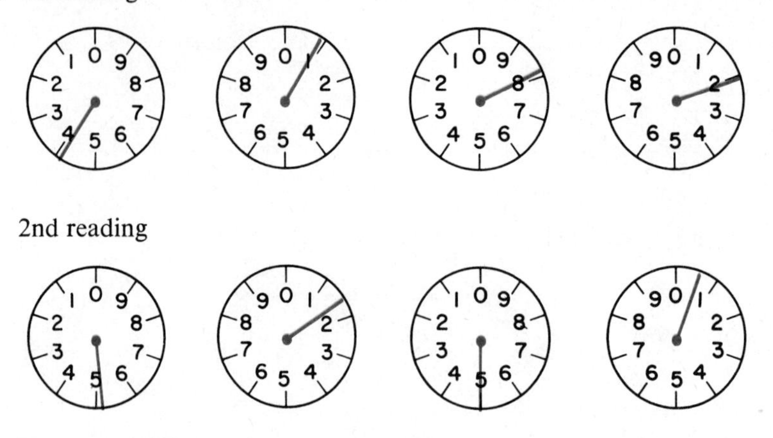

2nd reading

How many kilowatt-hours were used?

16. Add: $\begin{array}{r} 31° 21' 30'' \\ +\ 24° 27' \\ \hline \end{array}$

17. Add: $\begin{array}{r} 43° 34' 29'' \\ +\ 15° 32' 47'' \\ \hline \end{array}$

18. Subtract: $\begin{array}{r} 25° 38' 29'' \\ -\ 12° 24' 13'' \\ \hline \end{array}$

19. Subtract: $\begin{array}{r} 49° 13' 24'' \\ -\ 19° 29' 36'' \\ \hline \end{array}$

20. Use a standard protractor to measure this angle to the nearest degree. $x = \underline{\ ?\ }$.

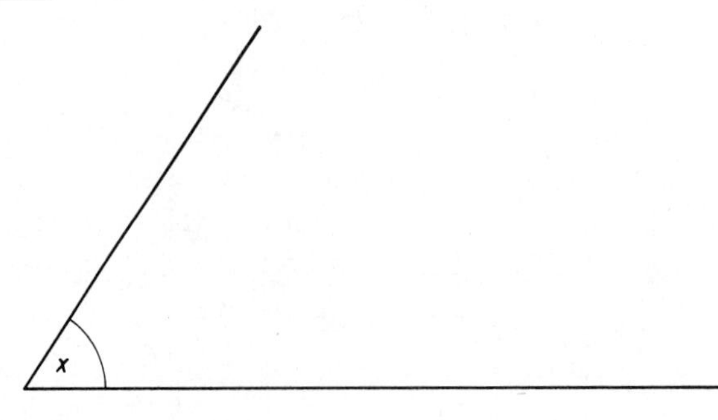

21. Measure this angle to the nearest degree. $y = \underline{\ ?\ }$.

MAINTAINING YOUR SKILLS

Add.

1. $\begin{array}{r} 52 \\ +\ 25 \\ \hline \end{array}$

2. $\begin{array}{r} 27 \\ 36 \\ +\ 56 \\ \hline \end{array}$

3. $\begin{array}{r} 247 \\ 339 \\ 333 \\ +\ 133 \\ \hline \end{array}$

4. $\begin{array}{r} 556 \\ 9656 \\ 37 \\ +\ 755 \\ \hline \end{array}$

5. $\begin{array}{r} 11{,}111 \\ 9{,}999 \\ 77 \\ +\ 222 \\ \hline \end{array}$

6. $\begin{array}{r} 729 \\ 19{,}201 \\ 1{,}655 \\ +\ 78 \\ \hline \end{array}$

Subtract.

7. $\begin{array}{r} 666 \\ -\ 555 \\ \hline \end{array}$

8. $\begin{array}{r} 925 \\ -\ 630 \\ \hline \end{array}$

9. $\begin{array}{r} 2730 \\ -\ 525 \\ \hline \end{array}$

10. $\begin{array}{r} 7652 \\ -\ 236 \\ \hline \end{array}$

11. $\begin{array}{r} 9927 \\ -\ 8901 \\ \hline \end{array}$

12. $\begin{array}{r} 72{,}403 \\ -\ 67{,}027 \\ \hline \end{array}$

Multiply.

13. $\begin{array}{r} 55 \\ \times\ 25 \\ \hline \end{array}$

14. $\begin{array}{r} 41 \\ \times\ 95 \\ \hline \end{array}$

15. 313×25

16. 955×65

17. 425×905

18. 987×543

Divide.

19. $7\overline{)175}$

20. $9\overline{)1350}$

21. $13\overline{)351}$

22. $15\overline{)3525}$

23. $14\overline{)2660}$

24. $25\overline{)2650}$

Simplify.

25. $\frac{1}{4} + \frac{1}{2} = ?$

26. $\frac{1}{8} + \frac{3}{4} = ?$

27. $\frac{1}{5} + \frac{3}{5} = ?$

28. $\frac{1}{16} + \frac{1}{8} + \frac{1}{4} = ?$

29. $\frac{3}{8} \times \frac{3}{4} = ?$

30. $\frac{1}{2} \times \frac{7}{8} = ?$

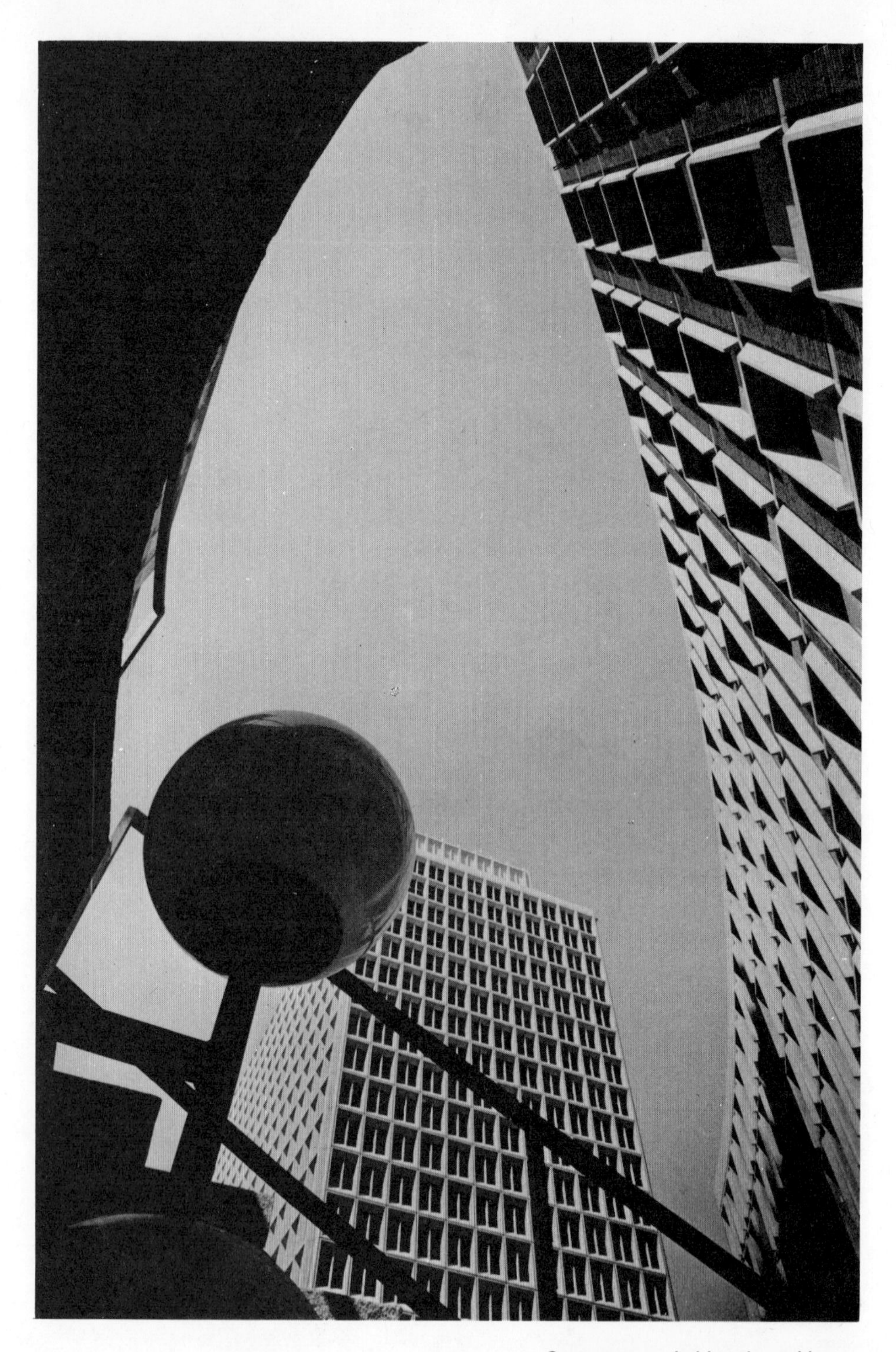

Our towns and cities abound in examples of geometric forms, as in this photograph taken in Boston, Mass.

Geometric Figures

OBJECTIVES

1. To learn about lines and angles in the plane.
2. To draw figures with protractor and compass.
3. To learn the names of special polygons and some of their properties.
4. To learn about common 3-dimensional figures and their construction from patterns.
5. To study the lines and angles associated with the circle.

People working in industry are aware of the importance of manufacturing products in mass quantity. A few of the patterns and tools required for such work were mentioned in the preceding sections. The design of tools and the construction of patterns involve an understanding of many geometric figures and relationships. To review and extend your knowledge in this field is the purpose of this chapter.

Plane Figures

3–1 Planes and Lines TM p. 9 , 3-1

A **plane** is a flat surface which extends indefinitely. Parts of planes are represented by the top of your desk, the chalkboard, a wall of your classroom.

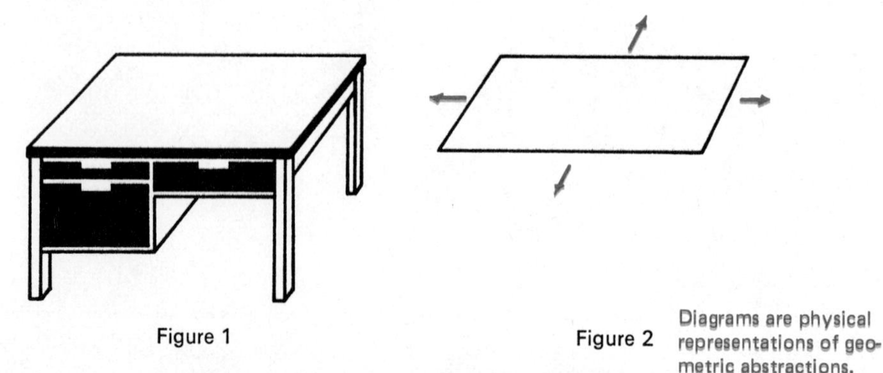

Figure 1 Figure 2

Diagrams are physical representations of geometric abstractions.

We cannot draw a plane, but we represent a part of a plane by drawing a figure such as Figure 2 above. The arrows remind us that the plane extends beyond the lines indicated. In actual practice we do not draw the arrows, but we remember that a plane has no boundaries.

In geometry the term **line** means a *straight* line, unlimited in length. The usual symbol for the line through the two points A and B is $\overleftrightarrow{AB}$, read "line AB." The arrowheads symbolize the fact that the line extends indefinitely beyond A and B. Sometimes lines are named by a small letter written near the line, as l below.

$\overleftrightarrow{AB}$ Line ℓ

A part of a line which has one endpoint and extends in one direction only is called a **ray.** A ray is named by using the endpoint and any other point on the ray. The ray with endpoint A and passing through point B is named by the symbol $\overrightarrow{AB}$, as in the figure below.

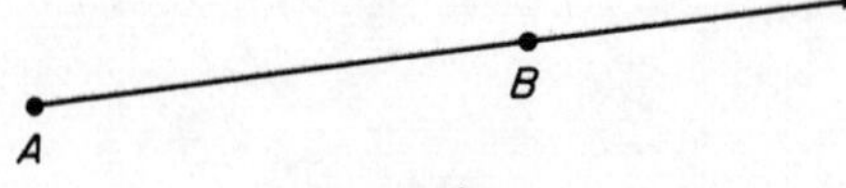

$\overrightarrow{AB}$

It is important to recognize that the symbol $\overrightarrow{BA}$ names a different ray, one that starts at B and passes through A.

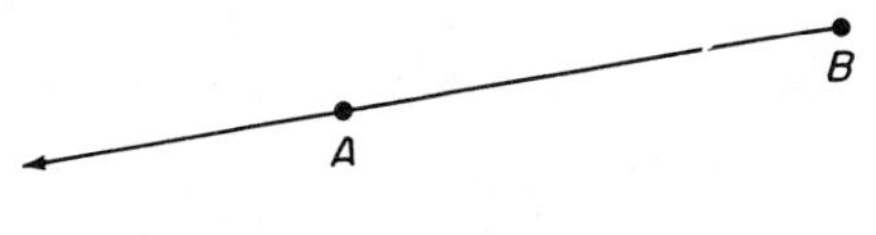

$\overrightarrow{BA}$

In this text "segment" will always mean "line segment."

A **line segment,** or **segment,** is a part of a line, and has two distinct endpoints. The symbol used for the line segment with endpoints A and B is $\overline{AB}$.

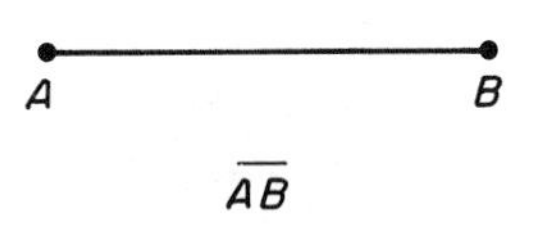

$\overline{AB}$

Notice that the symbol for a line segment has no arrowheads, in order to indicate that a segment has a definite length. We will write $m\overline{AB}$ for the length of line segment $\overline{AB}$. You will find it easy to remember the meaning of this symbol since the m stands for "the measure of." Another way of referring to the length of segment $\overline{AB}$ is simply to write AB, without any other symbol. To understand the ideas in this chapter, it is important for you to know the difference between the meaning of the symbols $\overleftrightarrow{AB}$, $\overrightarrow{AB}$, $\overrightarrow{BA}$, $\overline{AB}$, $m\overline{AB}$, and AB. Stress this.

If two lines are in a plane, they may intersect or not intersect. In the first diagram below, $\overleftrightarrow{MN}$ intersects $\overleftrightarrow{XY}$ at O. Lines in a plane which do not intersect are called **parallel lines.** Such lines are always the same distance apart. We read $\overleftrightarrow{AB} \parallel \overleftrightarrow{CD}$ as "line AB is parallel to line CD,"

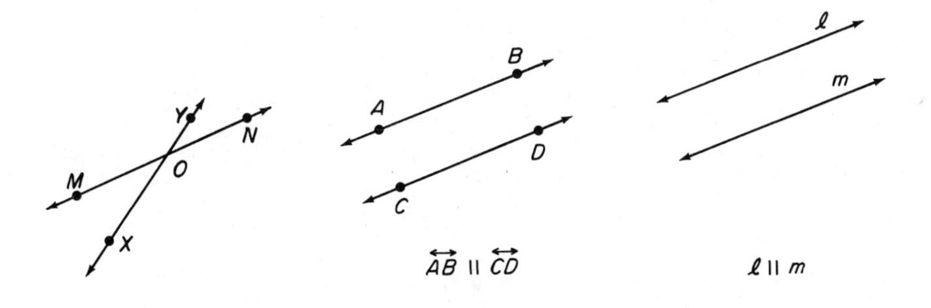

$\overleftrightarrow{AB} \parallel \overleftrightarrow{CD}$ $\ell \parallel m$

and $l \parallel m$ as "line l is parallel to line m."

Two line segments are parallel if they are parts of two parallel lines. Thus, in the center diagram above, $\overline{AB} \parallel \overline{CD}$ because $\overleftrightarrow{AB} \parallel \overleftrightarrow{CD}$.

EXERCISES

Draw a sketch to illustrate each figure named below. Label the parts of your figures.

These exercises will help students become familiar with the symbols used.

A

1. $\overline{AB}$
2. $\overrightarrow{AB}$
3. $\overleftrightarrow{AB}$
4. $\overrightarrow{BA}$
5. $\overleftrightarrow{AB} \parallel \overleftrightarrow{CD}$
6. $r \parallel s$
7. Line l intersecting parallel lines $\overleftrightarrow{CD}$ and $\overleftrightarrow{EF}$
8. Ray $\overrightarrow{CD}$ intersecting line $\overleftrightarrow{ST}$
9. $\overleftrightarrow{AB}$ intersecting $\overrightarrow{CD}$, which intersects $\overline{EF}$
10. $\overleftrightarrow{AB} \parallel \overleftrightarrow{CD} \parallel \overleftrightarrow{EF}$

3–2 Angles

An **angle** is a geometric figure formed by two rays with the same endpoint.

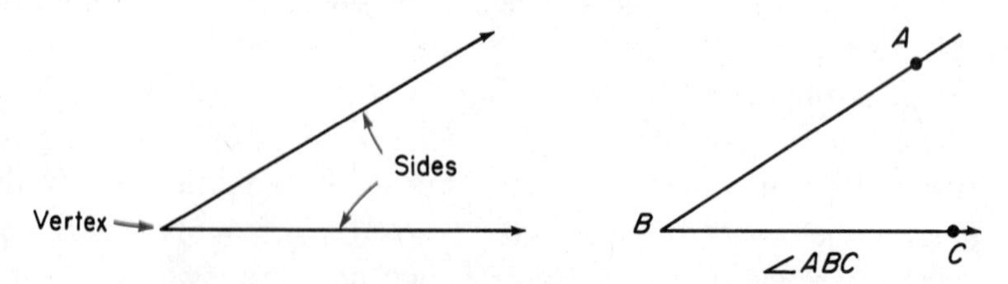

Angles are usually named with three letters, as $\angle ABC$. The letter naming the **vertex** always appears in the middle. Sometimes, when no confusion will result, an angle is named by a single letter, the letter at the vertex.

Important.

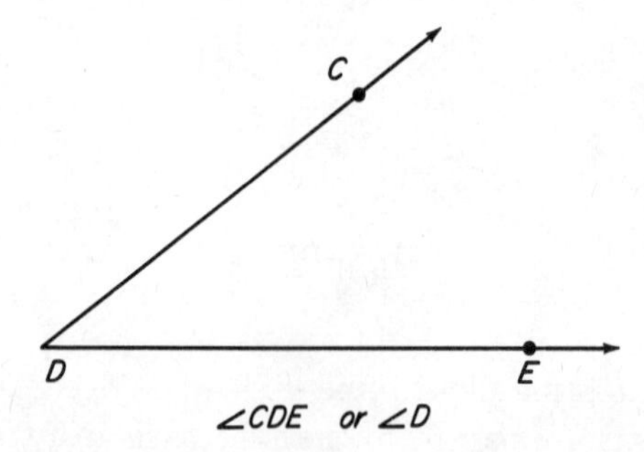

Angles are measured with a protractor, as you learned on page 77.

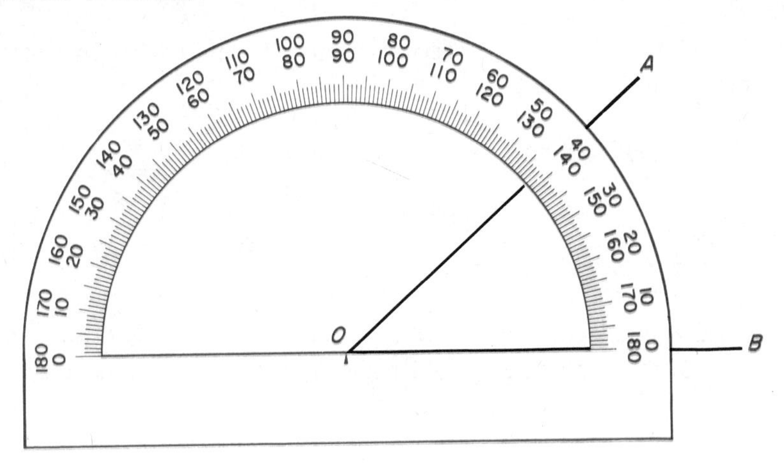

The measure of $\angle AOB$ is 42°, which we will write as $m\angle AOB = 42°$.

Angles with measures between 0° and 90° are called **acute** angles. A **right** angle is one with a measure of 90°. **Obtuse** angles are angles with measures between 90° and 180°. TM p. 9 , 3-2(1)

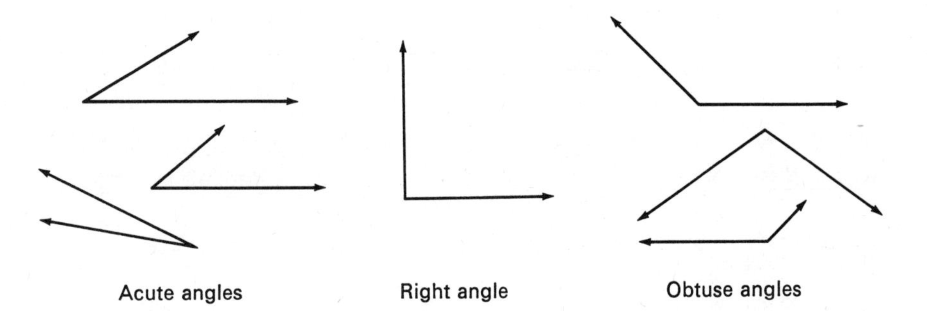

Acute angles Right angle Obtuse angles

Lines which meet to form angles of 90° are called **perpendicular** lines.

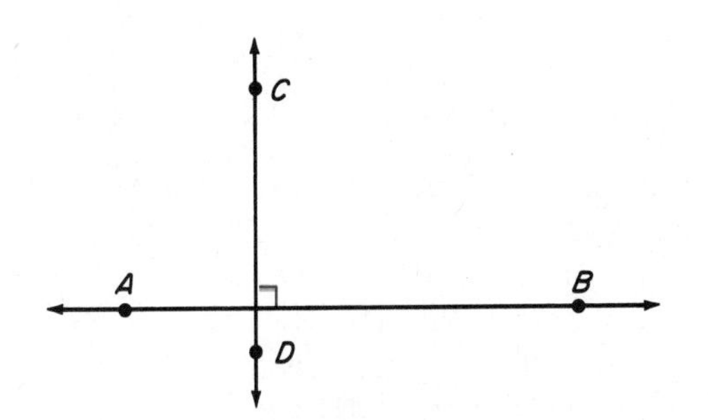

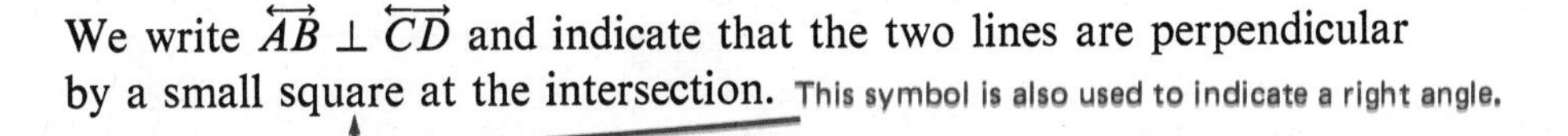

We write $\overleftrightarrow{AB} \perp \overleftrightarrow{CD}$ and indicate that the two lines are perpendicular by a small square at the intersection. This symbol is also used to indicate a right angle.

Two angles whose measures total 90° are called **complementary angles.** TM p. 9 , 3-2(2)

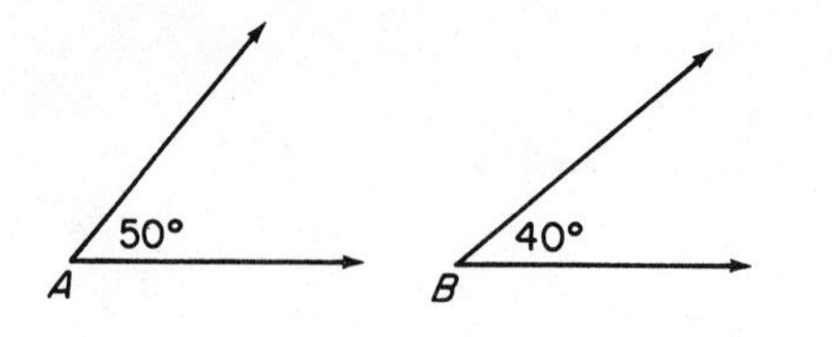

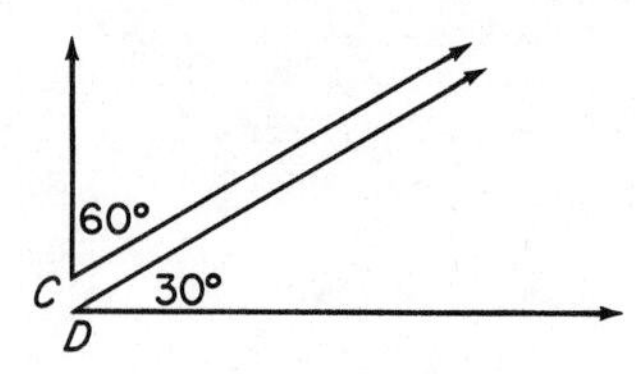

Angle *A* is the complement of angle *B*.
Angle *B* is the complement of angle *A*.

Angles *C* and *D* are complementary angles.

Two angles whose measures total 180° are called **supplementary angles.**

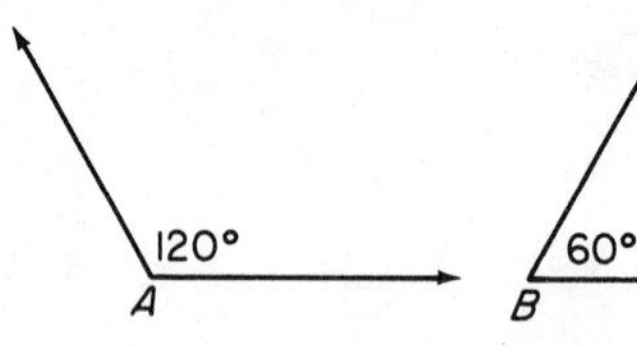

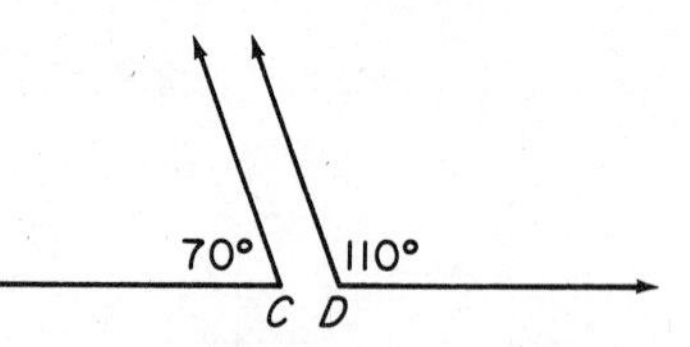

Angle *A* is the supplement of angle *B*.
Angle *B* is the supplement of angle *A*.

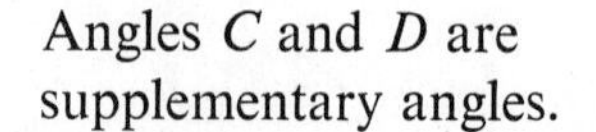

Angles *C* and *D* are supplementary angles.

Point out that complementary angles and supplementary angles do not have to be adjacent (that is, share a common vertex and a common side).

EXERCISES

Use your protractor and a sharp pencil for these exercises.

A

1. Draw an acute angle of 50°. Letter the angle *ABC*.
2. Draw a right angle. Letter the angle *MNO*.
3. Draw an obtuse angle of 120°. Letter the angle *PQR*.
4. Draw an angle of 180° about point *A*. Letter it *EAG*. (Such an angle is known as a *straight angle*.)
5. Bisect an obtuse angle of 160°. (Draw the line which divides the angle into two angles with equal measures.) How many degrees in each angle? Letter the angles, using *A*, *B*, *C*, and *D*, so that *B* appears as the vertex of the angles. The method of constructing the bisector of an angle with the compass is given on page 262. Here we rely on the protractor.

Use a protractor to measure these two angles. Then find the measures of the complements of these angles.

6. **7.**

Use a protractor to measure the angles below. Then find the measure of the supplement of each angle.

8. **9.**

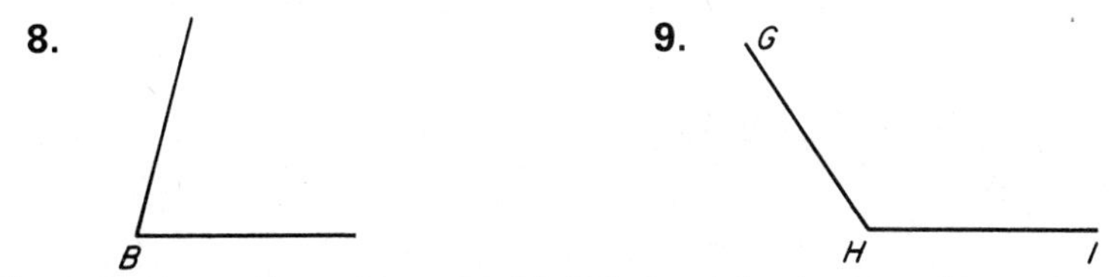

The student may wish to review pages 79-80 before doing these exercises.

B **10.** Find the measure of the angle which is the complement of an angle whose measure is 27° 30′.

11. Find the measure of the angle which is the complement of an angle whose measure is 42° 31′ 27″.

12. Find the measure of the angle which is the supplement of an angle whose measure is 39° 43′.

13. Find the measure of the angle which is the supplement of an angle whose measure is 137° 33″.

3–3 Polygons

Geometric figures such as those shown below are polygons. A

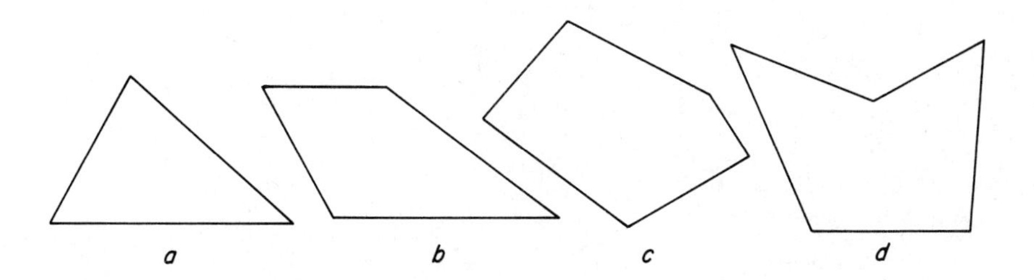

polygon is formed by line segments which meet at their endpoints, do not cross, and completely enclose a part of the plane. The line segments

Emphasize the importance of the three requirements in the definition of a polygon.

are called the **sides** of the polygon and the vertices of the angles formed are called the **vertices of the polygon.** In the figure below the sides are $\overline{AB}$, $\overline{BC}$, $\overline{CD}$, $\overline{DE}$, and $\overline{EA}$. The vertices are A, B, C, D, and E.

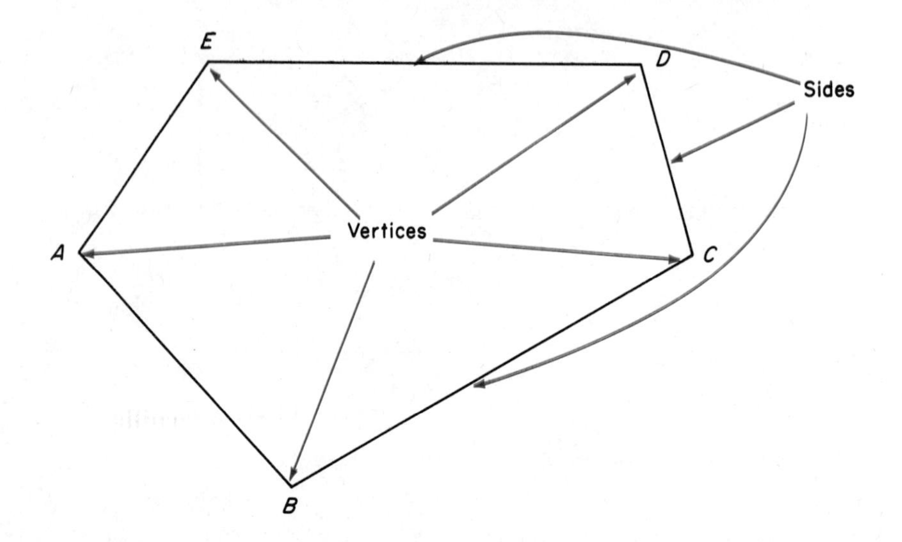

Polygons are named according to the number of their sides. Some of the more common ones are shown below.

Urge the students to test each polygon shown below against the definition on page 109.

Triangle: 3 sides

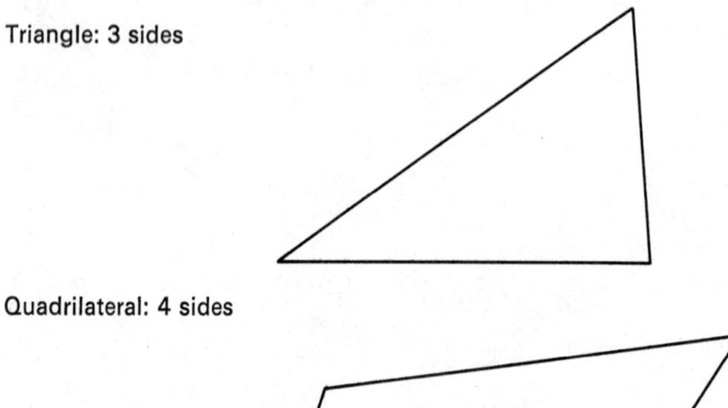

Quadrilateral: 4 sides

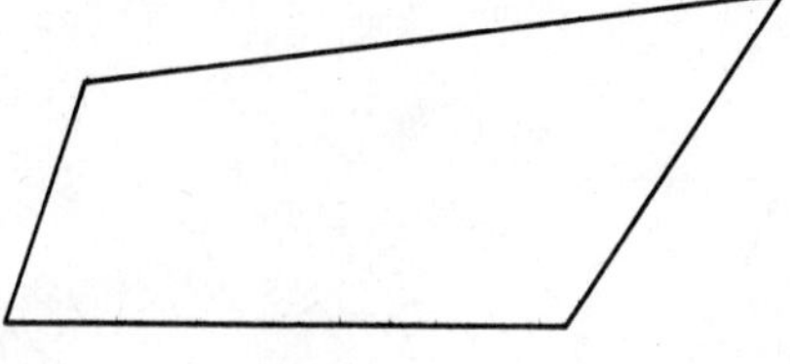

Pentagon: 5 sides

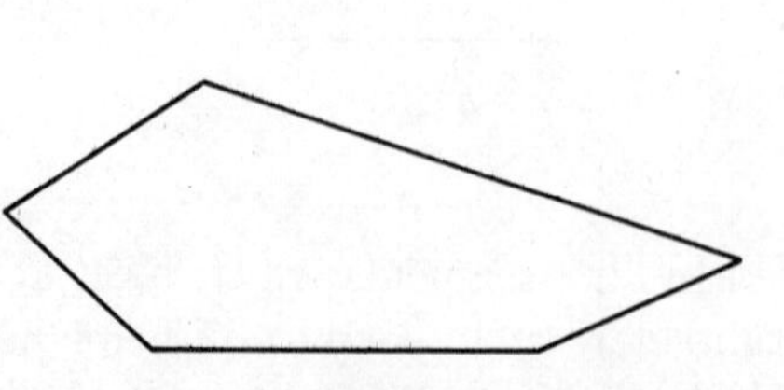

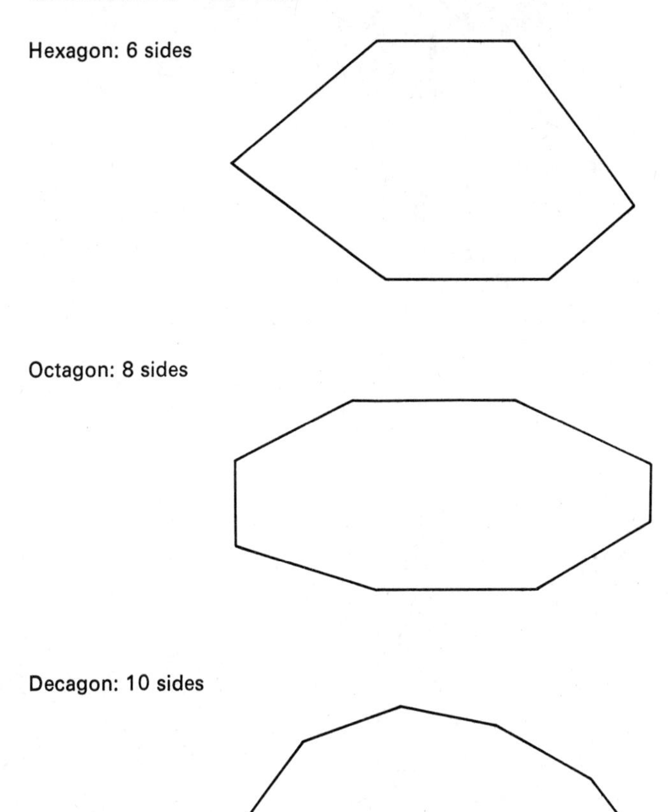

The teacher may wish to introduce the terms equiangular and equilateral here.

A polygon with all angles equal and all sides the same length is called a **regular polygon.**

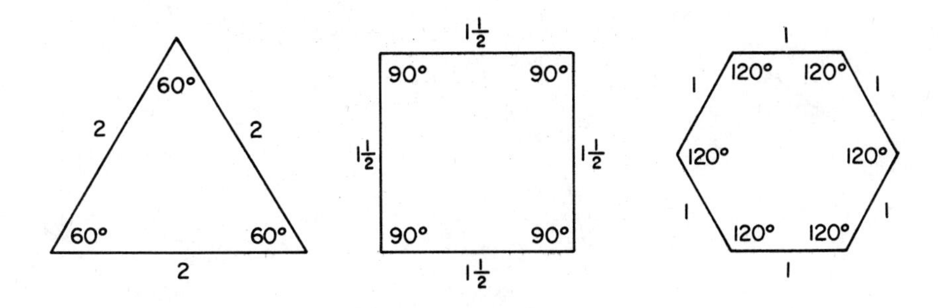

Regular polygons

EXERCISES

Name the types of polygons pictured below.

A **1.** **2.** **3.** **4.** **5.** **6.** **7.** **8.**

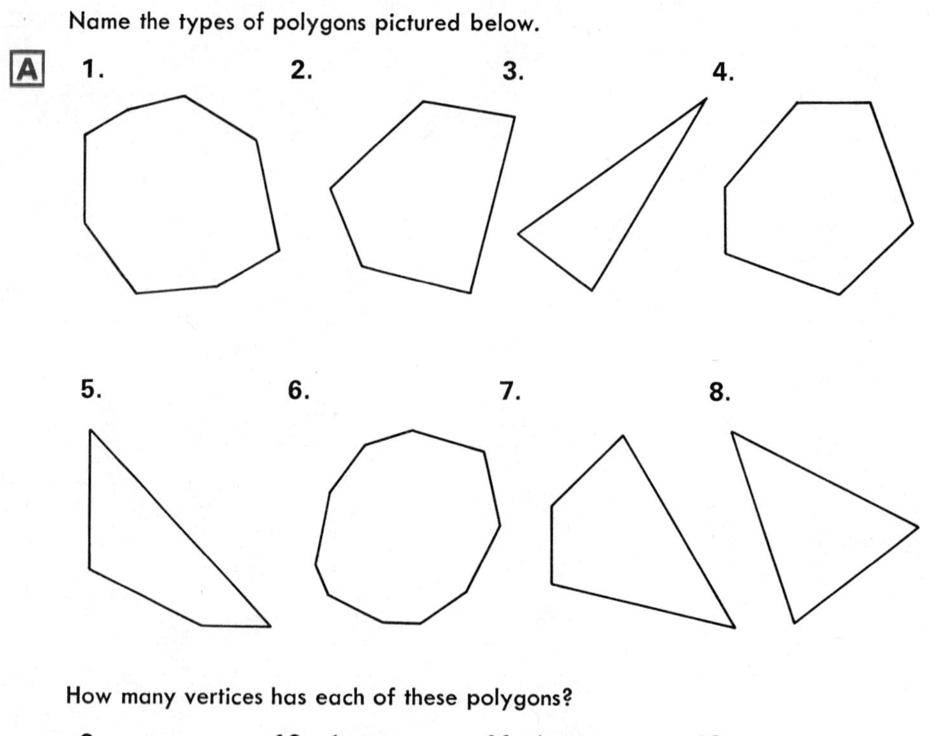

How many vertices has each of these polygons?

9. octagon **10.** decagon **11.** hexagon **12.** pentagon

In Exercises 13 and 14 use a ruler and a protractor to measure each side and each angle. Copy and complete the table on page 113.

13. **14.**

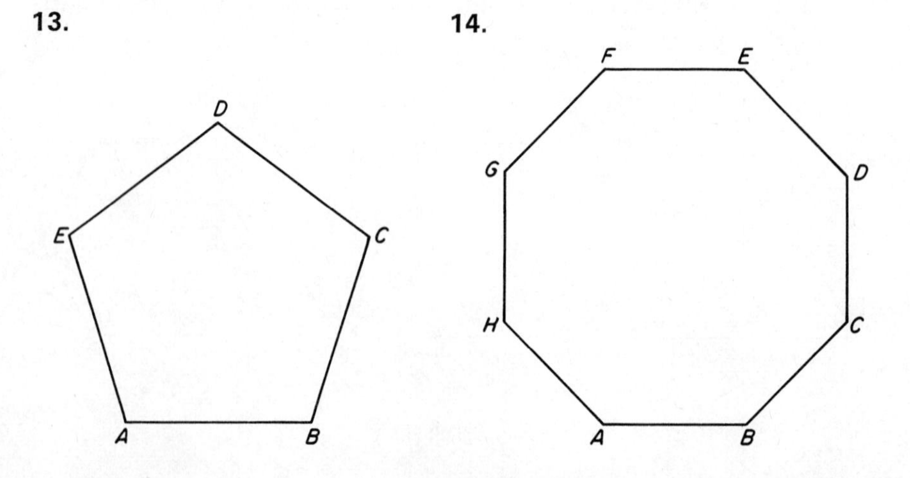

	Ex. 13	Ex. 14
Name of polygon		
$m\overline{AB}$ = __?__ inch		
Are all sides equal?		
$m\angle ABC$ = __?__ degrees		
Are all angles equal?		
Is the polygon regular?		

3–4 Triangles

The two ways to classify triangles are (a) by sides, and (b) by angles. The types of triangles in each group are illustrated below.

A. Triangles Classified by Sides

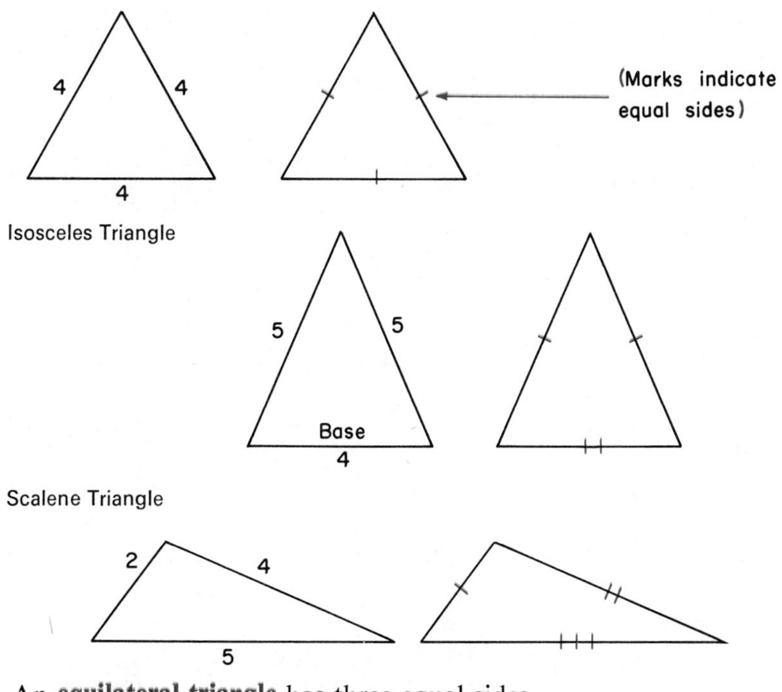

An **equilateral triangle** has three equal sides.
An **isosceles triangle** has two equal sides.
A **scalene triangle** has no two sides equal.

B. Triangles Classified by Angles

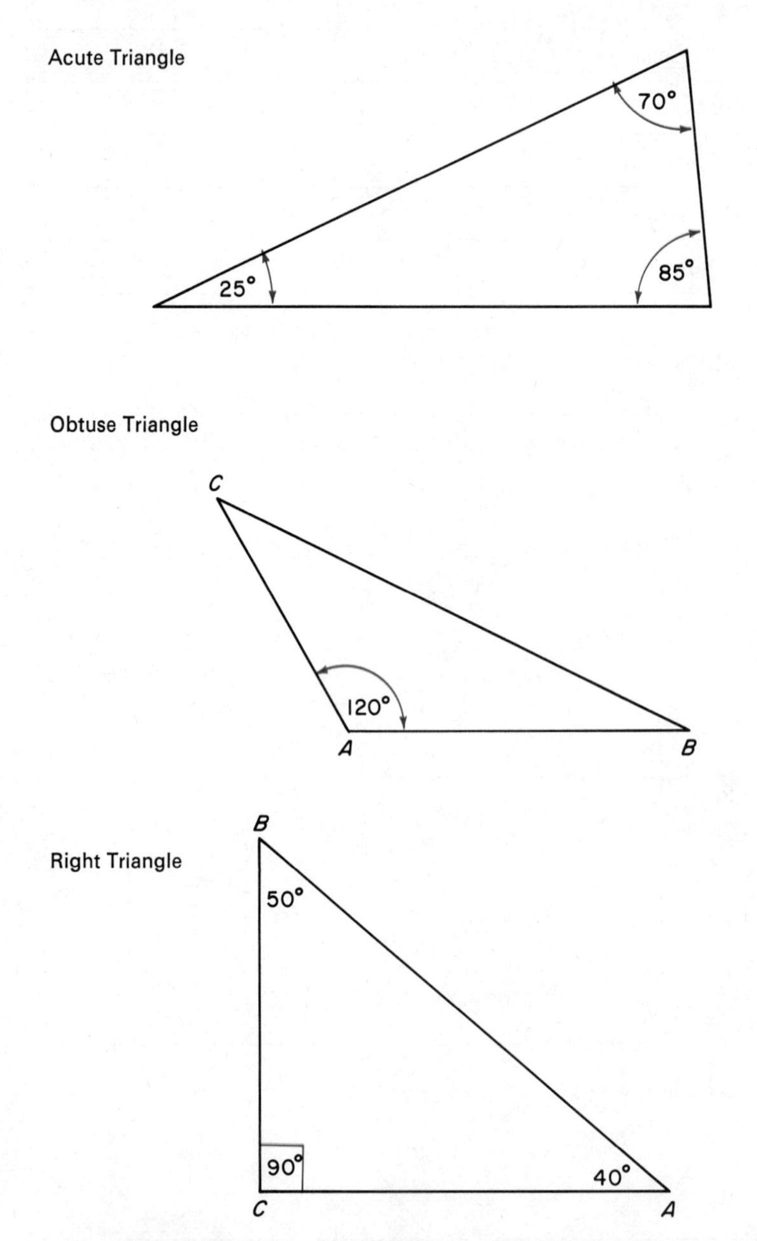

An **acute triangle** is one in which every angle is less than 90°.

An **obtuse triangle** is one which contains an obtuse angle.

A **right triangle** is one which contains a right angle, that is, an angle of 90°.

Notice the red lines in these triangles. They are the altitudes of the triangle. Every triangle has three altitudes. An **altitude of a triangle** is the segment from a vertex perpendicular to the line containing the opposite side. Compare this meaning of altitude with its use on page 56 in connection with the altimeter.

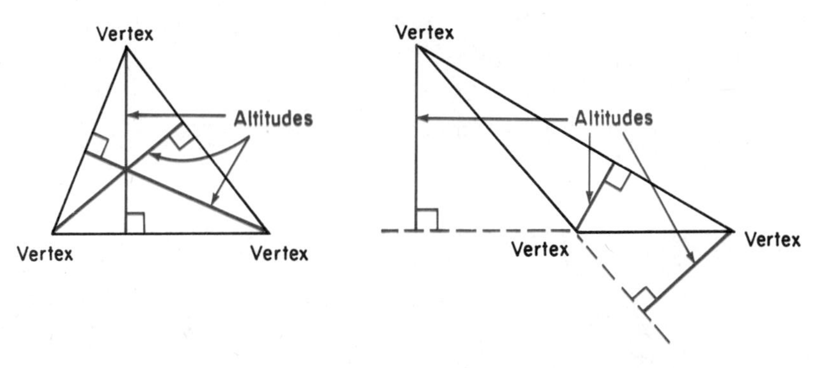

ACTIVITY: ***Measuring the angles of a triangle.*** See TM p. 10, 3-4 for an alternative method.

Purpose: To discover the sum of the measures of the angles of any triangle.

Materials: Paper, pencil, straightedge, protractor.

Plan:

1. Draw a triangle as large as your paper allows.
2. Measure each angle with your protractor. Record your measurements.
3. Add the measures found in Step 2.
4. Compare your sum with those of others in your class.
5. Would you now agree with the following statement?

Encourage the students to analyze the possible sources of errors in their measurements.

> The sum of the measures of the angles of any triangle is 180°.

EXERCISES

A

1. Draw an obtuse triangle and letter the obtuse angle A. Call the other two angles B and C. What is the sum of angles B and C? Can you have a triangle with more than one obtuse angle?

2. Draw a triangle ABC ($\triangle ABC$) with $m\angle C = 90°$. Is $\angle A$ the complement of $\angle B$?

3. Are the acute angles of a right triangle always complementary?

Exercises 4–8 refer to the figure below.

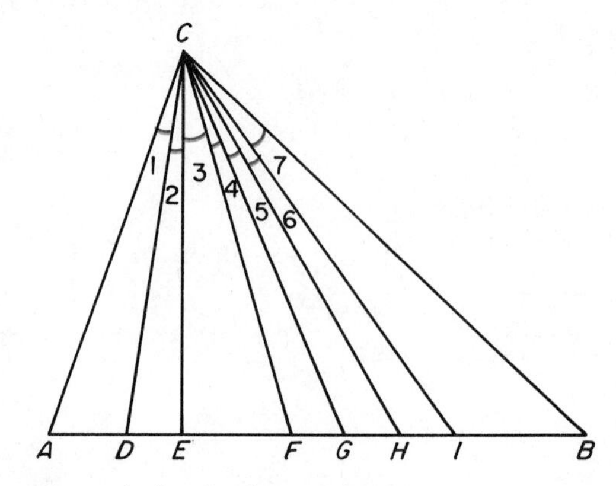

4. Measure each angle in the figure above.

$m\angle 1 = \underline{\ ?\ }$ $m\angle 4 = \underline{\ ?\ }$ $m\angle 6 = \underline{\ ?\ }$
$m\angle 2 = \underline{\ ?\ }$ $m\angle 5 = \underline{\ ?\ }$ $m\angle 7 = \underline{\ ?\ }$
$m\angle 3 = \underline{\ ?\ }$

5. Which lines in the figure are perpendicular?

6. Which line is an altitude of $\triangle ABC$?

7. Which line is the shortest distance from C to $\overline{AB}$?

Point out that the altitude is always the shortest distance from a vertex to the opposite side (extended, if necessary).

ACTIVITY: *Constructing a triangle.*

Purpose: To construct a triangle, given three sides, p, q, r.

p ______________ q ______________ r ______________

Materials: Compass, straightedge, pencil and paper.

Procedure:

1. Draw a line segment longer than p, and on it mark a point A.
2. To copy segment p, place the point of your compass at one end of p and adjust compass so that the pencil tip is at the other end of p. (Recall page 52.)

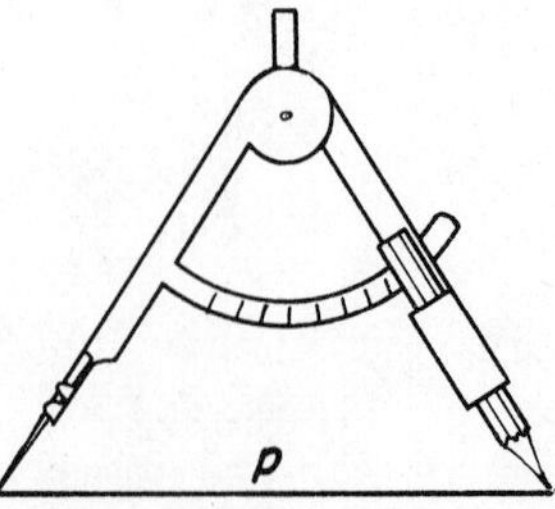

3. Without changing the compass, mark off the length of p on the line segment, and locate point B.

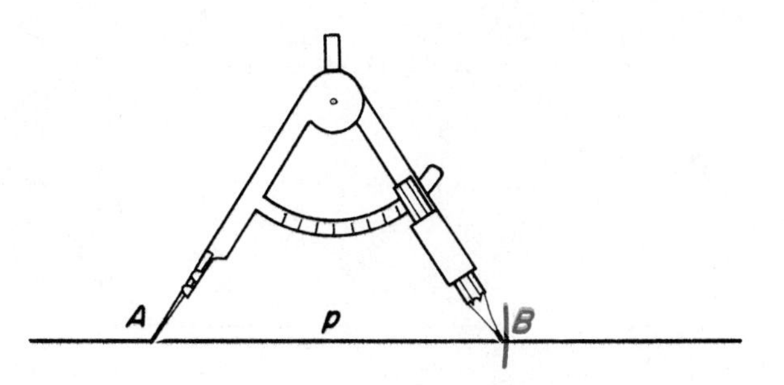

4. Use your compass to measure side q. Place the point of the compass on point A and draw an arc.

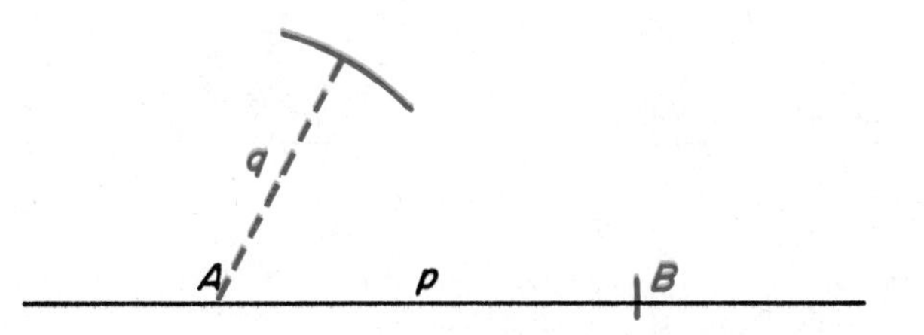

5. Repeat Step 4 using the length of side r and point B to locate point C.

If the first arc must be extended, remind the student to reset the compass to length $\underline{q}$.

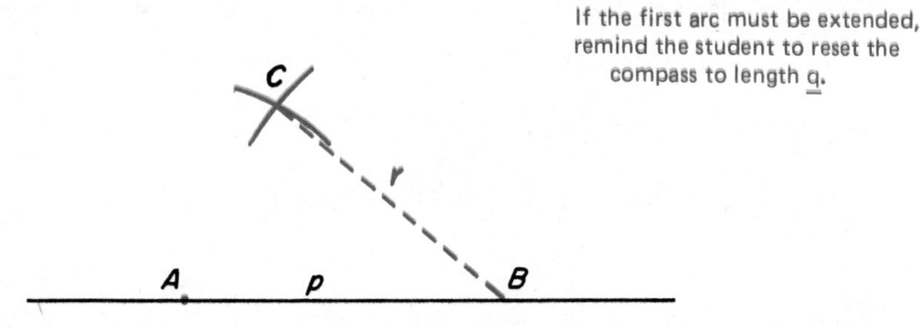

6. Connect points A and C, and B and C, to give triangle ABC with sides p, q, r.

Have students compare their constructions to evaluate accuracy.

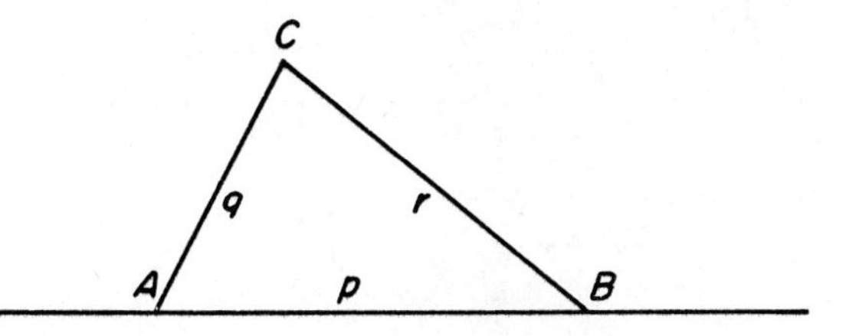

EXERCISES

A

1. Construct four triangles with the given segments.

a. p q r

b. p q r

c. p q r

d. p q r

2. Construct an equilateral triangle with 3″ sides.

3. Construct an isosceles triangle with sides of 3″ and a 5″ base. Emphasize this property. ↓

4. Construct a scalene triangle with sides 2″, 4″, and 5″.

5. Measure the sides of each triangle in Problem 1. Is the sum of the lengths of any two sides of a triangle greater than the length of the third side?

6. Is it possible to construct a triangle with sides of 2″, 2″, and 4″? If not, give your reason.

7. Measure the angles and classify each of the triangles at the top of page 119 by their angles. You can use the flow chart below to help you.

Exercises 7 and 8 illustrate the two methods of classifying triangles.

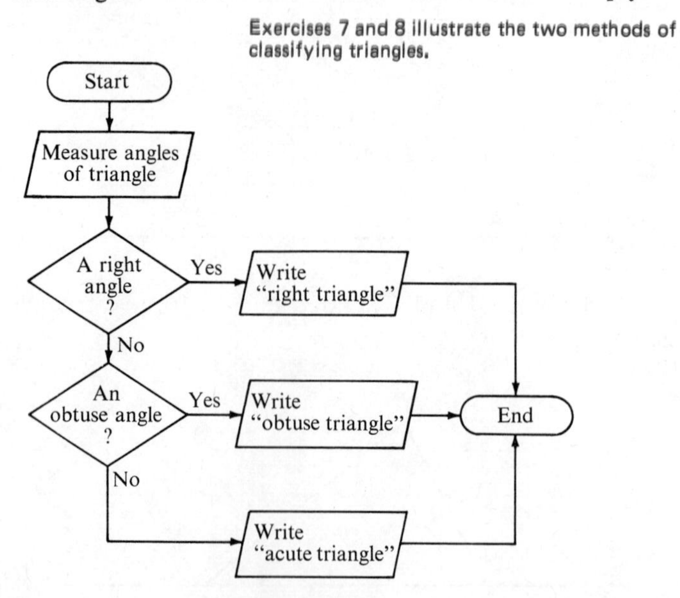

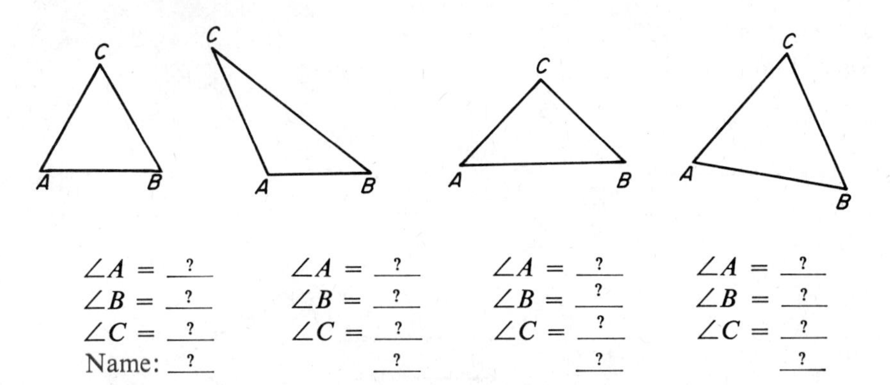

8. Measure the sides of each triangle in Exercise 7 and classify the triangles by their sides. Use the flow chart below to help you.

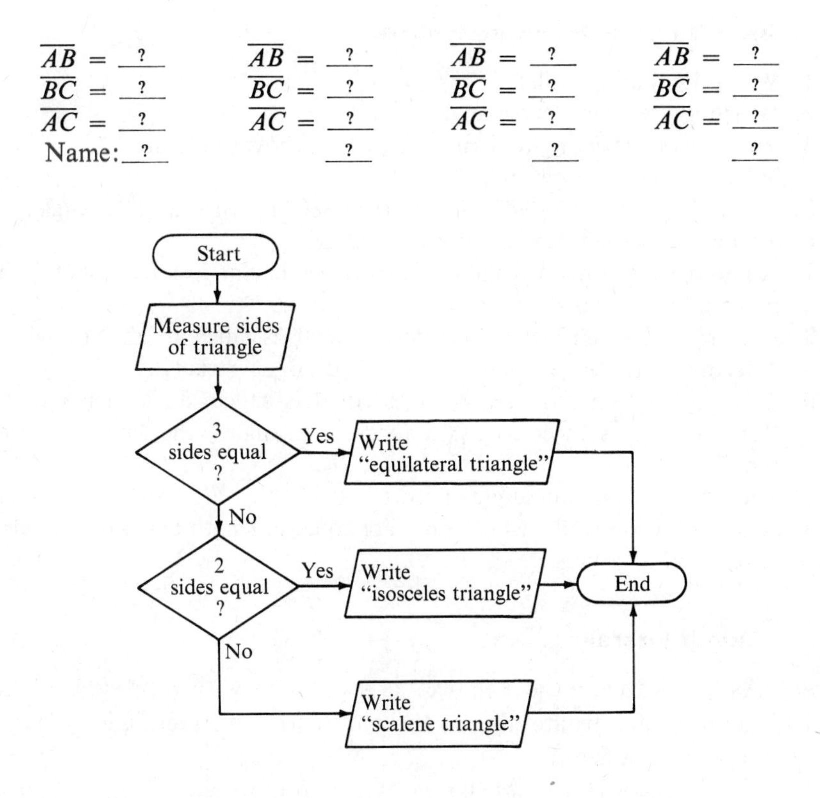

9. a. Draw a triangle with base 3″ and base angles of 60° and 50°.
b. Measure the length of the two sides formed.
c. What is the measure of the third angle?

10. Draw an obtuse triangle having a 120° angle with the sides forming it each 2″.

11. Draw an equilateral triangle. Is this triangle also an acute triangle?

SELF-ANALYSIS TEST I

Time: 5 minutes

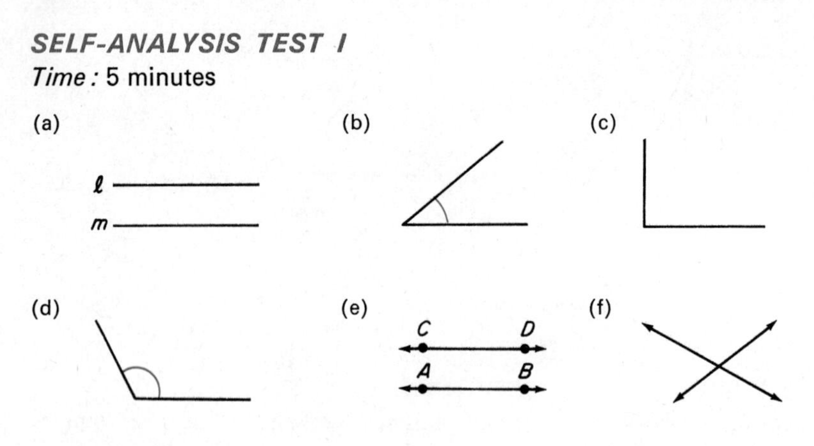

Exercises 1–4 refer to the diagrams above.

1. Which lines are parallel?
2. Which figure is an obtuse angle?
3. Two lines intersecting to form 4 angles are shown in figure __?__.
4. Which figure is a right angle?
5. An angle greater than 90° and less than 180° is called an __?__ angle.
6. Two angles whose sum is 90° are called __?__.
7. A line segment drawn from a vertex perpendicular to the opposite side of a triangle is called an __?__.
8. A triangle in which each angle is less than 90° is called an __?__ triangle.
9. A triangle with three equal sides is called an __?__ triangle.
10. A triangle which has no two sides equal is called a __?__ triangle.
11. When two lines meet so as to form __?__ angles, the lines are perpendicular.
12. The supplement of an angle of 35° is __?__.
13. A __?__ polygon is one whose sides are equal in length and whose angles have equal measures.

A geoboard, if available, can be used to show the relationships among members of the family of quadrilaterals.

3–5 Quadrilaterals

As you know, a **quadrilateral** is a polygon with four sides. The most common quadrilaterals are the parallelogram, rectangle, square, rhombus, and trapezoid.

A **parallelogram** is a quadrilateral whose opposite sides are parallel.

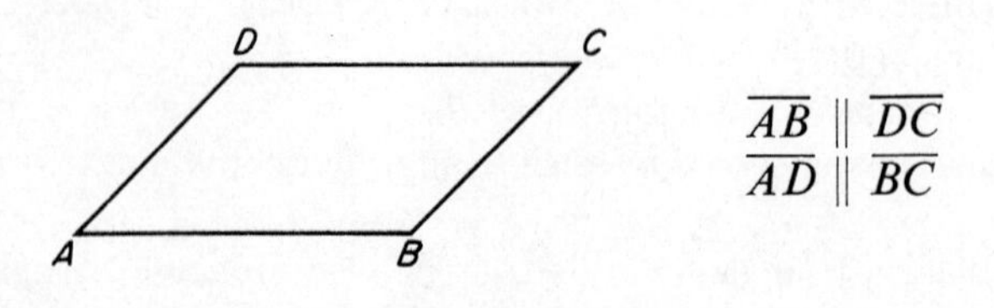

$\overline{AB} \parallel \overline{DC}$
$\overline{AD} \parallel \overline{BC}$

A **rectangle** is a parallelogram with four right angles.

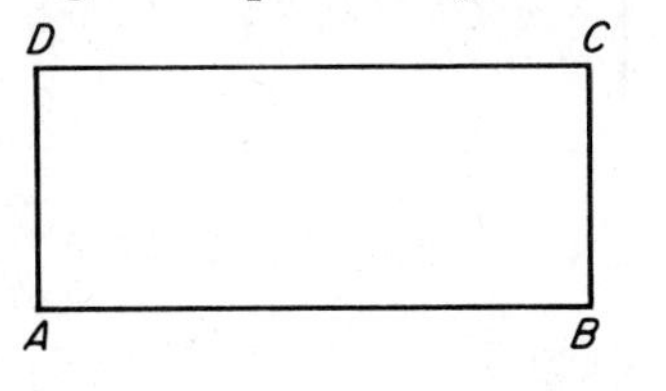

$\overline{AB} \parallel \overline{DC}$, $\overline{AD} \parallel \overline{BC}$
$\measuredangle A, B, C, D$ are right angles.

A **square** is a rectangle with all sides equal.

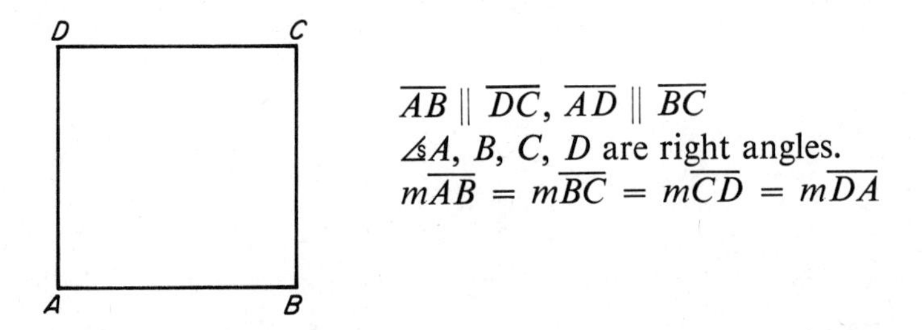

$\overline{AB} \parallel \overline{DC}$, $\overline{AD} \parallel \overline{BC}$
$\measuredangle A, B, C, D$ are right angles.
$m\overline{AB} = m\overline{BC} = m\overline{CD} = m\overline{DA}$

A **rhombus** is a parallelogram with all sides equal.

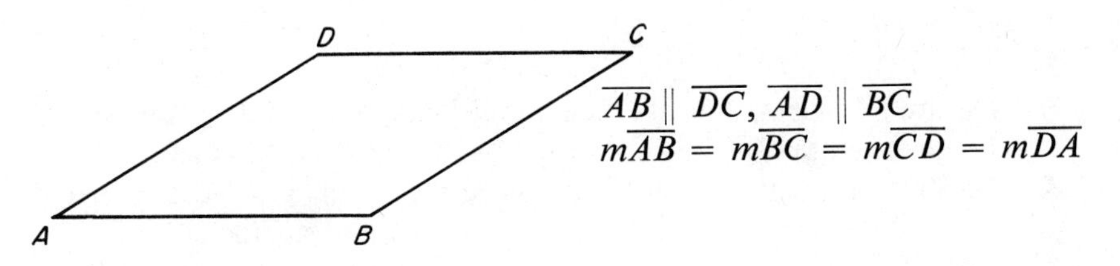

$\overline{AB} \parallel \overline{DC}$, $\overline{AD} \parallel \overline{BC}$
$m\overline{AB} = m\overline{BC} = m\overline{CD} = m\overline{DA}$

A **trapezoid** is a quadrilateral with only one pair of opposite sides parallel.

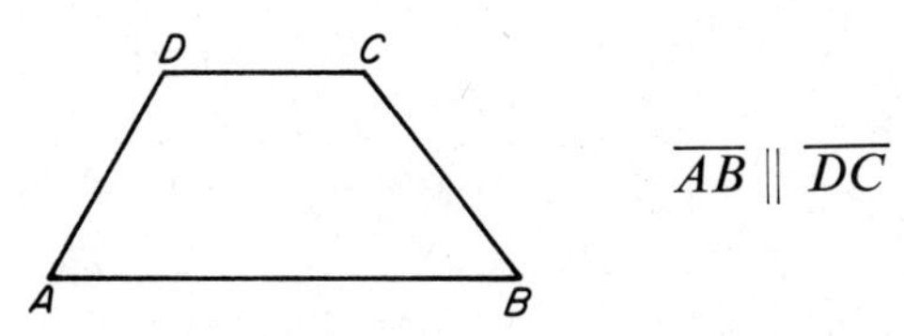

$\overline{AB} \parallel \overline{DC}$

An **isosceles trapezoid** has its two nonparallel sides equal.

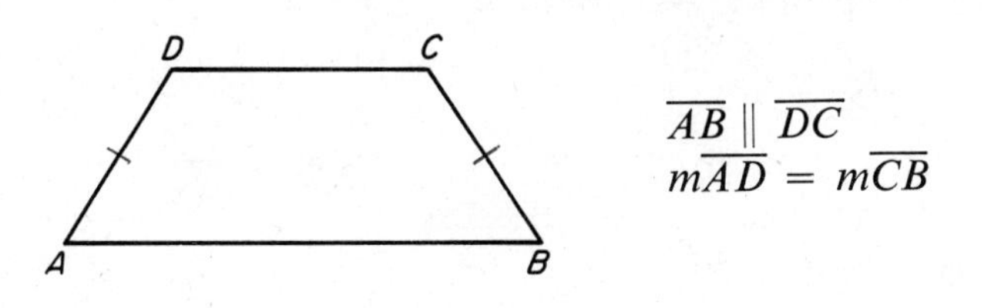

$\overline{AB} \parallel \overline{DC}$
$m\overline{AD} = m\overline{CB}$

EXERCISES

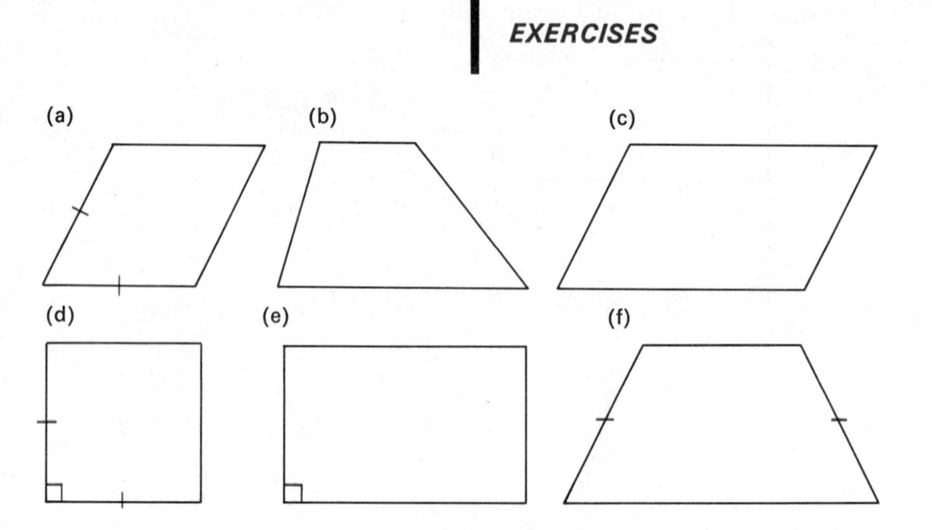

Note. Short cross marks indicate equal lengths; right angles are marked by small squares.

Exercises 6-10 are intended to point out the basic properties of parallelograms. Understanding these properties is important for work later in the text.

A

1. Which figures above are parallelograms?
2. Which figures are rectangles?
3. Which figure is a rhombus?
4. Which figures are trapezoids?
5. Which figure is an isosceles trapezoid?
6. Measure the opposite sides of all parallelograms. Are they equal?
7. Measure the opposite angles of each parallelogram. Are they equal?
8. Measure the angles of the rectangle and the square. What do they measure? Would this be true of all rectangles and squares?
9. Measure all sides of the square, and the sides of the rhombus. What are their lengths? In your opinion, what is the basic difference between a rhombus and a square?
10. Would you classify either the square or the rhombus as a regular polygon?

ACTIVITY: *Geometric Puzzle.*

Students enjoy working with puzzles. Encourage them to devise other shapes and to formulate a new set of questions about them.

Purpose: To review geometric shapes.

Materials: Paper or cardboard, ruler, pencil, scissors.

Plan:

1. Copy the diagram at the top of page 123 on paper or cardboard.
2. Cut out all the geometric shapes. Be sure to label each figure as shown — *A, B, C,* and so on.

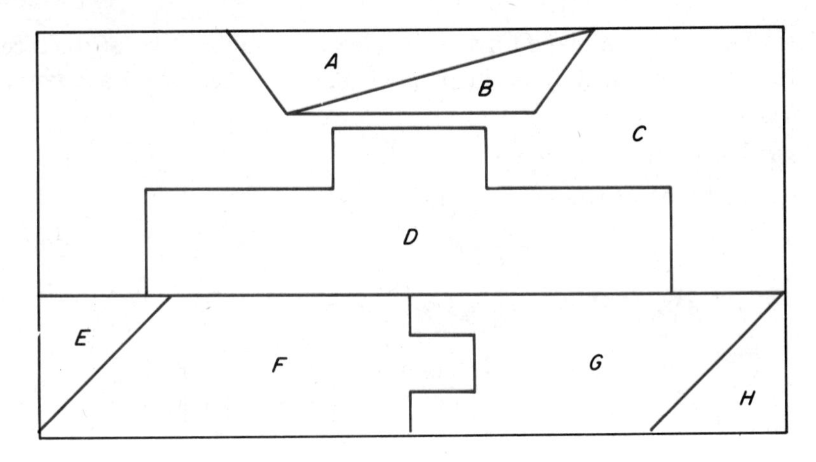

3. We shall now use two or more of these "cut-outs" to form some geometric figures you have just studied.

Questions

1. What 2 figures may be combined to obtain a parallelogram?
   Answer. *F* and *G*.

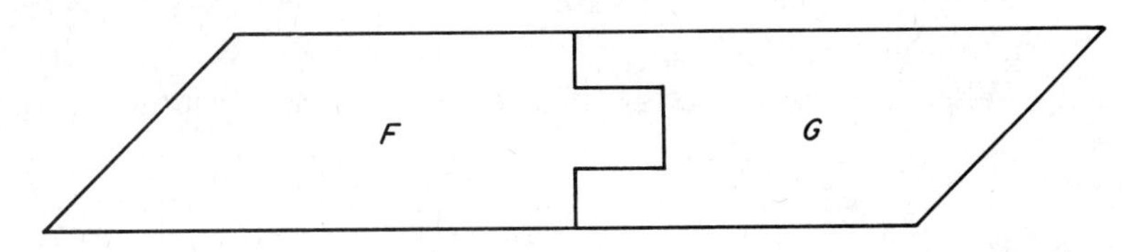

2. What 2 figures may be combined to obtain an isosceles trapezoid?
3. What 4 figures may be combined to form a rectangle? (Two ways)
4. What 2 figures may be combined to make a rectangle?
5. How many of the figures must you use to obtain a square?

■ Polyhedrons

3–6 Prisms TM p. 10, 3-6

The general term used to describe closed 3-dimensional figures formed by planes is **polyhedron** (pŏly-**hē**-drŏn). Polyhedrons can have a great variety of shapes.

Certain polyhedrons are called **prisms.** The figures on the next page show some prisms and the names of different parts of these solids. Study the figures in connection with the following terms.

Face: The part of a plane forming a side of the solid. Two of the faces are called **bases;** they lie in parallel planes. The others are **lateral faces.**

Edge: The segment formed by the intersection of two faces.

Vertex: The point where three sides meet.

Altitude: A segment perpendicular to the bases, as $\overline{AB}$ in the diagrams.

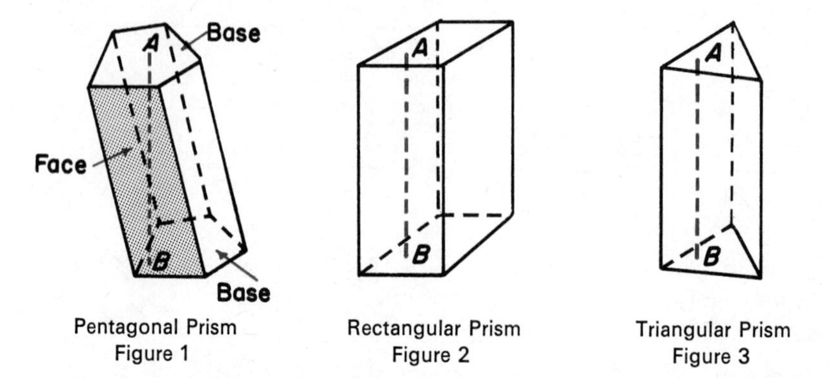

Pentagonal Prism
Figure 1

Rectangular Prism
Figure 2

Triangular Prism
Figure 3

Figure 1 is called an *oblique* prism because its edges are not perpendicular to the bases. Figures 2 and 3 are *right* prisms because their edges *are* perpendicular to the bases.

The names given to prisms, as above, come from the shape of the bases. When the bases are regular polygons, the prisms are called **regular.**

ACTIVITY: *Construction of a right triangular prism.*

Purpose: Construct a right triangular prism whose bases are triangles with sides 2″, 3″, and 4″, and whose altitude is 6″.

Materials: Cardboard, scissors, straightedge, compass, and tape.

Plan:

1. Construct two triangles on cardboard, with sides 2″, 3″, and 4″. (Recall page 116.)
2. Cut out the triangles with scissors.
3. Draw 3 rectangles on cardboard. The first one should be 2″ × 6″, the second one 3″ × 6″, and the third 4″ × 6″.

2" 3" 4"

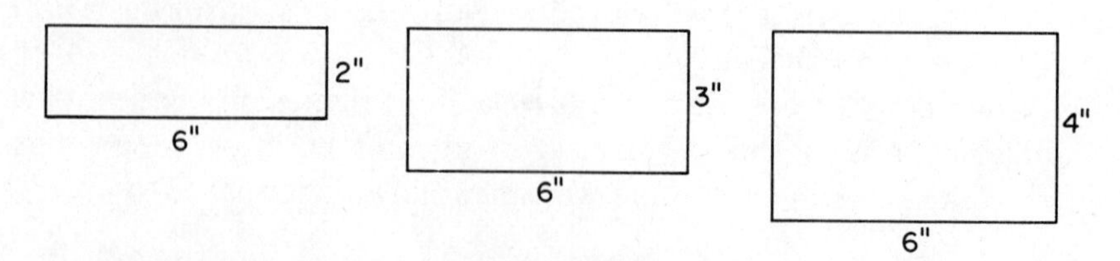

4. Cut out the rectangles.
5. Connect the edges with tape, so that equal base edges are parallel.

Final construction

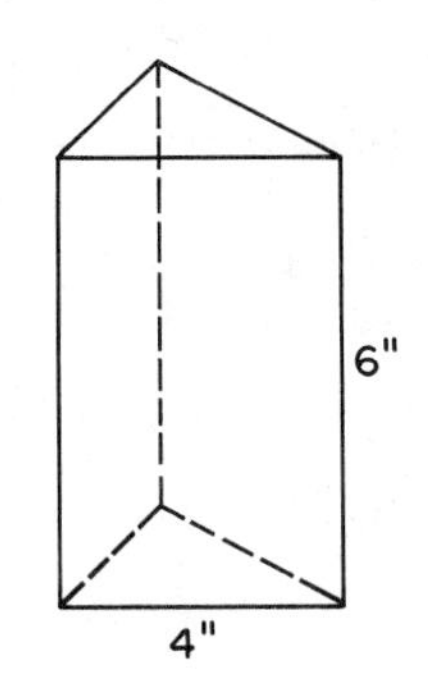

6. Label the parts in ink: (a) bases; (b) a lateral face; (c) a lateral edge; (d) an altitude.

EXERCISES

A

1. Is the figure you constructed a regular prism? If not, why?
2. Is the lateral edge which you labeled an altitude of the prism? Is this true of the other lateral edges?
3. Draw freehand a regular prism whose bases have 6 sides. Label all parts.
4. Construct a pattern for the figure in Exercise 3.
5. Draw a pattern and construct an oblique prism.
6. Would you consider a rectangular box a prism? Bring a box to class and discuss its characteristics.

3–7 Pyramids

A **pyramid** is a polyhedron whose base is a polygon and whose faces are triangles with a common vertex. If the faces are all the same size and shape, the pyramid is called *regular*.

One of the Three Great Pyramids of Egypt

Pyramids are classified by their bases. A pyramid with a triangular base is called a **triangular pyramid,** or **tetrahedron.**

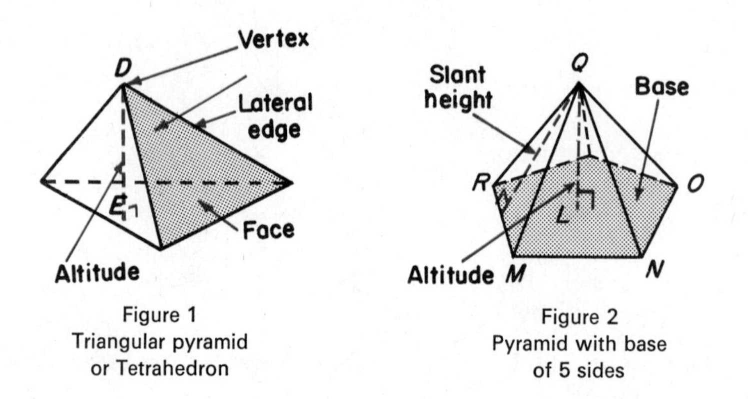

Figure 1
Triangular pyramid
or Tetrahedron

Figure 2
Pyramid with base
of 5 sides

The **altitude of a pyramid** is the line segment from the vertex perpendicular to the plane of the base. In Figure 1 the altitude is $\overline{DE}$. What is the altitude of the pyramid in Figure 2?

When a pyramid is a regular one, we often speak of its **slant height** that is, the altitude of a face, as in Figure 2. Point out the two different applications of the word "altitude" used here.

ACTIVITY: *Construction of a regular pyramid.*

Purpose: To construct a regular pyramid with a square base.
Materials: Cardboard, scissors, tape, compass, ruler.
Plan:

1. Draw a 4″ square on the cardboard.

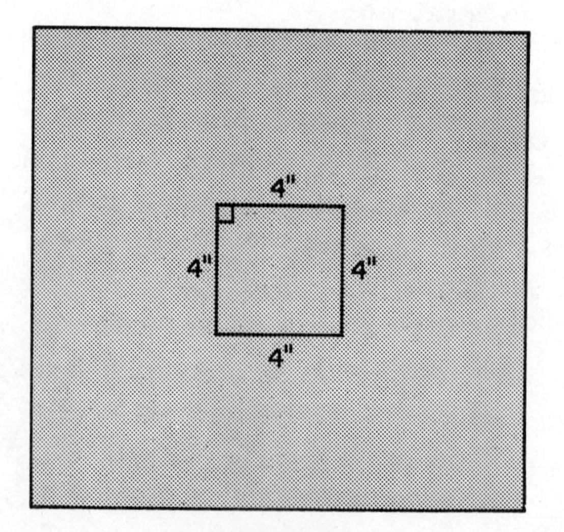

2. On each side of the square construct an isosceles triangle with equal sides of 5″. (The base of each triangle is one of the sides of the square.)

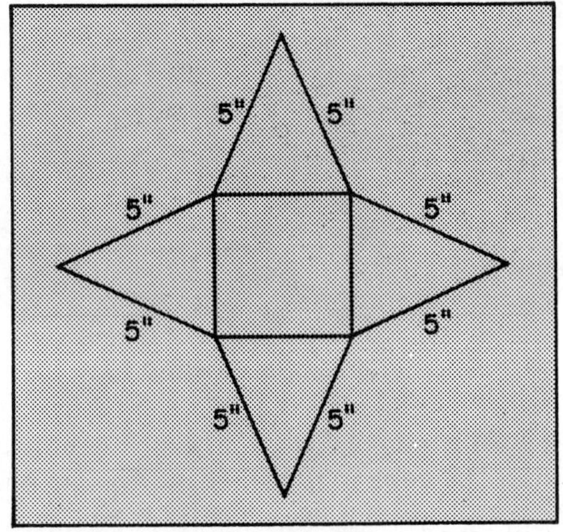

3. Cut out the figure and connect the edges with tape. Work carefully so that the triangles will meet at the vertex.

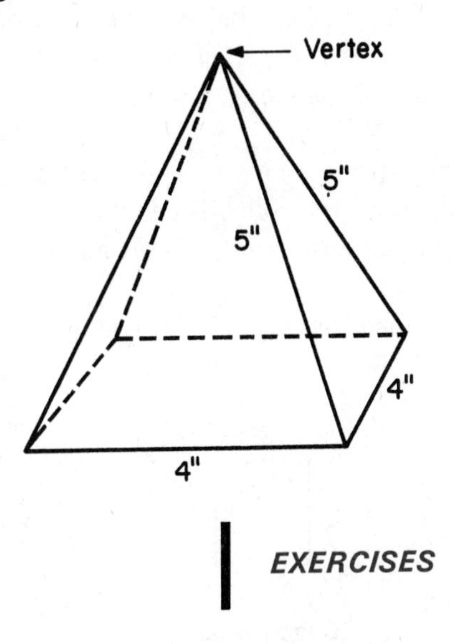

EXERCISES

A

1. Make a model of a rectangular pyramid whose base is 3″ × 4″ and whose lateral edges are 4″.

2. Draw freehand a regular triangular pyramid. Label the lateral edges, the altitude of the pyramid, the vertex, and the altitude of one of the triangular faces (slant height).

3. Make a model of a regular triangular pyramid whose lateral edges are 2″. Have the students label this model as in Exercise 2.

B **4.** Make a model of the oblique rectangular pyramid shown below. Notice that the altitude must be measured outside the pyramid.

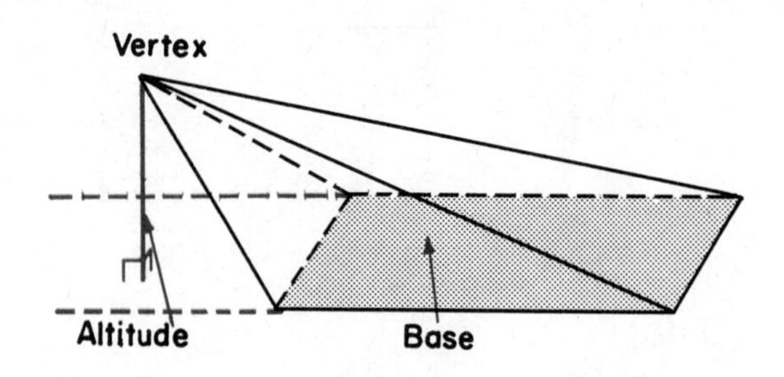

ACTIVITY: *Construction of regular polyhedrons.*

A **regular polyhedron** is a polyhedron whose faces are regular polygons of the same size. The cube is probably the regular polyhedron most familiar to you. In this Activity you will learn how to make models of the cube and the four other regular polyhedrons.

Purpose: To construct the five types of regular polyhedrons: (1) tetrahedron, 4 faces; (2) cube, 6 faces; (3) octahedron, 8 faces; (4) dodecahedron, 12 faces; (5) icosahedron, 20 faces.

Materials: Cardboard, scissors, tape, compass, ruler, protractor.

Plan:

1. Make your own patterns in a size to fit your cardboard. Follow the patterns shown, using the following facts.
   Tetrahedron: the faces are equilateral triangles.
   Cube: the faces are squares.
   Octahedron: the faces are equilateral triangles.

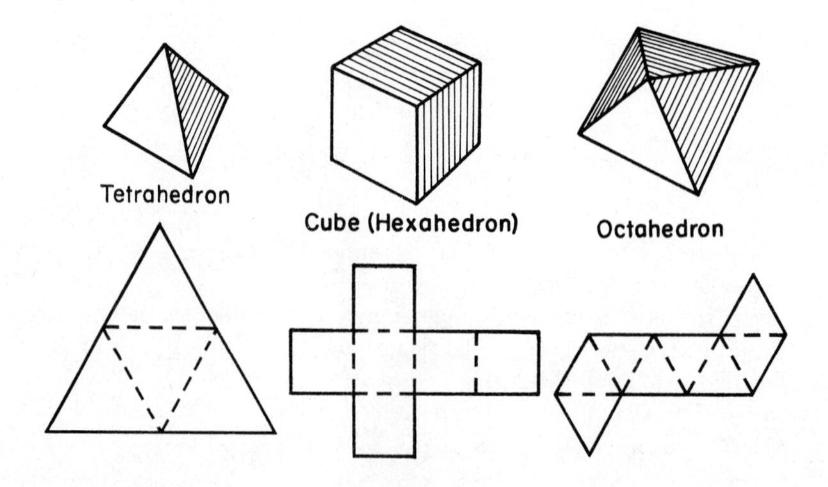

Dodecahedron: the faces are regular pentagons.
Each angle of a regular pentagon measures 108°. ← Use a protractor to draw these angles.
Icosahedron: the faces are equilateral triangles.

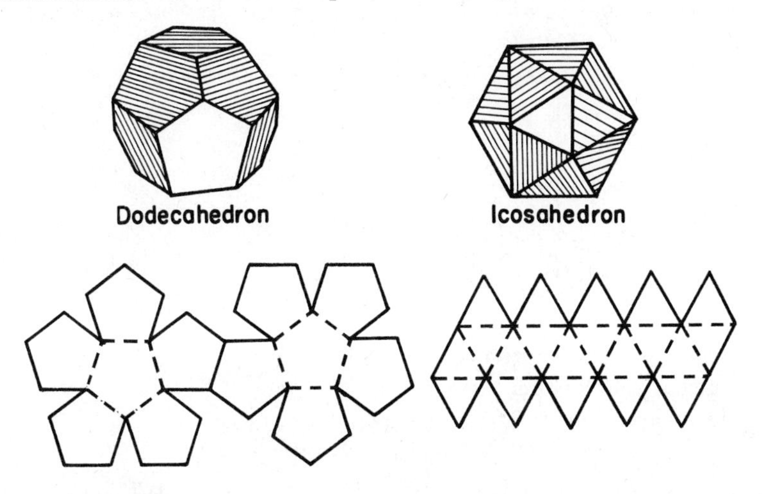

2. Fold the patterns and tape the edges together to form the solids. These five are the only types of *regular* polyhedrons.

Copy and complete this chart.

REGULAR POLYHEDRONS				
Name	No. of faces	Shape of each face	No. of edges	No. of vertices
tetrahedron				
cube				
octahedron				
dodecahedron				
icosahedron			30	12

SELF-ANALYSIS TEST II
Time: 10 minutes

1. A _?_ is a quadrilateral whose opposite sides are parallel.
2. A _?_ is a quadrilateral with one pair of opposite sides parallel.
3. A _?_ (two answers possible) is a parallelogram with all sides equal.

4. A polygon whose 5 sides are equal and whose 5 angles are equal is called a __?__.
5. A polyhedron is a geometric solid bounded by __?__.
6. A __?__ is a polyhedron whose faces are rectangles and whose bases are parallel.

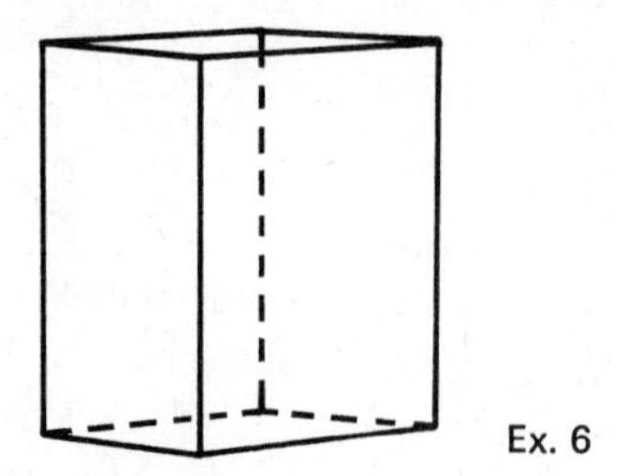

Ex. 6

7. A __?__ is a polyhedron whose base is a polygon and whose faces are triangles with a common vertex.
8. The diagram shows a triangular pyramid.
   a. Which line segment is the altitude of the pyramid?
   b. Which line segment is the altitude of a face of the pyramid?
   c. Name the 6 lateral edges of the pyramid.

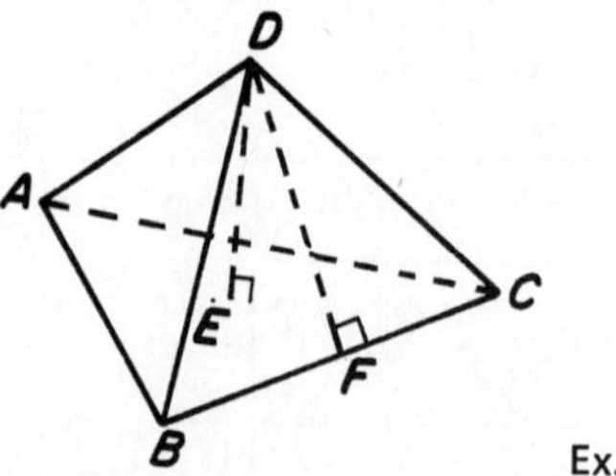

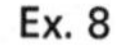

Ex. 8

9. The diagram shows a prism.
   a. What type of prism is this?
   b. Line __?__ is the altitude of the prism.
   c. A prism has __?__ bases.

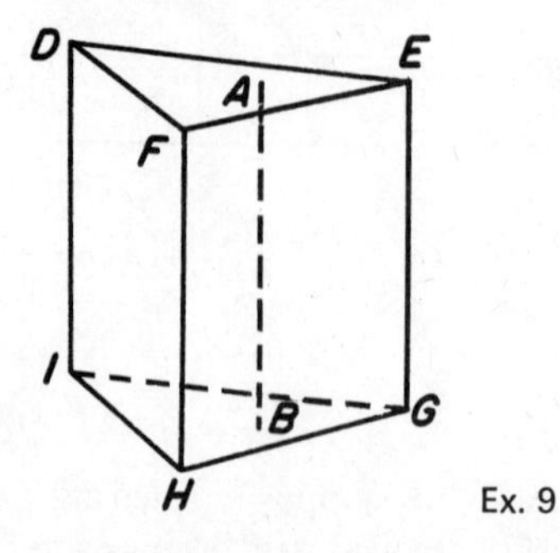

Ex. 9

10. The regular polyhedron having 12 edges and 6 vertices is an __?__.

■ Circles and Angle Measurement

3–8 Circles; Central Angles

Not all geometric figures are of the type we have been studying, that is, formed by lines and planes. One of the most common and useful plane figures is the circle. Circular shapes are found in almost all areas of industry.

A **circle** is a closed plane curve every point of which is the same distance from a given point called the center. TM p. 10 , 3-8(1)

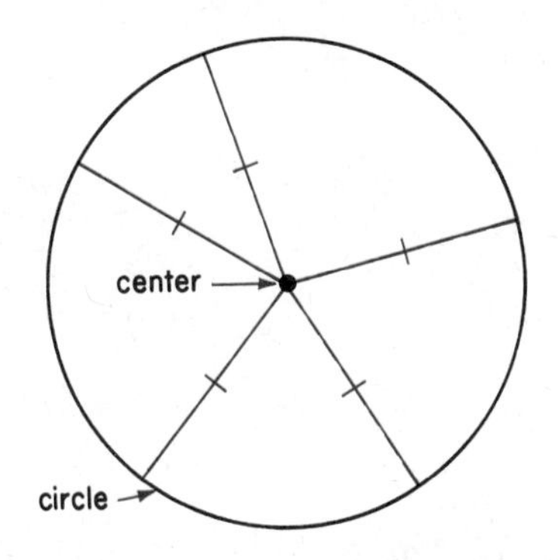

A circle has many special terms associated with it. Several are listed below and illustrated in the diagrams. Be sure the student understands these terms.

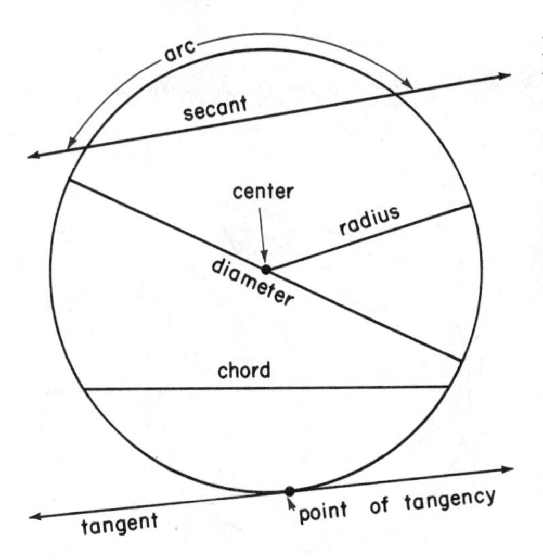

Arc: a part of a circle.
Radius: a line segment with one endpoint on the circle and the other endpoint at the center.
Chord: a line segment with endpoints on the circle.
Diameter: a chord which passes through the center of the circle.
Secant: a line which intersects a circle at two points.
Tangent: a line which intersects a circle at one and only one point (called the *point of tangency*).

Concentric circles: two or more circles with the same circle.
Central angle: an angle with its vertex at the center of a center.

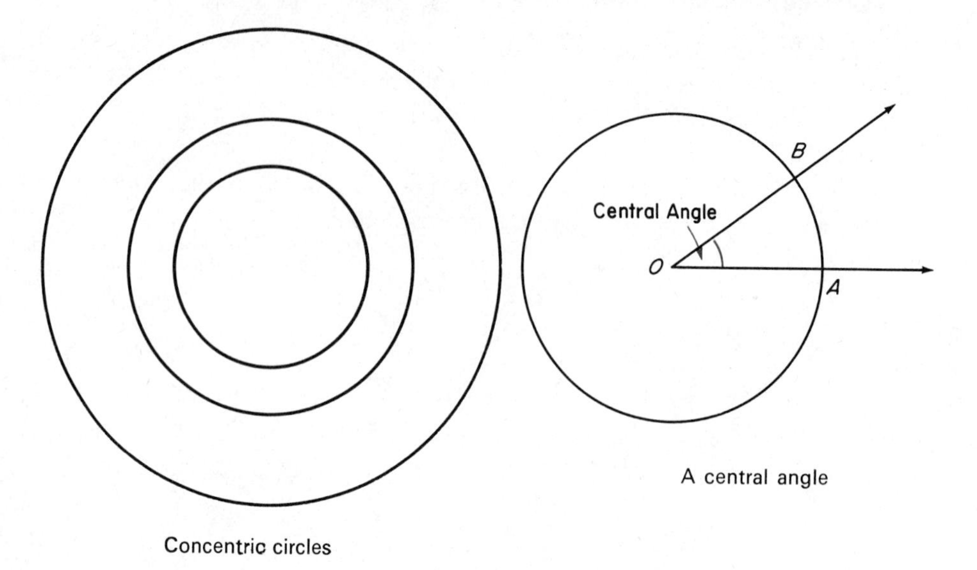

A central angle

Concentric circles

In the circle at the right above, $\angle AOB$ cuts off, or **intercepts,** the arc AB. (Notice that AB names two arcs. We shall mean the smaller of the two arcs.) We write arc AB as $\widehat{AB}$. Stress this.

We measure arcs in degrees (recall page 77) by reference to certain associated angles. An important fact to remember is this:

A central angle and its intercepted arc have the same measure.

In this diagram,

$$m\angle AOB = m\widehat{AB}.$$

Since $m\angle AOB = 60°$, we know that $m\widehat{AB}$ is 60° also; that is, $\widehat{AB}$ is an arc of 60°.

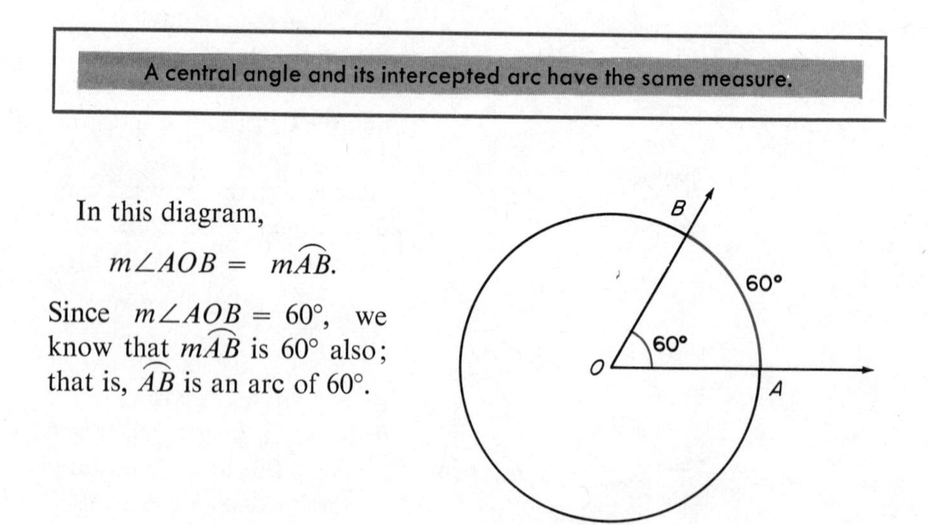

Practical Applications of Circles

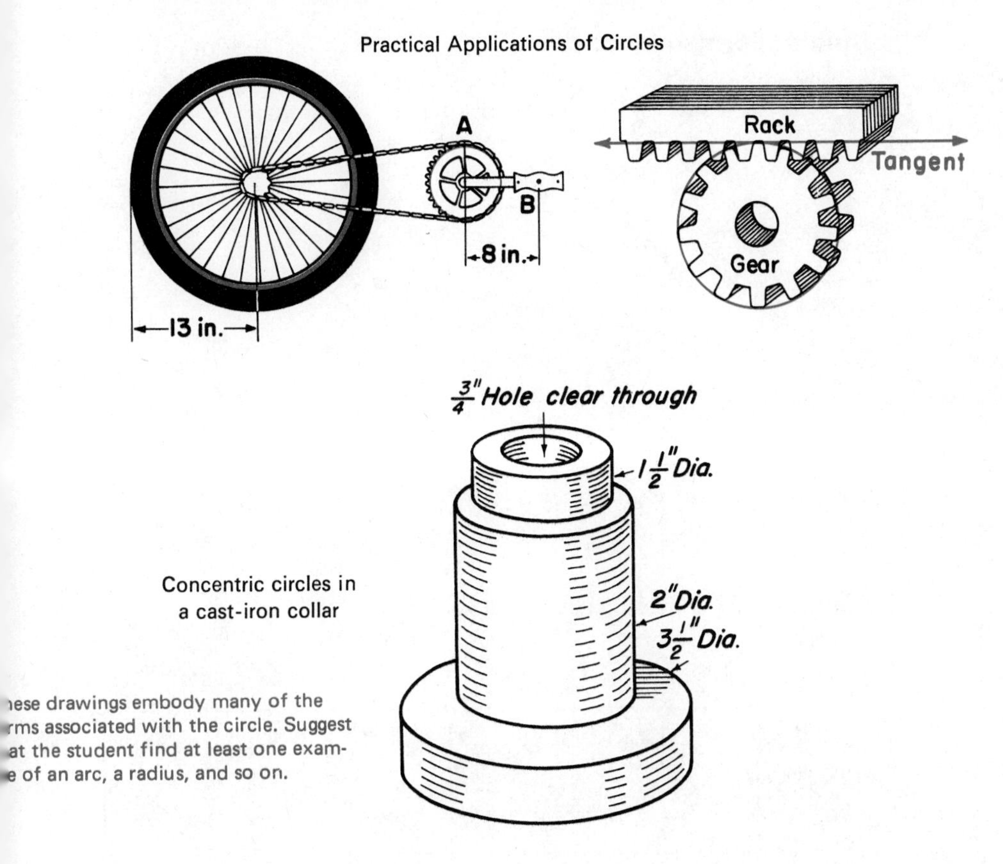

Concentric circles in a cast-iron collar

ıese drawings embody many of the rms associated with the circle. Suggest at the student find at least one exam- e of an arc, a radius, and so on.

EXERCISES

Refer to the diagram at the right.

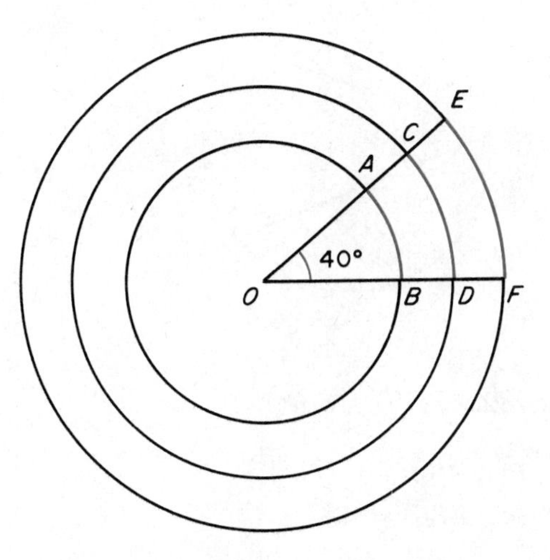

A

1. How many degrees in $\widehat{AB}$? in $\widehat{CD}$? in $\widehat{EF}$?

M p. 10, -8(2) →

2. Are the three arcs named in Exercise 1 equal in arc degrees?
3. Are they equal in length?
4. Draw a circle and show a central angle $XOY = 55°$.
5. What is the measure of $\widehat{XY}$?
6. How many arc degrees in the larger arc $\widehat{XY}$? (Recall that a circle measures 360°.)

3–9 Angles Formed by Chords

$\angle B$ in the figure below is called an **inscribed angle.**

Encourage the student to formulate a definition of an inscribed angle, and to compare it with the one in the Glossary, page 397.

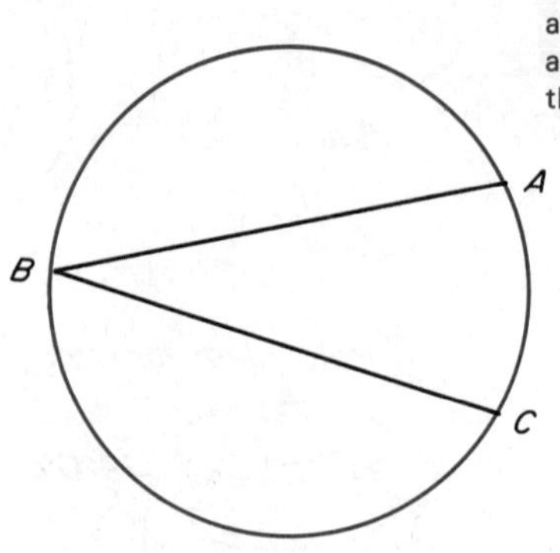

The following is a useful fact to know.

> An inscribed angle is measured by $\frac{1}{2}$ the measure of its intercepted arc.
>
> $$m\angle ABC = \tfrac{1}{2}m\widehat{AC}$$

EXAMPLE 1

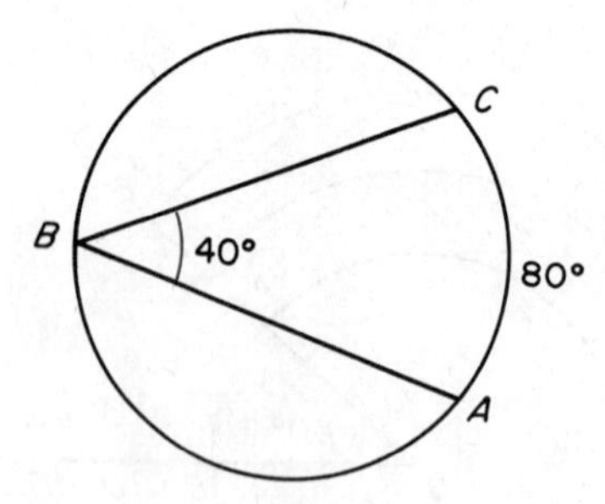

$$m\angle ABC = \frac{1}{2}m\widehat{AC}$$
$$m\angle ABC = \frac{1}{2}(80°)$$
$$m\angle ABC = 40°$$

EXAMPLE 2

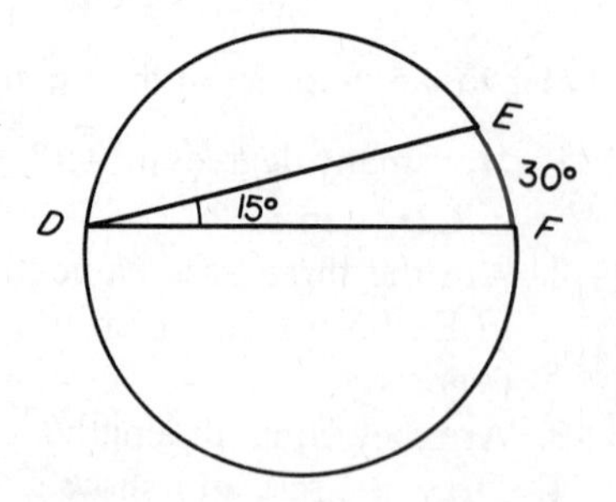

$$m\angle EDF = \frac{1}{2}m\widehat{EF}$$
$$15° = \frac{1}{2}m\widehat{EF}$$
$$30° = m\widehat{EF}$$

EXERCISES

A

1.

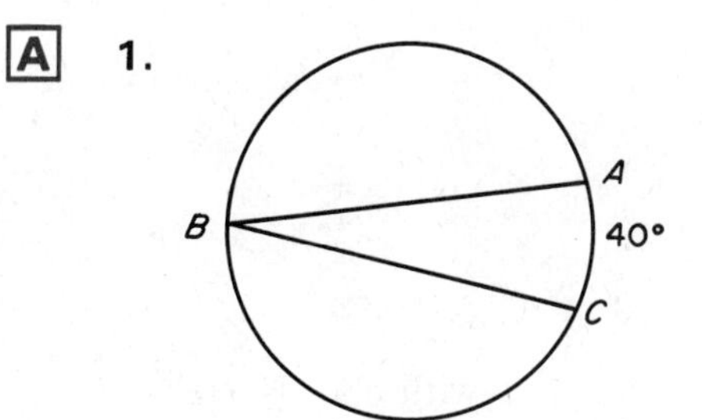

$m\angle ABC = \underline{\ ?\ }$

2.

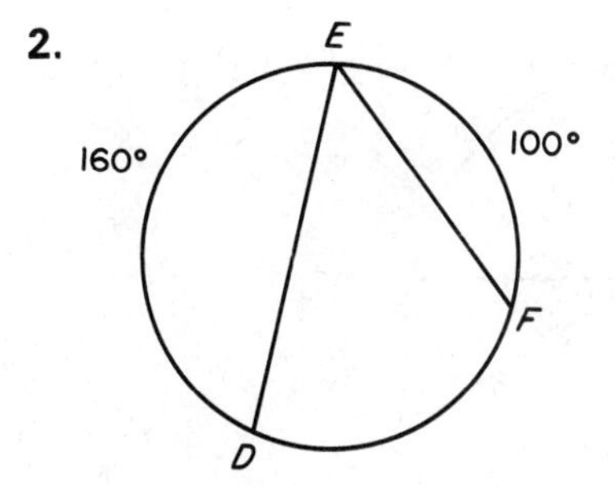

$m\angle DEF = \underline{\ ?\ }$
Hint. Find $\widehat{DF}$ first.

3.

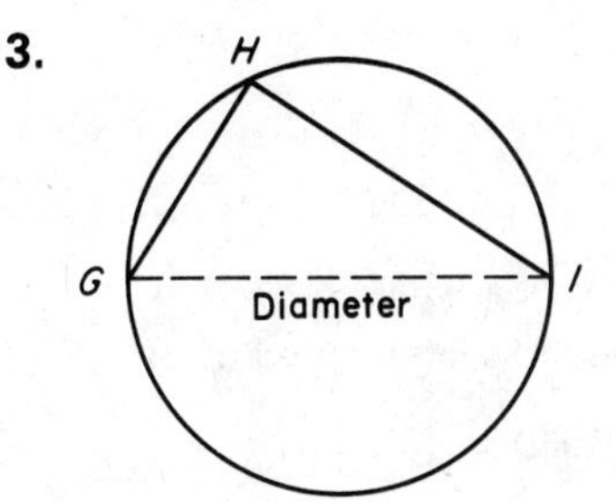

$m\angle GHI = \underline{\ ?\ }$
What do you notice about an angle inscribed in a semicircle (half a circle)?

Remind students that a semicircle measures 180°. See also TM p. 11 , 3-9 for an interesting application of this problem.

4.

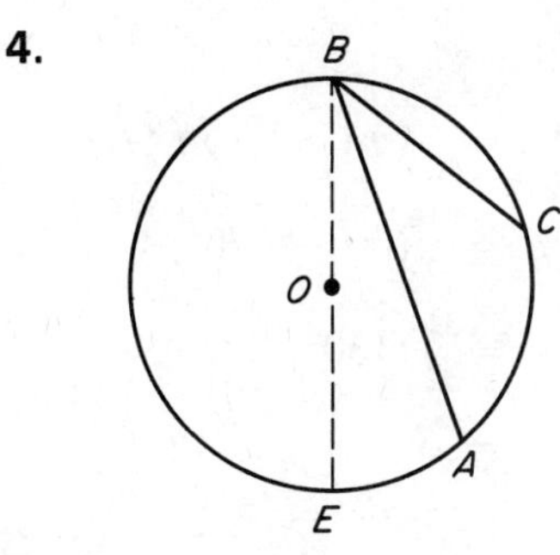

$m\widehat{CE} = 105°$
$m\widehat{EA} = 40°$
$m\angle ABC = \underline{\ ?\ }$

Point out that a diameter is a special chord.

5.

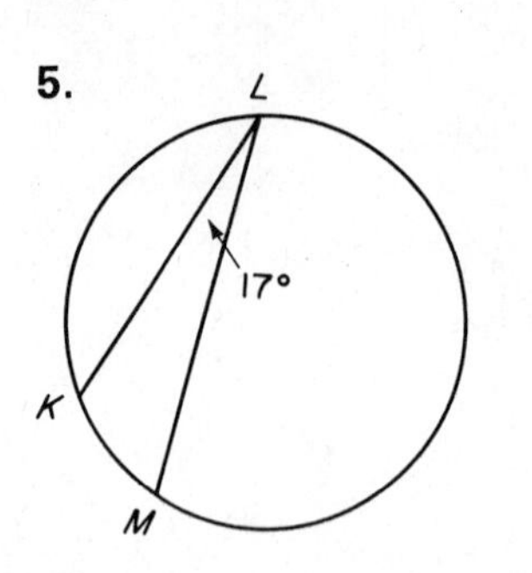

$m\angle KLM = 17°$
$m\widehat{LK} = 110°$
Find $m\widehat{ML}$.

When the chords intersect within the circle, as with chords DE and FG in the figure below, the formula for measuring the angle is a little more complicated.

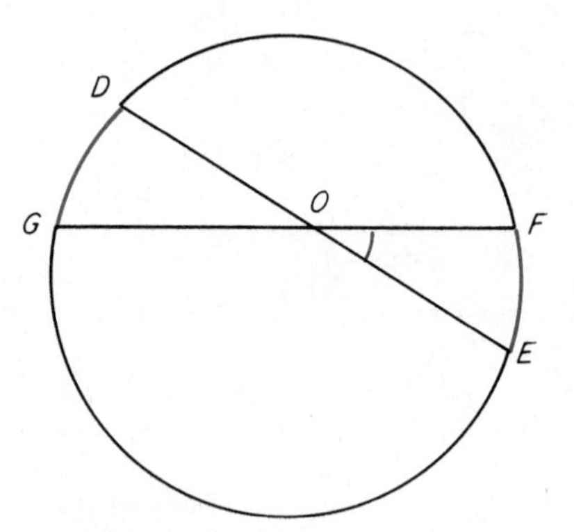

We use the following rule:

> **An angle formed by two chords intersecting within a circle is measured by $\frac{1}{2}$ the sum of the measures of its intercepted arcs.**
>
> $$m\angle FOE = \tfrac{1}{2}(m\widehat{FE} + m\widehat{DG})$$

EXAMPLE 1

$$m\angle COB = \frac{1}{2}(m\widehat{CB} + m\widehat{AD})$$

$$m\angle COB = \frac{1}{2}(60° + 70°)$$

$$= \frac{1}{2}(130°)$$

$$= 65°$$

EXAMPLE 2

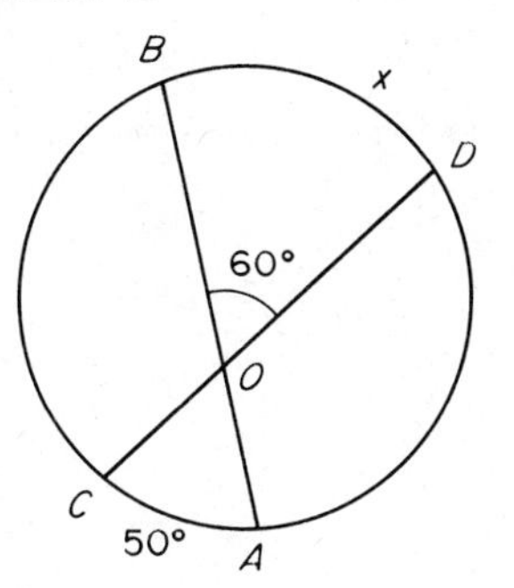

$$m\angle BOD = \frac{1}{2}(m\widehat{BD} + m\widehat{AC})$$
$$60^\circ = \frac{1}{2}(x + 50^\circ)$$
$$120^\circ = x + 50^\circ$$
$$x = 70^\circ$$

Exercises requiring this method of solution are reserved for B sections.

EXERCISES

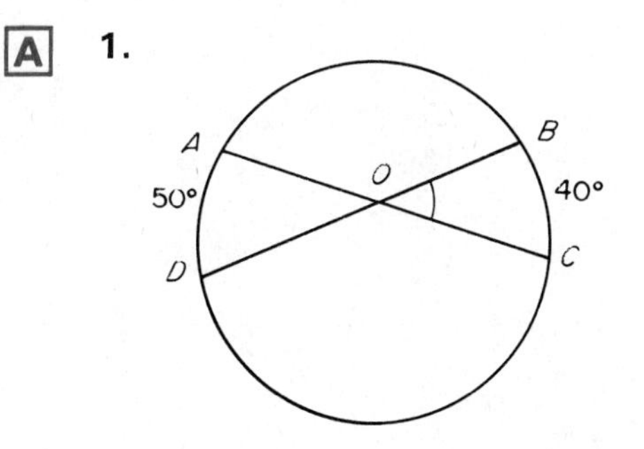

$m\angle COB =$ ___?___

2.

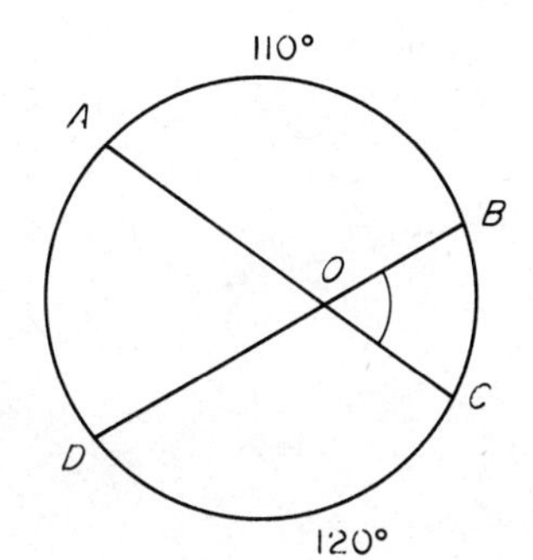

$m\widehat{AB} = 110^\circ$
$m\widehat{CD} = 120^\circ$
$m\angle BOC =$ ___?___

3.

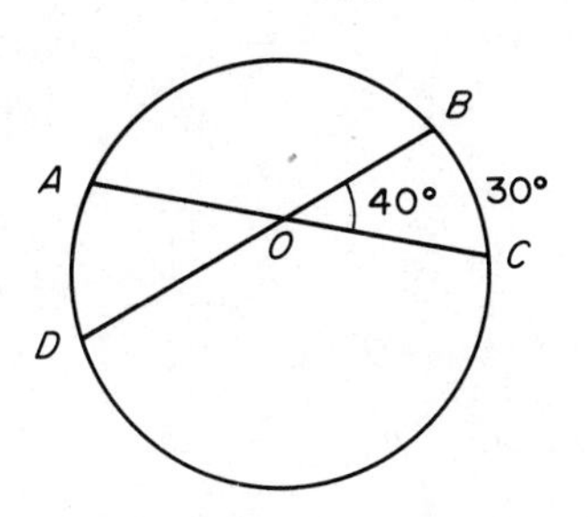

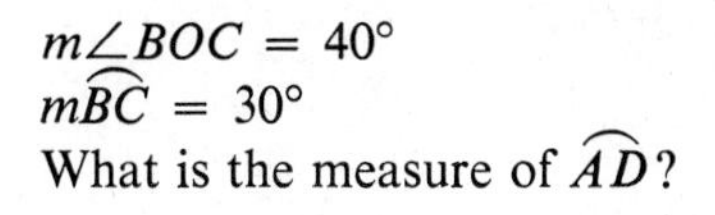
$m\angle BOC = 40^\circ$
$m\widehat{BC} = 30^\circ$
What is the measure of $\widehat{AD}$?

4. The circle shown is divided according to the hours on a clock. Each 5 minutes the minute hand makes an arc of 30°. Find

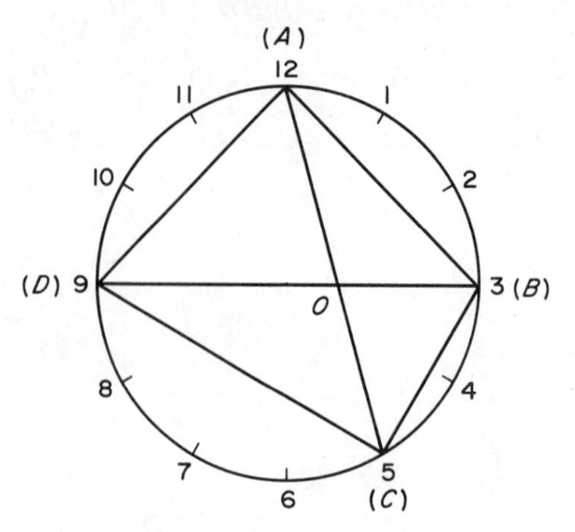

$m\widehat{AB}$, $m\widehat{BC}$, $m\widehat{CD}$, $m\widehat{AD}$, $m\angle BOC$, $m\angle COD$, $m\angle BAC$, $m\angle BAD$.

The teacher may wish to use a real clock and several small rods for a vivid presentation of this exercise.

SELF-ANALYSIS TEST III

Time: 15 minutes

1. An angle formed at the center of a circle is called a __?__ angle.

2. An angle formed by two chords drawn from the same point on the circle is called an __?__ angle.

3. An angle formed by the intersection of two chords is measured by __?__.

4. $m\angle BOA = 50°$
$m\widehat{AB} =$ __?__

5. $m\angle ABC = 30°$
$m\widehat{AC} =$ __?__

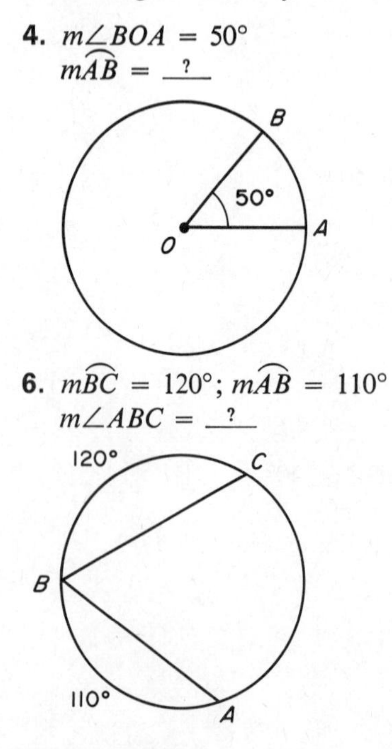

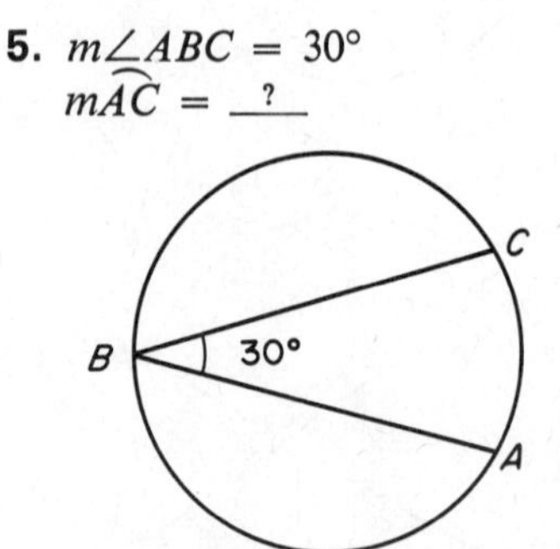

6. $m\widehat{BC} = 120°$; $m\widehat{AB} = 110°$
$m\angle ABC =$ __?__

7. $m\angle AOC = 70°$
$m\angle ABC =$ __?__

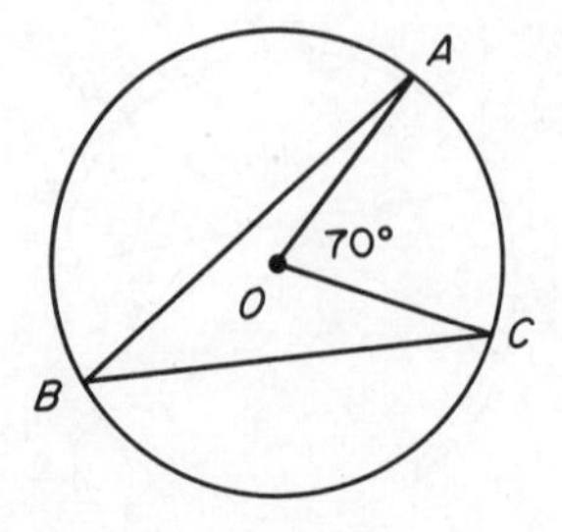

8.

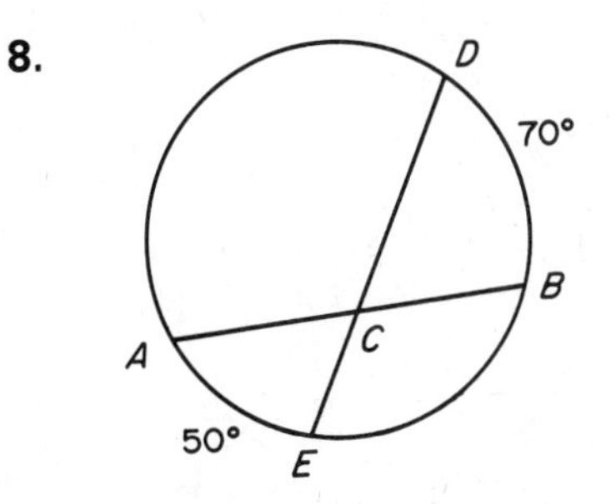

$m\widehat{AE} = 50°; m\widehat{BD} = 70°$
$m\angle ACE = \underline{\ ?\ }$

3–10 Angles Formed by Tangents and Chords

The formula used in finding the measure of an inscribed angle applies also to angles formed by a tangent and a chord.

> **An angle formed by a tangent and a chord is measured by $\frac{1}{2}$ the measure of its intercepted arc.**
>
> $$m\angle ABC = \tfrac{1}{2} m\widehat{AB}$$

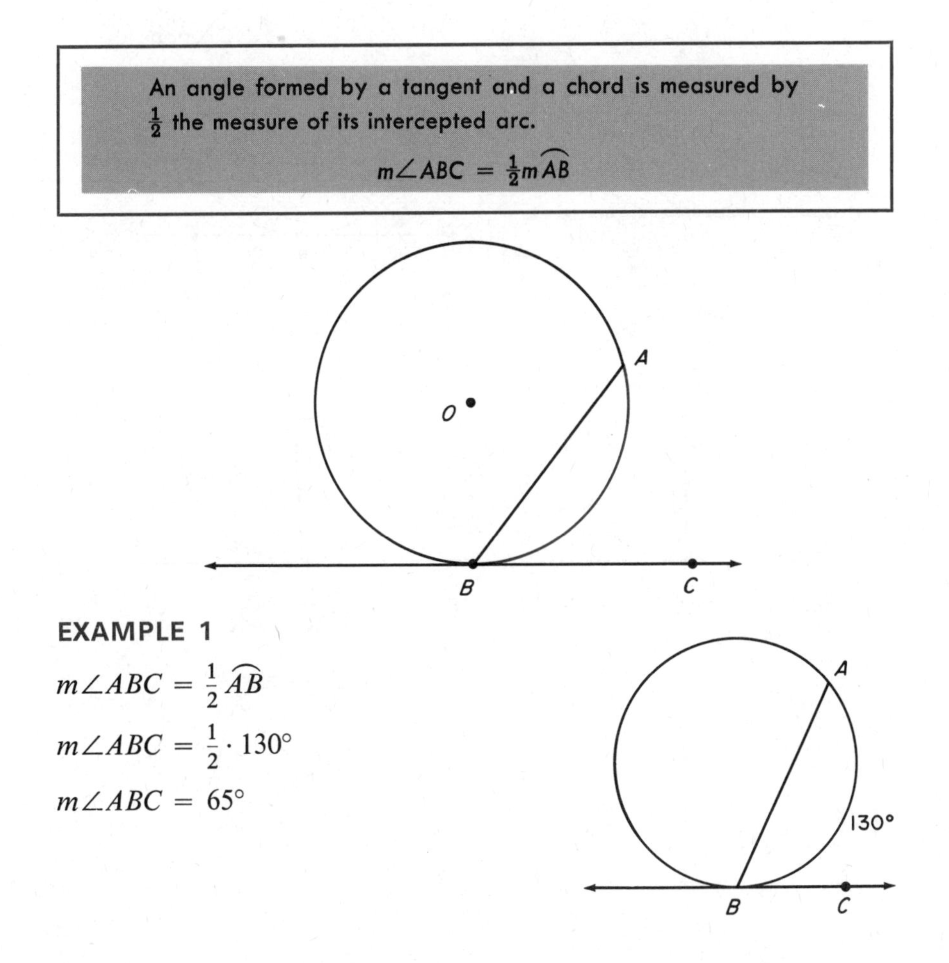

EXAMPLE 1

$m\angle ABC = \frac{1}{2}\widehat{AB}$

$m\angle ABC = \frac{1}{2} \cdot 130°$

$m\angle ABC = 65°$

EXAMPLE 2

$m\angle ABC = \frac{1}{2} m\widehat{AXB}$

$m\angle ABC = \frac{1}{2} \cdot 220°$

$m\angle ABC = 110°$

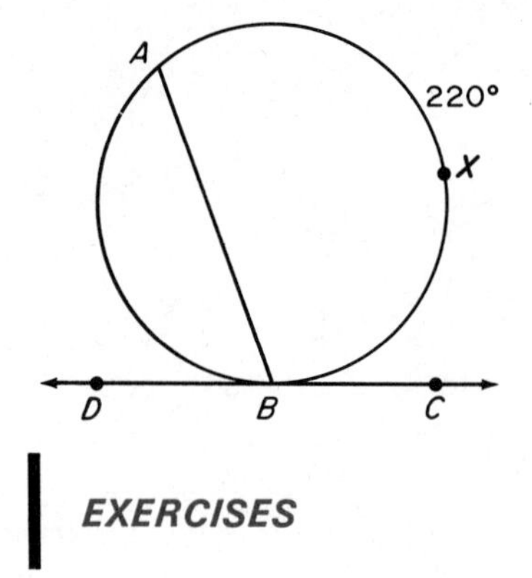

EXERCISES

Find $m\angle ABC$ in Exercises 1–4.

TM p. 11, 3-10

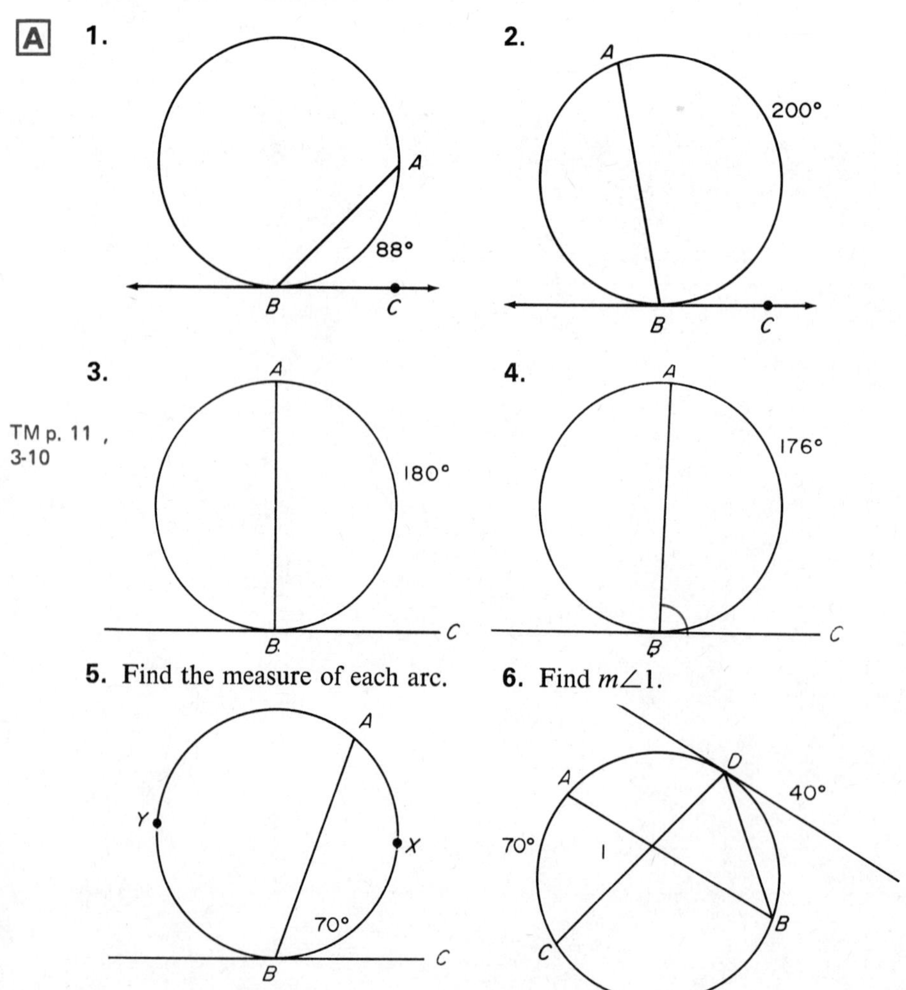

7. Find the measures of angles 1, 2, 3, 4, 5, and 6. (Hint: Find the arcs first.)

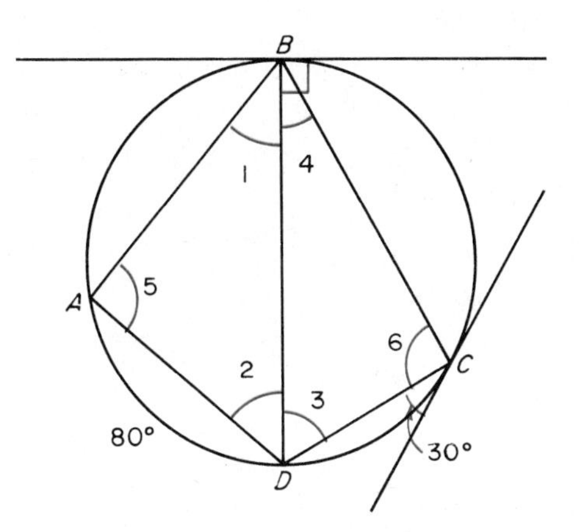

3–11 Angles Formed by Tangents and Secants

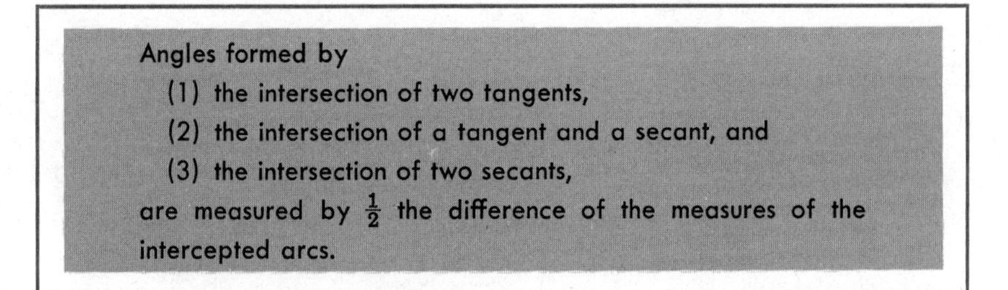

Angles formed by
(1) the intersection of two tangents,
(2) the intersection of a tangent and a secant, and
(3) the intersection of two secants,
are measured by $\frac{1}{2}$ the difference of the measures of the intercepted arcs.

This rule is repeated as formulas for each of the three cases.

(1) Two tangents $m\angle B = \frac{1}{2}(m\widehat{APC} - m\widehat{AC})$

It may be useful to point out that both tangents are the same length.

EXAMPLE 1

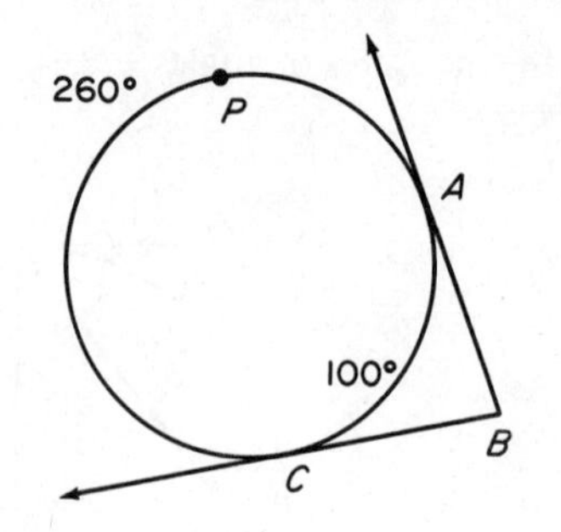

$$m\angle B = \frac{1}{2}(m\widehat{APC} - m\widehat{AC})$$

$$m\angle B = \frac{1}{2}(260° - 100°)$$

$$m\angle B = \frac{1}{2} \cdot 160°$$

$$m\angle B = 80°$$

EXAMPLE 2

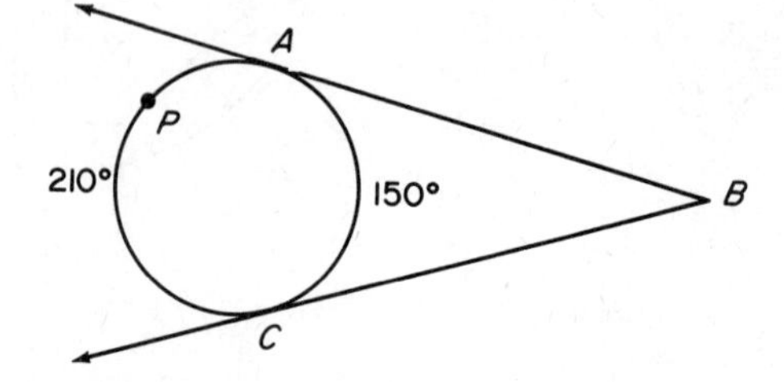

$$m\angle B = \frac{1}{2}(m\widehat{APC} - m\widehat{AC})$$

$$m\angle B = \frac{1}{2}(210° - 150°)$$

$$m\angle B = \frac{1}{2} \cdot 60°$$

$$m\angle B = 30°$$

(2) Tangent and secant $\quad m\angle B = \frac{1}{2}(m\widehat{AD} - m\widehat{AC})$

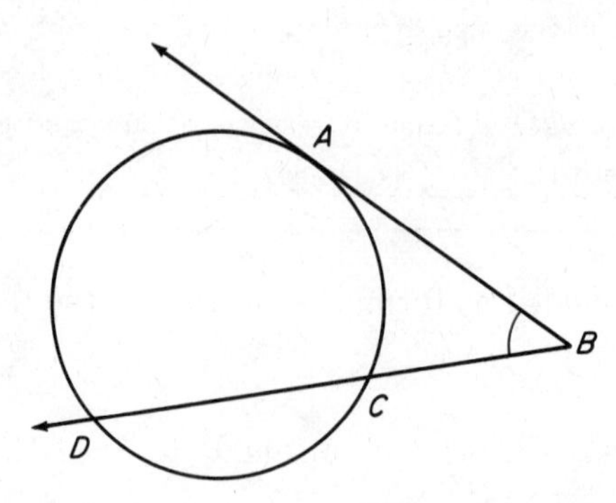

EXAMPLE 3

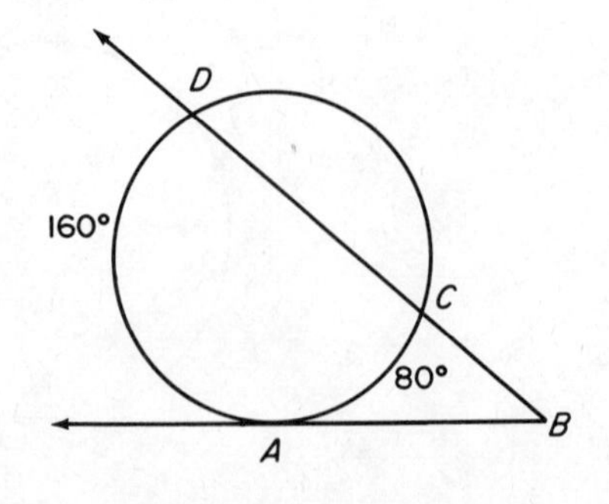

$$m\angle B = \frac{1}{2}(m\widehat{AD} - m\widehat{AC})$$

$$m\angle B = \frac{1}{2}(160° - 80°)$$

$$m\angle B = \frac{1}{2} \cdot 80°$$

$$m\angle B = 40°$$

EXAMPLE 4

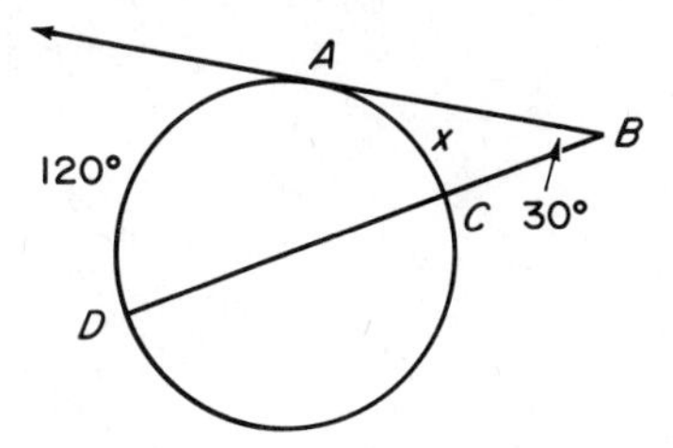

$$m\angle B = \frac{1}{2}(m\widehat{AD} - m\widehat{AC})$$

$$30^\circ = \frac{1}{2}(120^\circ - x)$$

$$60^\circ = 120^\circ - x$$

$$x = 60^\circ$$

Exercises based on Examples 4 and 6 are reserved for B sections.

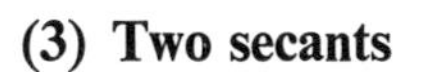

(3) Two secants $\quad m\angle B = \frac{1}{2}(m\widehat{AE} - m\widehat{DC})$

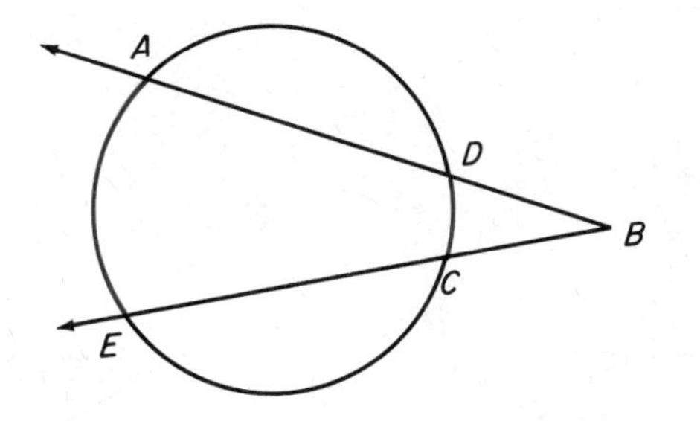

EXAMPLE 5

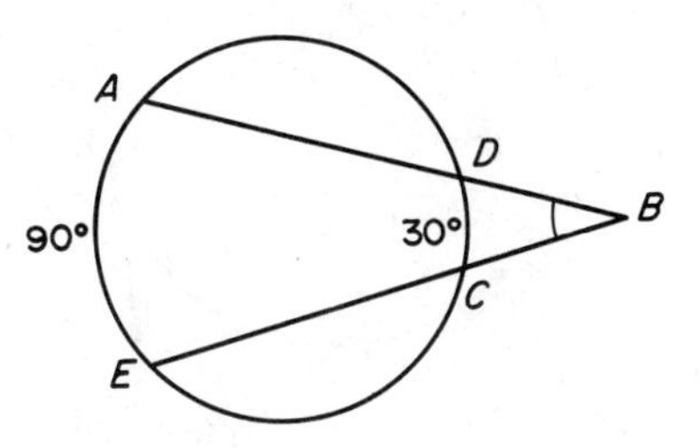

$$m\angle B = \frac{1}{2}(m\widehat{AE} - m\widehat{DC})$$

$$m\angle B = \frac{1}{2}(90^\circ - 30^\circ)$$

$$m\angle B = 30^\circ$$

EXAMPLE 6

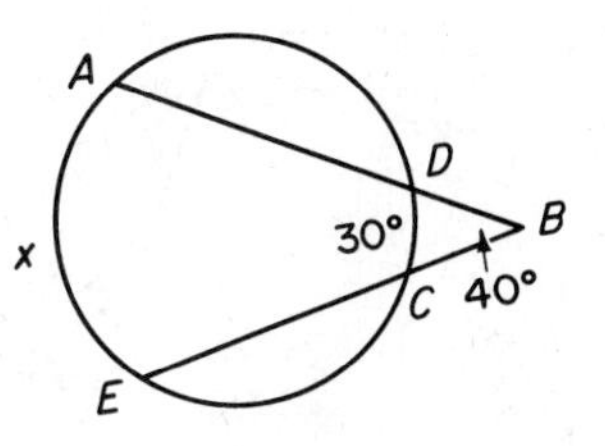

$$m\angle B = \frac{1}{2}(m\widehat{AE} - m\widehat{DC})$$

$$40^\circ = \frac{1}{2}(x - 30^\circ)$$

$$80^\circ = x - 30^\circ$$

$$x = 110^\circ$$

EXERCISES

A

1. Find $m\angle B$.

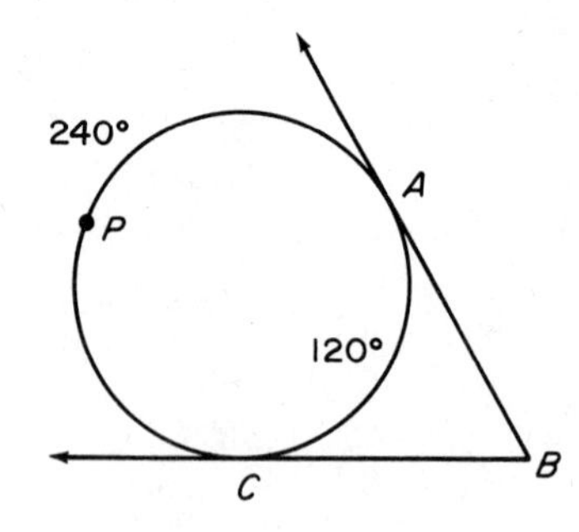

2. Find $m\angle B$.

A
B
100°
C
P

3. Find $m\angle B$.

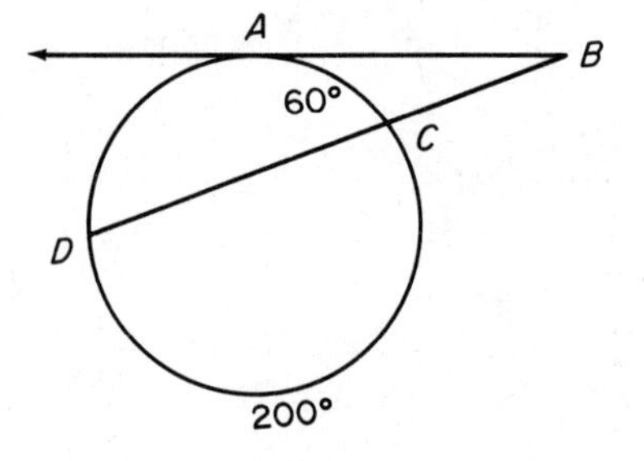

4. Find $m\angle B$.

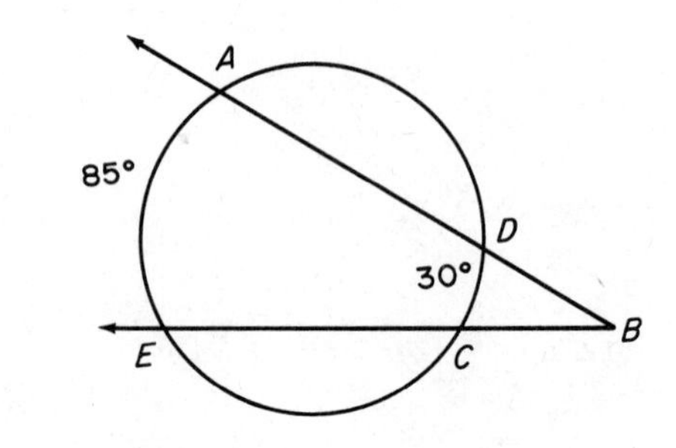

B

5. Find $m\widehat{AD}$.

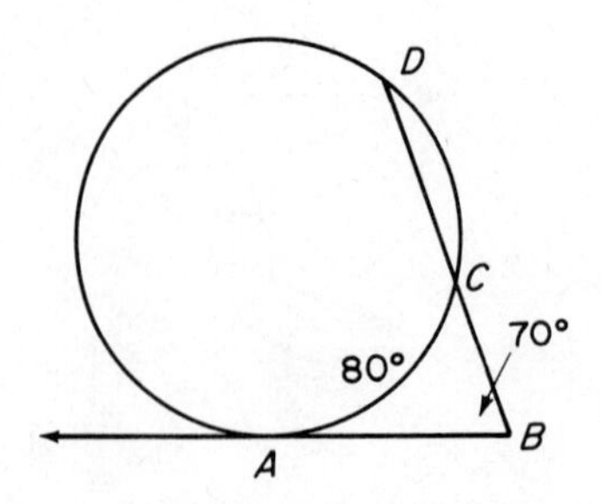

6. Find $m\widehat{AE}$.

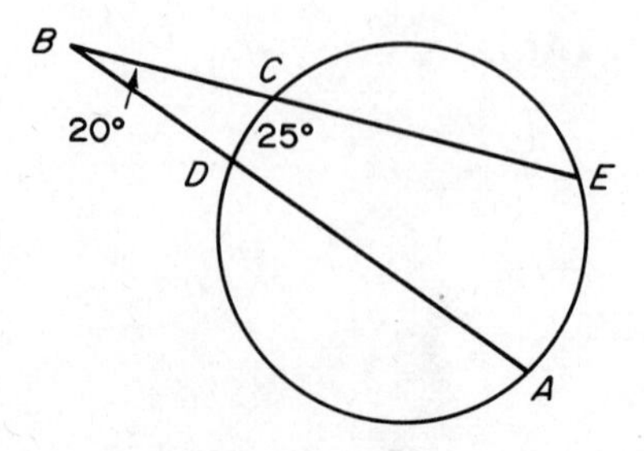

SELF-ANALYSIS TEST IV

Time: 30 minutes

A

1. An angle formed by a tangent and a chord is measured by _?_.
2. An angle formed by a tangent and a secant is measured by _?_.

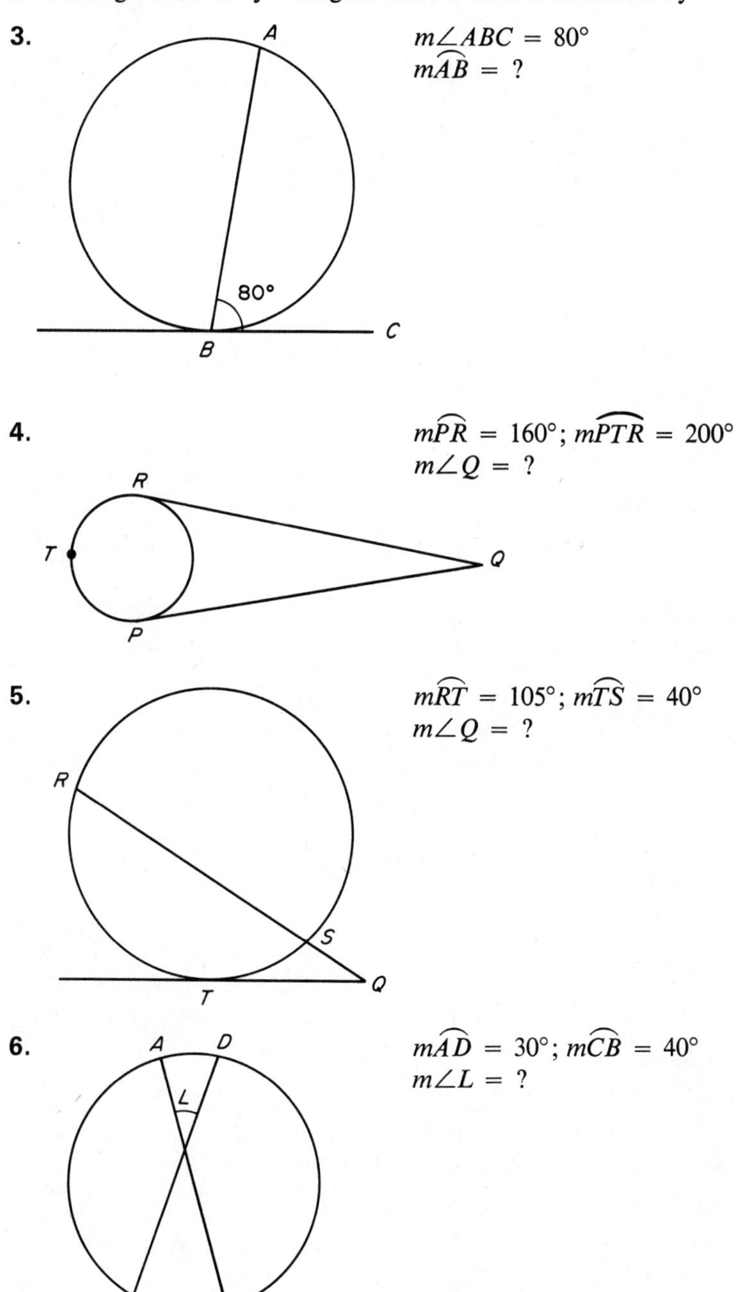

3. $m\angle ABC = 80°$
   $m\widehat{AB} = ?$

4. $m\widehat{PR} = 160°$; $m\widehat{PTR} = 200°$
   $m\angle Q = ?$

5. $m\widehat{RT} = 105°$; $m\widehat{TS} = 40°$
   $m\angle Q = ?$

6. $m\widehat{AD} = 30°$; $m\widehat{CB} = 40°$
   $m\angle L = ?$

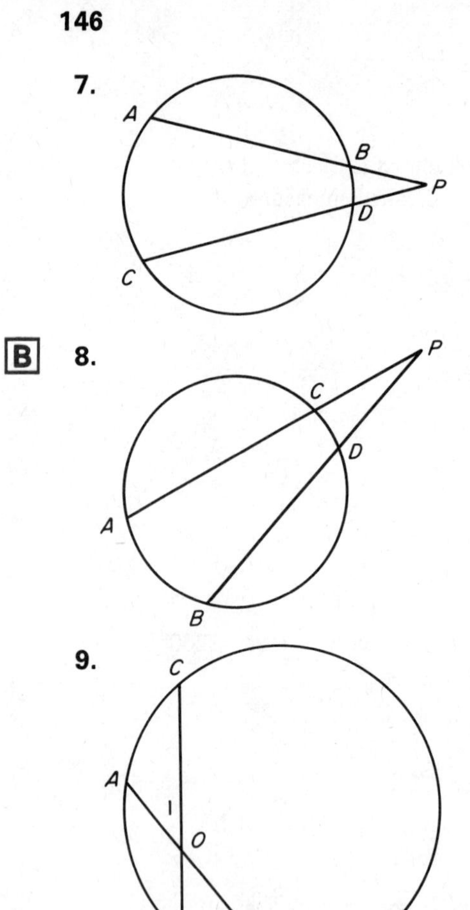

7. $m\widehat{AC} = 80°$; $m\widehat{BD} = 25°$
$m\angle P = ?$

B **8.** $m\angle P = 25°$; $m\widehat{CD} = 30°$
$m\widehat{AB} = ?$

9. $m\angle 1 = 40°$; $m\widehat{AC} = 30°$
$m\widehat{AD} = 60°$; $m\angle ABE = ?$

10. $m\angle B = 75°$; $m\widehat{BC} = 90°$
$m\widehat{FC} = 100°$; $m\angle$s $x, y, z = ?$

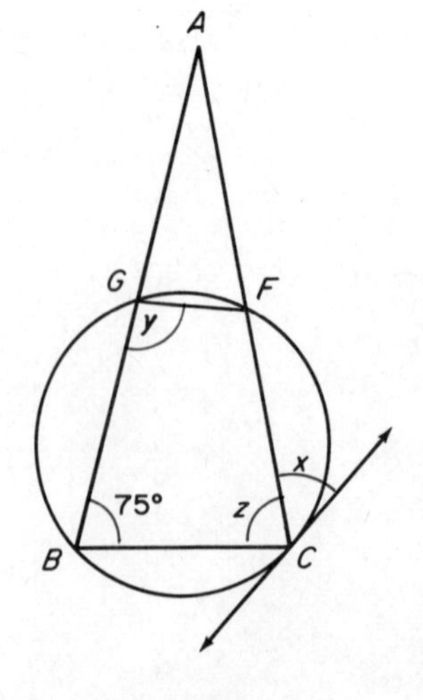

■ Solids with Circular Bases

3–12 Cylinders and Cones TM p. 11, 3-12

A **right circular cylinder** is a closed surface formed by rotating a rectangle about one side. You might demonstrate this with a cardboard model. The **bases** are circles, and the line segment joining the centers of the circles is called the **axis.** In a right circular cylinder, the

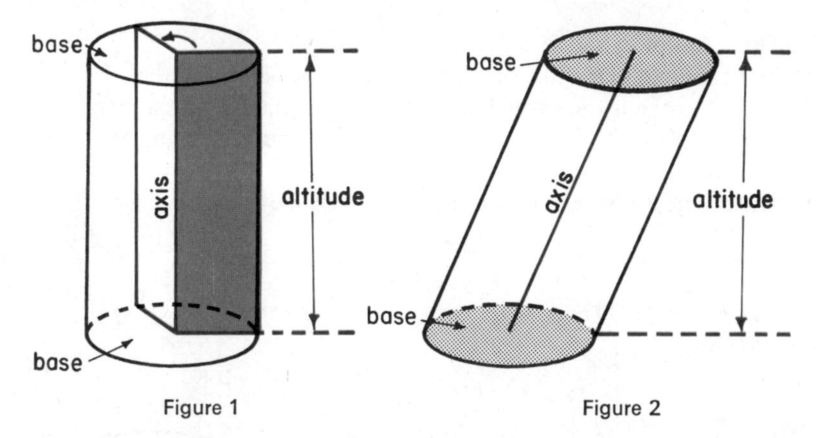

Figure 1 Figure 2

axis is perpendicular to the bases (Figure 1). Figure 2 shows an **oblique** cylinder. Its bases are also circles in parallel planes, but notice that the axis is *not* perpendicular to the bases. In each case, the *altitude* is the distance between the planes containing the bases.

A **right circular cone** is a closed surface formed by rotating a right triangle about one of the sides of the right angle. The **base** is a circle

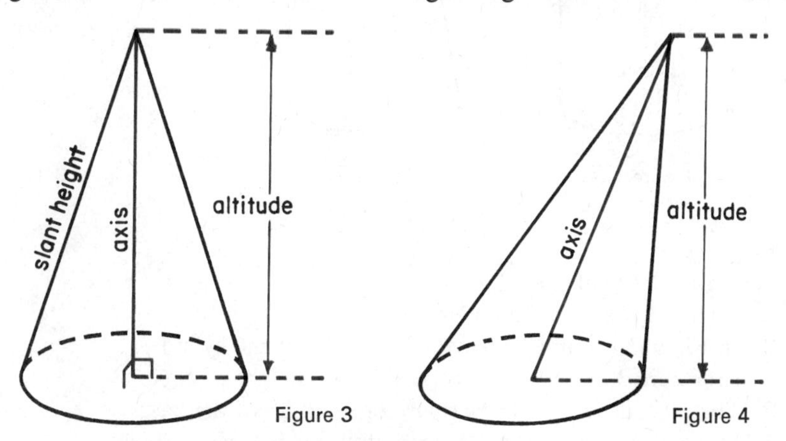

Figure 3 Figure 4

and the line segment from the vertex to the center of the base is called the **axis.** In a right circular cone the axis is perpendicular to the base. Figure 4 shows an *oblique* cone, where the axis is not perpendicular to the base. In each case the **altitude** is the distance between the vertex and the plane of the base. In a right circular cone (Figure 3) the length of a segment joining the vertex and a point on the circle is called the **slant height.** Compare the meaning of "slant height" here with that for a pyramid on page 126.

EXERCISES

A

1. The bases of cylinders and cones are __?__.
2. In a right circular cylinder, the __?__ is perpendicular to the __?__.
3. An __?__ cone is one whose axis is not perpendicular to the base.
4. In a cone the __?__ is the distance between the vertex and the plane of the base.
5. The shortest distance between the bases of a cylinder is called the __?__.

SELF-ANALYSIS TEST V

Time: 10 minutes

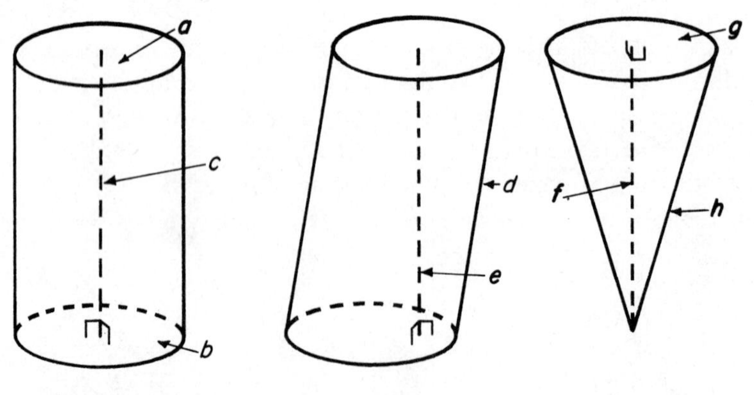

Figure 1 Figure 2 Figure 3

1. Figure 1 is called a __?__.
2. Figure 2 is an __?__ cylinder.
3. In Figure 1, *a* and *b* are called the __?__ of the cylinder.
4. In Figure 3, *h* is referred to as the __?__ height of cone.
5. The altitude of a right circular cone is __?__ to the base.
6. In an oblique cone the __?__ may fall outside the base.
7. A cone has __?__ base(s); a cylinder has __?__ base(s).
8. The line segment joining the centers of the bases of a cylinder is called the __?__ of the cylinder.

CHAPTER SUMMARY

1. A right angle is one with a measure of 90°. The lines which form a right angle are perpendicular lines.
   An acute angle has a measure between 0° and 90°.
   An obtuse angle has a measure between 90° and 180°.
2. Two angles whose measures total 90° are called complementary angles. Two angles whose measures total 180° are called supplementary angles.
3. Polygons are two-dimensional figures formed by line segments. They are named according to the number of their sides.
4. A regular polygon is a polygon having all its angles equal and all its sides the same length.
5. Triangles are further classified by sides and by angles.
6. Quadrilaterals are subdivided into parallelograms, rectangles, and so on.
7. A polyhedron is a closed 3-dimensional figure formed by intersecting planes. Prisms and pyramids are common polyhedrons.
8. Angles formed by lines associated with a circle are the means by which we measure intercepted arcs, and vice versa.
9. Circular cylinders and cones are common 3-dimensional figures.

CHAPTER TEST

1. Match the parts of the circle listed in the right-hand column with the most appropriate term in the other column.

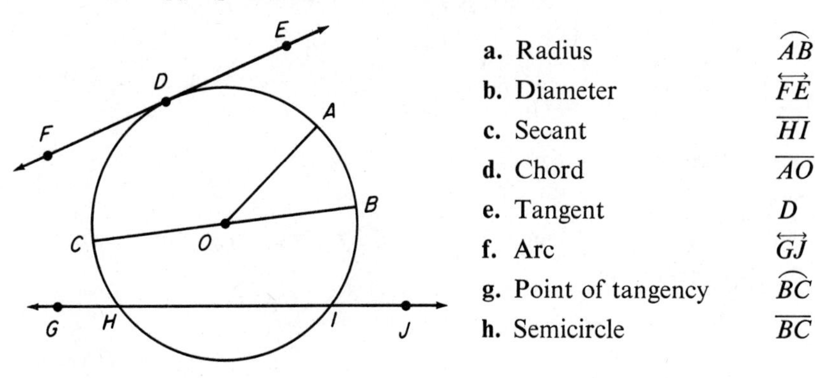

a. Radius	$\overset{\frown}{AB}$
b. Diameter	$\overleftrightarrow{FE}$
c. Secant	$\overline{HI}$
d. Chord	$\overline{AO}$
e. Tangent	D
f. Arc	$\overleftrightarrow{GJ}$
g. Point of tangency	$\overset{\frown}{BC}$
h. Semicircle	$\overline{BC}$

If the following statements (Exercises 2–21) are true, write T. If false, write F, and rewrite the statement to make it true. (Hint: It may help you to draw pictures to illustrate the questions.)

2. A triangle with three equal sides is usually called an isosceles triangle.
3. An angle greater than 90° but less than 180° is called a supplementary angle.
4. The supplement of an angle of 135° is an angle of 35°.
5. A line drawn from a vertex perpendicular to the opposite side of a triangle is called an altitude.
6. The complement of an angle of 23° is an angle of 67°.
7. Two lines which meet at an angle of 23° must intersect.
8. A regular polygon is a polygon whose sides are equal, but whose angles are not always equal.
9. A triangle having an angle of 115° is called an acute triangle.
10. A quadrilateral is a triangle with four sides.
11. A trapezoid whose 2 nonparallel sides are equal is called a rhombus trapezoid.
12. A polygon with 5 sides is called a pentagon.
13. A regular hexagon is a polygon with 6 equal sides and 6 equal angles.
14. A polyhedron is a geometric solid bound by angles.
15. A triangular prism is a prism whose bases are trapezoids.
16. A pyramid is a polyhedron whose base is a polygon and whose faces are triangles with a common vertex.
17. An angle formed at the center of the circle is called an obtuse angle.
18. An angle formed by two chords drawn from the same point is called an acute angle.
19. An angle formed by the intersection of two chords is measured by $\frac{1}{2}$ the sum of the measures of its intercepted arcs.
20. An angle formed by a tangent and a chord is measured by $\frac{1}{2}$ the difference of the measures of its intercepted arcs.
21. An angle formed by 2 secants is measured by $\frac{1}{2}$ the sum of the measures of its intercepted arcs.

22. $m\widehat{BA} = 60°$
$m\angle BOA = \underline{\ ?\ }$

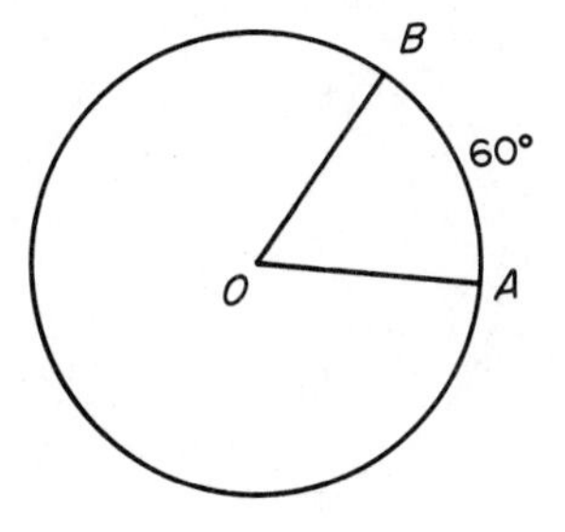

23. $m\widehat{BC} = 130°$
$m\widehat{AB} = 100°$
$m\angle ABC = \underline{\ ?\ }$

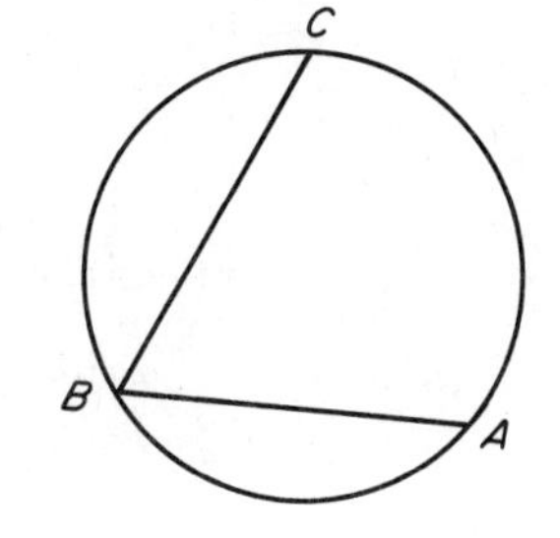

24. $m\angle AOC = 80°$
$m\angle ABC = \underline{\ ?\ }$

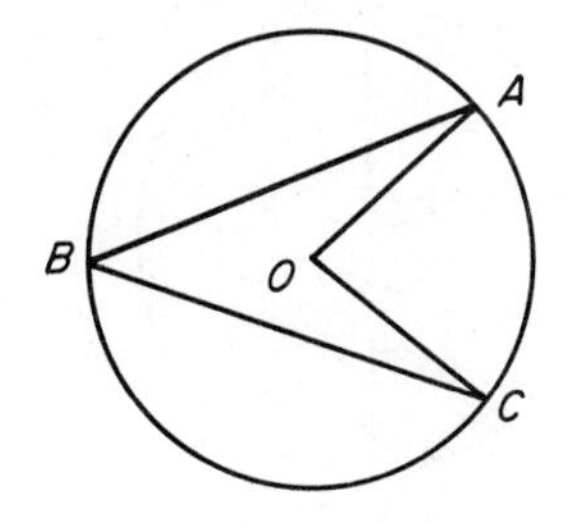

25. $m\widehat{AE} = 98°$
$m\widehat{BD} = 60°$
$m\angle ACE = \underline{\ ?\ }$

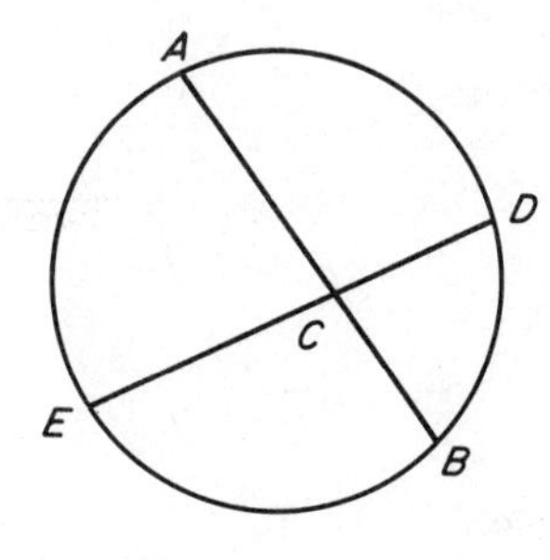

26. $m\angle ABC = 140°$
$m\widehat{APB} = \underline{\ ?\ }$

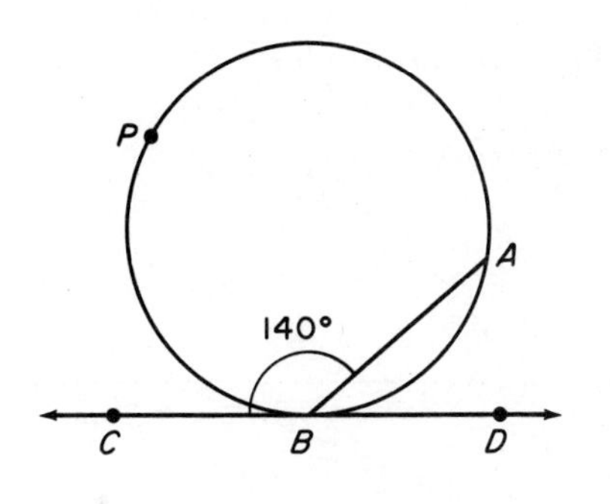

27. $m\widehat{APB} = 300°$
$m\angle ABC = \underline{\ ?\ }$

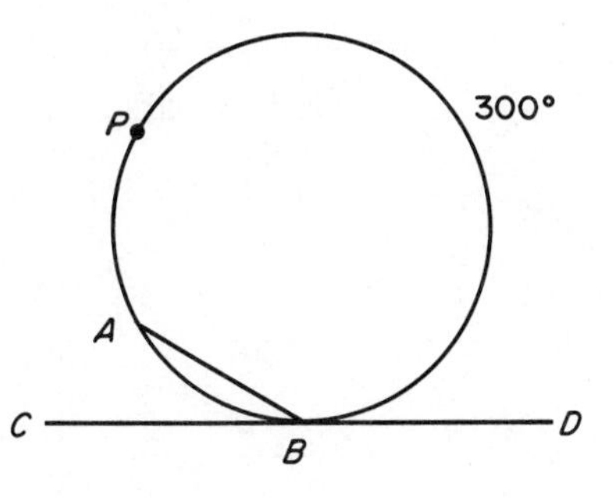

28. $m\widehat{BPC} = 280°$
$m\widehat{BC} = 80°$
$m\angle A = \underline{\ ?\ }$

29. $m\widehat{AC} = 50°$
$m\widehat{DC} = 120°$
$m\angle B = \underline{\ ?\ }$

30. $m\widehat{AE} = 90°$
$m\widehat{DC} = 40°$
$m\angle B = \underline{\ ?\ }$

31. $m\angle ABC = 40°$
$m\widehat{DE} = 60°$
$m\angle 1 = \underline{\ ?\ }$

32. $m\angle AOC = 160°$
$m\angle B = \underline{\ ?\ }$

33. (Optional) $m\angle P = 70°$
$m\widehat{CD} = 20°$
$m\widehat{AB} = \underline{\ ?\ }$

34. (Optional) $m\widehat{AC} = 40°$
$m\angle AFC = 25°$
$m\angle B = \underline{\ ?\ }$

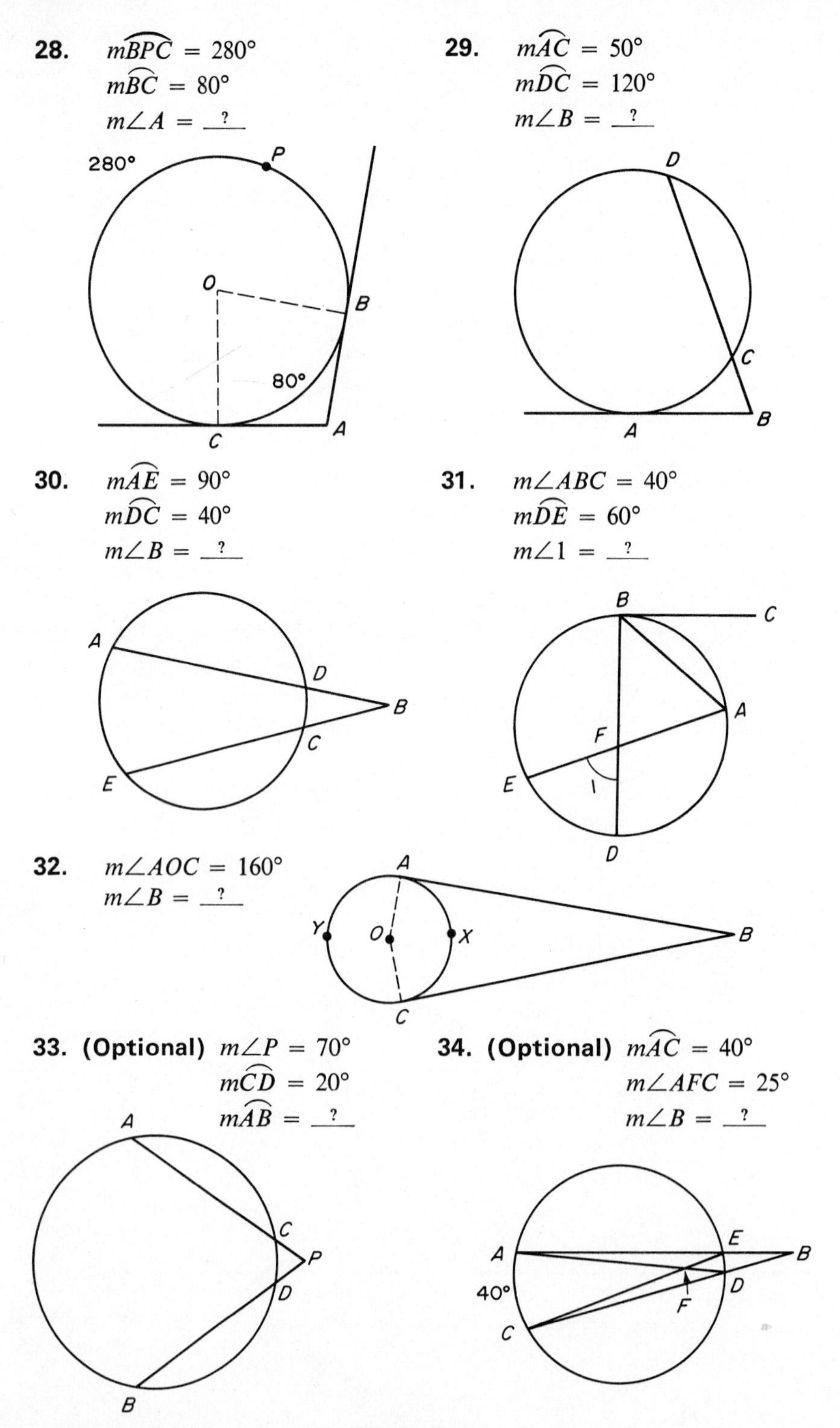

MAINTAINING YOUR SKILLS

Add.

1. $\begin{array}{r} 35 \\ +\ 96 \\ \hline \end{array}$

2. $\begin{array}{r} 52 \\ 27 \\ +\ 98 \\ \hline \end{array}$

3. $\begin{array}{r} 836 \\ 527 \\ 255 \\ +\ 666 \\ \hline \end{array}$

4. $\begin{array}{r} 728 \\ 4125 \\ 216 \\ +\ \ 91 \\ \hline \end{array}$

5. $\begin{array}{r} 18{,}052 \\ 7{,}025 \\ 25 \\ +\ \ 555 \\ \hline \end{array}$

6. $\begin{array}{r} 496 \\ 14{,}305 \\ 1{,}444 \\ +\ \ 65 \\ \hline \end{array}$

Subtract.

7. $\begin{array}{r} 229 \\ -\ 198 \\ \hline \end{array}$

8. $\begin{array}{r} 855 \\ -\ 542 \\ \hline \end{array}$

9. $\begin{array}{r} 1{,}999 \\ -\ 464 \\ \hline \end{array}$

10. $\begin{array}{r} 6886 \\ -\ 106 \\ \hline \end{array}$

11. $\begin{array}{r} 1913 \\ -\ 1001 \\ \hline \end{array}$

12. $\begin{array}{r} 26{,}500 \\ -\ 15{,}222 \\ \hline \end{array}$

Multiply.

13. 35×15

14. 44×25

15. 625×17

16. 216×68

17. 712×5.05

18. 22.3×1.55

Divide.

19. $15\overline{)825}$

20. $37\overline{)1628}$

21. $35\overline{)5775}$

22. $27\overline{)3105}$

23. $4.5\overline{)4725}$

24. $1.8\overline{)10.44}$

Simplify.

25. $\frac{3}{8} + \frac{1}{3} = ?$

26. $\frac{7}{8} + \frac{1}{16} = ?$

27. $\frac{5}{6} \times \frac{3}{4} = ?$

28. $\frac{1}{8} \times \frac{1}{4} \times \frac{3}{8} = ?$

29. $1\frac{1}{2} + 5\frac{3}{4} = ?$

30. $4\frac{5}{8} - 2\frac{1}{2} = ?$

The Houston astrodome. Its construction required the use of many geometric formulas.

Geometric Formulas

OBJECTIVES

1. To review plane and solid geometric figures.

2. To learn how to use formulas in finding areas.

3. To learn how to use formulas in finding volumes.

In the preceding chapter we studied the characteristics of various plane and solid figures. In the practical applications of geometry it is often necessary to find measurements of these figures. This chapter will show you how to do this by means of formulas.

■ Plane Figures

4–1 Triangles

Any side of a triangle may be called the **base.** As you know (page 115), an *altitude* is the line segment drawn from a vertex, perpendicular to the line containing the opposite side. TM p. 12, 4-1(1)

TM → p. 12 4-1(2)

The **area** of any triangle is equal to one half the product of the measures of the base and the altitude drawn to it. The **perimeter** is the sum of the lengths of the three sides. Expressed as formulas,

Commonly referred to as the "distance around" the figure.

$$A = \frac{1}{2}bh, \text{ where } A = \text{area}, b = \text{base}, h = \text{altitude}.$$

$$P = a + b + c, \text{ where } P = \text{perimeter, and } a, b, c \text{ are sides.}$$

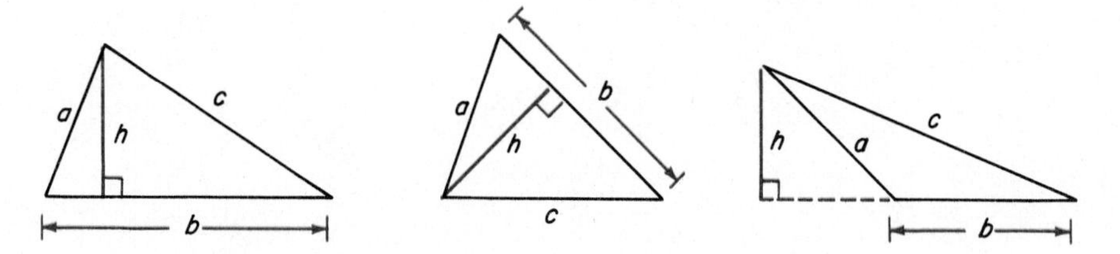

EXAMPLES

1. Find the area.

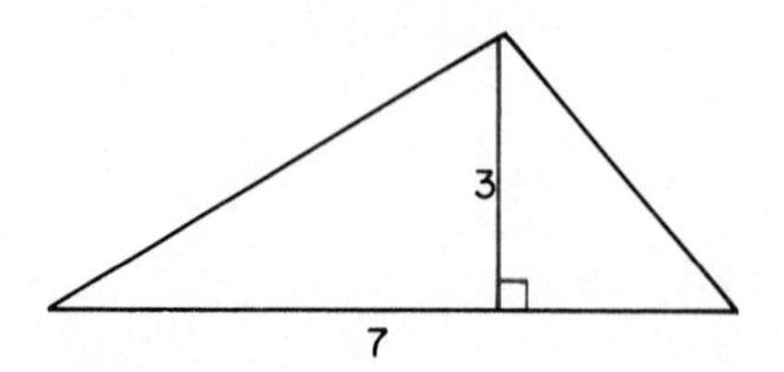

Solution. $A = \frac{1}{2}bh$

$A = \frac{1}{2} \cdot 7 \cdot 3 = \frac{21}{2}$

$= $ **10.5 (sq. units)**

2. Find the perimeter.

Solution. $P = a + b + c$

$P = 4 + 5 + 6$

$P = $ **15 (units)**

Solutions are given in terms of units to preserve the generality of the method. See also TM p. 8 2-7.

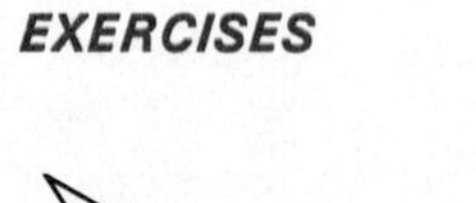

EXERCISES

Find the perimeter.

A

1.

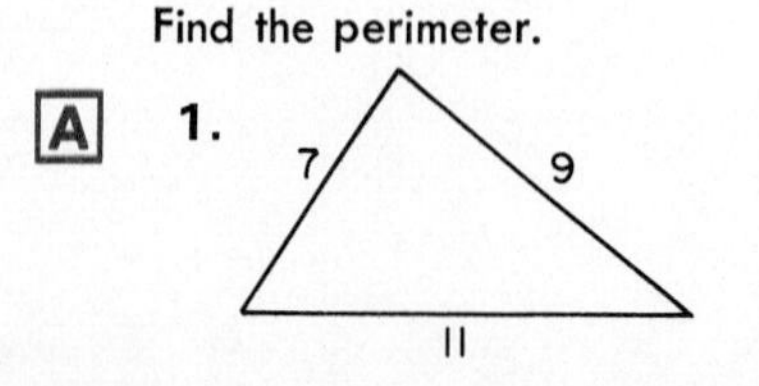

2.

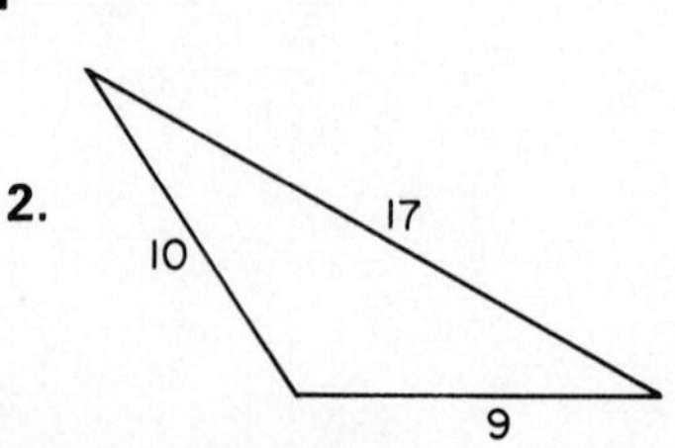

Find the area.

3.

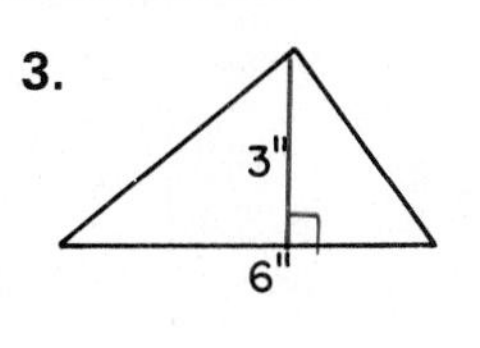

4.

5.

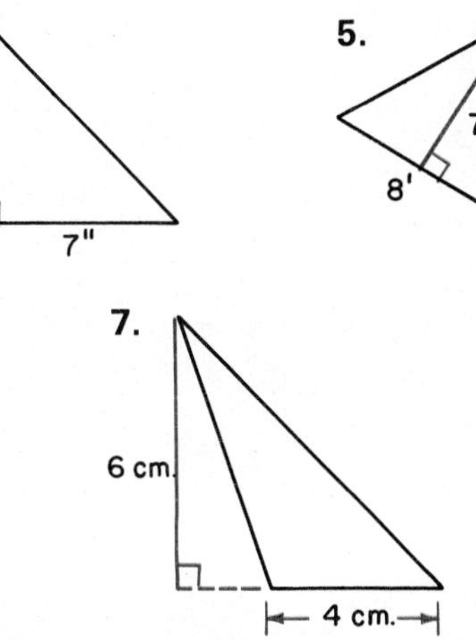

6.

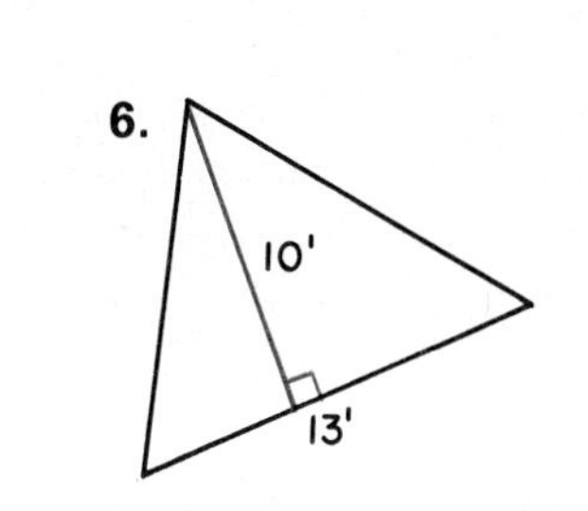

7.

8.

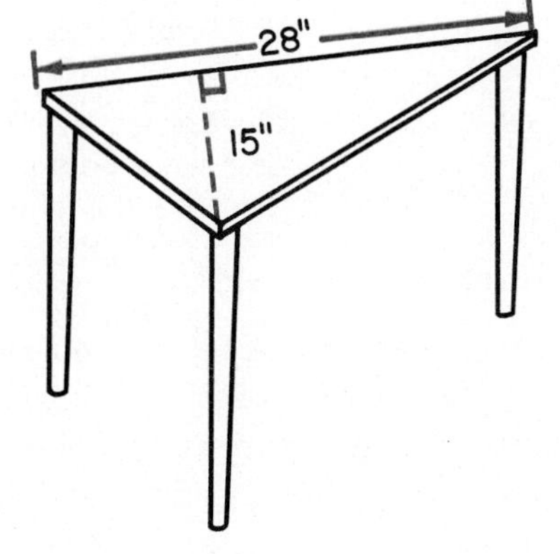

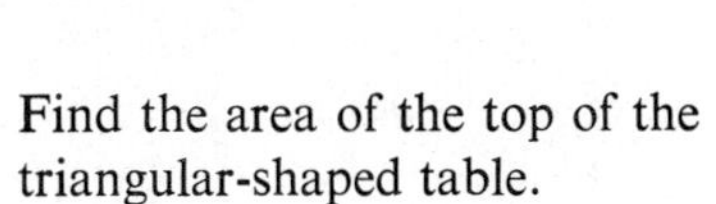

Find the area of the top of the triangular-shaped table.

9.

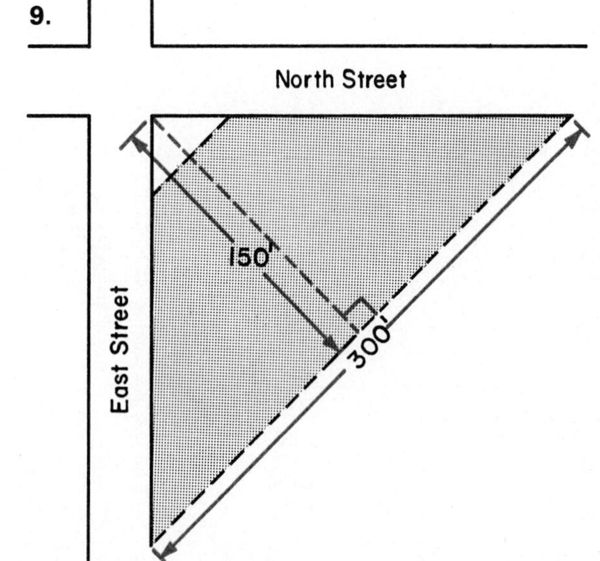

Find the area of the shaded portion of the lot, if the base is 300′ and the altitude of the lot is 150′.
The area of the small triangular lot (not shaded) is 900 sq. ft.

Measure with your ruler. Then use the formula for area.

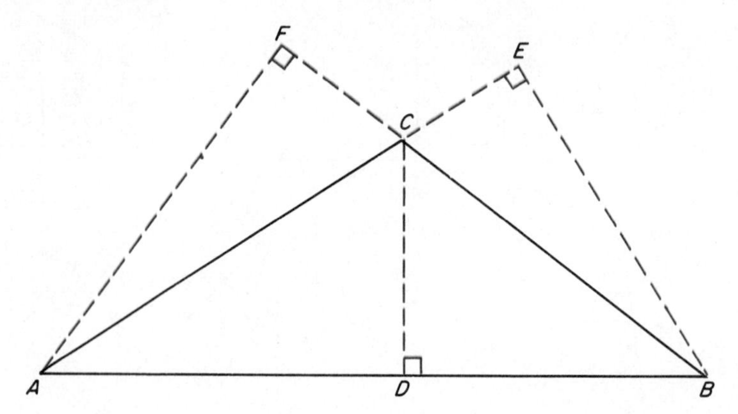

B **10.** Find the area of the triangle ABC by using the measures of $\overline{AB}$ and $\overline{CD}$.

11. Find the area of the triangle ABC by using the measures of $\overline{CB}$ and $\overline{AF}$.

12. Find the area of the triangle ABC by using the measures of $\overline{AC}$ and $\overline{BE}$.

13. Do your results in Exercises 10, 11, and 12 agree? They may not be identical, but they should be close. Point out that in theory the three results should agree, but in fact, they may not. Discuss the possible sources of difference.

4–2 Parallelogram, Rectangle, Rhombus

The area of a rectangle, a parallelogram, and a rhombus may be found by use of the same formula. Remember that the *altitude* is the perpendicular distance from the base to the opposite side. The *area* is the product of the measures of the base and the altitude. The *perimeter* is the sum of the lengths of the sides. TM p. 12, 4-2(1)

Any side of these three figures can be considered the base.

$$A = bh$$ TM p. 12, 4-2(2)

$$P = a + b + c + d$$

d h a c b   d a h c b   d a h c b

EXAMPLE 1

Find the area.

Solution. $A = bh$

$A = 2 \cdot 4$

$A = \mathbf{8}$ **(sq. units)**

2 4

EXAMPLE 2

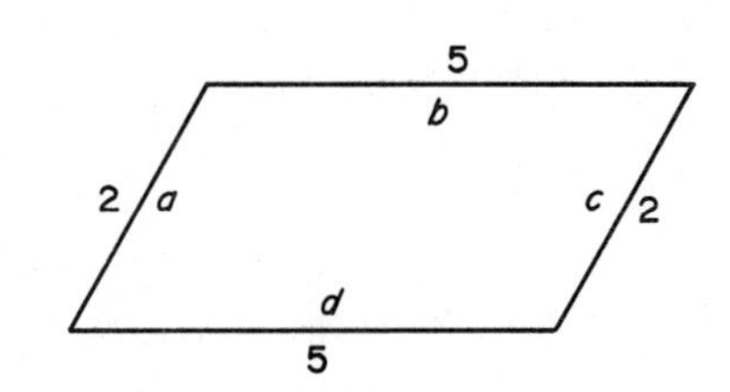

Find the perimeter.

Solution. $P = a + b + c + d$

$P = 2 + 5 + 2 + 5$

$P = \mathbf{14}$ **(units)**

EXAMPLE 3

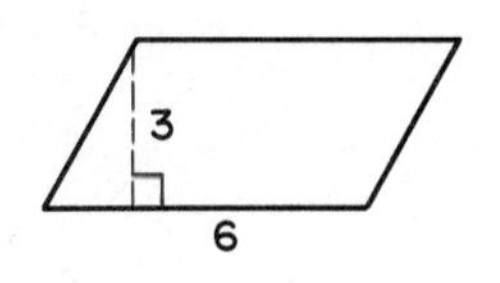

Find the area.

Solution. $A = bh$

$A = 6 \cdot 3$

$A = \mathbf{18}$ **(sq. units)**

EXERCISES

Find the areas.

A

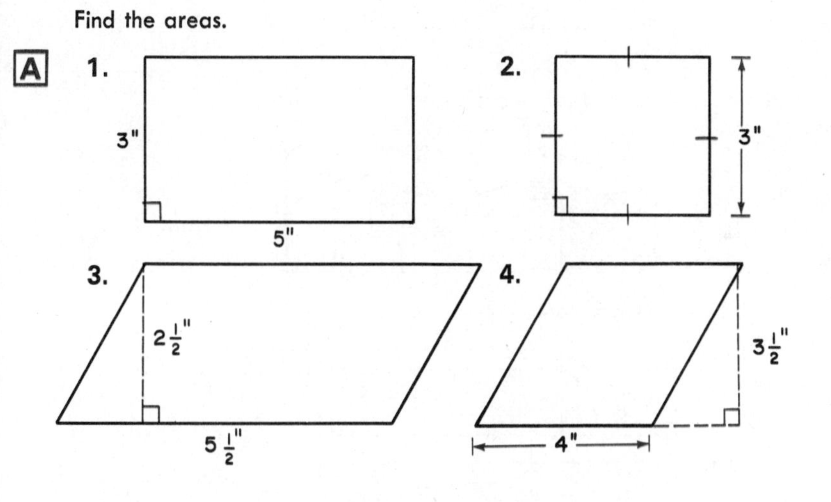

5. Find the area of the rectangle $ABCD$.
Find the area of the parallelogram $EFCD$.
Are they equal?

This problem can be vividly demonstrated on a geoboard, if available.

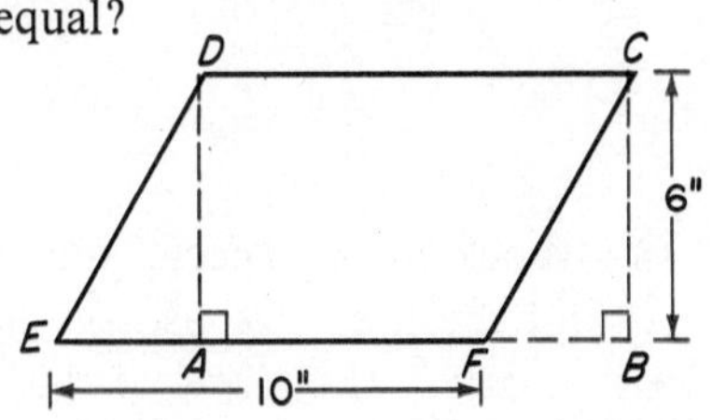

Find the perimeters.

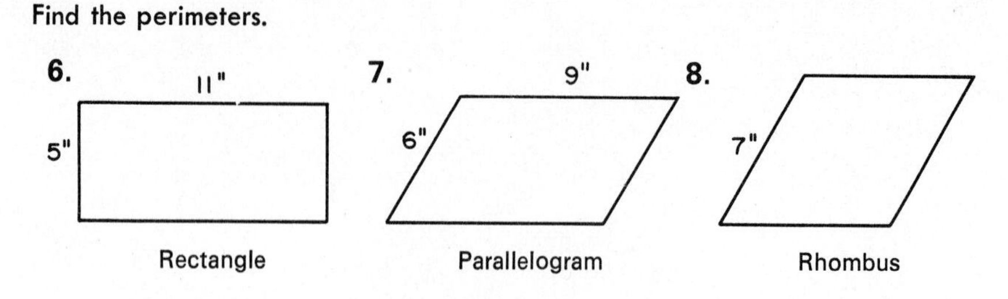

B **9.** Find the perimeter and area of the cardboard box illustrated.

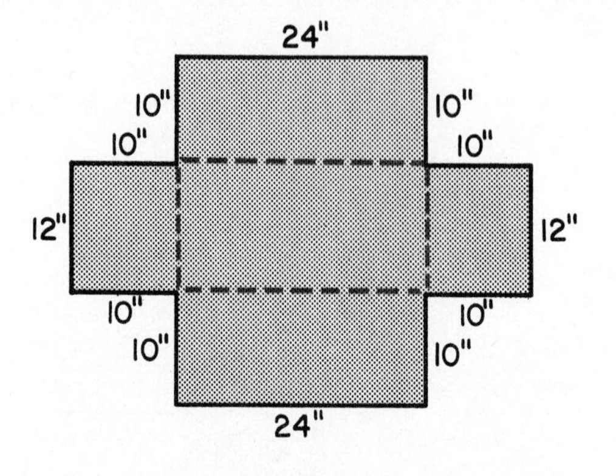

10. Find the area of the rectangular die face as illustrated.

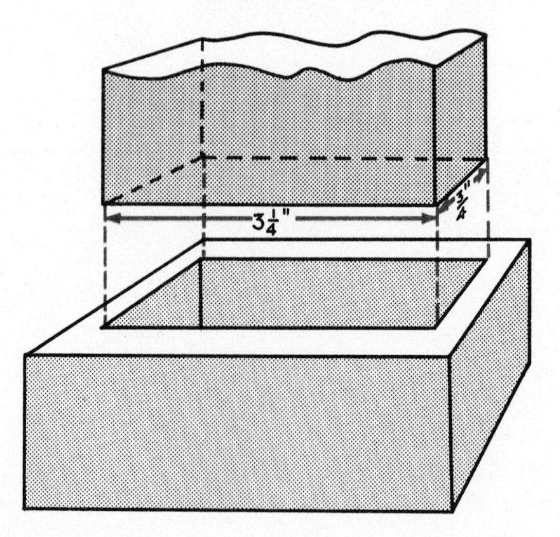

You may wish to alter the dimensions given here to review the ideas of tolerance and dimension limits. Refer to pages 63-65.

4–3 Trapezoid

You will recall that the trapezoid is a special quadrilateral, with only two sides parallel. To find the area, we use the average of the length of the two parallel sides, called the *bases* of the trapezoid. In

Be sure the student understands the difference between b_2 and b^2.

the diagram they are labeled b_1 and b_2, read "b-sub-1" and "b-sub-2." (The small numerals 1 and 2 are called *subscripts.*) The average of b_1 and b_2 is $\frac{1}{2}(b_1 + b_2)$.

The *area* is the product of the length of the altitude and the average of the lengths of the bases. The *perimeter* is the sum of the lengths of the four sides.

$$A = h \cdot \frac{1}{2}(b_1 + b_2),$$

or

$$\mathbf{A = \frac{1}{2} h(b_1 + b_2)}$$

$$\mathbf{P = a + b_1 + c + b_2}$$

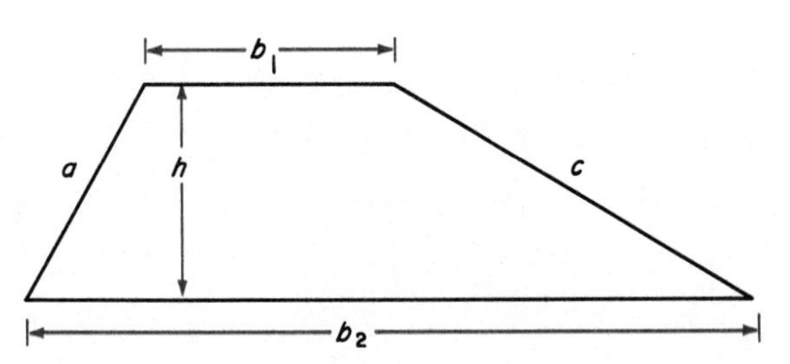

EXAMPLE 1

Find the area of the trapezoid shown.

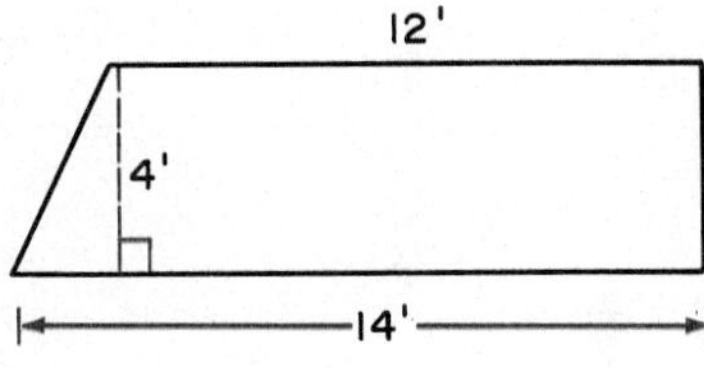

Solution. $A = \frac{1}{2}(4)(12 + 14)$
$A = 2(26) =$ **52 (sq. ft.)**

EXAMPLE 2

Find the perimeter of the trapezoid shown.

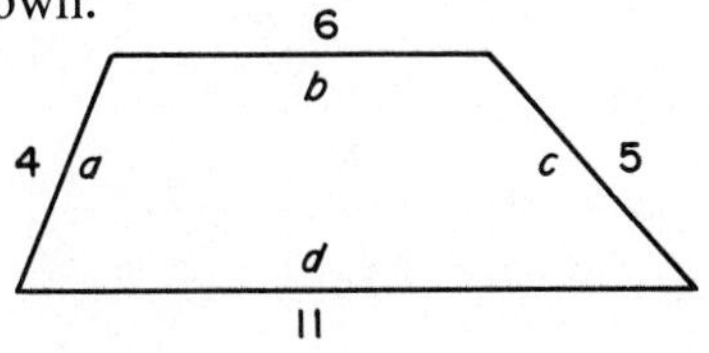

Solution. $P = a + b + c + d$
$P = 4 + 6 + 5 + 11$
$P =$ **26 (units)**

EXERCISES

Find the areas of the trapezoids.

A

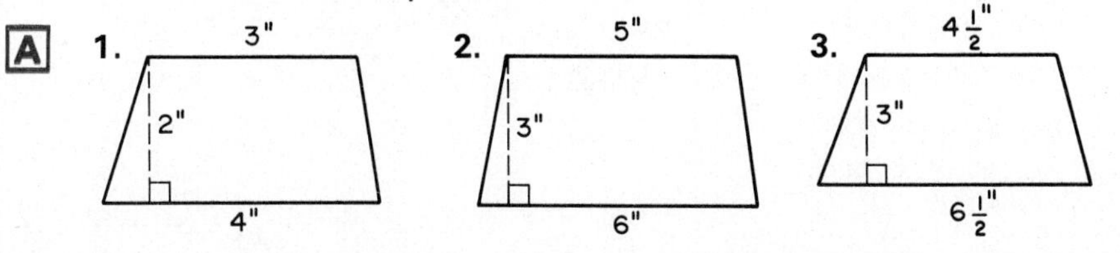

Find the areas of the trapezoids.

4.

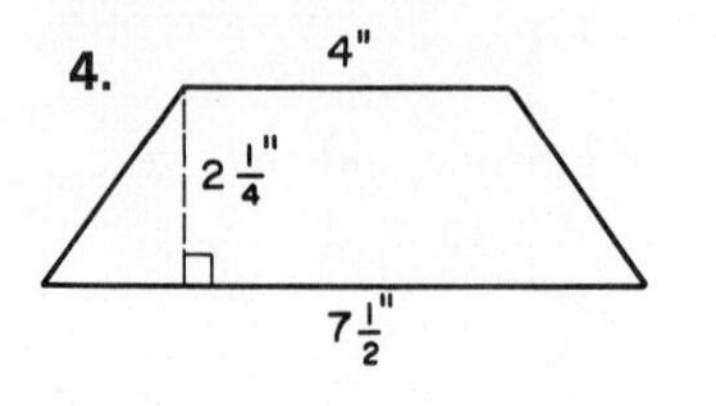

5.

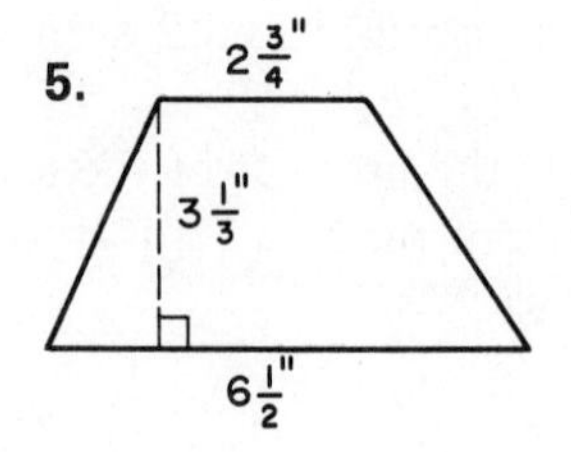

Find the perimeters of the trapezoids.

6. **7.**

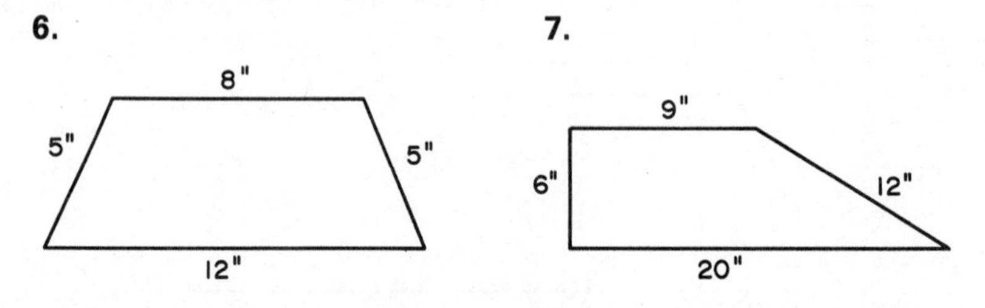

8. Find the area of the patio roof.

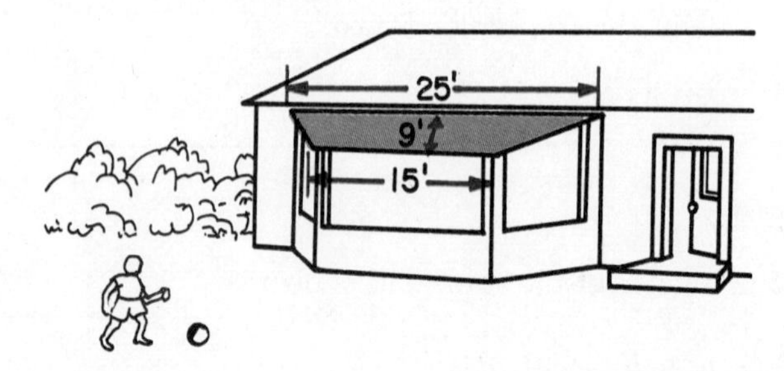

9. Find the total area of the wagon, if *a* and *d* are trapezoids, and *b*, *c*, and *e* are rectangles.

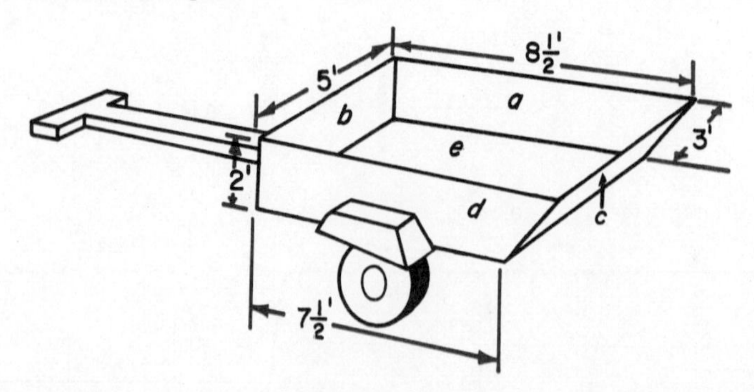

4–4 Circles

The Greek letter π (pī) represents a special number; this number is the quotient of the circumference of a circle divided by its diameter. For practical work we usually use the approximate values $\frac{22}{7}$ or 3.14 for π.

The area, A, of a circle is the product of π and the square of the length of the radius, r. The perimeter of a circle, called the **circumference,** C, is given by twice the product of π and the length of the radius.

Point out that for technical work more accurate values of π are necessary; for example, 3.14159 is a closer approximation.

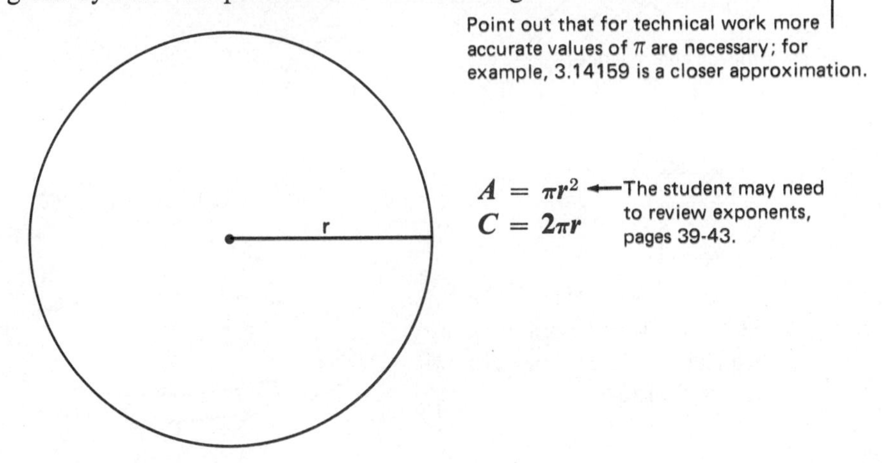

$$A = \pi r^2$$
$$C = 2\pi r$$

The student may need to review exponents, pages 39-43.

EXAMPLE 1

Find the area of the circle.

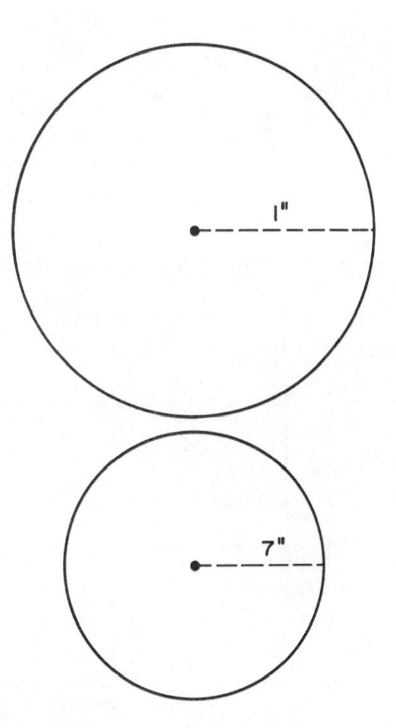

Solution. $A = \pi r^2$

$A = \frac{22}{7}(1^2) = \frac{22}{7} \times 1 \times 1$

$A = \mathbf{\frac{22}{7}}$ **(sq. in.)**

EXAMPLE 2

Find the circumference of the circle.

Solution. $C = 2\pi r$

$C = 2(\frac{22}{7})7$

$C =$ **44 (in.)**

EXERCISES

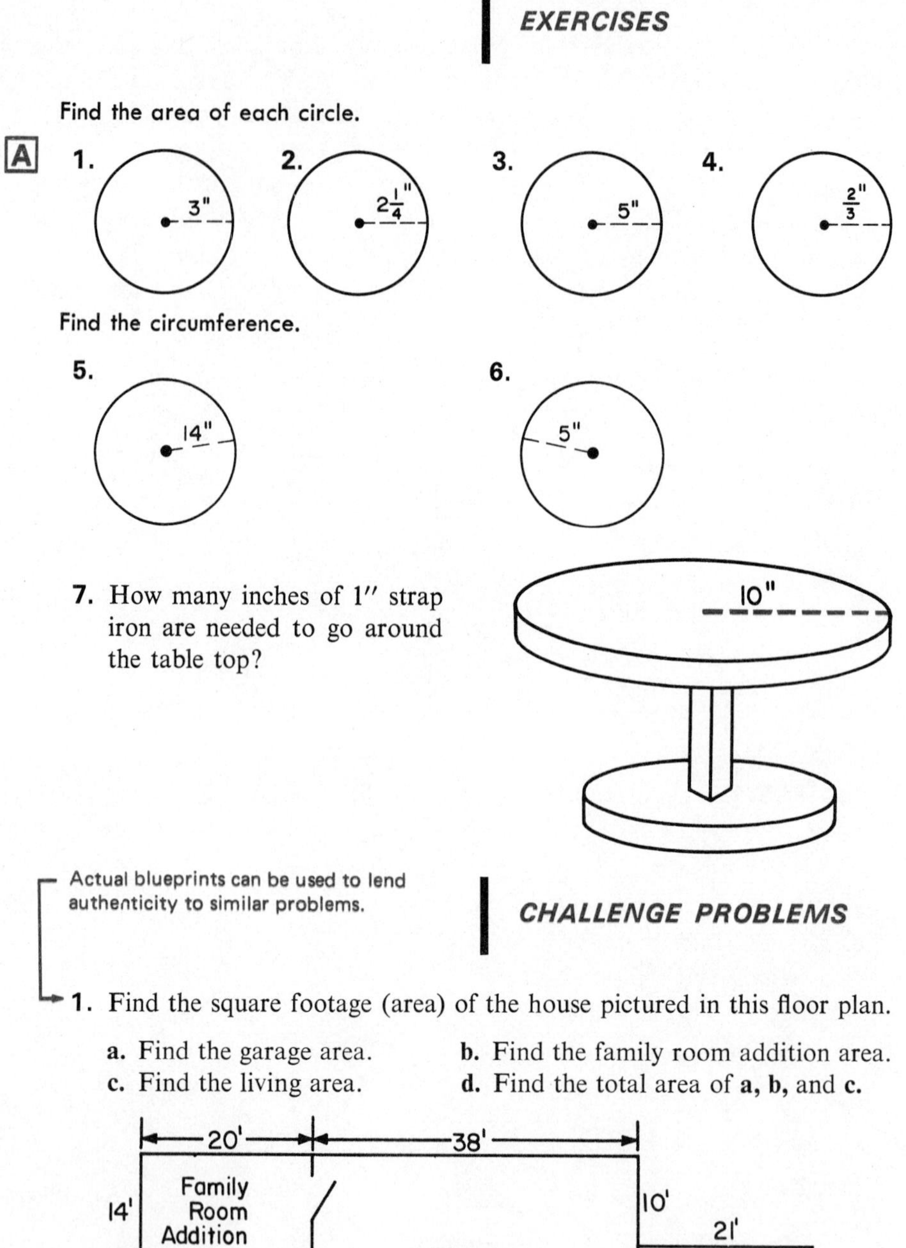

Find the area of each circle.

A 1. 2. 3. 4.

Find the circumference.

5. 6.

7. How many inches of 1″ strap iron are needed to go around the table top?

Actual blueprints can be used to lend authenticity to similar problems.

CHALLENGE PROBLEMS

1. Find the square footage (area) of the house pictured in this floor plan.

   a. Find the garage area. **b.** Find the family room addition area.
   c. Find the living area. **d.** Find the total area of **a, b,** and **c.**

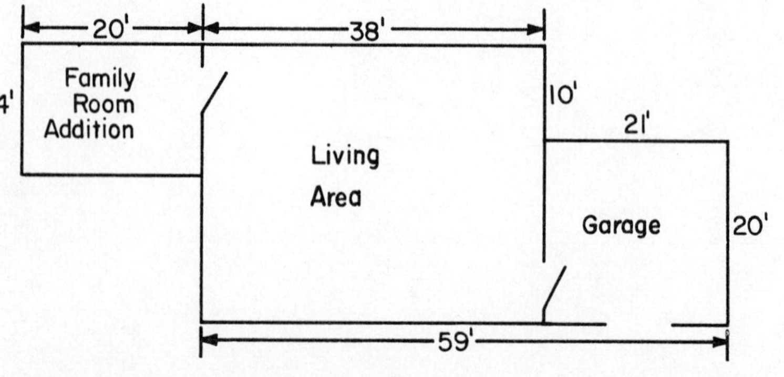

2. Find the frontal area of the barn.

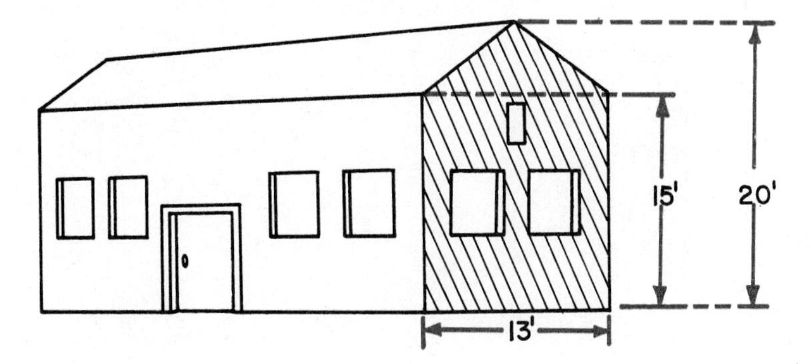

3. Find the area of the template. (*DEFG* is a parallelogram.)

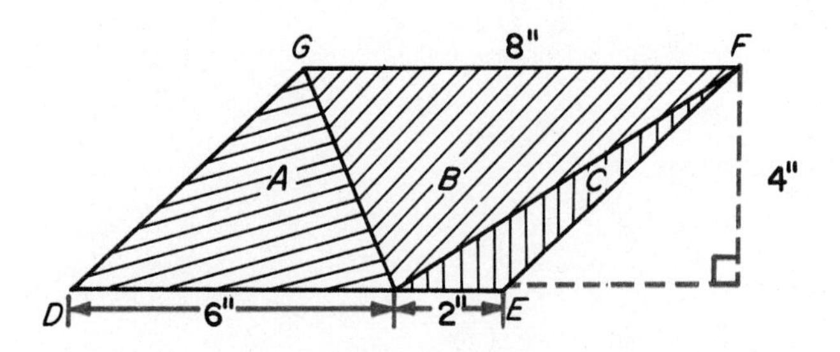

a. Find the area of triangle *A*.
b. Find the area of triangle *B*.
c. Find the area of triangle *C*.
d. Find the total area of parallelogram *DEFG*.

4. *ABCD* is a rectangle. Find the area of:

a. triangle *AEF*
b. trapezoid *EFDG*
c. rectangle *EBCG*
d. pentagon *BEFDC*
e. rectangle *ABCD*

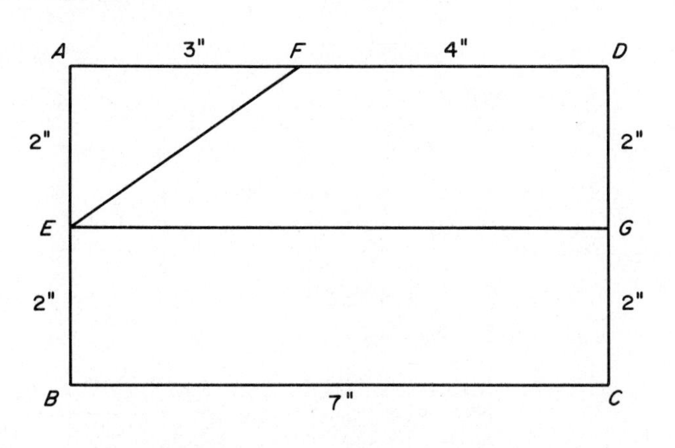

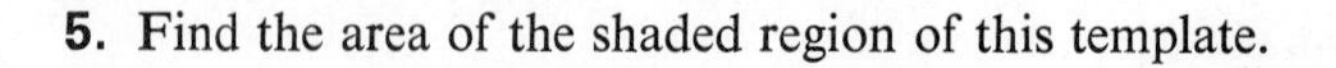

5. Find the area of the shaded region of this template.

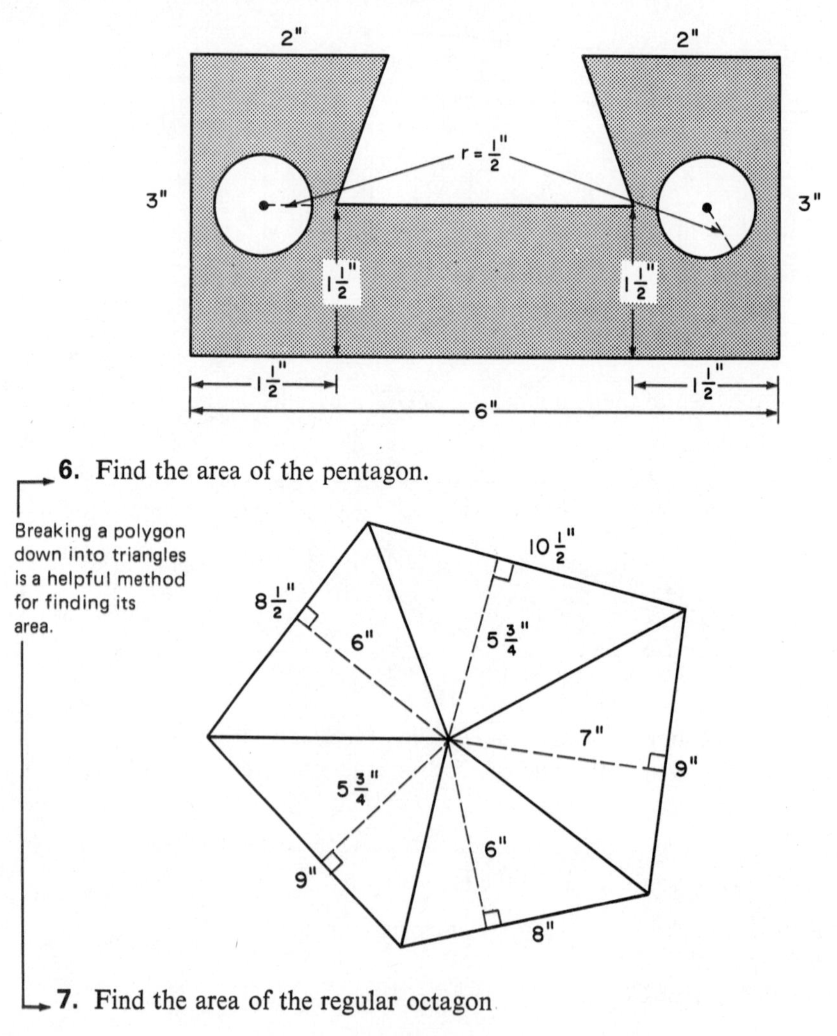

6. Find the area of the pentagon.

Breaking a polygon down into triangles is a helpful method for finding its area.

7. Find the area of the regular octagon

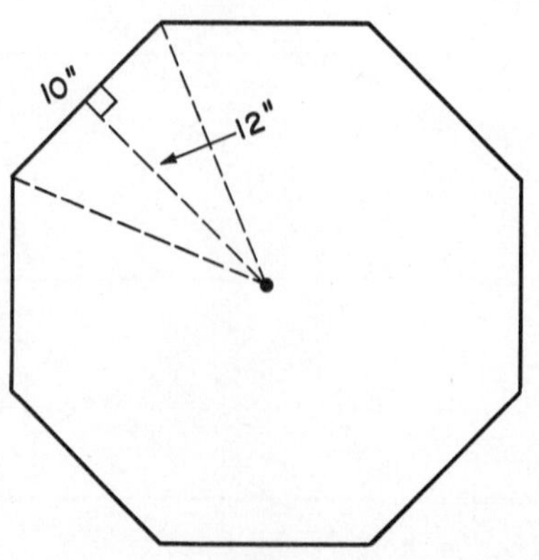

SELF-ANALYSIS TEST I

Time: 10 minutes

Find the perimeters of the figures below (1–4).

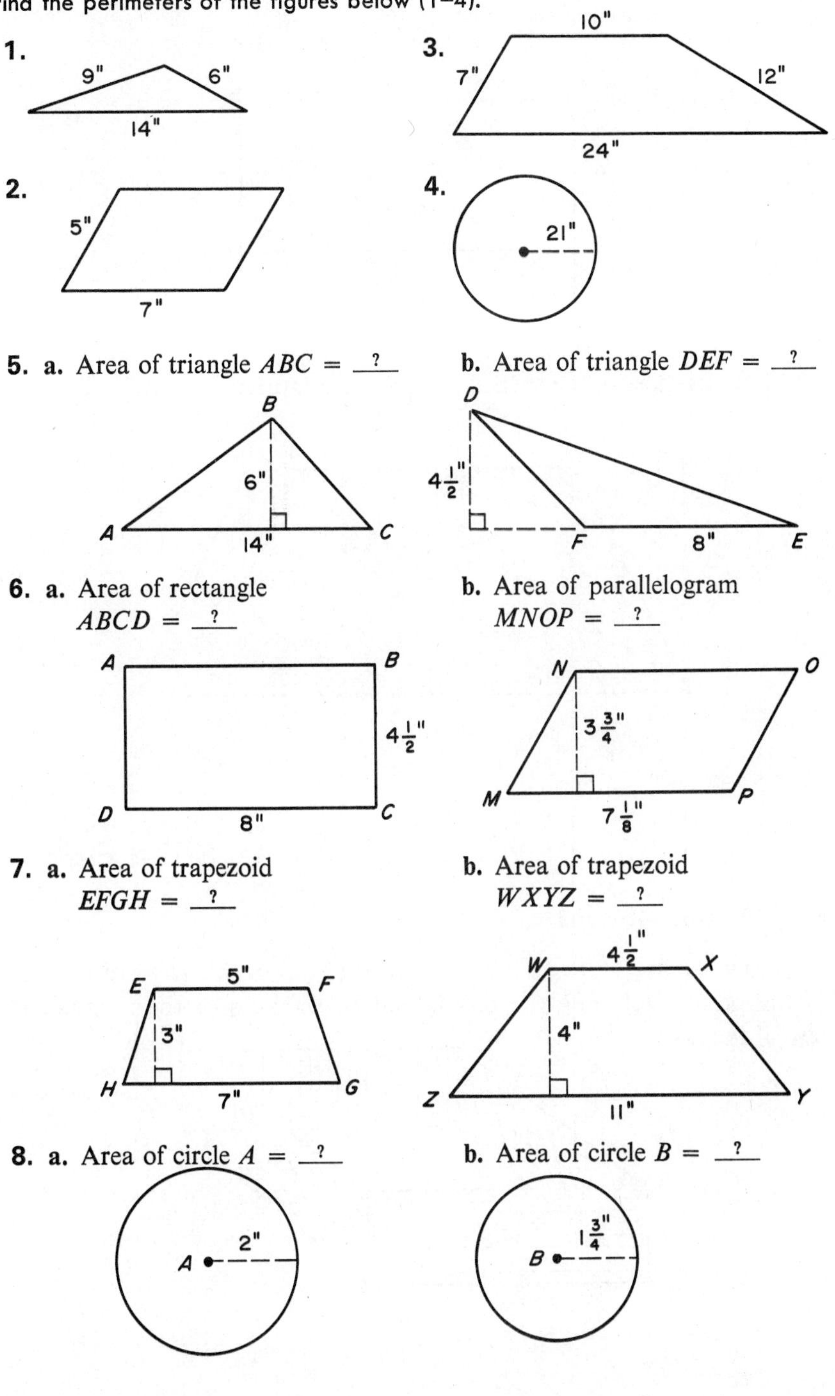

9. *ACIH* is a rectangle.
   a. Find the area of triangle *BFE*.
   b. Find the area of trapezoid *ABED*.
   c. Find the area of rectangle *ACIH*.

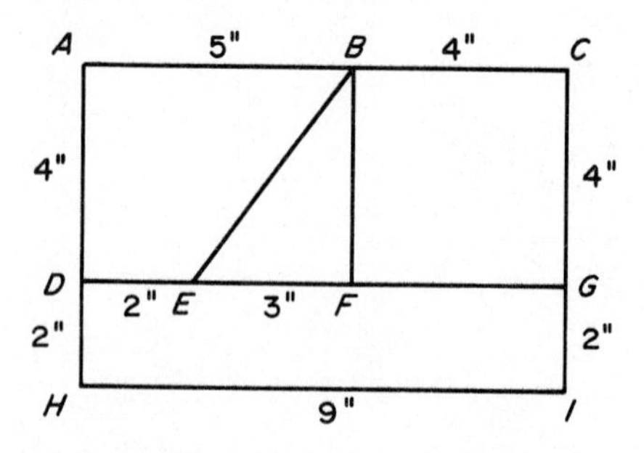

10. Find the area of the shaded region of the trapezoid.

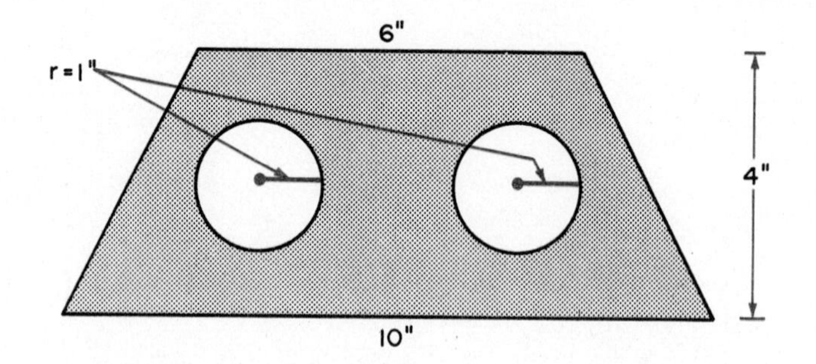

Solid Figures

4–5 Prisms — Areas

The **lateral area, *L*, of a prism** is the sum of the areas of the faces of the prism excluding the bases, that is, the sum of the areas of the lateral faces.

The student may wish to review the terms associated with polyhedrons on page 124.

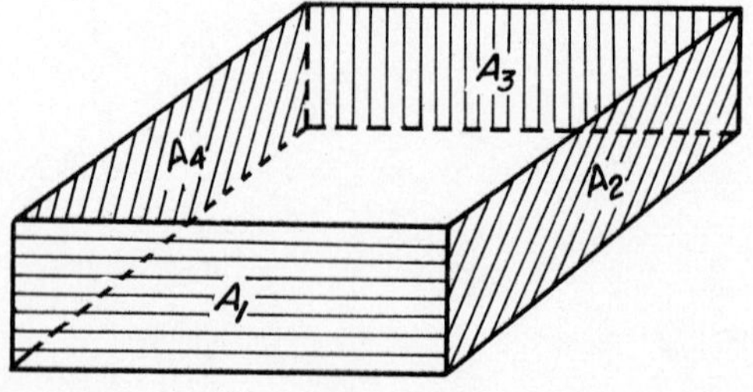

$$L = A_1 + A_2 + A_3 + A_4$$

The symbol S stands for surface area.

The **total area, S,** of a prism is the sum of the areas of all the faces.

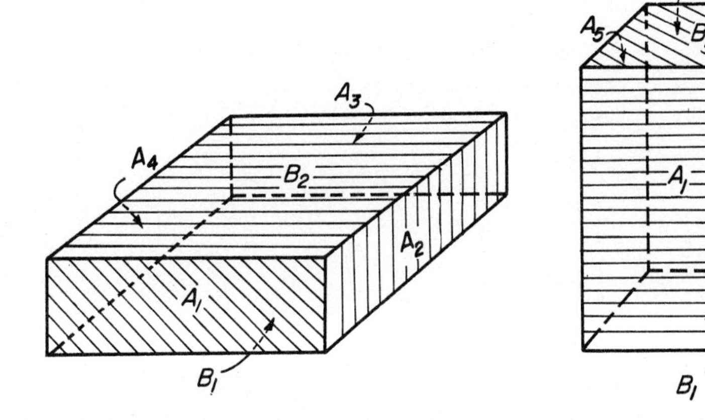

$$S = A_1 + A_2 + A_3 + A_4 + A_5 + B_1 + B_2$$

EXAMPLE 1

Find the lateral area of this prism.

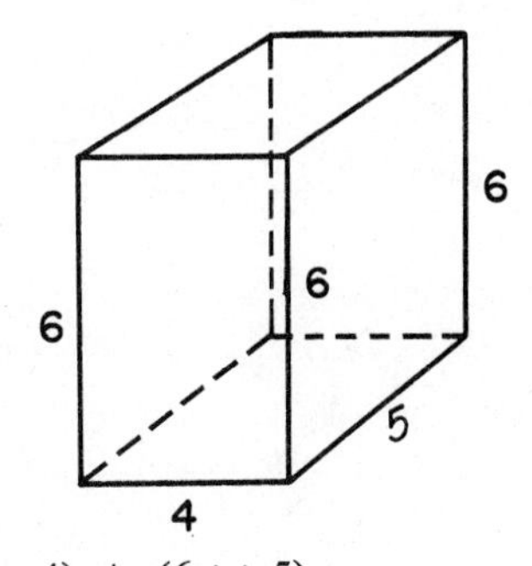

Solution. Find the area of all four rectangular faces; add to get the lateral area.

$$\begin{aligned} L &= (6 \times 4) + (6 \times 5) + (6 \times 4) + (6 \times 5) \\ &= 24 + 30 + 24 + 30 \\ &= \mathbf{108 \text{ (sq. units)}} \end{aligned}$$

Remind the student to simplify within the grouping symbols first.

EXAMPLE 2

Find the total area of the four walls and roof of the building.

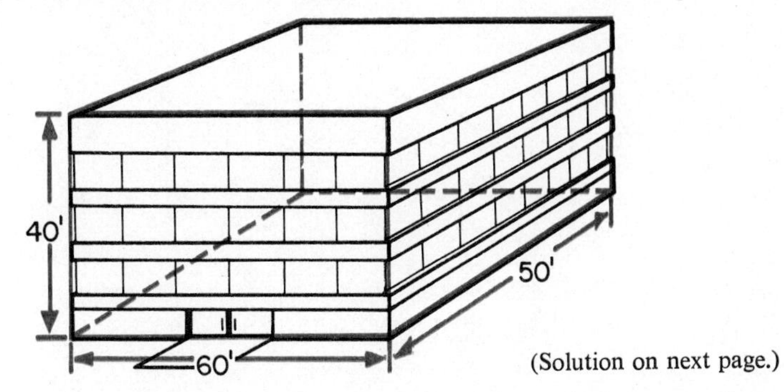

(Solution on next page.)

Solution. Find the area of all four lateral faces, and the area of one base.

$$\begin{aligned} S &= (40 \times 60) + (40 \times 50) + (40 \times 60) + (40 \times 50) \\ &\quad + (50 \times 60) \\ &= 2400 + 2000 + 2400 + 2000 + 3000 \\ &= \mathbf{11{,}800 \text{ (sq. ft.)}} \end{aligned}$$

EXERCISES

Find the lateral area of the following:

A

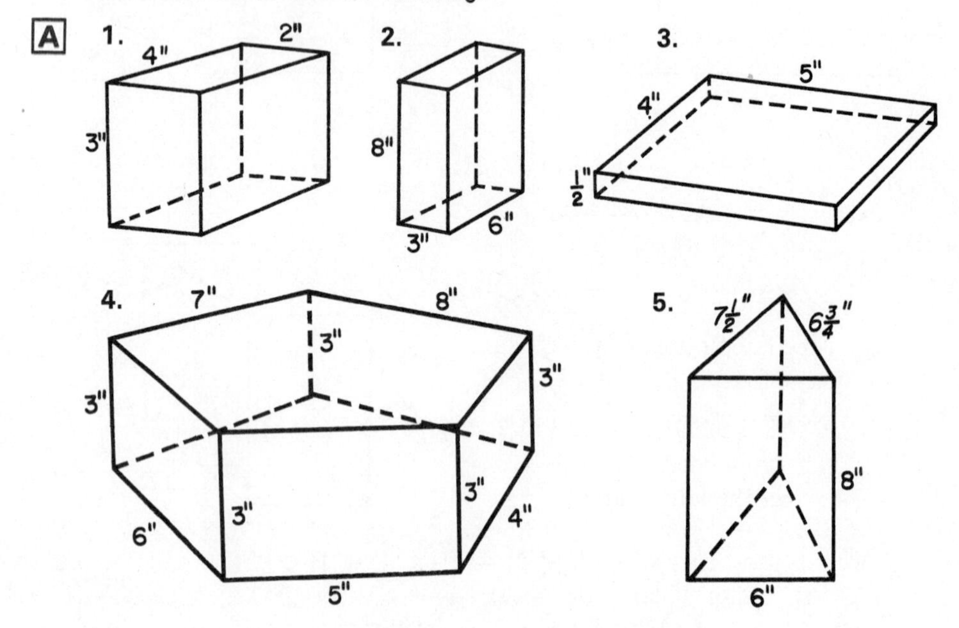

6. Find the lateral area of the "T" block illustrated.

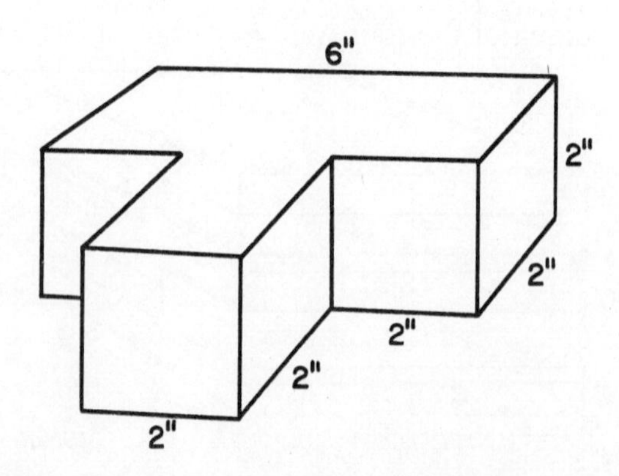

Find the total area of each of the following:

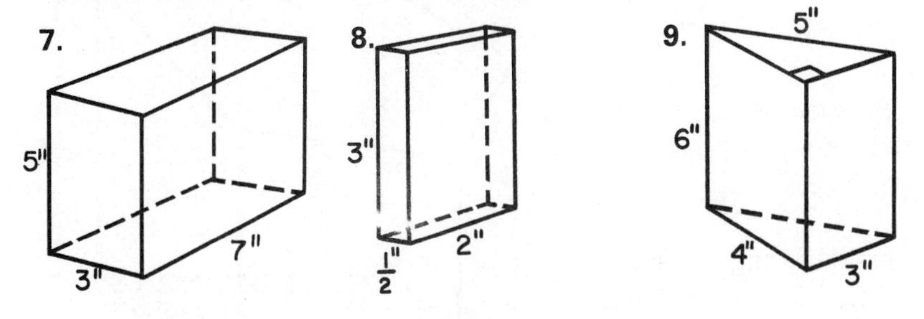

B **10.** Find the total area of this regular hexagonal prism.

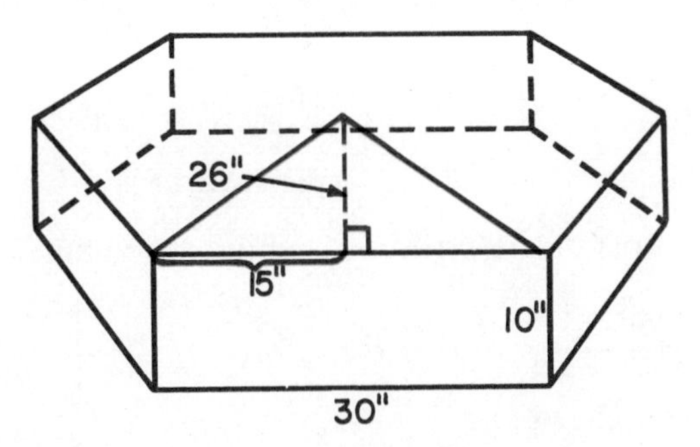

11. Find the total area. (Hint: Be careful not to include overlapping areas.)

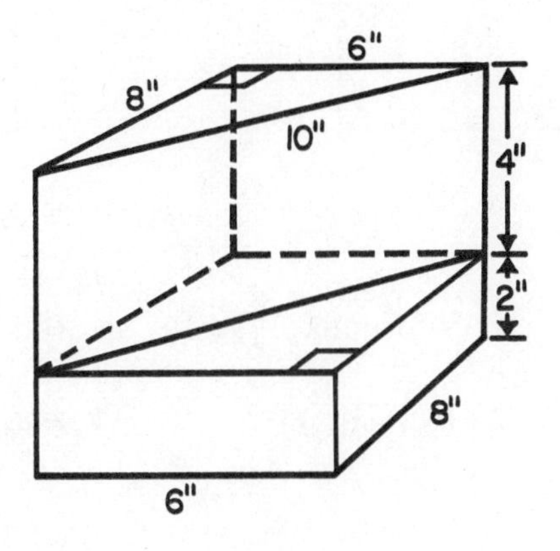

4–6 Prisms — Volume

Finding the volumes of prisms anticipates the work in Chapter 6 on determining the capacity of rectangular containers.

The **volume of a prism** is the product of the area of a base and the length of the altitude. To calculate the area of the base, B, you will have to use what you know about polygons.

Note: Beginning at this point, we shall be working with right prisms only.

Important

The formula for finding the volume of a prism is

$$V = Bh$$

where V = the volume, B = the area of the base, and h = the altitude of the prism.

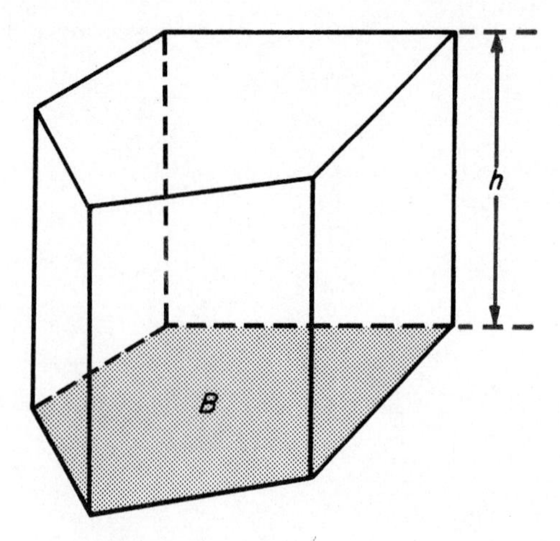

EXAMPLE 1

Find the volume of the prism.

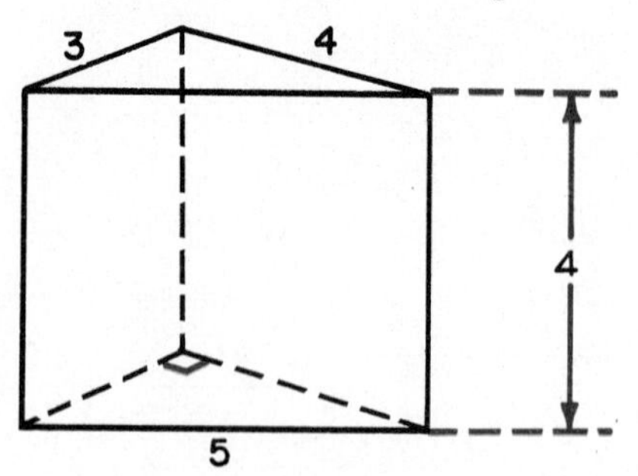

Solution. $V = Bh$

$B = \frac{1}{2} \cdot 3 \cdot 4$ (triangle formula)
$B = 6$
Thus $V = 6 \cdot 4$
$V =$ **24 (cu. units)**

EXAMPLE 2

Find the volume.

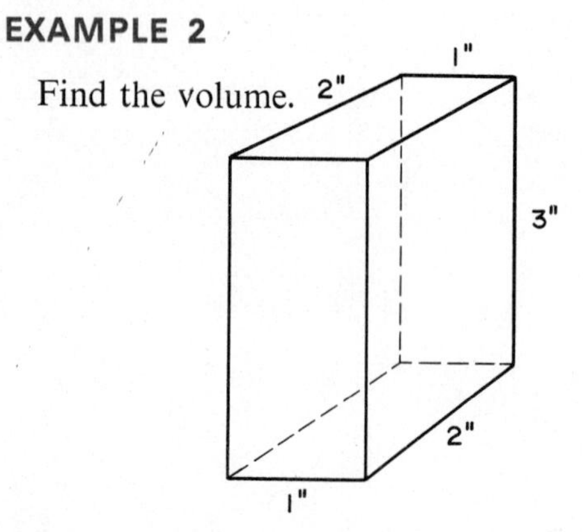

Solution. $V = Bh$

B, area of base,
$= 1 \times 2 = 2$ (sq. in.)
$V = 2 \times 3$
$V =$ **6 (cu. in.)**

EXAMPLE 3

Find the volume of this triangular prism.

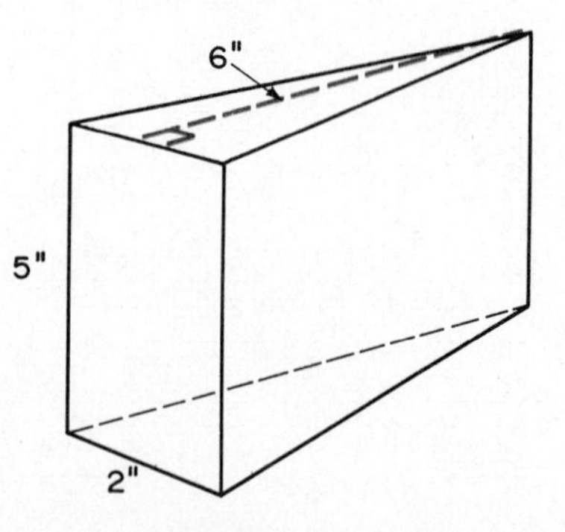

Solution. $V = Bh$

B, area of base, $= \frac{1}{2}bh$
$B = \frac{1}{2}(2)(6) = 6$ (sq. in.)
$V = 6 \times 5$
$V =$ **30 (cu. in.)**

EXERCISES

Find the volume of each of the following right prisms.

A

1. Rectangular prism

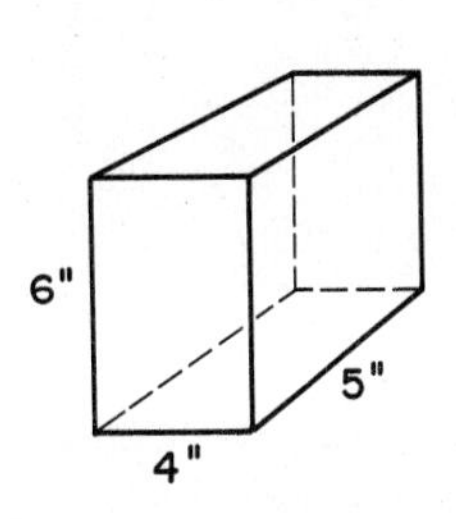

2. Triangular prism

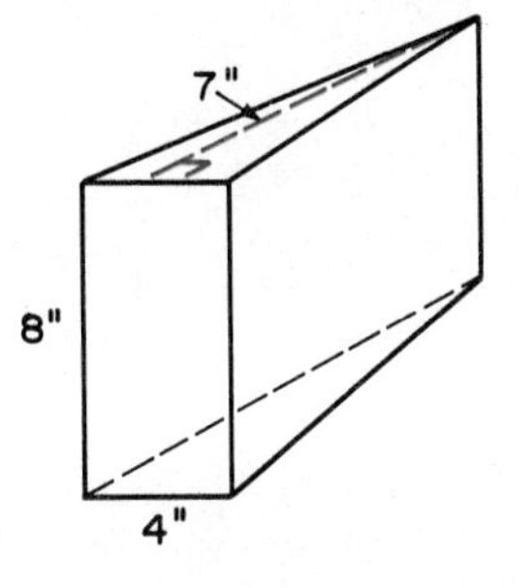

3. Rectangular prism

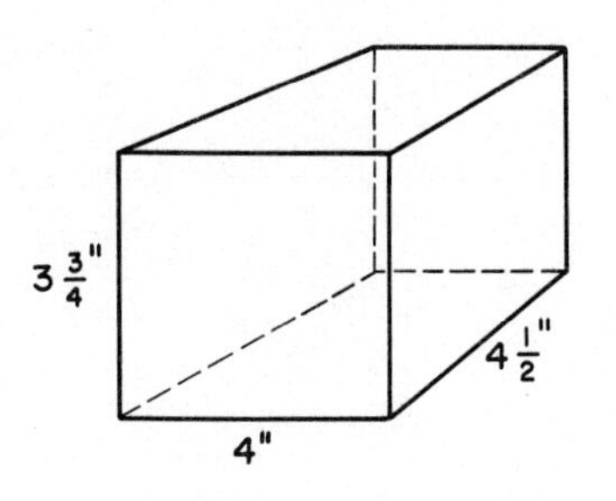

4. Triangular prism

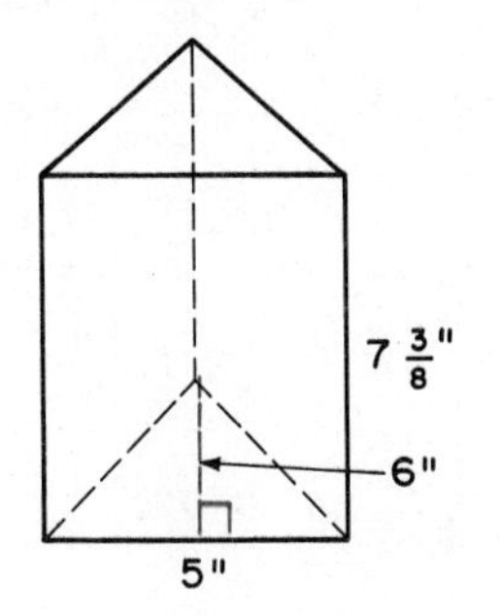

B

5. Hexagonal prism.
   (*ABCDEF* is a regular hexagon.)
   a. Find the volume.
   b. Find the lateral area.
   c. Find the total area.

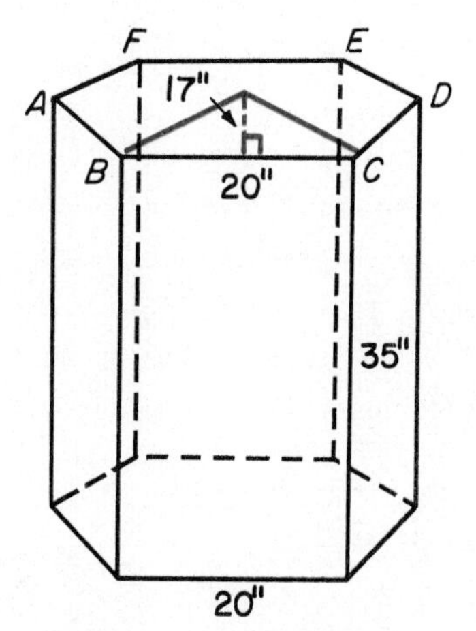

6. A swimming pool is to be 42 ft. long, 20 ft. wide, and have an average depth of 6 ft. If a truck can load 5 cu. yd., how many truckloads of dirt are removed while excavating for the pool? (1 cu. yd. = 27 cu. ft.)

4–7 Pyramids — Area

The **lateral area, L, of a pyramid** is the sum of the areas of the lateral faces.

EXAMPLE 1

Find the lateral area of this pyramid. The base is a square.

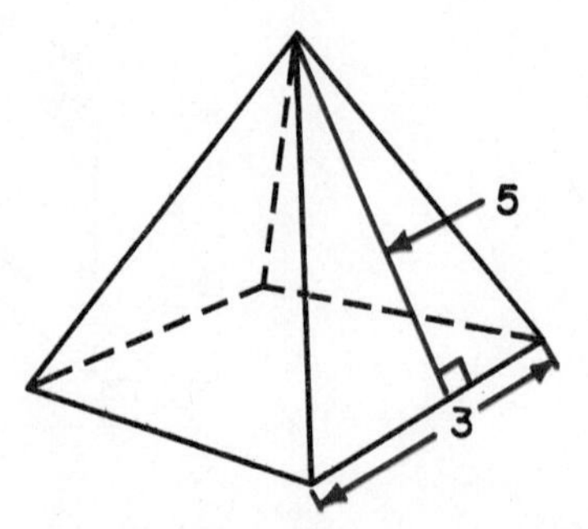

Solution. First find the area of each triangular face.

$A = \frac{1}{2}bh$

$A = \frac{1}{2} \cdot 3 \cdot 5 = \frac{15}{2}$ ← Point out that it is unnecessary to simplify this result since it will be used in the work which follows.

Since all four triangles have the same area,

$L = 4A$

$L = 4 \cdot \frac{15}{2}$

$L = \mathbf{30}$ **(sq. units)**

EXERCISES

Find the lateral area of each pyramid below.

A

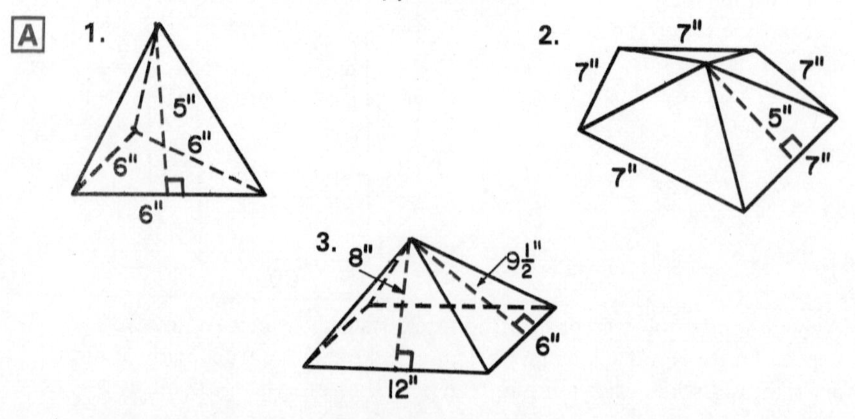

4. Find the lateral area of the shaded portion of the pyramid, if

$$\overline{AB} = \overline{BC} = \overline{AC} = 8'',$$
$$\overline{DE} = \overline{EF} = \overline{DF} = 4'',$$
$$\overline{GH} = 10''$$
$$\overline{GI} = 5''$$

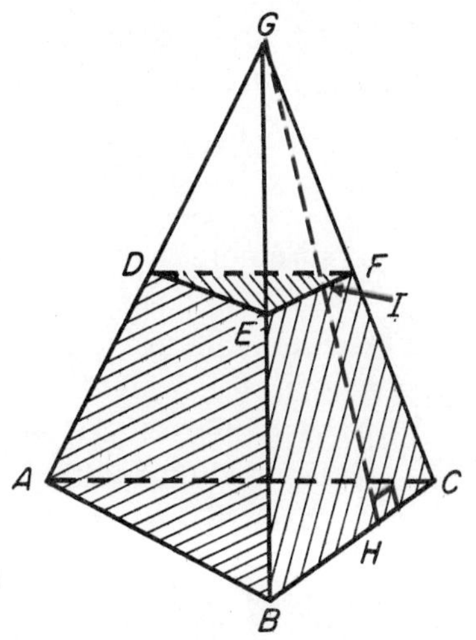

(Hint: Subtract lateral area of smaller pyramid from lateral area of larger pyramid.)

Encourage the students to check their solutions by finding the total area of the shaded trapezoids.

5. Find the lateral area of the figure.

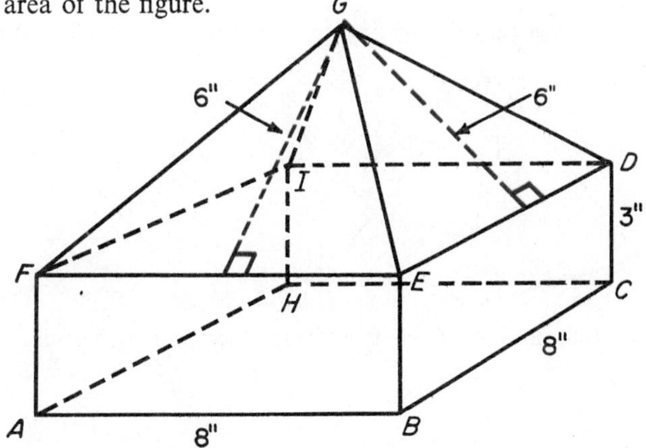

The **total area, S, of a pyramid** is the sum of the areas of the lateral faces, plus the area of the base.

EXAMPLE 2

Find the total area of the pyramid shown. The base is a square.

Solution. The total area is equal to the sum of the lateral areas and the area of the base.

$S = L + B$
$L = 30$ (from Example 1)
$B = 3 \times 3 = 9$
$S = 30 + 9$
$S =$ **39 (sq. units)**

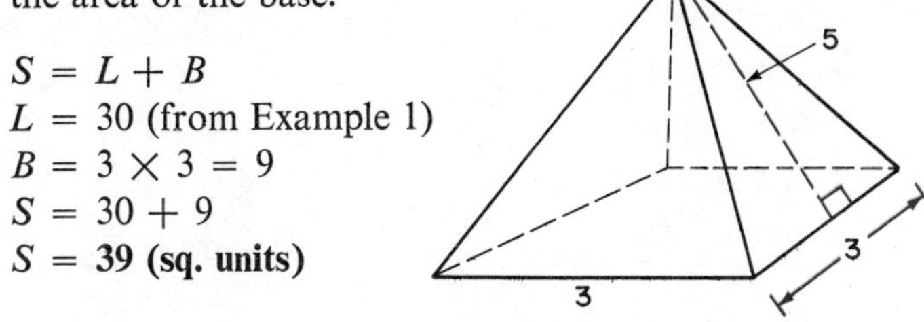

EXAMPLE 3

Find the total area of the regular triangular pyramid shown. This is a tetrahedron.

3.5 4 4 4 4

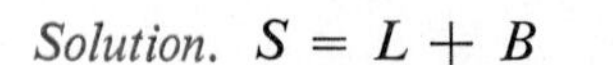

Solution. $S = L + B$

We note that the base has the same dimensions and shape as each lateral face. Hence

$$S = 3[\tfrac{1}{2}(4)(3.5)] + \tfrac{1}{2}(4)(3.5)$$
$$S = 21.0 + 7.0$$
$$S = \mathbf{28.0\ (sq.\ units)}$$

Call attention to the manner of simplification here.

EXERCISES

Find the total area of each pyramid below, if the bases are squares.

A 1.

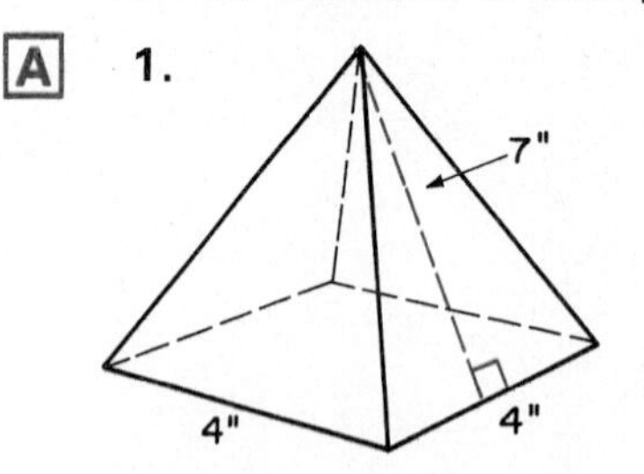

2.

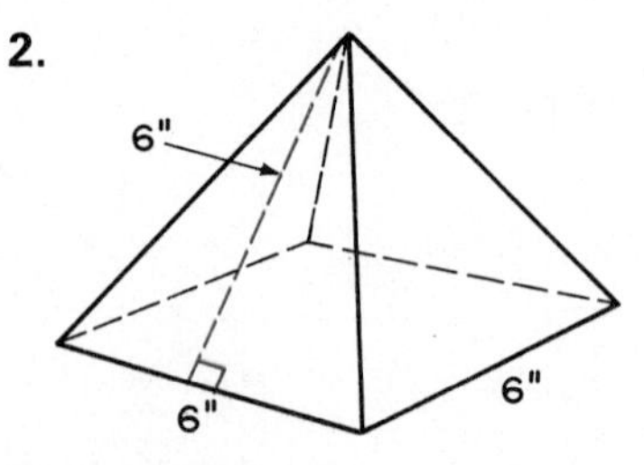

Find the total areas of the regular triangular pyramids.

3.

4.

Find the total areas.

B 5.

6.

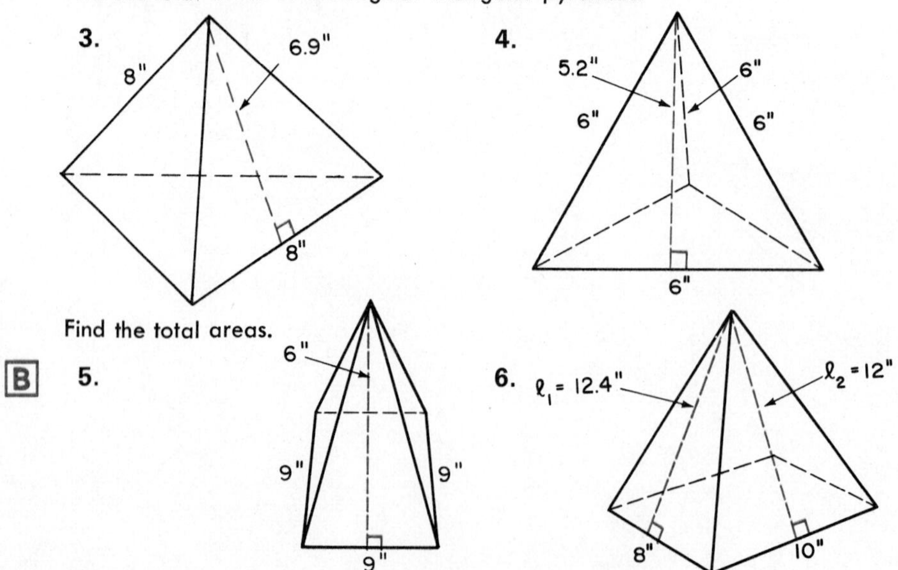

4–8 Pyramids — Volume

The **volume of a pyramid** is equal to one third the product of the area of the base and the length of the altitude.

$$V = \frac{1}{3}Bh$$

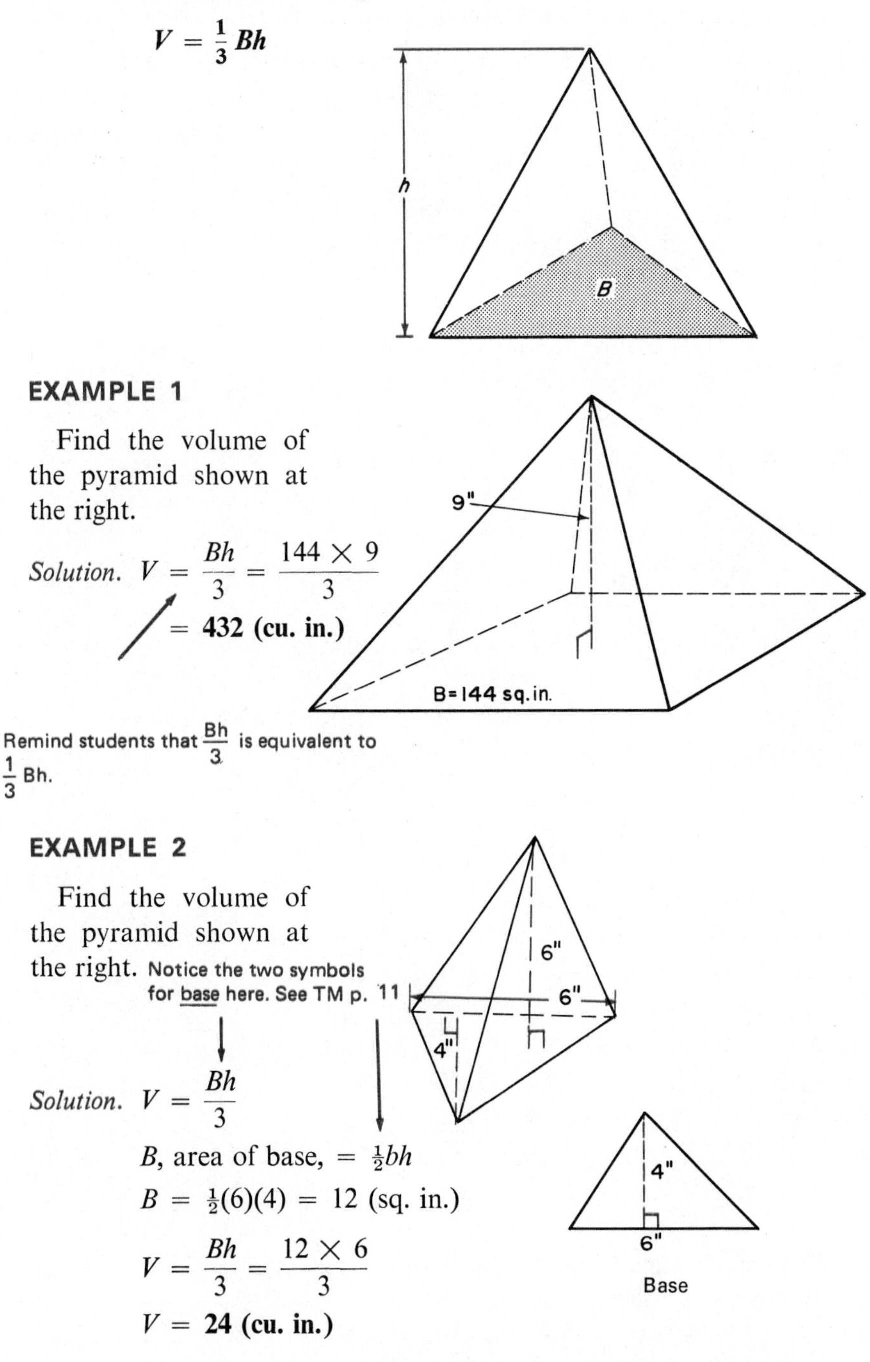

EXAMPLE 1

Find the volume of the pyramid shown at the right.

Solution. $V = \dfrac{Bh}{3} = \dfrac{144 \times 9}{3}$

$= \mathbf{432\ (cu.\ in.)}$

Remind students that $\frac{Bh}{3}$ is equivalent to $\frac{1}{3}$ Bh.

EXAMPLE 2

Find the volume of the pyramid shown at the right. Notice the two symbols for base here. See TM p. 11

Solution. $V = \dfrac{Bh}{3}$

B, area of base, $= \frac{1}{2}bh$

$B = \frac{1}{2}(6)(4) = 12$ (sq. in.)

$V = \dfrac{Bh}{3} = \dfrac{12 \times 6}{3}$

$V = \mathbf{24\ (cu.\ in.)}$

EXERCISES

Find the volumes of the following pyramids.

A

1. Rectangular pyramid

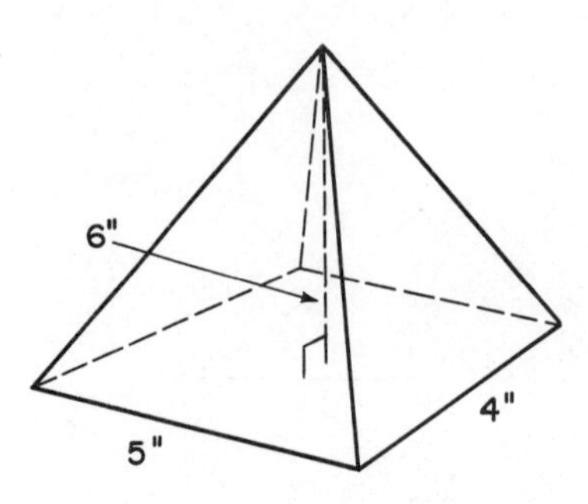

2. Triangular pyramid

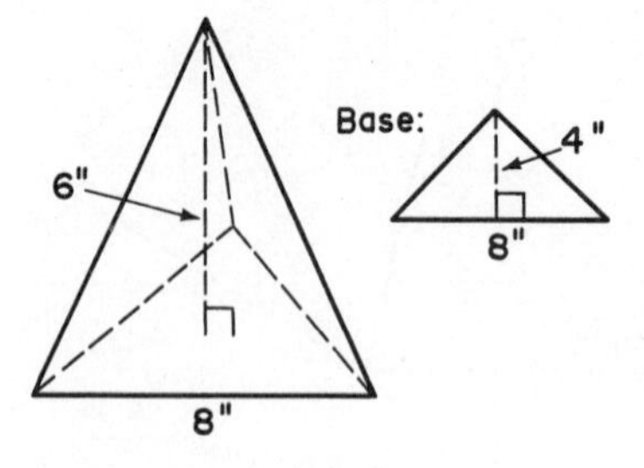

3. Rectangular pyramid

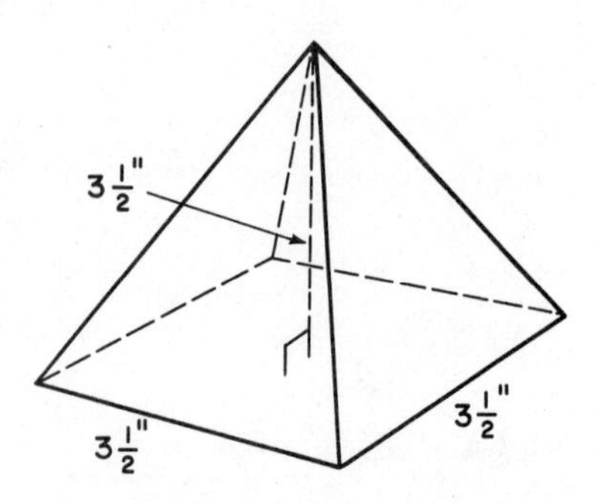

4. Triangular pyramid

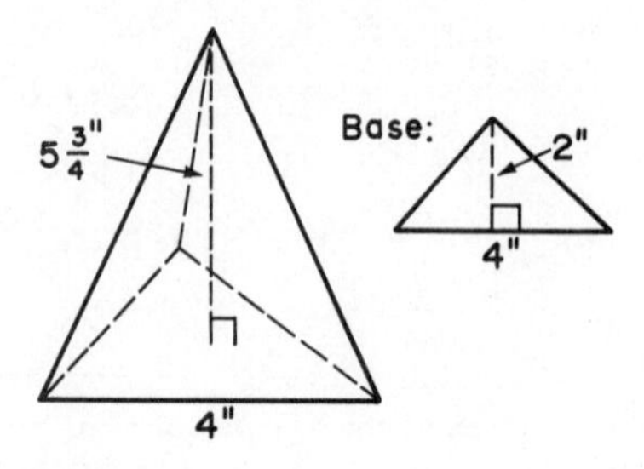

B

5. Regular pentagonal pyramid. (Base is a regular pentagon.)

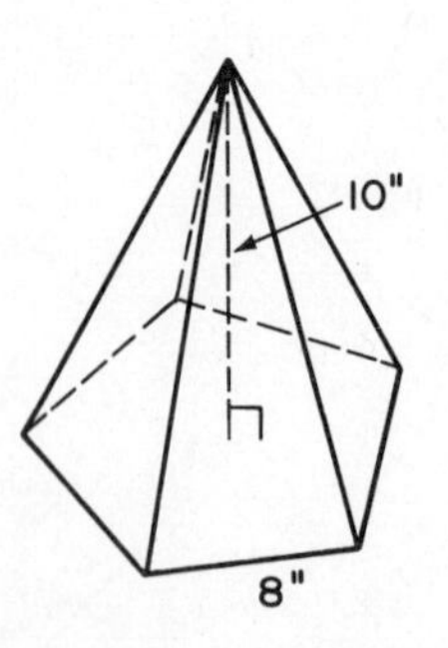

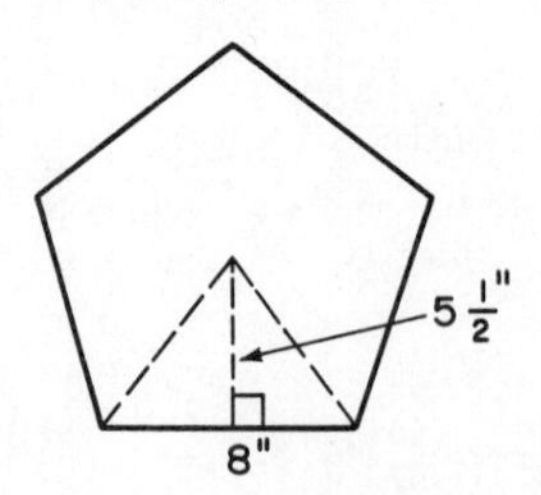

Base: Area of triangle $= \frac{1}{2}bh$
Area of base
$= 5 \times$ area of triangle

6. Find the volume of a pyramid if its altitude is $5\frac{1}{2}''$ and its base is a rhombus with diagonals 8″ and 10″. (Hint: The area of a rhombus is equal to one half the product of its diagonals.)

This formula gives the student a second way of finding the area of a rhombus.

SELF-ANALYSIS TEST II

Time: 30 minutes

1. Find the lateral area of the rectangular prism.

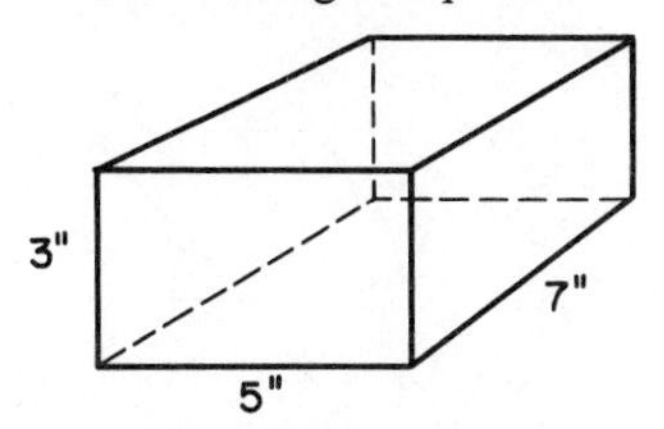

2. Find the lateral area of the rectangular prism.

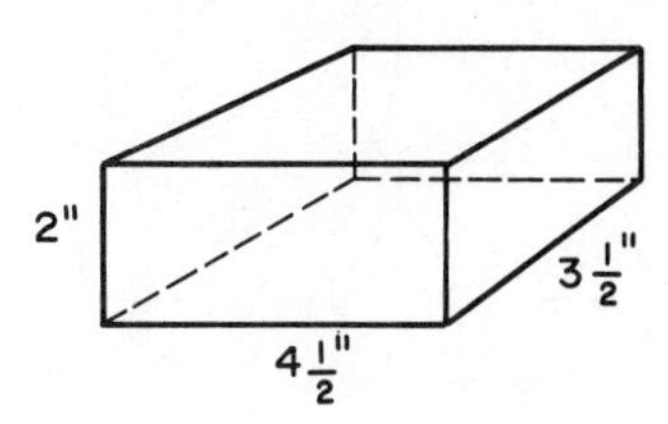

3. Find the total area of the triangular prism.

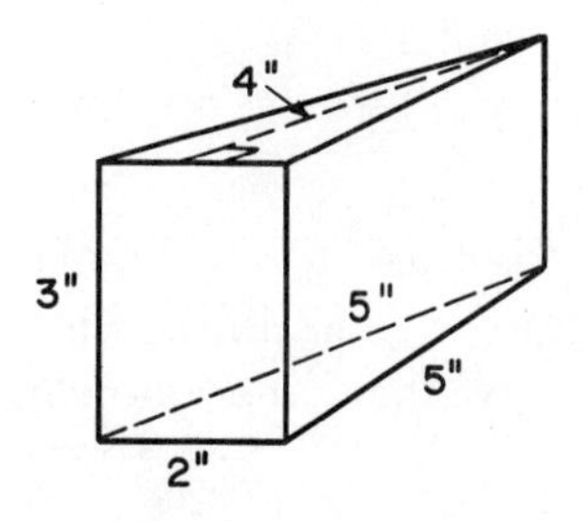

4. Find the total area of the rectangular prism.

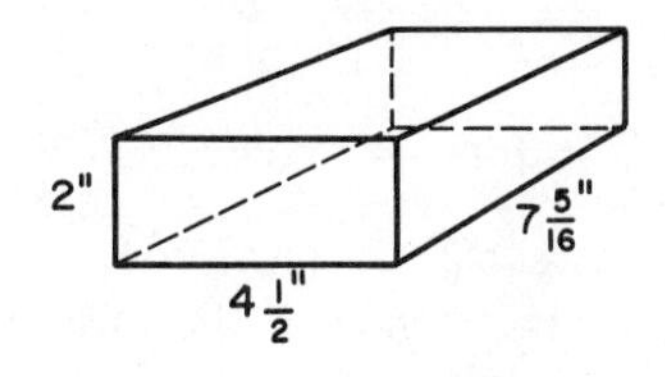

5. Find the volume of the triangular prism.

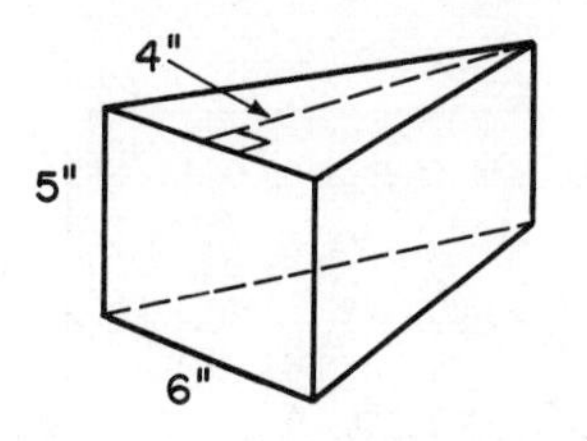

6. Find the volume of the rectangular prism.

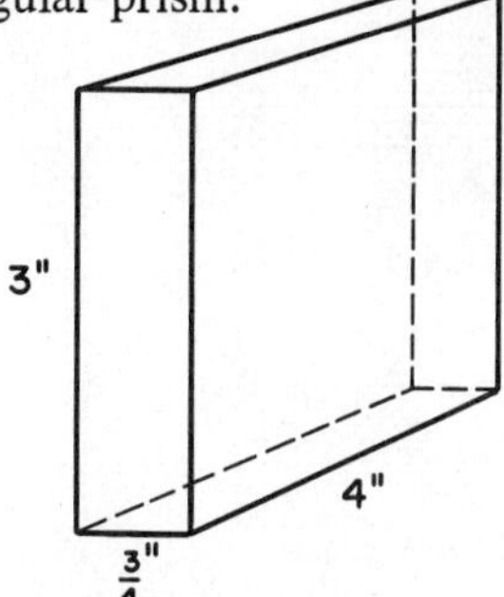

7. Find the lateral area of the regular triangular pyramid.

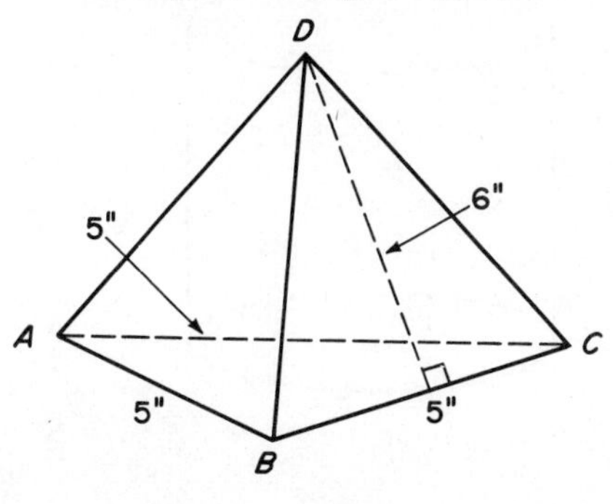

8. Find the lateral area of the rectangular pyramid.

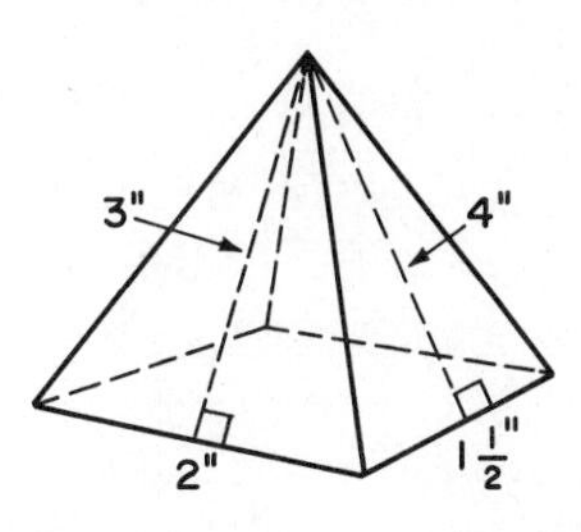

9. Find the total area of the square pyramid.

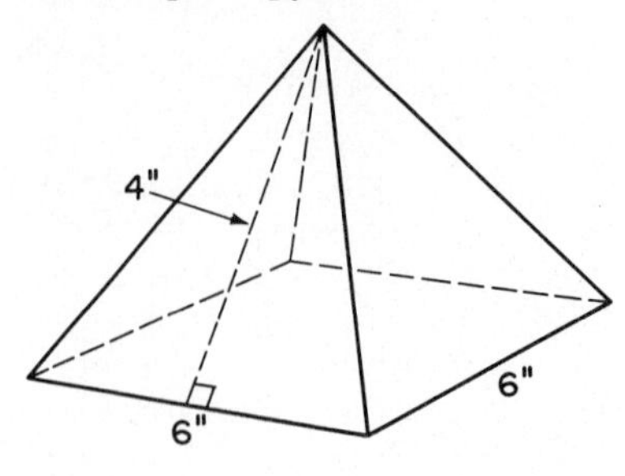

10. Find the volume of the pyramid.

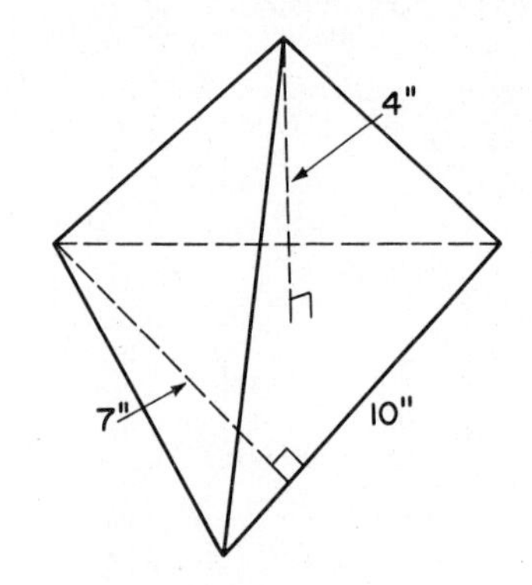

4–9 Cylinders — Area TM p. 12 , 4-9

The **lateral area, L, of a circular cylinder** is equal to the product of the circumference of the base and the length of the altitude. Since the circumference of a circle with radius r is $2\pi r$, we have the following formula for L.

$$\boldsymbol{L = 2\pi rh}$$

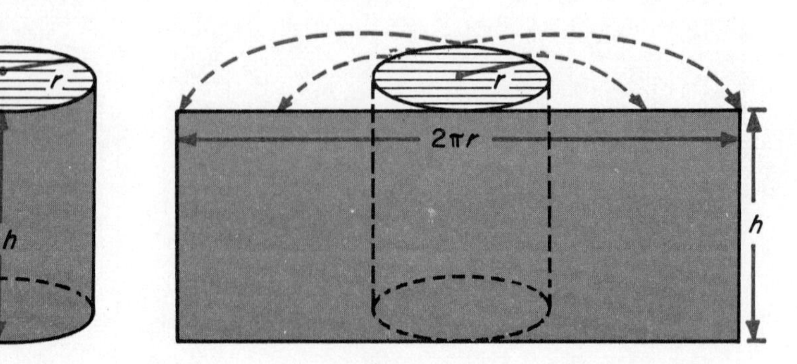

EXAMPLE

Find the lateral area.

Solution. $L = 2\pi rh$
$= 2(\frac{22}{7})(4)(7)$
$= \mathbf{176}$ **(sq. in.)**

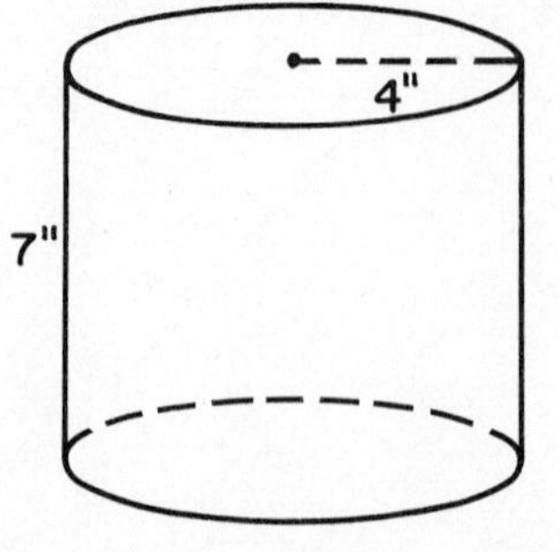

EXERCISES

Find the lateral area of the cylinders in Exercises 1 and 2.

A 1.

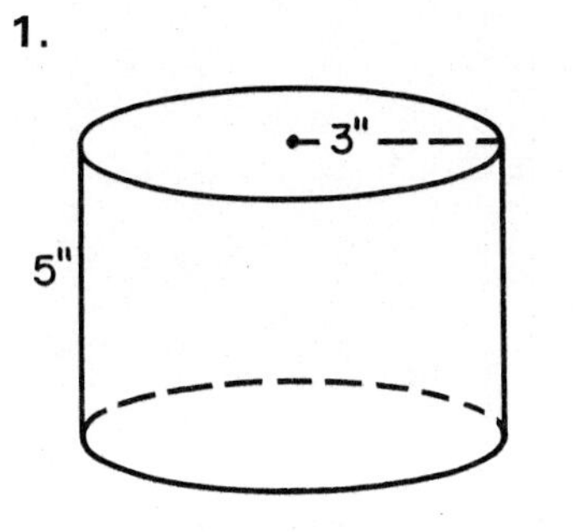

2.

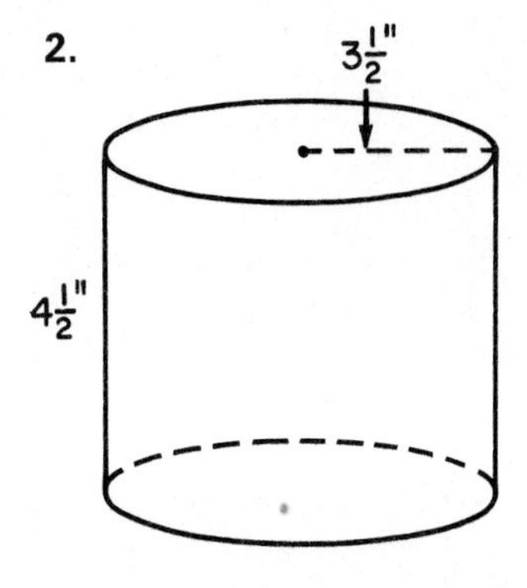

B 3. If $L = 44$ sq. in., find x.

4. Find the combined lateral area of the spool.

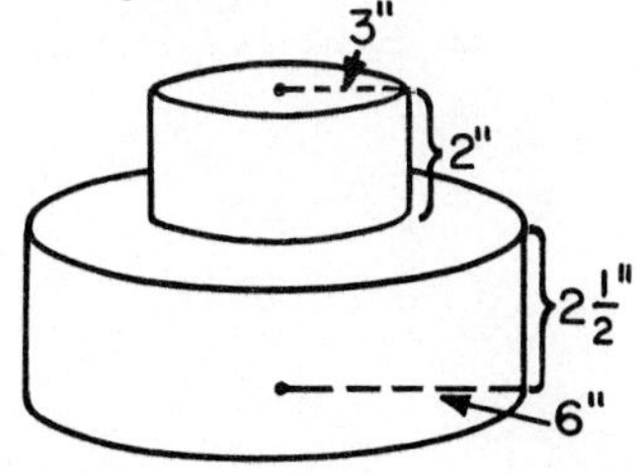

5.

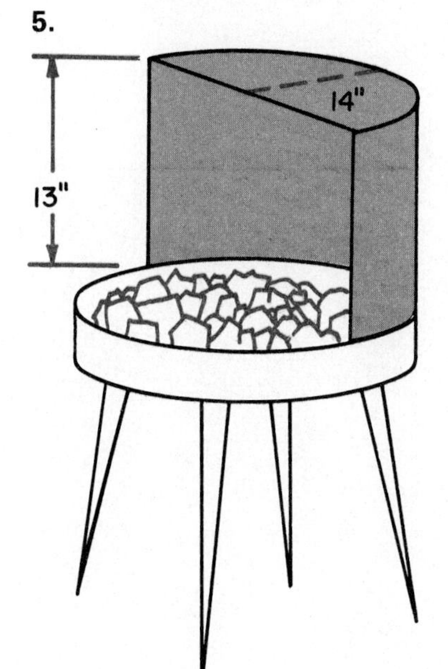

Find the lateral area of the semicircular barbecue hood as illustrated.

6. Find the cost of painting a tank 10 ft. high and 20 ft. in diameter if one gallon of paint costs \$8.00 and covers approximately 250 sq. ft.

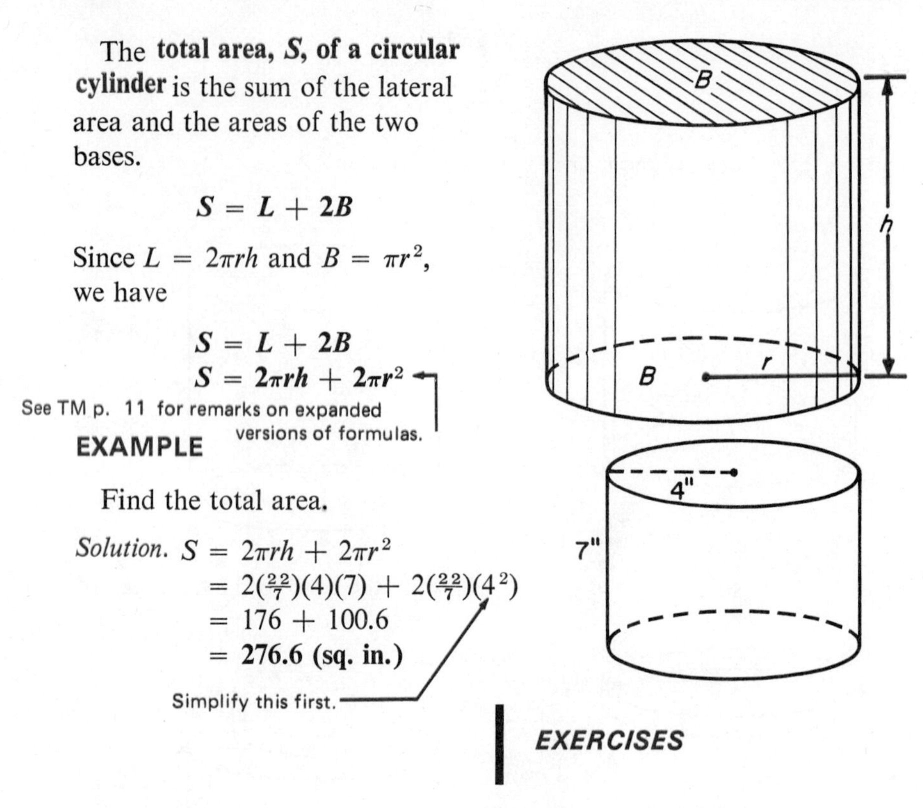

The **total area, S, of a circular cylinder** is the sum of the lateral area and the areas of the two bases.

$$S = L + 2B$$

Since $L = 2\pi rh$ and $B = \pi r^2$, we have

$$S = L + 2B$$
$$S = 2\pi rh + 2\pi r^2$$

See TM p. 11 for remarks on expanded versions of formulas.

EXAMPLE

Find the total area.

Solution. $S = 2\pi rh + 2\pi r^2$

$= 2(\frac{22}{7})(4)(7) + 2(\frac{22}{7})(4^2)$

$= 176 + 100.6$

$= \mathbf{276.6\ (sq.\ in.)}$

Simplify this first.

EXERCISES

Find the total area.

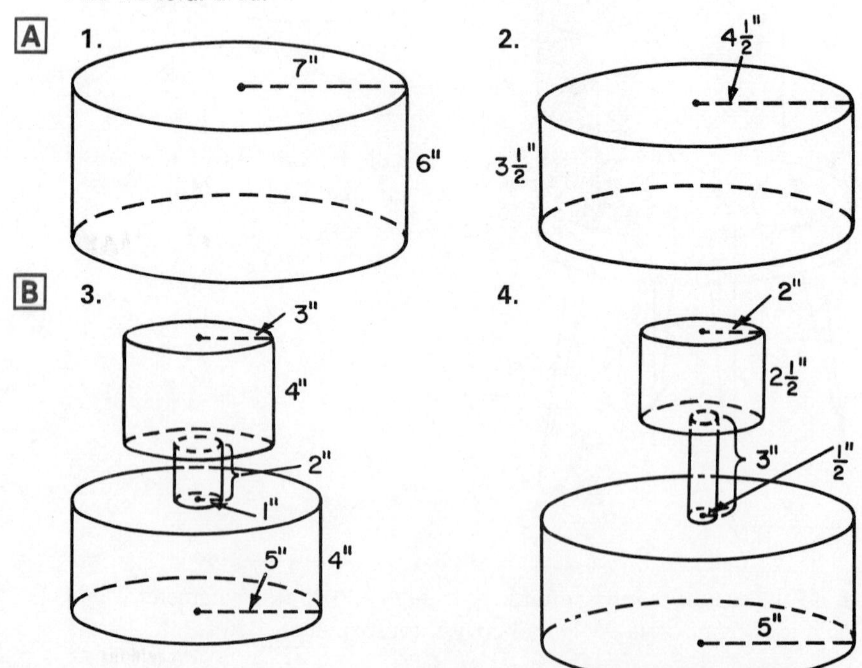

4–10 Cylinders — Volume

The **volume of a circular cylinder** is given by the product of the area of the base and the length of the altitude.

$$V = Bh$$

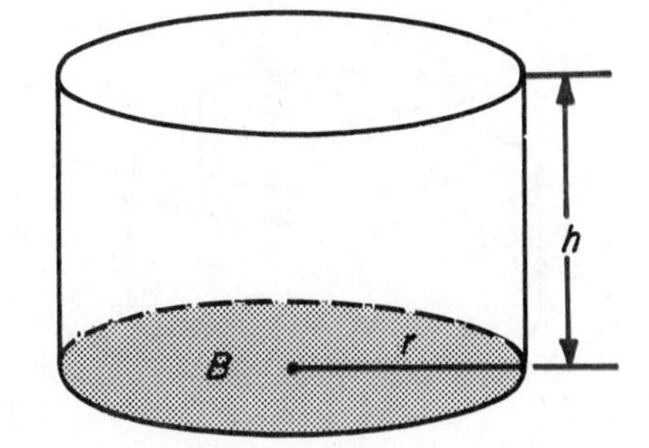

Since $B = \pi r^2$,

$$V = \pi r^2 h$$

EXAMPLE

Find the volume.

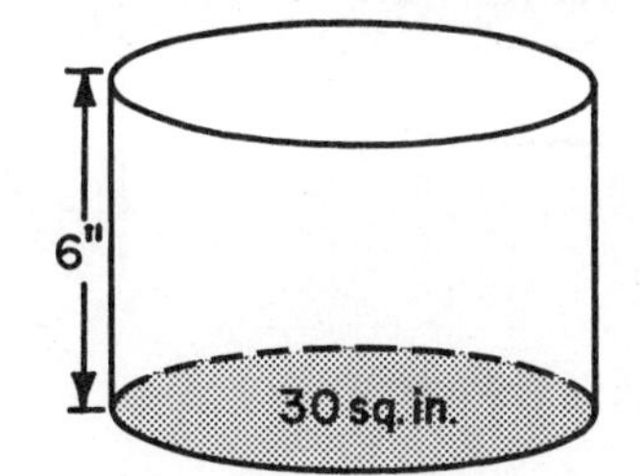

Solution. $V = Bh$
$= 30 \times 6$
$= \mathbf{180}$ **(cu. in.)**

EXERCISES

Find the volume.

A

1.

2.

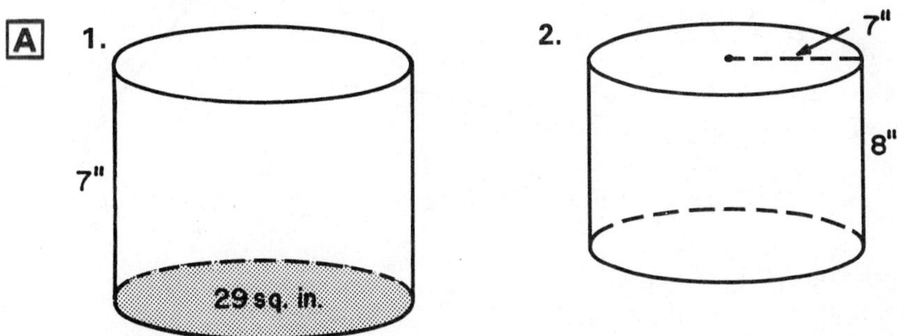

B

3. Find the volume of the steel pipe.

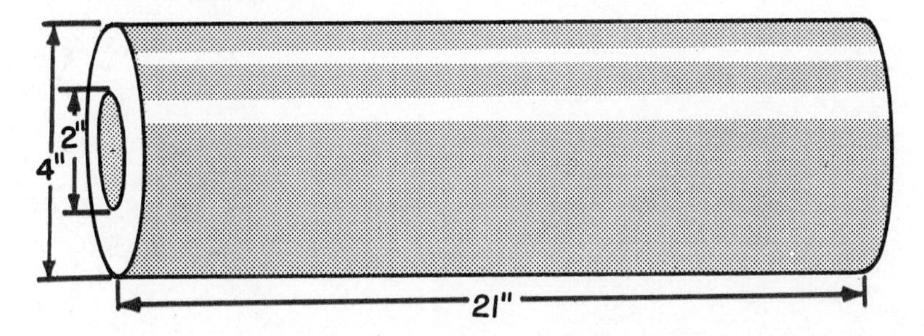

4. Find the volume.

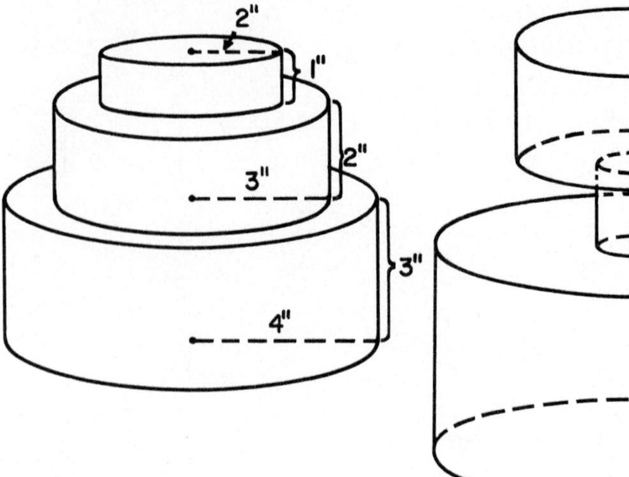

5. Find the volume.

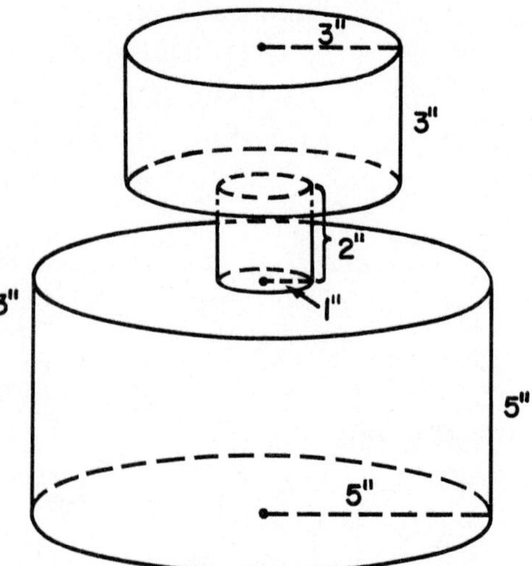

4–11 Cones

The **lateral area, L, of a right circular cone** is equal to one half the product of the circumference of the base and the length of the slant height.

$$L = \frac{1}{2}Cl$$

Since $C = 2\pi r$,
we have $L = \frac{1}{2} \cdot 2\pi rl$
or

$$L = \pi rl$$

The **total area, S, of a right circular cone** is the sum of the lateral area and the area of the base.

$$S = L + B$$

or

$$S = \pi rl + \pi r^2$$

See TM p. 11 for discussion of expanded version of formulas.

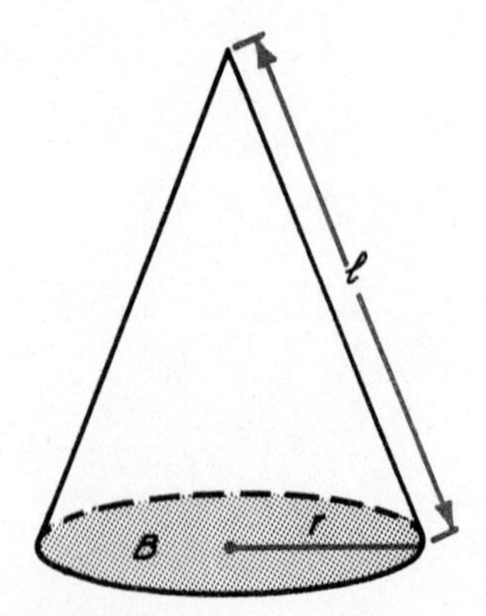

The **volume of a right circular cone** is equal to one third the product of the area of the base and the length of the altitude.

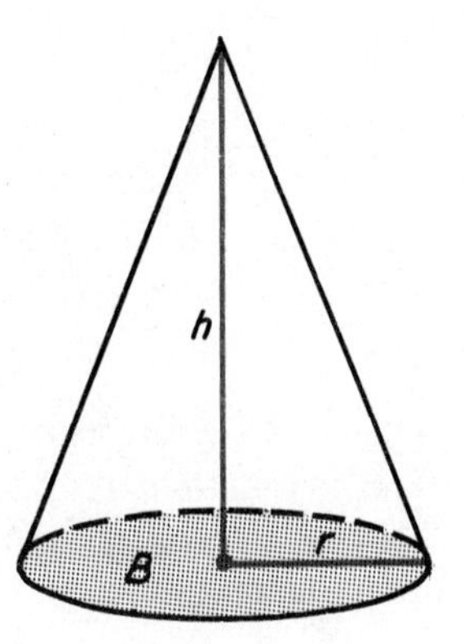

$$V = \frac{1}{3} Bh$$

Since $B = \pi r^2$,

$$V = \frac{1}{3} \pi r^2 h$$

EXAMPLE 1

Find the lateral area of a right circular cone if $r = 2''$ and $l = 7''$.

Solution. $L = \pi r l$

$L = (\frac{22}{7})(2)(7)$

$L = \mathbf{44}$ **(sq. in.)**

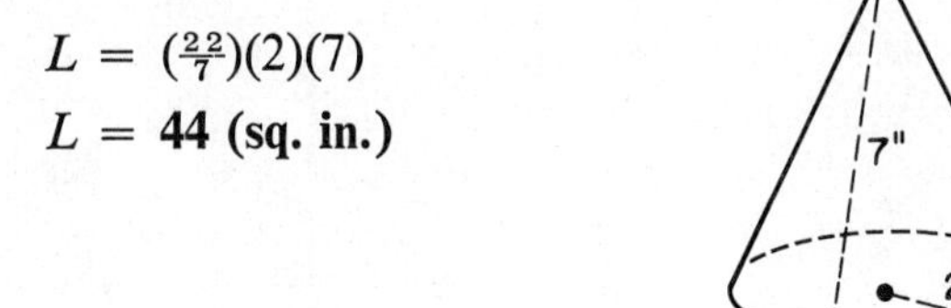

EXAMPLE 2

Find the total area of a right circular cone with $r = 4''$, $l = 14''$.

Solution. $S = \pi r l + \pi r^2$

$S = (\frac{22}{7})(4)(14) + (\frac{22}{7})(4)(4)$

$S = 176 + 50.3$

$S = \mathbf{226.3}$ **(sq. in.)**

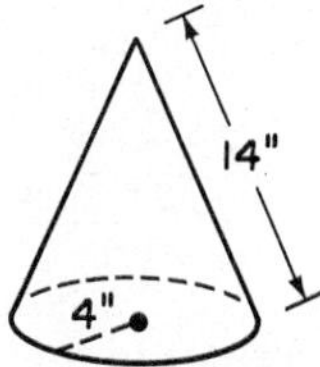

EXAMPLE 3

Find the volume of a right circular cone if $r = 10''$ and $h = 7''$.

Solution. $V = \frac{1}{3}\pi r^2 h$

$V = \frac{1}{3}(\frac{22}{7})(10)(10)(7)$

$V = \frac{2200}{3}$

$V = \mathbf{733.3}$ **(cu. in.)**

EXERCISES

For each of the following exercises, draw a cone, label its dimensions, and solve for the required information.
(All cones referred to are right circular cones.)

A

1. The lateral area of a cone with $r = 4''$ and $l = 14''$.
2. The lateral area of a cone with $r = 3.5''$ and $l = 12''$.
3. The total area of a cone with $r = 6.3''$ and $l = 12''$.
4. The volume of a cone with $r = 5''$ and $h = 21''$.
5. The volume of a cone with $r = 3.5''$ and $h = 9''$.

4–12 Spheres

A **sphere** is a solid figure all points of which are the same distance from a given point, its center. Ball bearings and golf balls are examples of spheres.

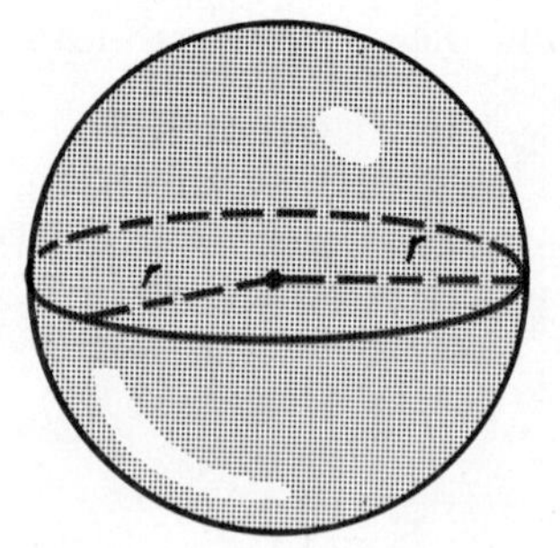

The **area of a sphere** is equal to four times the product of π and the length of the radius squared.

$$S = 4\pi r^2$$

EXAMPLE 1

Find the area of this sphere.

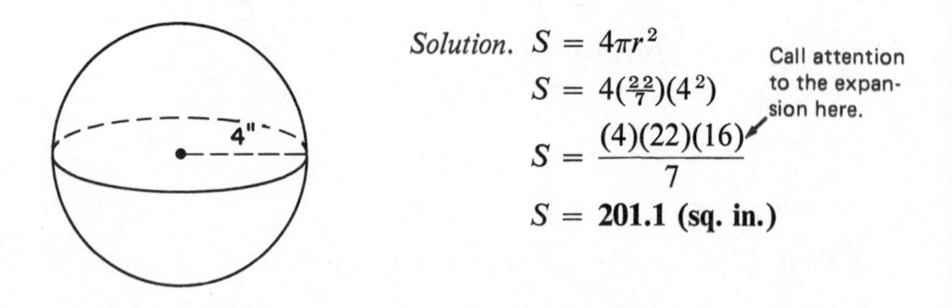

Solution. $S = 4\pi r^2$

$S = 4(\frac{22}{7})(4^2)$

$S = \frac{(4)(22)(16)}{7}$

$S = \mathbf{201.1}$ **(sq. in.)**

Call attention to the expansion here.

The **volume of a sphere** is equal to $\frac{4}{3}$ the product of π and the length of the radius cubed.

$$V = \frac{4}{3}\pi r^3$$

Remind students that this means the radius will be used as a factor three times.

EXAMPLE 2

Find the volume of this sphere.

Explain that the 3-inch radius is being cubed.

Solution. $V = \frac{4}{3}\pi r^3$
$V = (\frac{4}{3})(\frac{22}{7})(3)(3)(3)$
$V = \mathbf{113.1}$ **(cu. in.)**

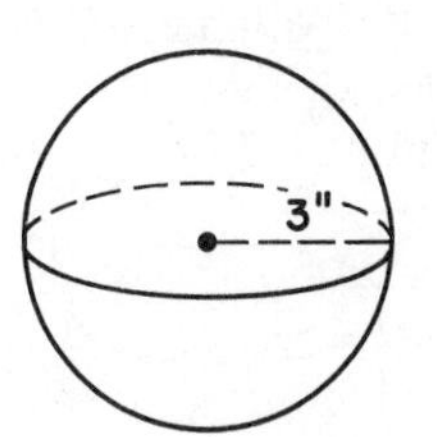

EXERCISES

Find the area and volume of each figure below.

A 1. 2. 3.

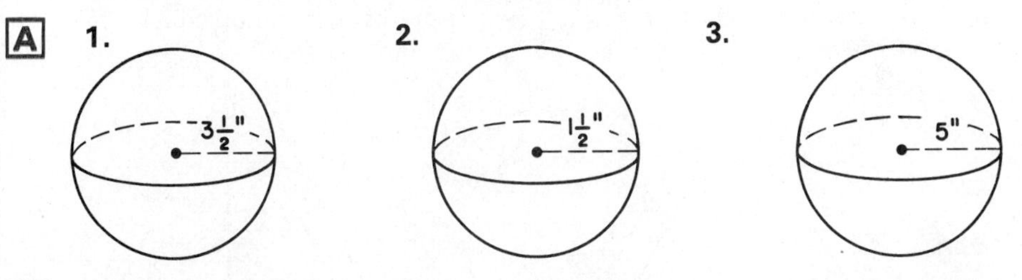

B 4. Find the area and volume of a barbell if each ball has a radius of $2\frac{1}{2}''$ and the diameter of the 4″ bar is 1″. (Consider the bar to be a cylinder, and the balls to be spheres.)

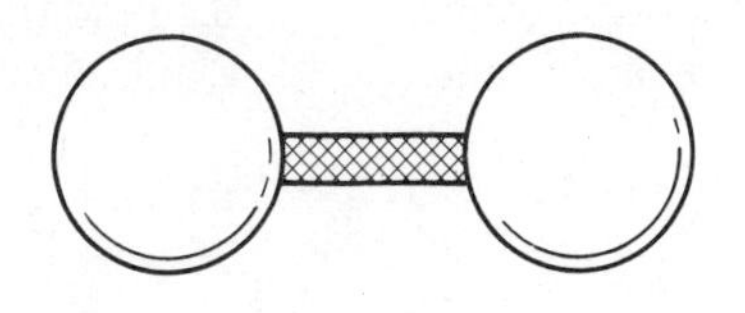

SELF-ANALYSIS TEST III

Time: 30 minutes

1. Find the lateral area of this right circular cylinder if $r = 2''$ and $h = 7''$.

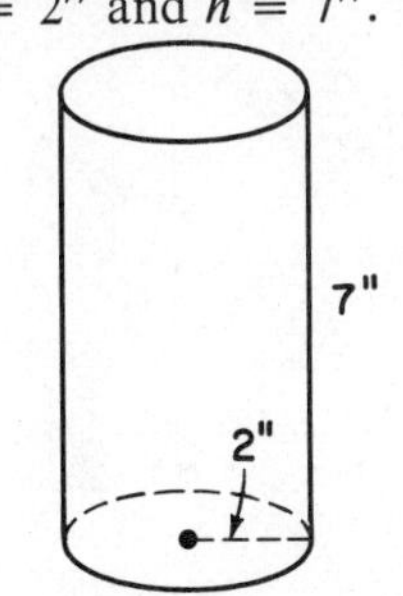

2. Find the total area of this right circular cylinder if $r = 14''$ and $h = 10''$.

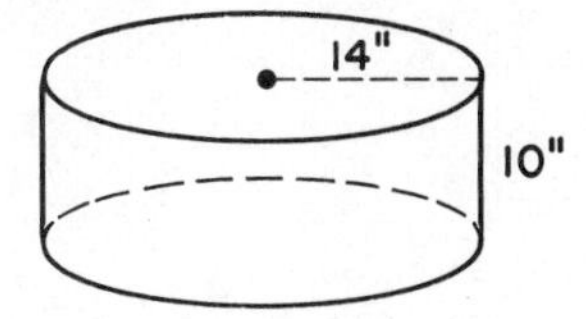

3. Find the volume of the right circular cylinder if $B = 20$ sq. in. and $h = 7$ in.

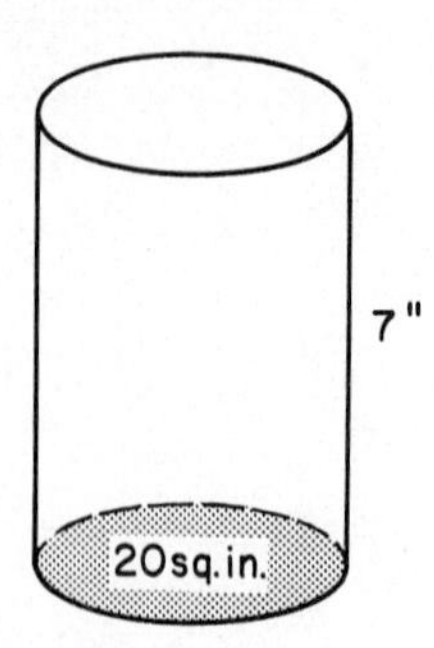

4. Find the volume of the right circular cylinder if $r = 21'$ and $h = 30'$.

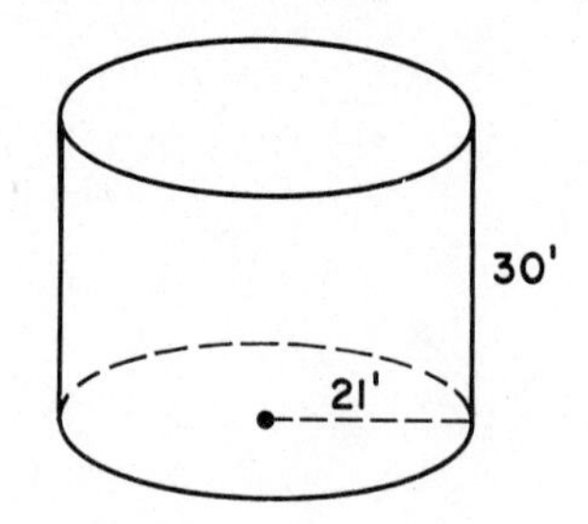

5. Find the lateral area of the right circular cone if $r = 3''$ and $l = 5''$.

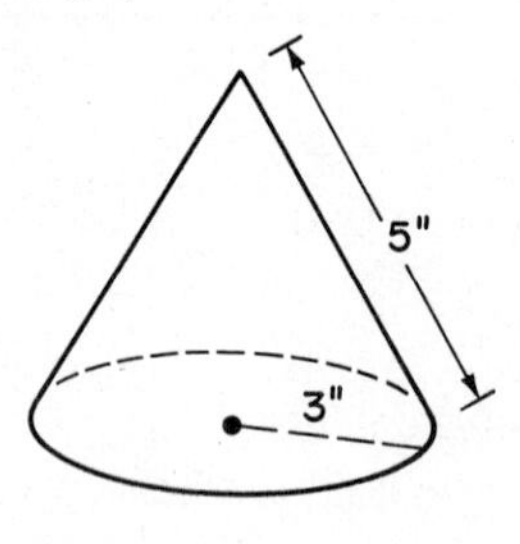

6. Find the lateral area of the right circular cone if $r = 3\frac{1}{8}''$ and $l = 6''$.

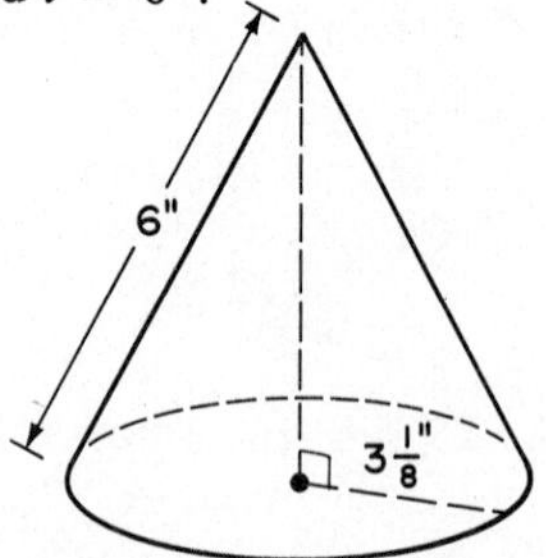

7. Find the total area of the right circular cone if $r = 7''$ and $l = 16''$.

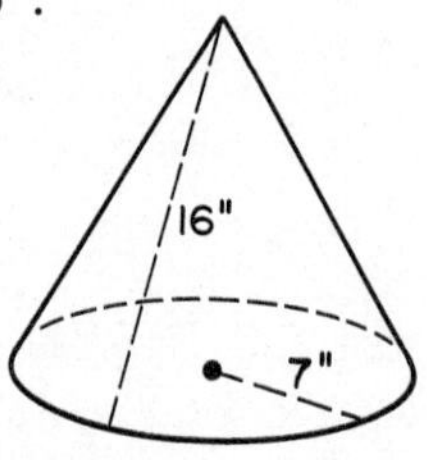

8. Find the total area of the right circular cone if $r = 2\frac{3}{4}''$ and $l = 6''$.

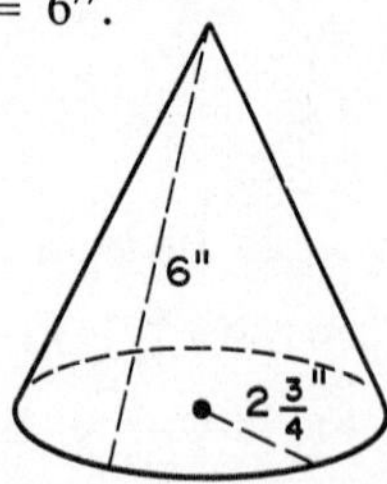

9. Find the volume of the right circular cone if $r = 3\frac{1}{2}''$ and $h = 12''$.

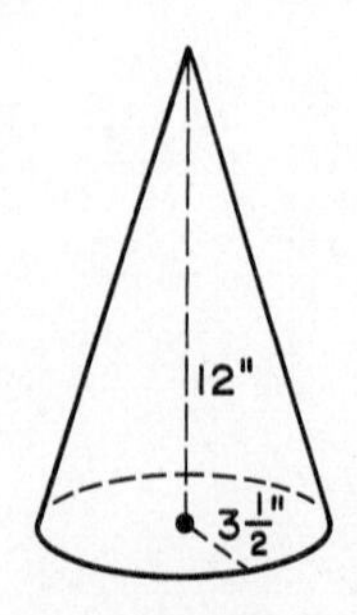

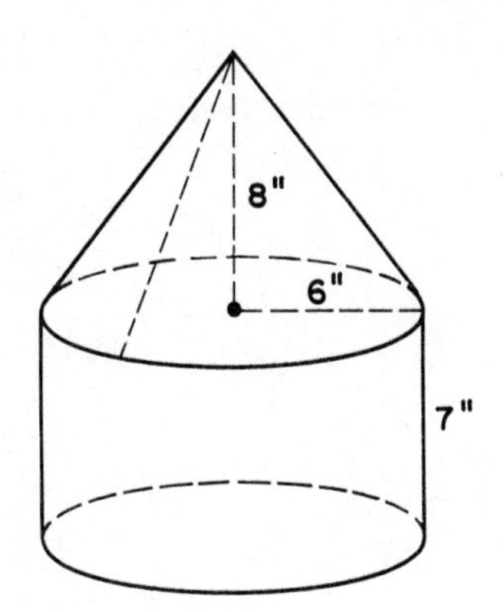

10. Find the volume of the right circular cylinder and cone at the right if $r = 6''$, the height of the cone equals $8''$, and the height of the cylinder equals $7''$.

11. Find the area of a sphere with a radius of $20'$.

12. Find the area of a sphere with a radius of $10\frac{1}{2}'$.

13. Find the volume of a sphere with a radius of $4'$.

14. Find the volume of a sphere with a radius of $2\frac{1}{2}''$.

CHAPTER SUMMARY

1. PLANE FIGURES

Notation

A area

$a, b, c, \ldots$ sides

b base

C circumference

h height or altitude

$\pi(\text{pi}) = \frac{22}{7}$

P perimeter

r radius

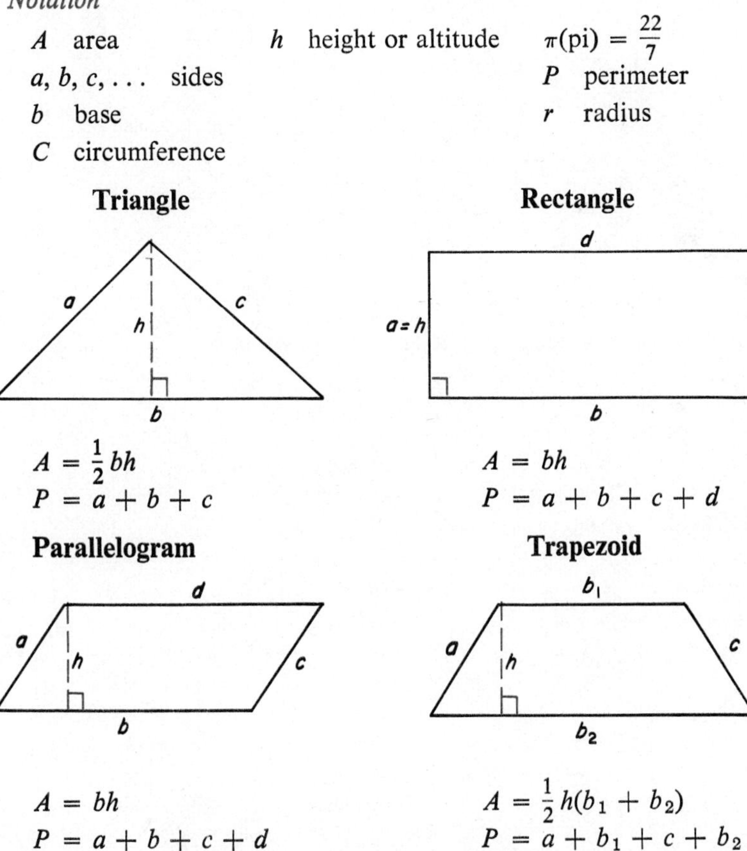

Triangle

$A = \frac{1}{2} bh$

$P = a + b + c$

Rectangle

$A = bh$

$P = a + b + c + d$

Parallelogram

$A = bh$

$P = a + b + c + d$

Trapezoid

$A = \frac{1}{2} h(b_1 + b_2)$

$P = a + b_1 + c + b_2$

Circle

$C = 2\pi r$
$A = \pi r^2$

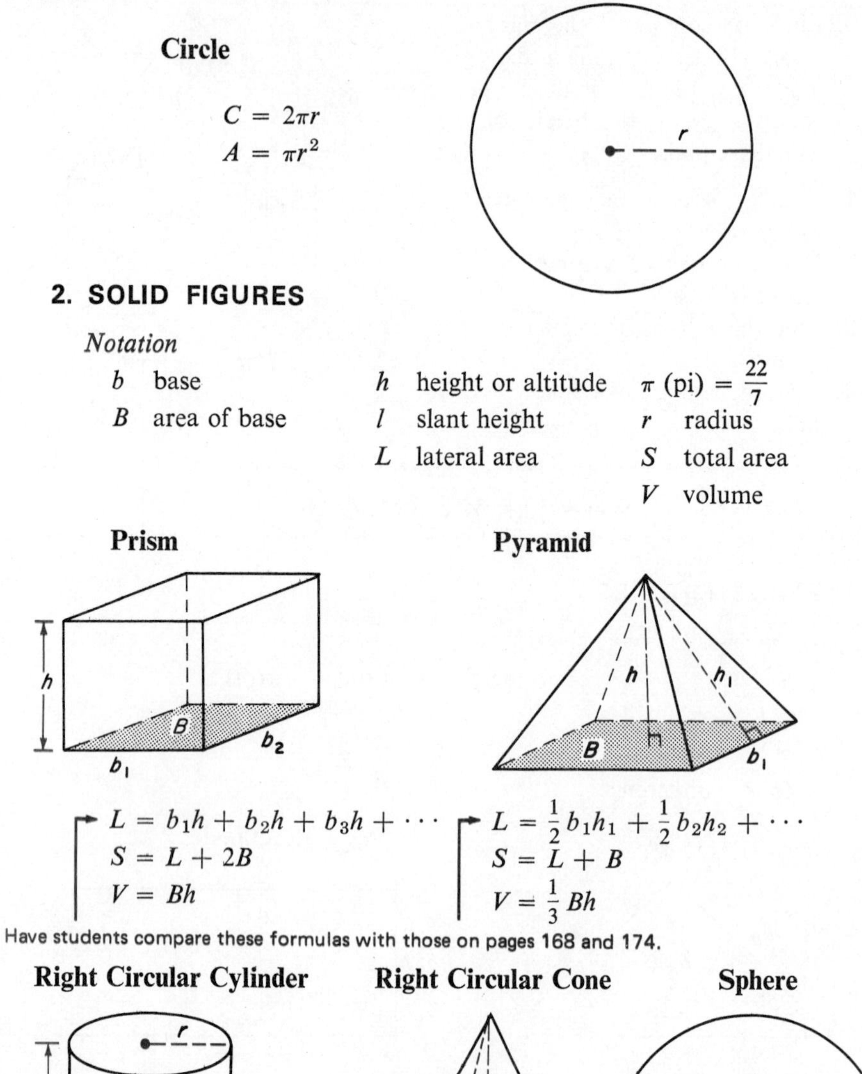

2. SOLID FIGURES

Notation

b	base	h	height or altitude	π (pi) $= \frac{22}{7}$	
B	area of base	l	slant height	r	radius
		L	lateral area	S	total area
				V	volume

Prism

$L = b_1h + b_2h + b_3h + \cdots$
$S = L + 2B$
$V = Bh$

Pyramid

$L = \frac{1}{2}b_1h_1 + \frac{1}{2}b_2h_2 + \cdots$
$S = L + B$
$V = \frac{1}{3}Bh$

Have students compare these formulas with those on pages 168 and 174.

Right Circular Cylinder

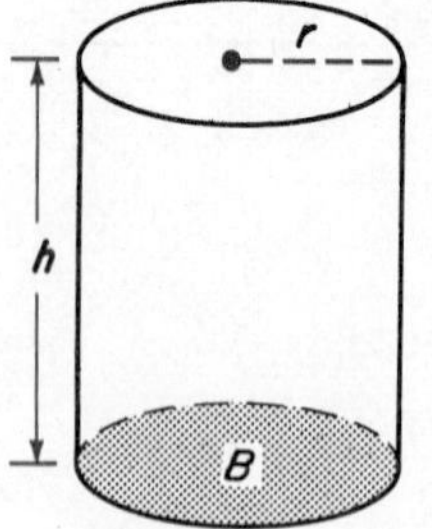

$L = 2\pi rh$
$S = 2\pi rh + 2\pi r^2$
$V = \pi r^2h$ or Bh

Right Circular Cone

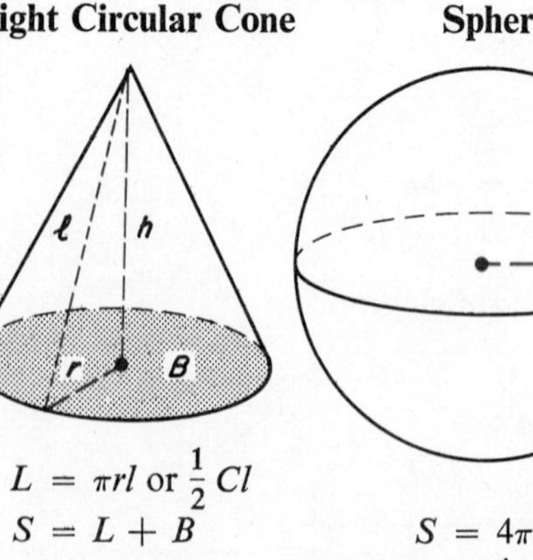

$L = \pi rl$ or $\frac{1}{2}Cl$
$S = L + B$
$S = \pi rl + \pi r^2$
$V = \frac{1}{3}\pi r^2h$

Sphere

$S = 4\pi r^2$
$V = \frac{4}{3}\pi r^3$

CHAPTER TEST

Find the areas of the geometric figures in Exercises 1–4.

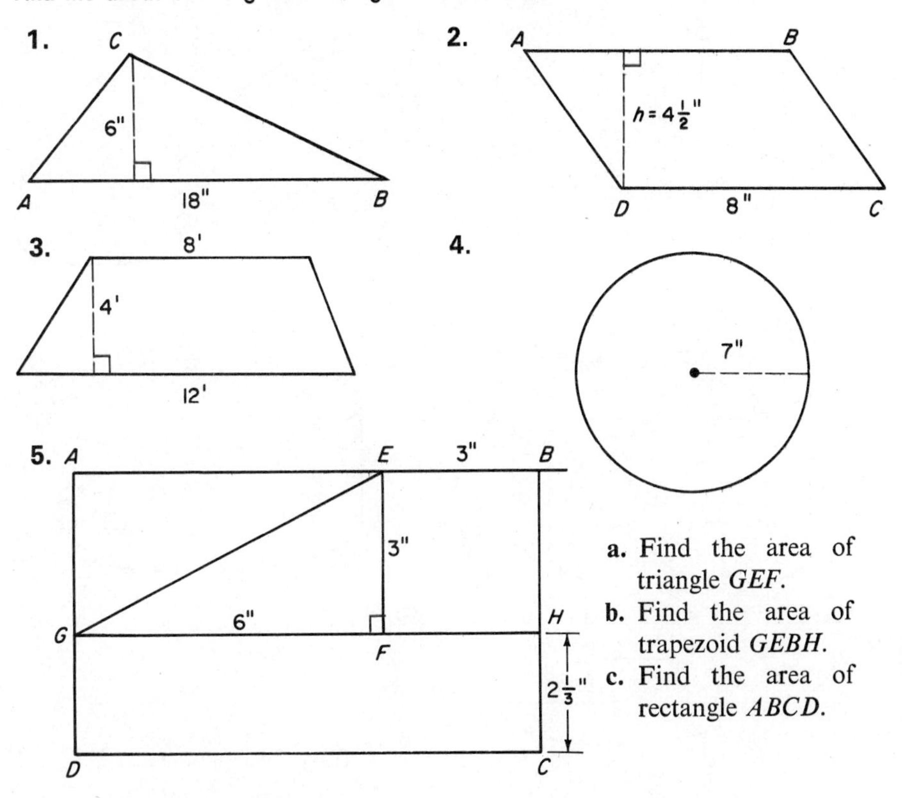

a. Find the area of triangle *GEF*.
b. Find the area of trapezoid *GEBH*.
c. Find the area of rectangle *ABCD*.

6. Find the lateral area of the following rectangular prism.

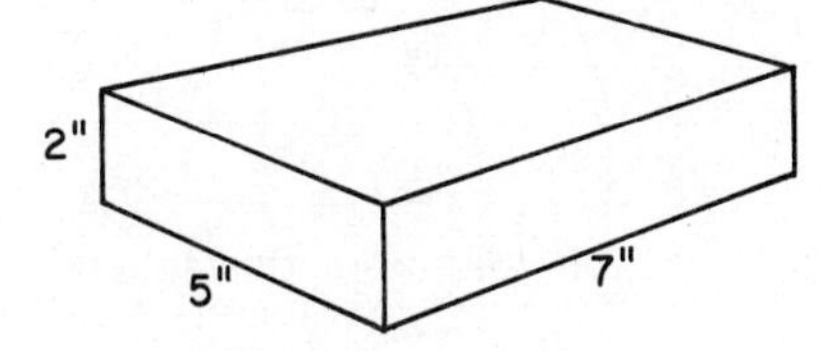

7. Find the total area of this prism.

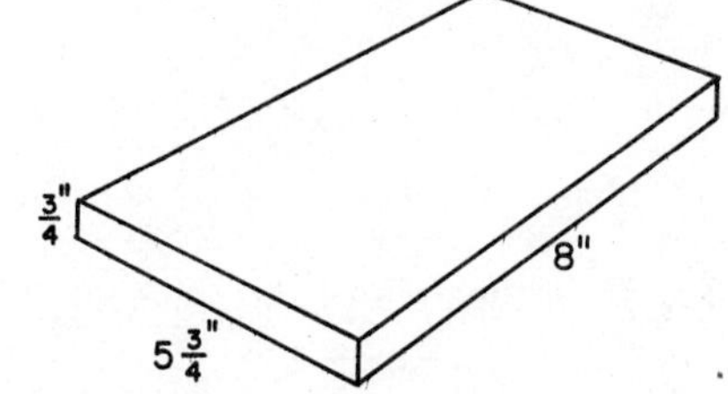

8. Find the volume.

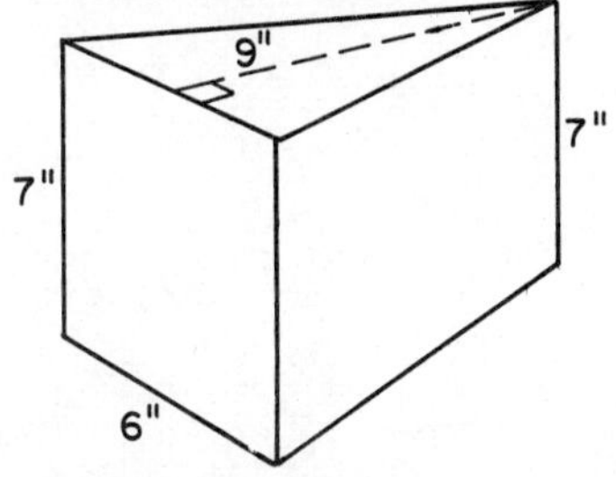

9. Find the lateral area of this pyramid; its base is a square.

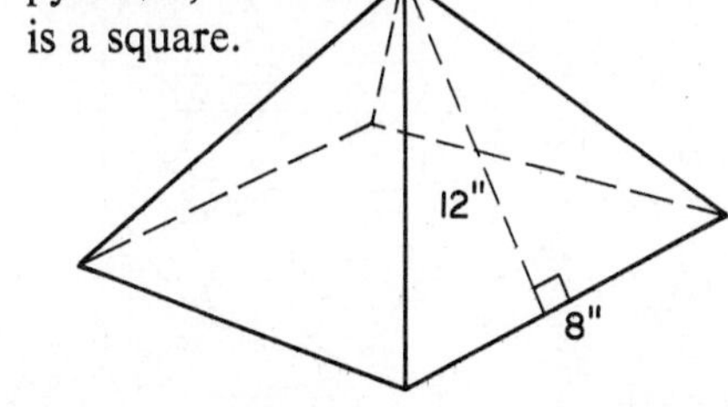

10. Find the total area of the pyramid if the base is an equilateral triangle and all faces are alike.

11. Find the volume of this pyramid; the base is a rectangle.

12. Find the lateral area.

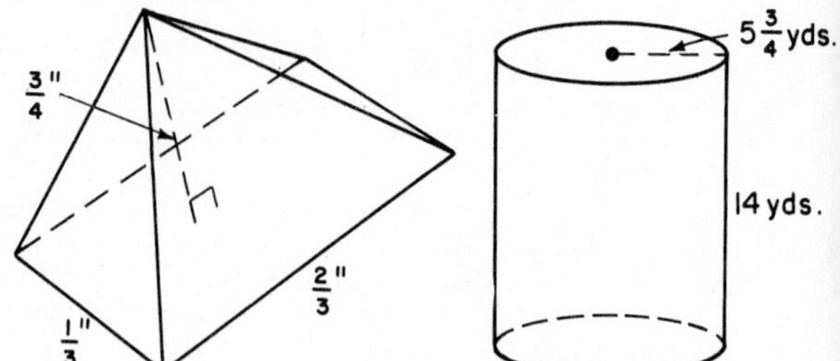

13. Find the total area of the cylinder.

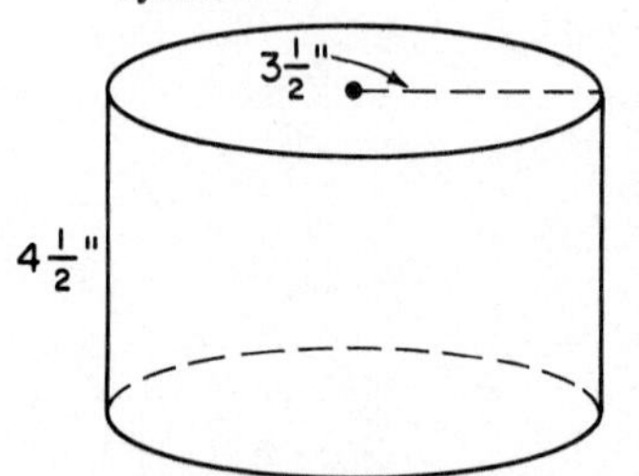

14. Find the volume of the cylinder.

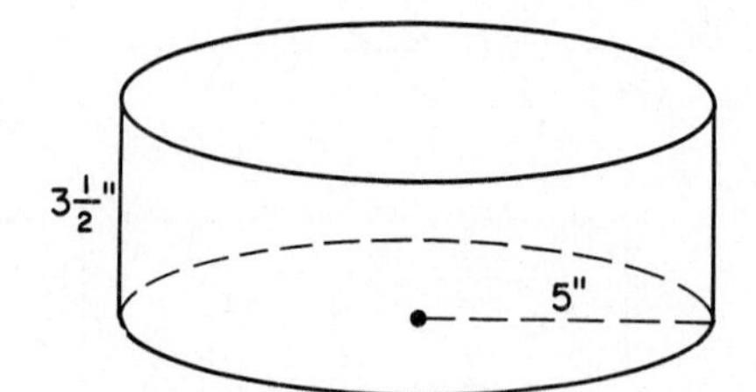

15. Find the lateral area of the cone.

$r = 21''$
$l = 40''$

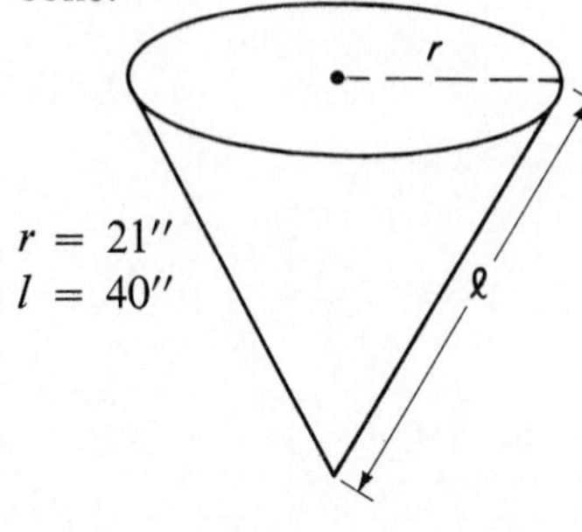

16. Find the volume of the cone.

$h = 48''$
$r = 7''$

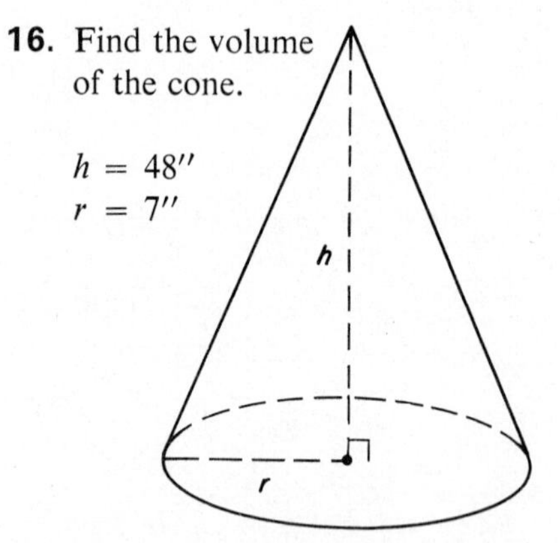

17. Find the area of the sphere.

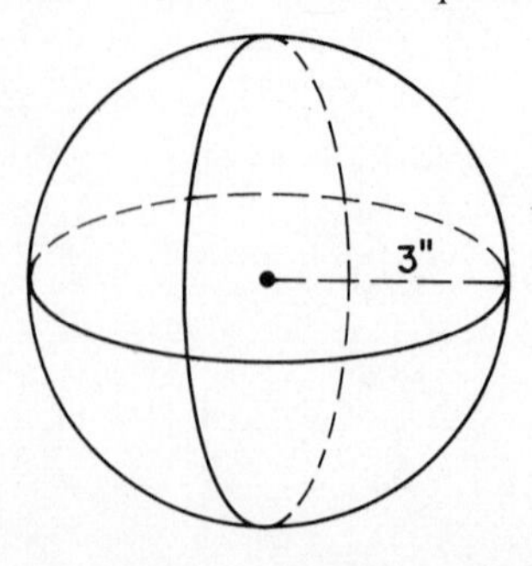

18. Find the volume of this sphere.

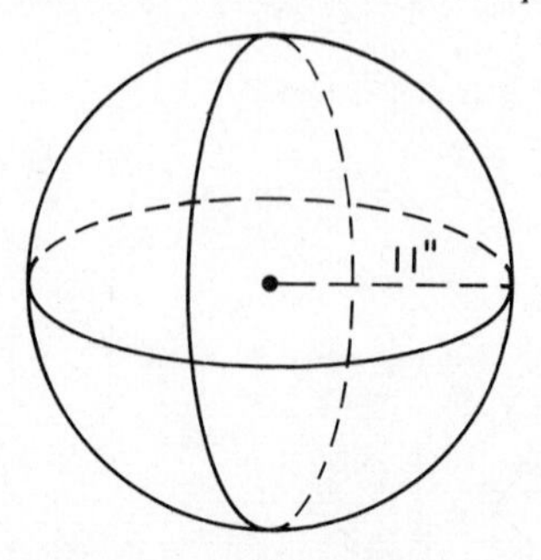

MAINTAINING YOUR SKILLS

Add.

1. $\begin{array}{r} 86 \\ +\ 33 \\ \hline \end{array}$

2. $\begin{array}{r} 45 \\ 93 \\ +\ 84 \\ \hline \end{array}$

3. $\begin{array}{r} 630 \\ 655 \\ 720 \\ +\ 935 \\ \hline \end{array}$

4. $\begin{array}{r} 278 \\ 4526 \\ 82 \\ +\ 925 \\ \hline \end{array}$

5. $\begin{array}{r} 18{,}885 \\ 1{,}250 \\ 45 \\ +\ 745 \\ \hline \end{array}$

6. $\begin{array}{r} 150 \\ 9{,}936 \\ 11{,}214 \\ +\ 25 \\ \hline \end{array}$

Subtract.

7. $\begin{array}{r} 256 \\ -\ 122 \\ \hline \end{array}$

8. $\begin{array}{r} 558 \\ -\ 427 \\ \hline \end{array}$

9. $\begin{array}{r} 1355 \\ -\ 165 \\ \hline \end{array}$

10. $\begin{array}{r} 7686 \\ -\ 157 \\ \hline \end{array}$

11. $\begin{array}{r} 3290 \\ -\ 2003 \\ \hline \end{array}$

12. $\begin{array}{r} 28{,}344 \\ -\ 3{,}457 \\ \hline \end{array}$

Multiply.

13. 18×25 **14.** 15×75 **15.** 135×95

16. 755×665 **17.** 25×8.25 **18.** $32.4 \times .255$

Divide.

19. $10\overline{)3500}$ **20.** $85\overline{)1275}$ **21.** $35\overline{)4375}$

22. $70\overline{)16{,}450}$ **23.** $1.5\overline{)2700}$ **24.** $.7\overline{)24.85}$

Simplify.

25. $\frac{3}{8} + \frac{1}{8} + \frac{3}{4} = ?$ **26.** $\frac{1}{4} + \frac{3}{4} - \frac{1}{16} = ?$ **27.** $\frac{3}{8} \times \frac{1}{5} = ?$

28. $1\frac{1}{2} \times \frac{1}{4} = ?$ **29.** $\frac{1}{2} \div \frac{1}{4} = ?$ **30.** $\frac{3}{4} \div \frac{1}{2} = ?$

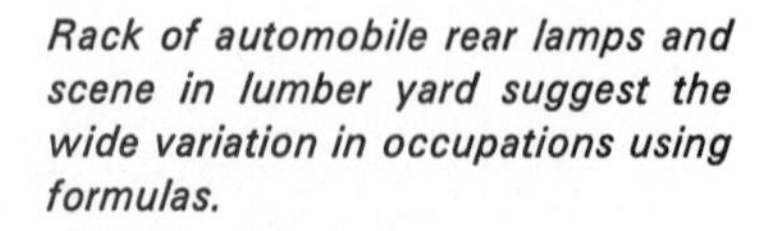

Rack of automobile rear lamps and scene in lumber yard suggest the wide variation in occupations using formulas.

Formulas from Industry

OBJECTIVES

1. To learn how to use estimates in practical applications.
2. To learn how to use formulas in industrial applications.

In the last chapter you learned about a number of useful formulas related to the area and volume of geometric figures. All of these find application in everyday occupations. However, trades and industries use many specialized formulas. This chapter will help you to become familiar with a number of them.

Lumber; Building Trades

5–1 Lumber

Lumber is measured in board feet. One **board foot** is a piece of wood 1 inch thick and 1 foot square, or its equivalent. For example, each of the following represents one board foot. A total of 144 cubic inches.

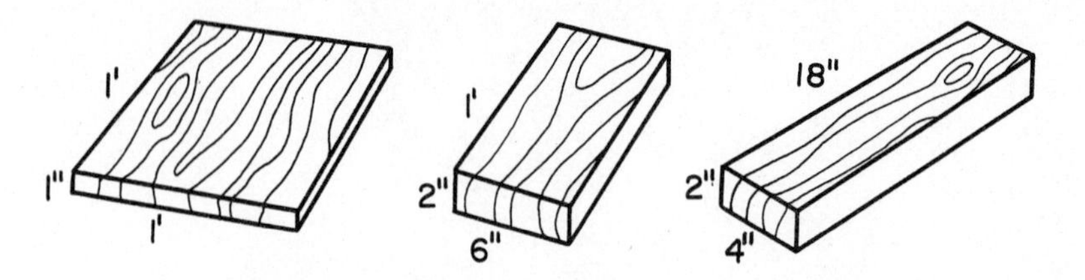

TM p. 13 5-1(1)

If you were checking a bill for lumber, you would need to know how to figure the number of board feet in certain stock. The rule for finding board feet is: Multiply the length and width expressed in feet and the thickness expressed in inches. Thus,

$$\textbf{Bd. ft.} = L \times W \times T$$

where L = length in feet, W = width in feet,
and T = thickness in inches

EXAMPLE

Find the number of board feet in a piece of lumber $2'' \times 8'' \times 6'$.

Solution. Since 8 inches = $\frac{8}{12}$ foot, we use $\frac{8}{12}$ in our calculations.

No. of bd. ft. = $2 \times \frac{8}{12} \times 6$

No. of bd. ft. = **8**

EXERCISES TM p. 13, 5-1(2)

Find the number of board feet in the lumber specified.

A

1. Piece of oak $5'' \times 2' \times 10'$.
2. Piece of yellow pine $2'' \times 10'' \times 4'$.
3. 10 pieces of antique elm each $1'' \times 14'' \times 3'$. Remind students to multiply by the number of pieces.
4. 20 pieces of black walnut each $2'' \times 7\frac{1}{2}'' \times 14\frac{2}{3}'$.
5. Find the cost of the elm in Exercise 3 if it costs 55¢ per board foot.

B

6. Large orders are priced per 1000 board feet. The following formula gives the cost; c = cost per 1000 bd. ft., C = total cost.

$$C = \frac{\text{bd. ft.}}{1000} \times c$$

Find the cost of 300 pieces of lumber 1″ × 10″ × 12′, at $17.20 per M. (M = 1000)

7. Complete the following purchase order on a separate piece of ruled paper by calculating the number of board feet and the amount of each item. Find the total cost of the purchase.

An adding machine, if available, can be used to check answers.

PURCHASE ORDER No. 12733

G&C Lumber Co. Yards at: Cedartown, Fair Oaks

Date: March 28, 19--

For: Taylor and Sons, Builders Phone: 549-1459

Address: 124 Brunswick St. City: Decatur, Ga. 30030

	Quan.	Size	Length	Description	Board Ft.	Price/Bd. Ft.	Amount
1	54	2" x 4"	8'	Studding		.09	
2	2	4" x 6"	12'	Horiz. header		.11	
3	1	4" x 8"	15'	Outside header		.12	
4	1	4" x 6"	12'	Inside header		.11	
5	8	1" x 6"	16'	Wind brace		.13	
6	12	4" x 6"	16'	Rafter		.11	
7	1	4" x 10"	12'	Beam		.16	
8	18	3/4" x 36"	8'	Exterior ply.		.19	
9	16	1/2" x 36"	8'	Interior ply.		.17	
10	10	1/2" x 24"	8'	Spruce paneling		.27	
11	6	1/2" x 24"	8'	Elm paneling		.33	
12	4	1" x 12"	10'	Shelf material		.17	
13							
14							
15							
						Total	

5–2 Estimating Measurements

The ability to make reasonable estimates is a useful tool in many practical situations.

There are many applications in the building trades that do not require an exact computation, but only a good estimate. Ordinarily, estimates are made before building starts, to obtain a "rough idea" of the amount and cost of the building materials needed. In general, it is always a good idea to make an estimate to see if your actual calculations are reasonable.

EXAMPLE

Estimate the floor area of a room $20\frac{3}{4}$ ft. by $10\frac{1}{4}$ ft.

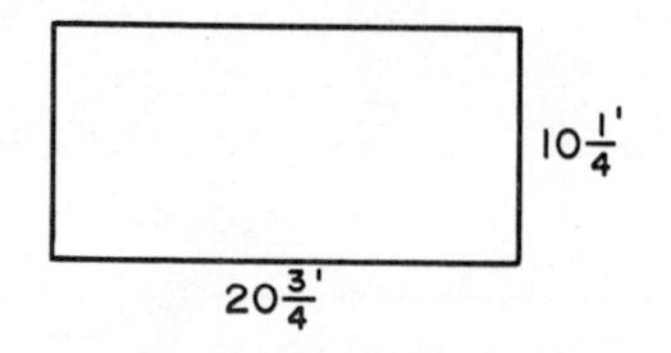

Solution. Since $20\frac{3}{4}'$ is about $21'$ and $10\frac{1}{4}'$ is about $10'$, we multiply 10×21 to obtain 210 as an *estimate* of the actual area, in square feet.

In this case the approximation is very close to the actual area obtained by computation.

$$10\frac{1}{4} \times 20\frac{3}{4} = 212\frac{11}{16} \text{ (sq. ft.)}$$

In the example above, we rounded off the mixed numbers to whole numbers. In situations like this we generally round off to the next greater whole number when the fractional part is $\frac{1}{2}$ or more. When the fractional part is less than $\frac{1}{2}$, we round off to the preceding whole number. Compare with the rule on page 36.

EXAMPLES

1. $10\frac{1}{8}'$ rounds off to $10'$.
2. $10\frac{1}{3}'$ rounds off to $10'$.
3. $10\frac{1}{2}'$ rounds off to $11'$.
4. $10\frac{2}{3}'$ rounds off to $11'$.
5. $10\frac{7}{8}'$ rounds off to $11'$.

Some situations require that we round to the next larger whole number regardless of what the fractional part is. For example, if we need $4\frac{1}{3}$ cu. yd. of concrete or a board $7\frac{1}{4}$ ft. long, we must order 5 cu. yd. of concrete or an 8-foot board or we will not be able to complete the job. Situations like these can be easily recognized.

Such estimates pertain to the <u>minimum</u> amount of materials needed to satisfy a given requirement.

EXAMPLE

Estimate the number of cubic yards of concrete needed for a 4″ thick patio floor whose dimensions are $15\frac{1}{4}'$ by $23\frac{3}{4}'$.

Solution.

$$V = l \times w \times h$$
$$4'' = \tfrac{4}{12}'$$
$$V = 15 \times 24 \times \tfrac{4}{12} \text{ (estimating in feet)}$$
$$V = 120 \text{ (cu. ft.)}$$
$$120 \text{ cu. ft.} = \tfrac{120}{27} \text{ cu. yd.} \quad (1 \text{ cu. yd.} = 27 \text{ cu. ft.})$$
$$= \mathbf{4\tfrac{12}{27}} \textbf{ cu. yd.}$$

Here we wish to round to the next greater whole number, and would order 5 cu. yd. of concrete.

You will notice that in this example we chose to estimate the volume of the patio floor in cubic feet, and then convert to cubic yards later. We can also estimate the volume of the floor in cubic yards first, and arrive at the final estimate directly.

Convenience, not logic, normally dictates which method to use.

$$V = l \times w \times h$$
$$= 15\tfrac{1}{4}' \times 23\tfrac{3}{4}' \times 4''$$
$$= 5 \text{ yd.} \times 8 \text{ yd.} \times \tfrac{1}{9} \text{ yd. (estimating in yards)}$$
$$V = \frac{40}{9} \text{ cu. yd.} = \mathbf{4\tfrac{4}{9}} \textbf{ cu. yd.}$$

Again, rounding the estimate to the next greater whole number shows that 5 cu. yd. of concrete will be needed.

EXERCISES

Estimate the following answers by rounding off measurements to the nearest whole foot. Check your estimates by calculation.

A

1. $10\frac{2}{3}' \times 15\frac{1}{3}' =$ _?_.
2. $12\frac{3}{4}' \times 14\frac{2}{3}' =$ _?_.
3. $14\frac{1}{2}' + 16\frac{3}{4}' + 17\frac{1}{3}' =$ _?_.
4. $(20\frac{1}{2}' \times 14\frac{3}{4}') \times 10\frac{1}{8}' =$ _?_.
5. $17\frac{2}{3}' + 19\frac{1}{4}' - 12\frac{3}{4}' =$ _?_.
6. Estimate the perimeter of this figure. Check by calculation.

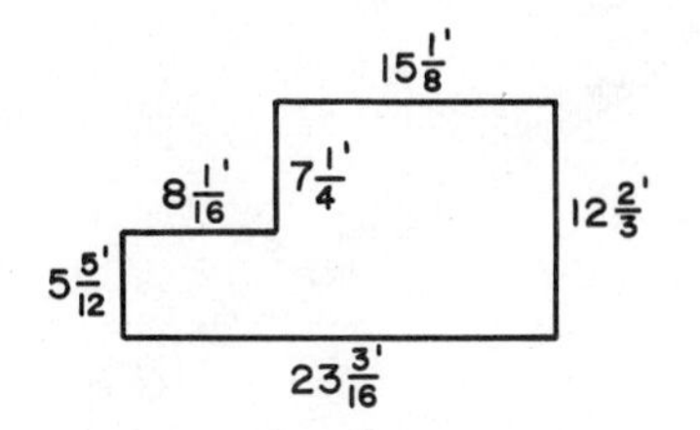

7. Estimate the circumference and the area of this circle. Check by calculation.

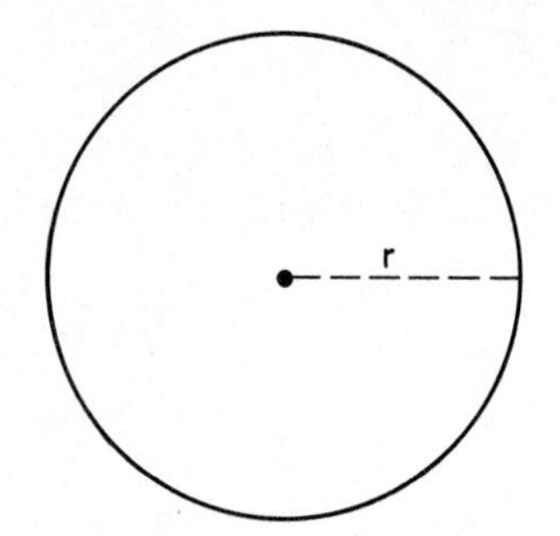

a. $C = 2\pi r$
b. $A = \pi r^2$ } $r = 10\frac{1}{3}''$, $\pi = 3\frac{1}{7}$

B

8. How much concrete is needed for $49\frac{1}{2}$ ft. of $36\frac{1}{4}''$ wide sidewalk, if it is $3\frac{3}{4}''$ thick?

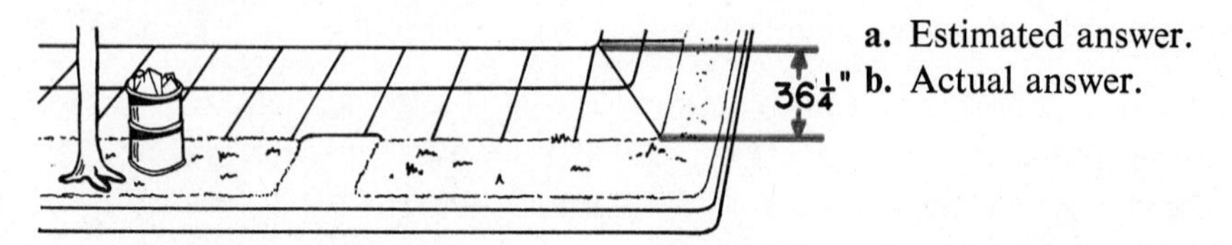

a. Estimated answer.
b. Actual answer.

9. A driveway is 40′ wide, $23\frac{3}{4}'$ long, and $2\frac{2}{3}''$ thick. How much asphalt was used in its construction?

a. Estimated answer. **b.** Actual answer.

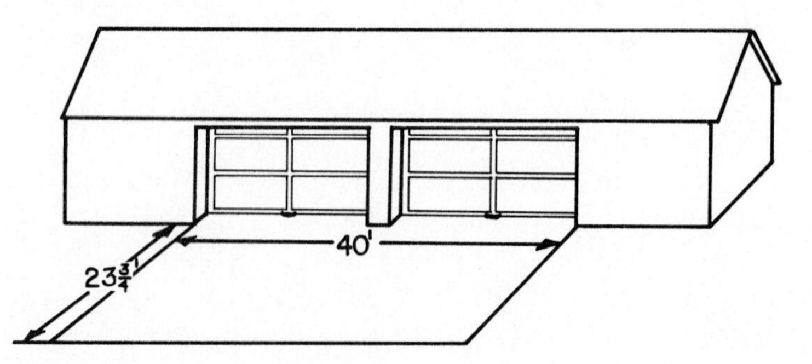

10. A $15\frac{3}{4}'$ square concrete slab floor is to be $5\frac{2}{3}''$ thick. How much concrete is needed for the floor?

a. Estimated answer. **b.** Actual answer.

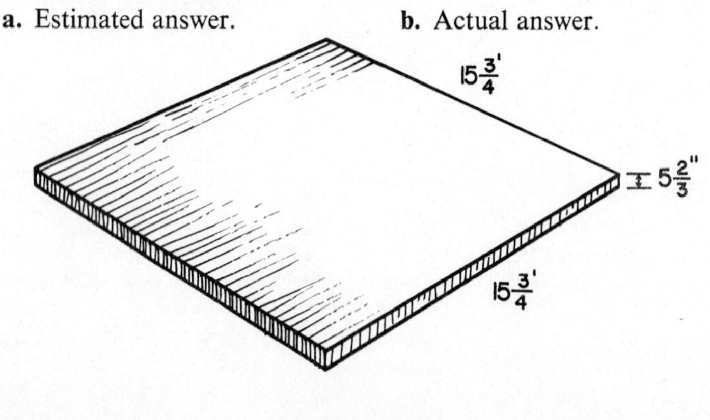

ACTIVITY: ***Estimating distances.***

Problem: To discover useful measurements for estimating distances.
Plan: To measure one's own thumb, hand span, and pace.

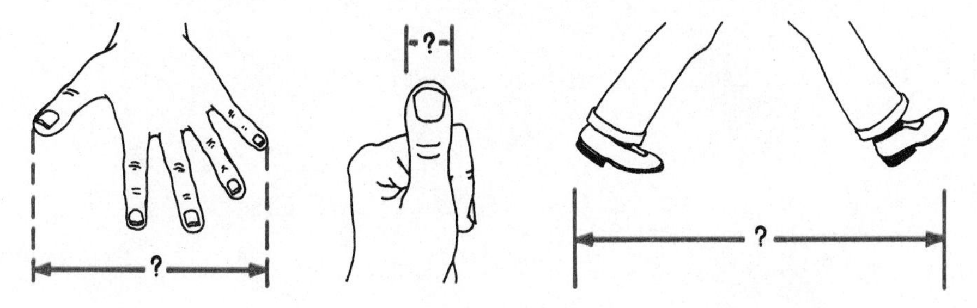

1. Make several measurements to determine (**a**) the width of your thumb, (**b**) the length of your hand span, and (**c**) your pace.
2. Decide on the measurements *you* will use as a result of Step 1.

Recall that many units of measure originated from reference to parts of the body.

The ability to make rough calculations of distances is one that should be acquired.

Try these. Stress this.

1. Using your thumb span, estimate the length of line segment *AB*. Use your ruler to check your estimate.

A ——————————————————————— *B*

2. Without measuring, estimate the width and height of the chalkboard in your room. Your teacher may wish you to prepare a table showing the class results.
3. Estimate the size of your classroom.
4. Estimate the length, width, and thickness of this textbook.

5–3 Roofing

Builders use the following terms in connection with pitched roofs. (See page 202.)

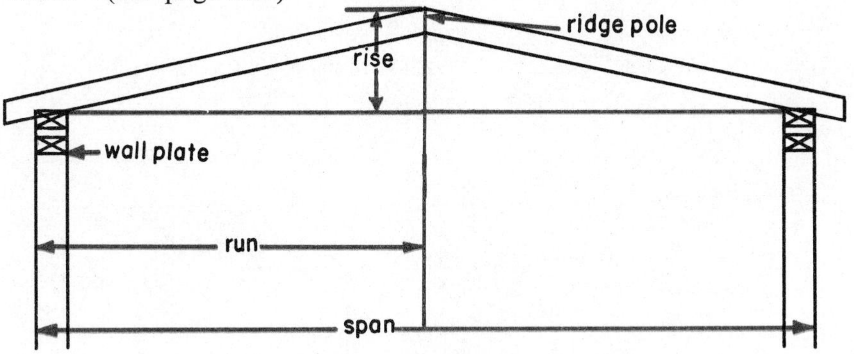

1. *Span* is the distance over the wall plates.
2. *Run* is half of the span.
3. *Rise* is the altitude of the right triangle formed by drawing lines from the top plate perpendicular to the line drawn through the center of the ridgepole.
4. *Pitch* is equal to the rise divided by the span.

The following formulas are useful:

The larger the fraction (pitch), the steeper the roof.

$$\textbf{Pitch} = \frac{\textbf{rise}}{\textbf{span}}$$

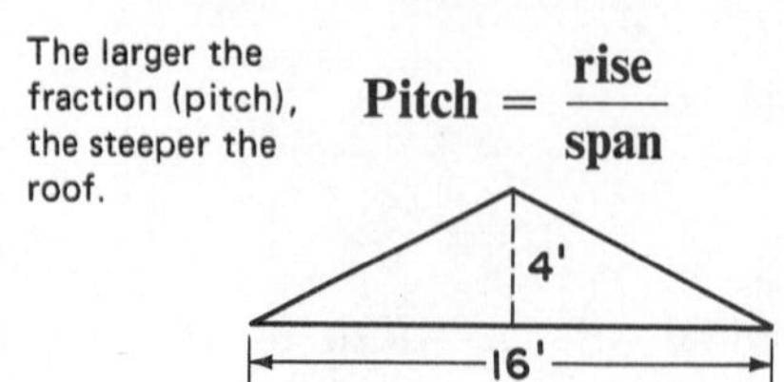

$$\textbf{Rise} = \textbf{pitch} \times \textbf{span}$$

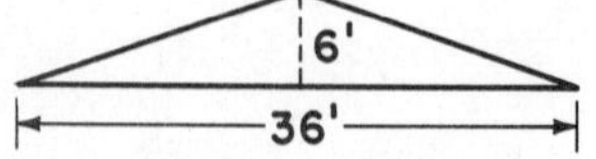

In this diagram the rise is 4′ and the span is 16′. Hence

$$\text{Pitch} = \frac{4}{16} = \frac{1}{4}$$

This is simply a ratio. Thus, no unit of measure is indicated.

In this diagram the span is 36′ and the pitch is $\frac{1}{6}$. Hence

$$\text{Rise} = \frac{1}{6} \times 36 = 6 \text{ (ft.)}$$

This is a dimension, and must be expressed in some unit of measure.

EXERCISES

A

1. Find the pitch of a roof, if the span is 24′ and the rise is 4′.
2. Find the pitch of a roof, if the span is 36′ and the rise is 6′.
3. Find the pitch of a roof, if the run is $16\frac{1}{2}$′ and the rise is 3′.
4. Find the rise, if the pitch is $\frac{1}{6}$ and the span is 30′.
5. Find the rise, if the pitch is $\frac{1}{4}$ and the span is 32′.
6. Find the rise, if the pitch is $\frac{1}{3}$ and the span is 39′.
7. Find the rise, if the pitch is $\frac{1}{7}$ and the run is 14′.

The student must double the run to find the span.

SELF-ANALYSIS TEST I

Time: 10 minutes

1. How many board feet are there in a piece of oak 7″ × 3′ × 8′?
2. How many board feet are there in 15 pieces of pine 2″ × 18″ × 7′?
3. Find the cost of 500 pieces of lumber if each is 2″ × 15″ × 24′ at \$23.00 per M. (M = 1000)
4. Estimate the number of board feet of $\frac{7}{8}$″ black walnut needed for the top, front and ends of the stereo cabinet.

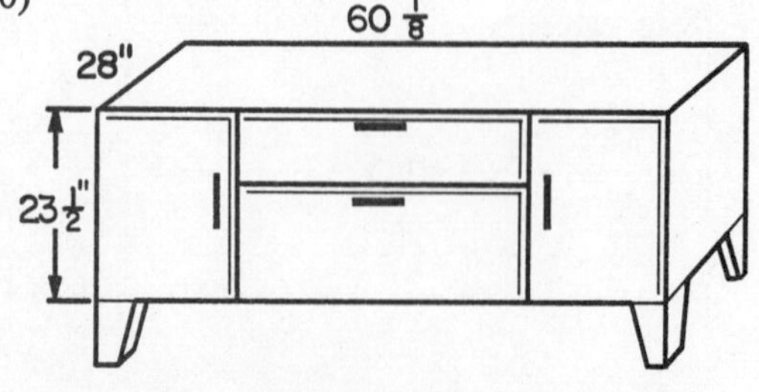

5. __?__ is equal to the rise divided by the span.
6. The distance over the wall plates is the __?__.
7. The __?__ is half the span.
8. The __?__ is the altitude of the right triangle formed by drawing lines from the top plate perpendicular to the line drawn through the center of the __?__ pole.
9. Find the pitch of a roof, if the span is 24′ and the rise is 10′.
10. Find the rise, if the pitch is $\frac{3}{8}$ and the span is 40′.

■ Work and Power Formulas

5–4 Work and Power TM p. 13 , 5-4

If we lift a heavy object, we say we are doing work. **Work** may be thought of as a flow of energy from one body to another. If we want to describe the *amount* of work, we need to know both the weight of the object moved and the distance it is moved. In industry this is exactly how work is defined — the product of force and distance.

Work = force × distance

$$W = f \times s$$

A common unit of work is the **foot-pound,** which is the work done when a force of 1 lb. is applied to an object for a distance of 1 ft.

EXAMPLE

Find the work done in lifting a weight of 3 lb. a distance of 2 ft.

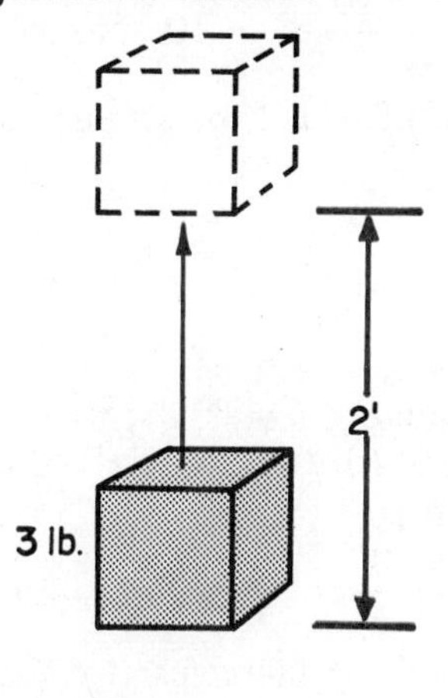

Solution. $W = f \cdot s$

$W = 3 \cdot 2$

$W =$ **6 (foot-pounds)**

EXERCISES

A

1. Find the work in foot-pounds if $f = 60$ lb. and $s = 30$ ft.
2. Find the work involved in moving a 500 lb. object a distance of 25 ft.
3. Find the distance an object is moved (displaced) if $W = 350$ ft.-lb. and $f = 5$ lb. $\left(s = \frac{W}{f}\right)$

4. Find the force if $W = 600$ ft.-lb. and $s = 15$ ft.
5. How much work is expended if an electric crane raises 3500 lb. of steel to a height of 20 ft.?
6. If 200 ft.-lb. of work is done by a man using a 2-foot wrench, how much force does he exert?

Power is the work done per unit of time. It is the rate of doing work.

Power is being used here in its more technical sense.

$$P = \frac{W}{t} \quad \text{or} \quad P = \frac{fs}{t}$$

EXAMPLE

Find the power if $f = 10$ lb., $s = 3$ ft., and $t = 5$ sec.

Solution. $P = \dfrac{f \cdot s}{t}$

A hyphen indicates multiplication. A slanted line means division. Compare with the formula at the left.

$$P = \frac{10 \times 3}{5} = \frac{30}{5}$$

$$P = 6$$

The power is 6 ft.-lb. per second, or **6 ft.-lb./sec.**

Repeat the example, changing the value of t to 3 sec. You will find that $P = \dfrac{10 \cdot 3}{3} = 10$. Notice that the smaller the time, the greater the power, provided the amount of work is the same.

EXERCISES

A

1. Find P if $f = 30$ lb., $s = 6$ ft., and $t = 5$ min.
2. Find P if $f = 2$ tons, $s = 3$ yd., and $t = 2$ hr. (1 ton = 2000 lb., 1 yd. = 3 ft.)
3. $t = \dfrac{W}{P}$ or $\dfrac{f \cdot s}{P}$. Find t if $f = 10$ lb., $s = 60$ ft., and $P = 5$ ft.-lb./sec.
4. Find the power exerted if a gasoline engine lifts 84 lb. a distance of 60 ft. in 12 sec.

5–5 Horsepower

We could always use foot-pounds per minute to express power, but the common unit is **horsepower** (hp). One horsepower is defined to be 33,000 foot-pounds per minute.

$$\mathbf{1\ hp = 33{,}000\ ft.\text{-}lb./min.}$$

or

$$\mathbf{1\ hp = 550\ ft.\text{-}lb./sec.}$$

One horsepower is the amount of power necessary to raise 33,000 pounds one foot in one minute, or 550 pounds one foot in one second.

$$\mathbf{hp = \frac{ft.\text{-}lb.\ of\ work\ per\ min.}{33{,}000}}$$

or

$$\mathbf{hp = \frac{ft.\text{-}lb.\ of\ work\ per\ sec.}{550}}$$

EXAMPLE

What is the horsepower necessary to raise a 2100-pound rock 50 ft. high in 3 min.?

Solution. $\text{ft.-lb./min.} = \frac{2100 \times 50}{3} = 35{,}000$

$$\text{hp} = \frac{35{,}000}{33{,}000} = 1\tfrac{2}{33}$$

TM p. 14 , 5-5

EXERCISES

A

1. What horsepower is necessary to raise 99,000 lb. a distance of 9 ft. in 3 min.?
2. What is the approximate horsepower needed to raise an elevator weighing 4000 lb. a distance of 360 ft. in 2 min.?
3. What is the approximate horsepower of an engine which can lift an airplane weighing 17 tons to the deck of a carrier 50 ft. high in 2 minutes?
4. A car being lifted into a junk pile weighs 5500 lb. If the engine needed to lift the car is rated at 5 hp and it takes 1 min. to reach the top of the pile, how high is the junk pile?

$$\text{Height} = \frac{\text{hp} \times 33{,}000 \times \text{time}}{\text{weight}}$$

5–6 Water Power

The term *horsepower* is also used to describe the power available in a waterfall or a dam. One cubic foot of water weighs about 62.4 pounds, so a force of 62.4 pounds falling a distance of *d* feet would produce $62.4 \times d$ foot-pounds of work. If we multiply this by the number of cubic feet of water falling per second, we have the number of foot-pounds of work per second.

Recall that horsepower may be found by the formula

$$\textbf{hp} = \frac{\textbf{ft.-lb. of work per sec.}}{\textbf{550}}$$

If we let F = flow of water in cubic feet per second
d = distance the water falls, in feet,

$$\text{then } \textbf{hp} = \frac{Fd \times 62.4}{550} \qquad \left(\frac{62.4}{550} = 0.113\right)$$

$$\textbf{hp} = \textbf{0.113}\,Fd$$

EXAMPLE

Find the horsepower of a waterfall 10 ft. high having a flow of 200 cu. ft. per second.

Solution. hp $= 0.113 \times 200 \times 10$
hp = 226

EXERCISES

A

1. Find the horsepower of a waterfall 30′ high with a flow of 800 cu. ft./sec.
2. Niagara Falls is about 160′ high and has a flow of 130,000 cu. ft./sec. Find its approximate potential horsepower. (The electricity thus generated serves a large area, including New York City.)
3. Hoover Dam has a flow of approximately 20,350 cu. ft./sec. and the water falls approximately 726 feet. Find its approximate horsepower.
4. How high must a dam be to generate 2808 hp, if the water flow is 550 cu. ft./sec.?

B

5. Which of two waterfalls of equal height but unequal water flow will produce the more horsepower?
6. Which of two waterfalls of equal water flow but unequal height will produce the more horsepower?

SELF-ANALYSIS TEST II

Time: 10 minutes

1. Work may be regarded as a __?__ of energy from one body to another.
2. __?__ is the work done per unit of time.
3. 1 hp is equal to __?__ ft.-lb./sec. or __?__ ft.-lb./min.
4. Every cubic foot of water weighs approximately __?__ lb.
5. The term __?__ refers to a unit of power.
6. Find the work in foot-pounds if a weight of 200 lb. is moved 30 feet.
7. Find the power required to lift a 20-pound box a distance of 5 ft. in 4 sec.
8. What is the horsepower necessary to raise a weight of 11,000 lb. a distance of 10 ft. in 5 min.?
9. Find the horsepower of a waterfall 30 ft. high having a flow of 100 cu. ft./sec.
10. Find the distance an object moves if $W = 700$ ft.-lb. and $f = 5$ lb. $\left(S = \frac{W}{f}\right)$

TM p. 14 , 5-7

■ Automobiles

5–7 Engine Horsepower

The horsepower of an automobile engine is calculated in two different ways, by reference to brakes and by reference to cylinders. The **brake horsepower** of a gasoline engine is determined by measuring the force exerted on a friction brake. Brake horsepower (bhp) is calculated by using the speed of the engine, the force on a scale at the end of an arm, and the length of the arm. The following formulas can be used to determine brake horsepower:

$$\mathbf{bhp} = \frac{2\pi RNW}{33{,}000} \qquad \mathbf{bhp} = \frac{RNW}{5252}$$

Point out that $\frac{2\pi}{33{,}000} = \frac{1}{5252}$.

where R = length of arm (from center of drum)
N = engine speed in rpm (revolutions per minute)
W = load on scale in pounds

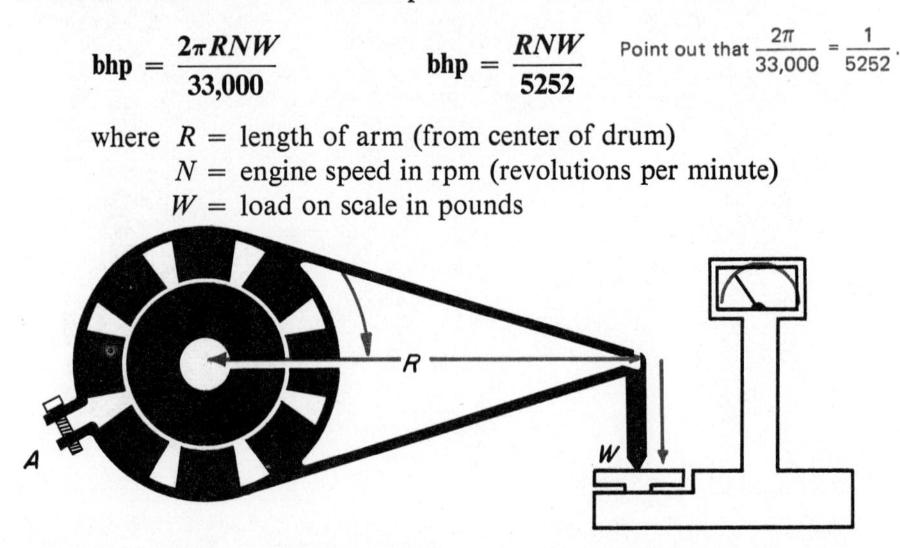

Prony brake (or dynamometer) for determining power output of engine: "A" is adjustment for tightening brake on brake drum; "R" is length of arm (from center of shaft to end supported on scales); and "W" is weight, or force, exerted on scales.

EXAMPLE

If the arm (R) is 3 ft. long, the load (W) is 100 lb., and the engine speed (N) is 1000 rpm, find the brake horsepower.

Engine horsepower ratings based on these two methods are seldom identical.

Solution. $\text{bhp} = \frac{RNW}{5252}$

$$\text{bhp} = \frac{3 \times 1000 \times 100}{5252} = \mathbf{57.12}$$

The SAE (Society of Automotive Engineers) horsepower rating is another method for comparing engines, based on the number of cylinders and their diameters (bore). The formula used is as follows:

$$\mathbf{SAE\ hp} = \frac{D^2 \times N}{2.5},$$

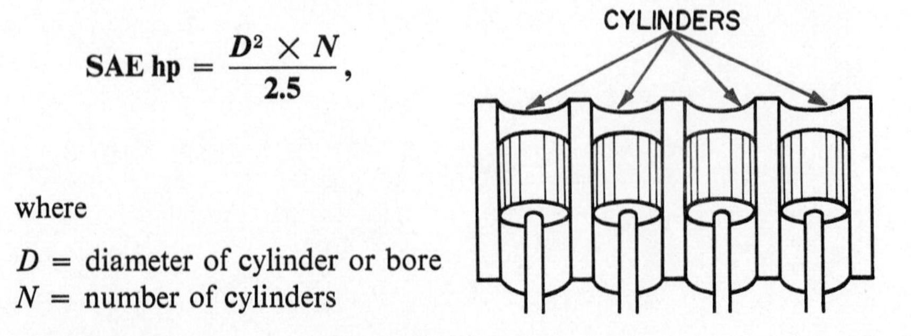

where

D = diameter of cylinder or bore
N = number of cylinders

This formula does not take into consideration such factors as mean effective pressure (mep), length of stroke, revolutions per minute (rpm), and so forth. A third method for calculating horsepower (not given here) uses these factors to find the "indicated" horsepower.

EXAMPLE

A Go-Car 6-cylinder engine has a bore of 3″. Find its SAE horsepower rating.

Solution. $\text{SAE hp} = \dfrac{D^2 \times N}{2.5}$

$$= \frac{3^2 \times 6}{2.5}$$

$$= \frac{9 \times 6}{2.5} = \frac{54}{2.5}$$

$$= \mathbf{21.6}$$

EXERCISES

A

1. Find the brake horsepower of a gasoline engine if the arm is 3 ft. long, the load (W) is 300 lb., and $N = 3000$ rpm.
2. Find the approximate brake horsepower of a Go-Car V-8 engine that, at 4600 rpm, registers 135 lb. at the end of a prony brake arm $2\frac{1}{2}$ ft. long.
3. Find the SAE horsepower of a V-8 gasoline engine with a bore of $3\frac{1}{2}$″.
4. Calculate the SAE horsepower for a V-4 power-plant engine with a $4\frac{1}{4}$″ bore.
5. Find the SAE horsepower of a 6-cylinder gasoline engine with a bore of 4″.

5–8 Engine Displacement

One factor which contributes directly to the horsepower rating of an engine is the size of its displacement. The displacement in a cylinder is the difference between the number of cubic inches of air in the cylinder when the piston is at the bottom of its stroke (bottom dead center) and the amount of air in the cylinder when the piston reaches the top of its stroke (top dead center). (Diagrams on page 210.)

We can use the following formula to find the total displacement of an engine.

$$\mathbf{d = \pi r^2 \times \text{stroke} \times \text{no. of cylinders}}$$

where r = radius of the bore ($\frac{1}{2}$ × the bore)

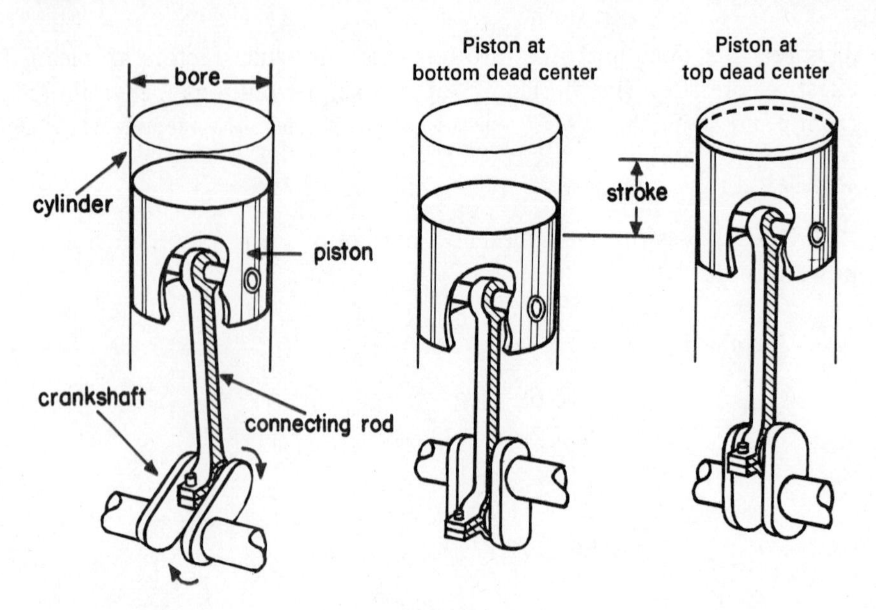

EXAMPLE

Find the displacement of an engine with a $3\frac{1}{2}''$ bore, a $3\frac{1}{2}''$ stroke, 8 cylinders. ($\pi = \frac{22}{7}$)

Solution. $r = \frac{1}{2} \times 3\frac{1}{2} = \frac{1}{2} \times \frac{7}{2} = \frac{7}{4}$

Remind students that $r = \frac{1}{2} \times$ bore.

$d = \frac{22}{7} \times (\frac{7}{4})^2 \times \frac{7}{2} \times 8$

$d = (\frac{22}{7} \times \frac{7}{4}) \times (\frac{7}{4} \times \frac{7}{2} \times 8)$

$d = \frac{11}{2} \times 7 \times 7 = \frac{539}{2} = 269.5$ (cu. in.), or **270 cu. in.**

TM p. 14 , 5-8

EXERCISES

Find the cubic-inch displacement of the following engines.

A

1. A V-8, when the bore is 4.125″ and the stroke is 3.750″.
2. A V-8, when the bore is 4.000″ and the stroke is 3.250″.
3. A 6, when the bore is 3.400″ and the stroke is 4.125″.
4. A V-8, when the bore is 3.75″ and the stroke is 3.25″.

5–9 Rear-Axle Ratio

Ratio will be studied in detail in Chapter 8.

To find the rear-axle ratio, r, of an automobile, divide the number of teeth on the ring gear, T, by the number of teeth on the pinion gear, t. Expressed as a formula,

$$r = \frac{T}{t}.$$

EXAMPLE

The ring gear has 34 teeth, and the pinion gear has 9. Find the rear-axle ratio.

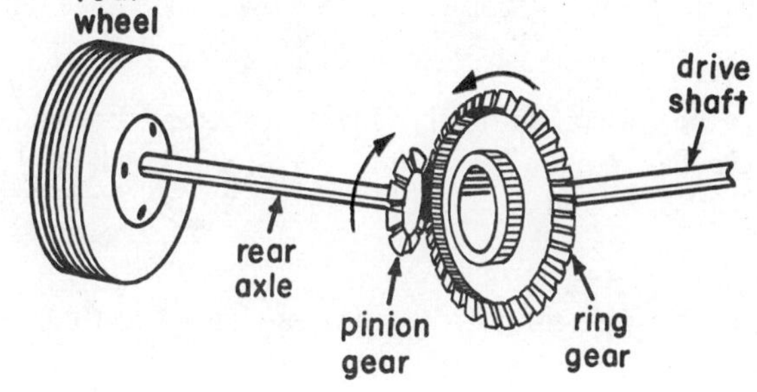

Solution. $34 \div 9 = 3.78$, to the nearest hundredth. The ratio is **3.78 to 1,** usually written **3.78:1.**

Note the use of the colon to represent "to."

The formula

$$T = rt$$

gives the number of teeth on the ring gear.

EXERCISES

Determine the rear-axle ratios for the following. Round off answers to the nearest hundredth.

A

1. Ring gear has 39 teeth, pinion gear 11 teeth.
2. Ring gear has 43 teeth, pinion gear 13 teeth.
3. Ring gear has 45 teeth, pinion gear 11 teeth.

Find the number of teeth on the ring gear.

B

4. Ratio is 4 to 1, and pinion gear has 9 teeth.
5. Ratio is 4.2 to 1, and pinion gear has 15 teeth.

SELF-ANALYSIS TEST III

Time: 15 minutes

1. The formula for the brake horsepower is __?__.
2. The formula for SAE horsepower is __?__.
3. The rear-axle ratio of an automobile is __?__.
4. The __?__ is the difference between the total number of cubic inches of air in the engine when the pistons are at the bottom of their stroke and the amount of air in the cylinders when the pistons reach the top of their stroke.

5. The formula for engine displacement is $\pi r^2 \times$ stroke $\times$ __?__.
6. Find the brake horsepower when the length of the arm is $2\frac{1}{2}$ ft., the load is 400 lb., and rpm is 3600.
7. What is the SAE horsepower of an 8-cylinder engine with a 3″ bore?

8. What is the cubic-inch displacement of a Go-Car 6-cylinder engine, with a $3\frac{3}{4}$″ bore and a 4″ stroke?

9. Find the rear-axle ratio if the ring gear has 44 teeth and the pinion has 13 teeth.
10. Find the number of teeth on the ring gear, if the rear-axle ratio is 3.2 to 1, and the pinion gear has 15 teeth.

Miscellaneous Formulas

5–10 Electricity

There are several terms used in electrical work that have to do with the flow of electricity.

The **ampere** is the unit used to measure the *rate* of flow of an electric current.

The **volt** is the unit used to measure the *amount* of pressure "pushing" the current through the conductor.

The **ohm** is the unit used to measure the *resistance* which the current meets in flowing through the conductor.

These three units are related in a simple but important formula, known as *Ohm's Law*. This law may be stated in any of these three forms.

Amperes	**Volts**	**Ohms**
(1) $I = \frac{E}{R}$	(2) $E = IR$	(3) $R = \frac{E}{I}$

I is the number of amperes. E is the number of volts. R is the number of ohms.

Use formula (1) to find the current. Use formula (2) to find the pressure. Use formula (3) to find the resistance.

EXAMPLE

Find I, the number of amperes (amps) in the following situation. The resistance, R, is 50 ohms and the pressure, E, is 110 volts.

Point out that most household appliances operate on 115 volts.

Solution. $I = \frac{E}{R}$

$$I = \frac{110}{50}$$

$$I = 2.2 \text{ amps}$$

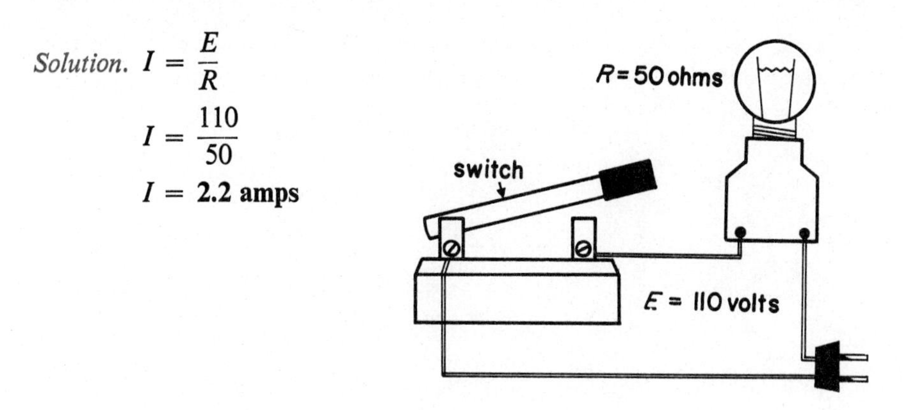

The chart shown at the left below, if properly used, will help you to remember the various forms of Ohm's Law. If you put your thumb over the I, you get E over R. This suggests that I (the letter covered) $= \frac{E}{R}$.

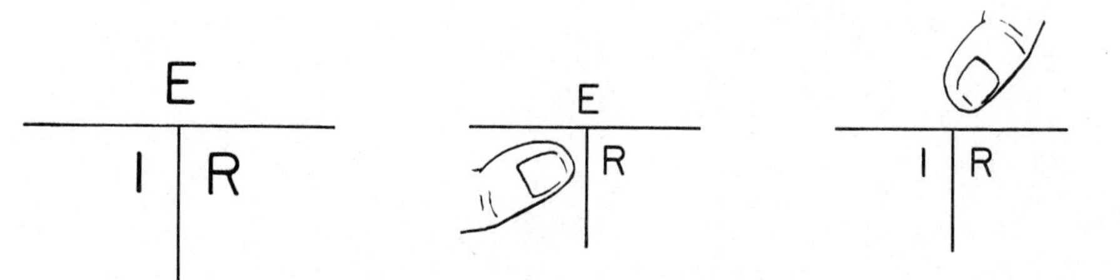

If you put your thumb over E, the figure suggests that E (the letter covered) $= I \times R$. Covering R suggests that $R = \frac{E}{I}$.

EXERCISES

Find the missing values in the following chart.

A

	Amperes I	Volts E	Ohms R
1.	?	220	5
2.	?	120	4
3.	24	220	?
4.	48	220	?
5.	12	?	4.5

In electricity the unit of power is the **watt.** The number of watts is equal to the number of volts times the number of amperes; that is,

$$\textbf{Watts} = \textbf{volts} \times \textbf{amperes}$$

One horsepower is equal to 746 watts.

$$\textbf{hp} = \frac{\textbf{watts}}{\textbf{746}}$$

or

$$\textbf{hp} = \frac{\textbf{volts} \times \textbf{amperes}}{\textbf{746}}$$

EXAMPLE

An electric motor running on a 220-volt line takes 30 amperes. What is its approximate horsepower?

Solution. $\text{hp} = \dfrac{\text{volts} \times \text{amperes}}{746}$

$$= \frac{220 \times 30}{746} = \frac{6600}{746}$$

$$= \textbf{8.8 hp (approx.)}$$

EXERCISES

A

1. What is the approximate horsepower of an electric motor taking 10 amperes on a 220-volt line?
2. What is the approximate horsepower of a motor if it requires a current of 60 amperes and a pressure of 440 volts?
3. An electric drill takes 4.2 amps at a voltage of 120. What is its horsepower?
4. An automobile engine starter takes 300 amps at 12 volts. What is its horsepower?
5. An electric hoist needs 40 amps at 220 volts to lift an engine. What is its horsepower?

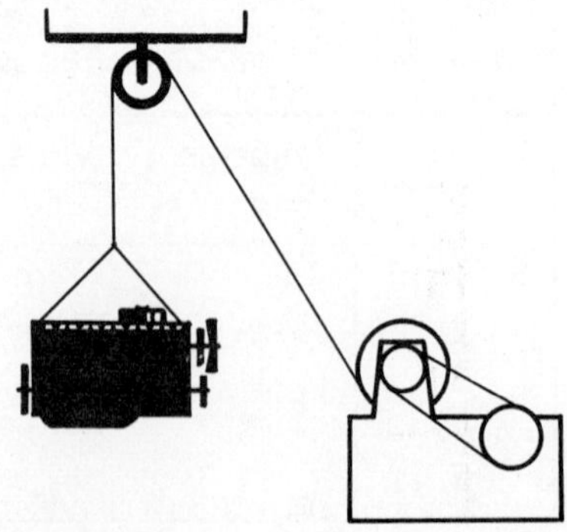

5–11 Distance

You are probably familiar with the **distance formula.** It is an extremely important one in relation to transportation by either surface or air.

There are three useful forms of this formula, in which D = distance, r = rate, and t = time.

(1) $\boldsymbol{D = r \cdot t}$ (2) $\boldsymbol{r = \frac{D}{t}}$ (3) $\boldsymbol{t = \frac{D}{r}}$

EXAMPLE These formulas can be shown in a chart as $\frac{D}{r \mid t}$.

Find the distance traveled by a jet liner in $2\frac{1}{2}$ hr. if the average speed is 650 mph (miles per hour).

Solution. $D = r \cdot t$
$= 650 \cdot 2\frac{1}{2}$
$D = \mathbf{1625}$ **(miles)**

EXERCISES

A

1. At an average speed of 550 mph, how far does an airplane go in 6 hr.?
2. If an airplane goes 1750 mi. at an average speed of 350 mph, how many hours will it take?
3. What is the rate of speed of an airplane if it goes 3250 mi. in 5 hr.?
4. An airplane flies 7500 mi. The first 6 hr. its speed is 600 mi. per hour. If its total time of flight is 12 hr., how fast did it go during the remaining time?
5. A man drives at the rate of 50 mph for $1\frac{1}{2}$ hr., rides in an airplane for 6 hr. at 625 mph, then goes by bus for 3 hr. at 45 mph. Find the total distance he traveled.

SELF-ANALYSIS TEST IV

Time: 10 minutes

1. The unit used to measure the rate of flow of an electric current is called an __?__.
2. The resistance to the flow of current is measured in __?__.
3. The number of watts is equal to the number of __?__ times the number of amperes.
4. Ohm's Law is expressed in the formula __?__.
5. The number of horsepower of an electrically powered machine is equal to the number of __?__ divided by 746.
6. Find the current (amperes) if the voltage is 110 and resistance is 45 ohms.
7. If an air conditioner draws a current of 16 amperes and has a resistance of 14 ohms, find the voltage.
8. Find the approximate horsepower of an electric lawn mower if its voltage is 120 and its current (amperes) is 11.
9. Find the distance traveled if an airplane's average speed is 500 mph and it travels for 5 hr.
10. What is the rate of speed of an airplane if it goes 3750 mi. in 7 hr.?

5–12 Pulley Formulas TM p. 14 , 5-12

The speed of a driven pulley and the speed of a driving pulley are related by the formula,

$$DS = ds$$

where
S = speed of driving pulley
s = speed of driven pulley
D = diameter of driving pulley
d = diameter of driven pulley

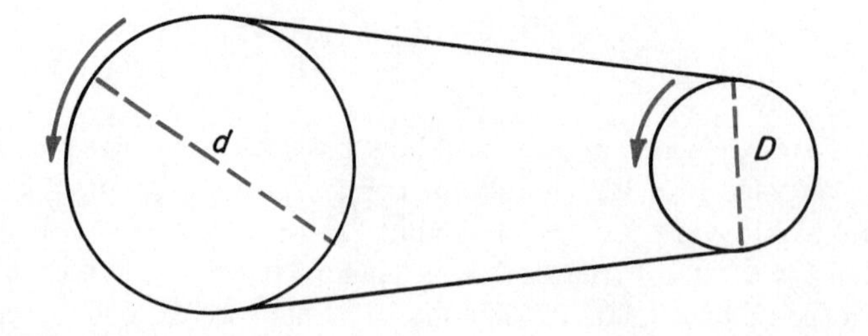

Four other forms of this formula are the following:

$$D = \frac{ds}{S} \qquad S = \frac{ds}{D} \qquad d = \frac{DS}{s} \qquad s = \frac{DS}{d}$$

EXAMPLE 1

The speed of the driving pulley is 280 rpm; the speed of the driven pulley is 420 rpm; the diameter of the driven pulley is 8 inches. Find the diameter of the driving pulley.

Solution. We choose the formula $D = \dfrac{ds}{S}$.

$$D = \frac{8 \times 420}{280}$$

$$D = \mathbf{12\ (in.)}$$

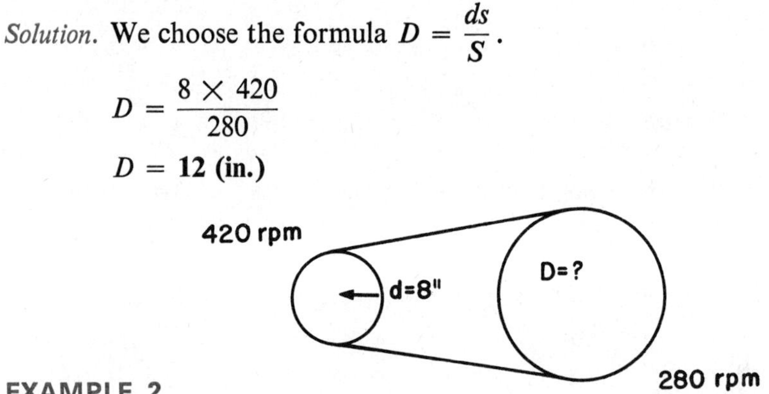

EXAMPLE 2

Find the speed of the driving pulley, when the speed of the driven pulley is 2700 rpm, the diameter of the driven pulley is 6″, and the diameter of the driving pulley is 9″.

Solution. $S = \dfrac{ds}{D}$

$$S = \frac{6 \times 2700}{9}$$

$$S = 6 \times 300$$

$$S = \mathbf{1800\ (rpm)}$$

EXERCISES

A

1. Find the diameter of the driving pulley, when the driven pulley is 9″ in diameter, the speed of the driven pulley is 360 rpm, and the speed of the driving pulley is 270 rpm.
2. Find the diameter of the driving pulley, when the driven pulley is 18 in. in diameter, the speed of the driven pulley is 320 rpm, and the speed of the driving pulley is 300 rpm.
3. Find the speed of the driving pulley, when the speed of the driven pulley is 630 rpm, the driven pulley is 12″ in diameter, and the driving pulley is 18″ in diameter.
4. Find the diameter of the driven pulley, when the driving pulley is 15 in. in diameter, the speed of the driving pulley is 450 rpm, and the speed of the driven pulley is 750 rpm.

The speed that the teeth of a circular saw blade are moving is called the **cutting speed** of the blade. This cutting speed is determined by the following formula.

$$S = \frac{C \times \text{rpm} \times D}{d \times 12}$$

where S = cutting speed of circular saw in ft./min.
C = circumference of saw blade (in inches)
rpm = revolutions per minute of the motor
D = diameter of the driving pulley
d = diameter of driven pulley (on the saw blade)

EXAMPLE

Find the cutting speed of a table saw if the circumference of the blade is 36″, the motor is turning at 1750 rpm, with a 4″ pulley on the motor and a 3″ pulley on the saw blade.

Solution. $S = \dfrac{C \times \text{rpm} \times D}{d \times 12} = \dfrac{36 \times 1750 \times 4}{3 \times 12}$

$S = \mathbf{7000\ ft./min.}$

To find the cutting speed of a **jointer saw,** used in shaping wood, we use the formula

$$S = \frac{C \times \text{rpm}}{12},$$

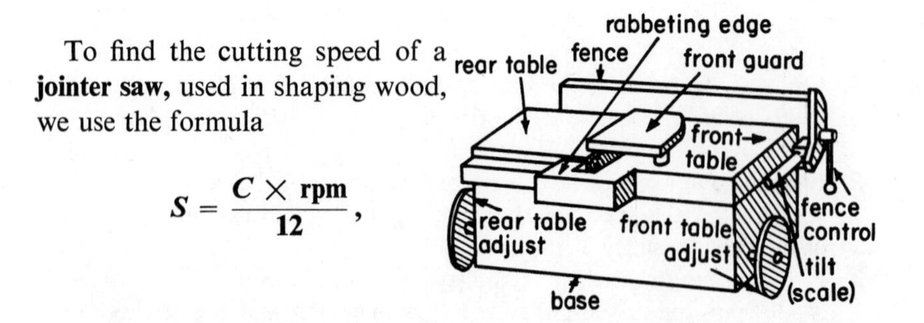

where S = cutting speed in feet per minute of the jointer blades
C = circumference of the cutter (in inches)
rpm = speed of pulley attached to cutter

EXAMPLE

Find the cutting speed in feet per minute of the jointer blades, if the circumference of the cutter is 15 inches, and the pulley rpm is 3600.

Solution. $S = \dfrac{C \times \text{rpm}}{12}$

$$S = \frac{15 \times 3600}{12}$$

$$S = \mathbf{4500\ ft./min.}$$

EXERCISES

A

1. Find the cutting speed of a circular saw, if the blade has a circumference of 42″, the motor is turning at 3450 rpm, with a 6″ pulley at the motor, and a 4″ pulley on the saw blade.
2. Find the cutting speed of a circular saw if the blade has a diameter of 14″, the motor turns at 1750 rpm, with a 6″ diameter pulley on the motor, and a 3″ pulley on the saw blade. (Hint: $C = \pi d$, where $\pi = \frac{22}{7}$)
3. Find the cutting speed of a jointer saw with a cutter blade of 21″ circumference, turning at 4800 rpm.
4. Find the cutting speed of a 6″ diameter jointer saw, if the blade pulley is rotating at 2800 rpm. (See Hint in Exercise 2.)

SELF-ANALYSIS TEST V

Time: 12 minutes

1. The formula for calculating the diameter of the driving pulley is _?_.
2. The formula for finding the cutting speed of a circular saw is _?_.
3. The formula for finding the cutting speed of a jointer saw is _?_.
4. Find the diameter of a driving pulley when the diameter of the driven pulley is 8″, the speed of the driving pulley is 400 rpm, and the speed of the driven pulley is 350 rpm.
5. Find the speed of the driving pulley if the diameter of the driven pulley is 5″, the speed of the driven pulley is 420 rpm, and the diameter of the driving pulley is 3″.
6. Find the cutting speed of a circular saw, if the circumference of the blade is 22″, the rpm is 2000, the diameter of the driving pulley is 3″, and the diameter of the driven pulley is 4″.
7. Find the cutting speed of a jointer saw if the circumference of the cutter is 14″ and the rpm of the pulley is 2400.

CHAPTER SUMMARY

Board Feet

$$\text{Bd. ft.} = L \times W \times T$$

L = length in feet
W = width in feet
T = thickness in inches

Roofing

$$\text{Pitch} = \frac{\text{rise}}{\text{span}}$$

$$\text{Rise} = \text{pitch} \times \text{span}$$

Work

$$W = f \times s$$

W = work in foot-pounds
f = force in pounds
s = distance in feet

Power

$$P = \frac{W}{t} \quad \text{or} \quad P = \frac{fs}{t}$$

W = work
t = time
f = force
s = distance

Horsepower

$$\text{hp} = \frac{\text{ft.-lb. of work per min.}}{33{,}000}$$

$$\text{hp} = \frac{\text{ft.-lb. of work per sec.}}{550}$$

Water Power

$$\text{hp} = \frac{Fd \times 62.4}{550}$$

$$\text{hp} = 0.113\,Fd$$

F = flow in cu. ft./sec.
d = distance water falls, in feet

Brake Horsepower

$$\text{bhp} = \frac{2\pi RNW}{33{,}000}$$

$$\text{bhp} = \frac{RNW}{5252}$$

R = length of arm
N = engine speed in rpm
W = load in pounds

SAE Horsepower

$$\text{SAE hp} = \frac{D^2 \times N}{2.5}$$

D = diameter of cylinder or bore
N = number of cylinders

Engine Displacement

$$d = \pi r^2 \times \text{stroke} \times \text{no. cylinders}$$

r = radius of bore

Rear-Axle Ratio

$$r = \frac{T}{t} \qquad T = rt$$

r = ratio
T = number of teeth on ring gear
t = number of teeth on pinion gear

Electricity

$I = \frac{E}{R} \qquad E = IR \qquad R = \frac{E}{I}$

I = current in amperes

E = pressure in volts

R = resistance in ohms

$\text{hp} = \frac{\text{watts}}{746}$

$\text{hp} = \frac{\text{volts} \times \text{amperes}}{746}$

Distance

$D = rt \qquad r = \frac{D}{t} \qquad t = \frac{D}{r}$

D = distance
r = rate
t = time

Pulleys

$DS = ds \qquad d = \frac{DS}{s}$

$D = \frac{ds}{S} \qquad s = \frac{DS}{d}$

$S = \frac{ds}{D}$

D = diameter of driving pulley
S = speed of driving pulley
d = diameter of driven pulley
s = speed of driven pulley

Cutting Speed of Circular Saw

$S = \frac{C \times \text{rpm} \times D}{d \times 12}$

C = circumference of saw blade
rpm = revolutions per minute
D = diameter of driving pulley
d = diameter of driven pulley

Cutting Speed of Jointer Saw

$S = \frac{C \times \text{rpm}}{12}$

C = circumference of cutter
rpm = revolutions per minute

CHAPTER TEST

1. Find the pitch of a roof, if the span is 50′ and the rise is 10′.
2. How many board feet in the plank shown below?

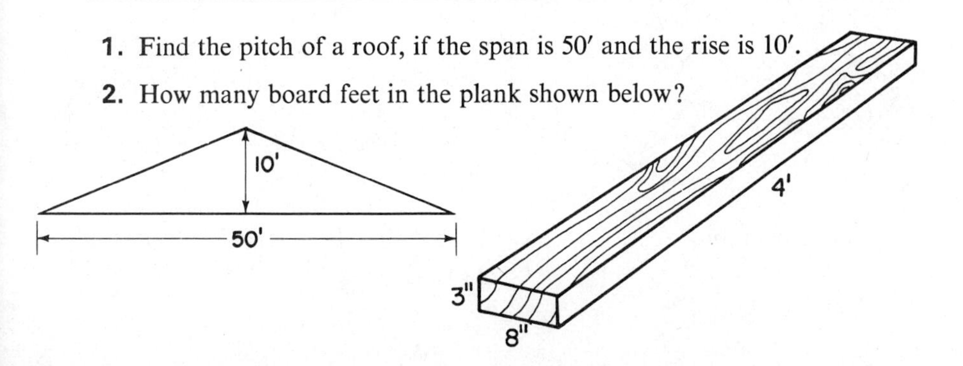

3. Find the work involved in lifting an engine 4 ft. if the engine weighs 400 lb. (Find the answer in foot-pounds.)

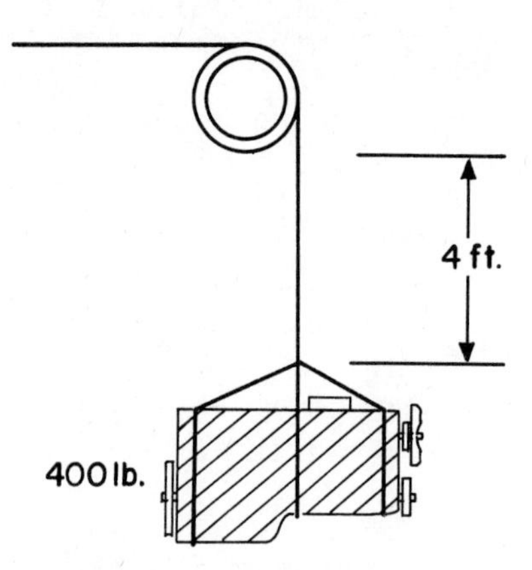

4. What horsepower is needed to raise 77,000 lb. a distance of 12 ft. in 4 min.?

5. Find the horsepower of a waterfall 20′ high with a flow of 350 cu. ft. per second.

6. Find the brake horsepower of an engine if the prony brake arm is 4 ft. long, the engine speed is 1200 rp.n, and the load is 120 lb.

7. Find the SAE horsepower of a 6-cylinder engine if the diameter of the cylinder is $3\frac{1}{2}''$.

8. Find the engine displacement in cubic inches if the engine has a $3\frac{1}{2}''$ bore, $3\frac{3}{4}''$ stroke, and is a V-8.

9. Find the rear-axle ratio if the ring gear has 36 teeth and the pinion gear 9.

10. Find the current (amperes) if the voltage is 115 volts and the resistance is 5 ohms.

11. Find the resistance if the voltage is 220 and the amperage is 44.

12. An electric motor running on a 110-volt line takes 5.1 amperes. What is its approximate horsepower?

13. How many hours will it take an airplane to go 2400 miles at 400 mi. per hour?

14. A man drives at the average rate of 40 mph for $2\frac{1}{2}$ hr., eats lunch, then travels at an average rate of 60 mph for $5\frac{1}{2}$ hr. How far did he travel?

15. Find the diameter of the driving pulley if the speed of the driving pulley is 240 rpm, the speed of the driven pulley is 360 rpm, and the diameter of the driven pulley is 6 inches.

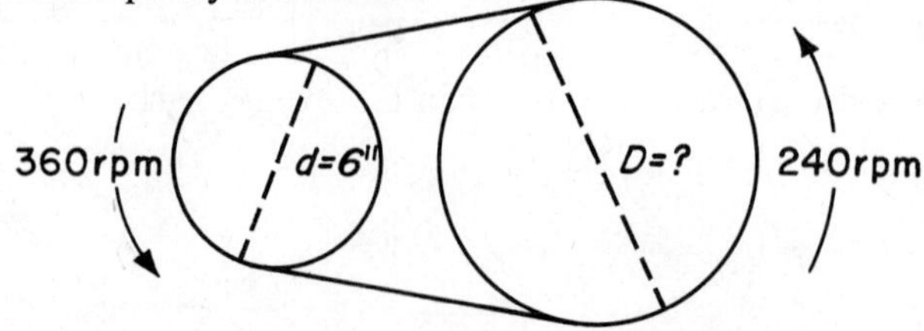

16. Find the cutting speed in feet per minute of the jointer blades if the circumference of the cutter is 11 in., and the pulley is turning at 2400 rpm.

MAINTAINING YOUR SKILLS

Add.

1. $\begin{array}{r} 22 \\ 47 \\ +\ 56 \\ \hline \end{array}$

2. $\begin{array}{r} 475 \\ 293 \\ +\ 777 \\ \hline \end{array}$

3. $\begin{array}{r} 10{,}550 \\ 9{,}275 \\ +\ \ 226 \\ \hline \end{array}$

4. $\frac{1}{4} + 2\frac{5}{8}$

5. $\frac{3}{5} + \frac{3}{10} + \frac{4}{5}$

6. $25.8 + 135.7 + 35.78$

Subtract.

7. $\begin{array}{r} 57 \\ -\ 23 \\ \hline \end{array}$

8. $\begin{array}{r} 27.5 \\ -\ 14.3 \\ \hline \end{array}$

9. $\begin{array}{r} 3{,}247 \\ -\ \ 179 \\ \hline \end{array}$

10. $\frac{5}{8} - \frac{1}{2}$

11. $(\frac{1}{4} + \frac{3}{4}) - \frac{1}{8}$

12. $3.75 - 2.54$

Multiply.

13. 27×35

14. $187 \times .25$

15. 27.90×2.6

16. 2.45×27.6

17. $\frac{1}{7} \times \frac{3}{5} \times \frac{7}{9}$

18. $\frac{11}{4} \times \frac{2}{7} \times \frac{3}{22}$

Divide.

19. $26\overline{)130}$

20. $15\overline{)30795}$

21. $756\overline{)15120}$

22. $.45\overline{)13590}$

23. $33\overline{)111.1}$

24. $2.5\overline{)2.756}$

Add or subtract as indicated.

25. $\begin{array}{r} 27^\circ\ 30' \\ +\ 15^\circ\ 22' \\ \hline \end{array}$

26. $\begin{array}{r} 38^\circ\ 25'\ 10'' \\ +\ \ 8^\circ\ \qquad 55'' \\ \hline \end{array}$

27. $\begin{array}{r} 47^\circ\ 40'\ 23'' \\ +\ 23^\circ\ 52'\ 47'' \\ \hline \end{array}$

28. $\begin{array}{r} 45^\circ\ 35'\ 24'' \\ -\ 23^\circ\ 19'\ 11'' \\ \hline \end{array}$

29. $\begin{array}{r} 67^\circ\ 27' \\ -\ 15^\circ\ 30' \\ \hline \end{array}$

30. $\begin{array}{r} 25^\circ\ \qquad 30'' \\ -\ 10^\circ\ 15'\ 40'' \\ \hline \end{array}$

The importance of measurement in industry is illustrated by these two pictures. The steel ring weighs 180,000 lb. and has a diameter of 22 ft. The designer is working on the development of an experimental sports car.

Systems of Measurement

OBJECTIVES

1. To review the units of measure in the United States Customary System of Measurement.

2. To learn how to convert measures in the United States system.

3. To become familiar with the International (Metric) System of Measurement and conversion within it.

4. To learn about conversion units between the United States and metric systems.

5. To learn how centigrade and Fahrenheit scales are related.

In the last chapter you learned many measurement formulas. In using these formulas in industry it is often necessary or convenient to change, or *convert,* from one unit of measurement to another. In this chapter you will review common units in the United States Customary System of Measurement. You will also learn about another important system, the International, or Metric, System.

United States Customary System of Measurement

6–1 Linear Measure

Stress this. Suppose you have a hall rug 10 ft. 6 in. long and 20 in. wide. To find its area, you know that both measurements must be expressed either in feet or in inches. Do you need to review the following familiar relations in our system of measurement? TM p. 15 , 6-1

LINEAR MEASURE

12 inches (in.) = 1 foot (ft.)
3 feet = 1 yard (yd.) = 36 inches
$5\frac{1}{2}$ yards or $16\frac{1}{2}$ feet = 1 rod (rd.)
5280 feet = 1 mile (mi.)

EXAMPLE 1

How many inches apart are two posts if a 14-foot board just fits between them?

Solution. 1 ft. = 12 in.
Therefore 14 ft. = 14 × 12 in. = **168 in.**

EXAMPLE 2

How many feet of pipe do you need to connect two pipes 132 in. apart?

Solution. 12 in. = 1 ft.
1 in. = $\frac{1}{12}$ ft.
132 in. = 132 × $\frac{1}{12}$ ft. = $\frac{132}{12}$ ft.
= **11 ft.**

Encourage the students to ask themselves if their results are consistent with experience. For instance, a measurement in inches should be much greater numerically (about 10 times) than a measurement in feet.

EXERCISES

A

1. How many inches are in 6 yd.?
2. How many feet are in 150 in.?
3. How many miles in 10,560 yd.?
4. How many yards are in 2 ft.?
5. How many inches in 1,760 yd.?
6. The distance from Detroit to Cleveland is 92 mi. What is this distance in feet? in yards?

7. How many pieces of string $4\frac{1}{2}$ in. long can be cut from a spool holding 225 yd.?

8. How many books $\frac{3}{4}''$ thick can be placed on a shelf $6\frac{1}{2}'$ long?

9. How many yards of chain-link fencing are needed to enclose a rectangular playground 148 ft. long and 122 ft. wide? (Hint: Find the perimeter first. Recall page 158.)

10. The four sides of an irregularly shaped tract of land measure 182 ft., 205 ft., 178 ft., and 194 ft., What is the perimeter of the lot in rods?

6–2 Square Measure

You will recall that areas are measured in square units (see page 65). Do you remember these relations of square measure in our United States system? The examples show how we change from a measurement in one unit to an equivalent one in another unit. The principle is exactly the same as for linear measure.

SQUARE MEASURE

144 square inches (sq. in.)	=	1 square foot (sq. ft.)
9 square feet	=	1 square yard (sq. yd.) or 1296 square inches
$30\frac{1}{4}$ square yards	=	1 square rod (sq. rd.) or $272\frac{1}{4}$ square feet
160 square rods	=	1 acre (A) or 4840 square yards

EXAMPLE 1

You wish to buy a carpet selling at $7.25 per square yard and the area to be covered is 153 sq. ft. How much will the carpet cost?

Solution. Since we know the cost per square yard, we need to know the number of square yards in 153 sq. ft.

$$
\begin{aligned}
9 \text{ sq. ft.} &= 1 \text{ sq. yd.} \\
1 \text{ sq. ft.} &= \tfrac{1}{9} \text{ sq. yd.} \\
153 \text{ sq. ft.} &= 153 \times \tfrac{1}{9} \text{ sq. yd.} \\
&= \tfrac{153}{9} \text{ sq. yd.} \\
&= 17 \text{ sq. yd.}
\end{aligned}
$$

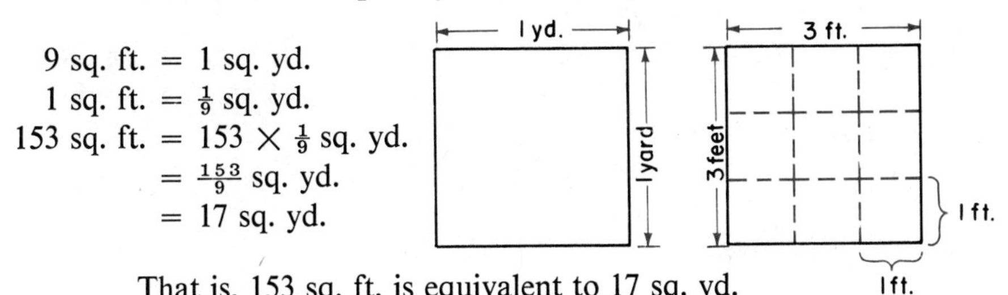

That is, 153 sq. ft. is equivalent to 17 sq. yd.

$$
\begin{aligned}
\text{Cost} &= 17 \times \$7.25 \\
&= \mathbf{\$123.25}
\end{aligned}
$$

EXAMPLE 2

Convert 24 sq. ft. to square inches.

Solution. 1 sq. ft. = 144 sq. in.
24 sq. ft. = 24 × 144 sq. in. = 3456 sq. in.

An area of 24 sq. ft. is equivalent to 3456 sq. in.

EXAMPLE 3

Convert 432 sq. in. to square feet.

Solution. 144 sq. in. = 1 sq. ft.
1 sq. in. = $\frac{1}{144}$ sq. ft.
432 sq. in. = 432 × $\frac{1}{144}$ sq. ft. = $\frac{432}{144}$ sq. ft. = 3 sq. ft.

Thus, an area of 432 sq. in. is equivalent to 3 sq. ft.

When you convert from square inches to square feet which numerical measure will be the larger? Ask this as a check when making conversions.

EXAMPLE 4

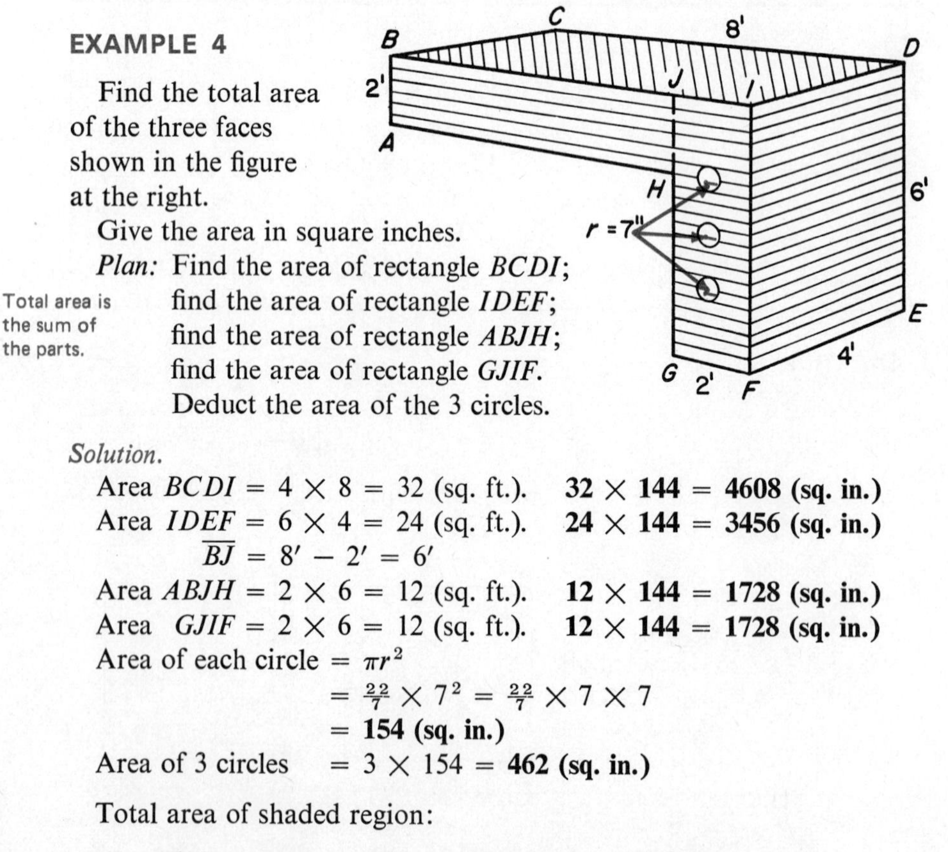

Find the total area of the three faces shown in the figure at the right.

Give the area in square inches.

Plan: Find the area of rectangle *BCDI*;
find the area of rectangle *IDEF*;
find the area of rectangle *ABJH*;
find the area of rectangle *GJIF*.
Deduct the area of the 3 circles.

Total area is the sum of the parts.

Solution.

Area *BCDI* = 4 × 8 = 32 (sq. ft.). **32 × 144 = 4608 (sq. in.)**
Area *IDEF* = 6 × 4 = 24 (sq. ft.). **24 × 144 = 3456 (sq. in.)**
$\overline{BJ}$ = 8′ − 2′ = 6′
Area *ABJH* = 2 × 6 = 12 (sq. ft.). **12 × 144 = 1728 (sq. in.)**
Area *GJIF* = 2 × 6 = 12 (sq. ft.). **12 × 144 = 1728 (sq. in.)**

Area of each circle = πr^2
$= \frac{22}{7} \times 7^2 = \frac{22}{7} \times 7 \times 7$
= **154 (sq. in.)**

Area of 3 circles = 3 × 154 = **462 (sq. in.)**

Total area of shaded region:

4608 + 3456 + 1728 + 1728 − 462 = **11,058 (sq. in.)**

EXERCISES

A

1. How many square inches are in 13 sq. ft.?
2. How many square feet are in 5 sq. yd.?
3. How many square inches are in 9 sq. yd.?
4. How many square yards are in 360 sq. ft.?
5. How many square feet are in 288 sq. in.?

B

6. Find the cost of two coats of paint for the outside of a barn, including the door. Paint costs $7.50 per gallon, and a gallon covers 250 sq. ft. Subtract the area of 8 windows at 25 sq. ft. each.

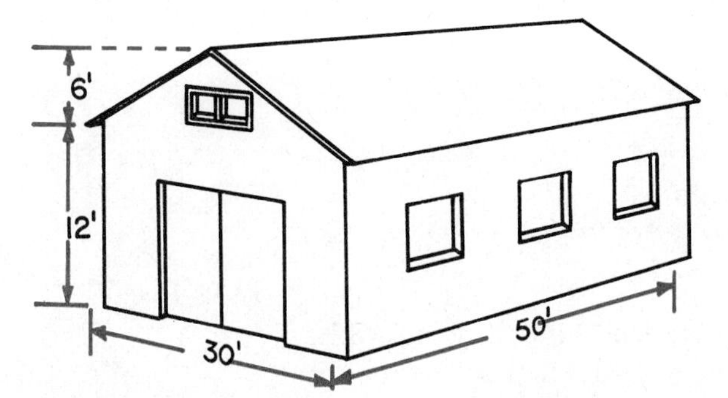

7. a. Find the lateral area of the cone in square inches.
   Formula: $L = \pi r l$, where r = radius of the base, and l = the slant height.
   b. Find the total area of the cone in square inches.
   Formula: $S = \pi r l + \pi r^2$.

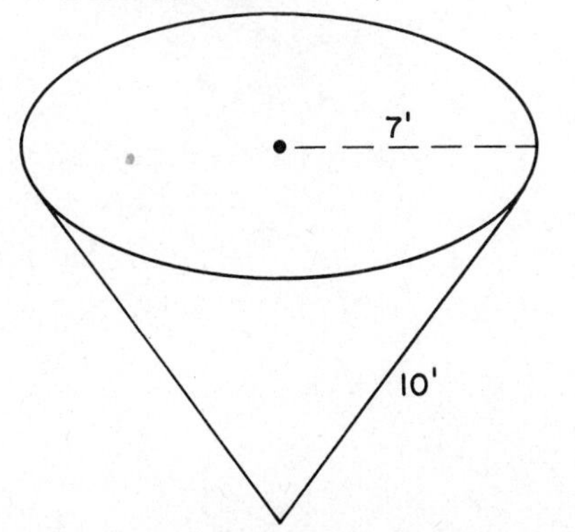

8. Find the total area of this cylinder in square yards, excluding the lower base. Formula: $S = 2\pi rh + \pi r^2$. ($\pi = \frac{22}{7}$)

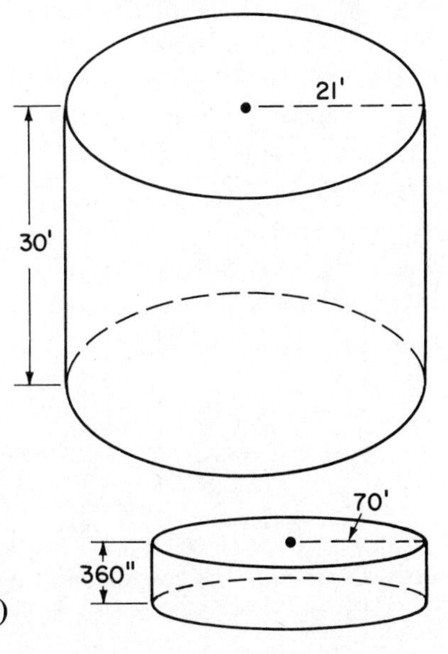

9. Find the total area of the cylinder at the right in square feet.
   Formula: $S = 2\pi rh + 2\pi r^2$. ($\pi = \frac{22}{7}$)

10. **a.** Find the perimeter in inches.
b. Find the area in square inches.
c. Find the area in square feet.

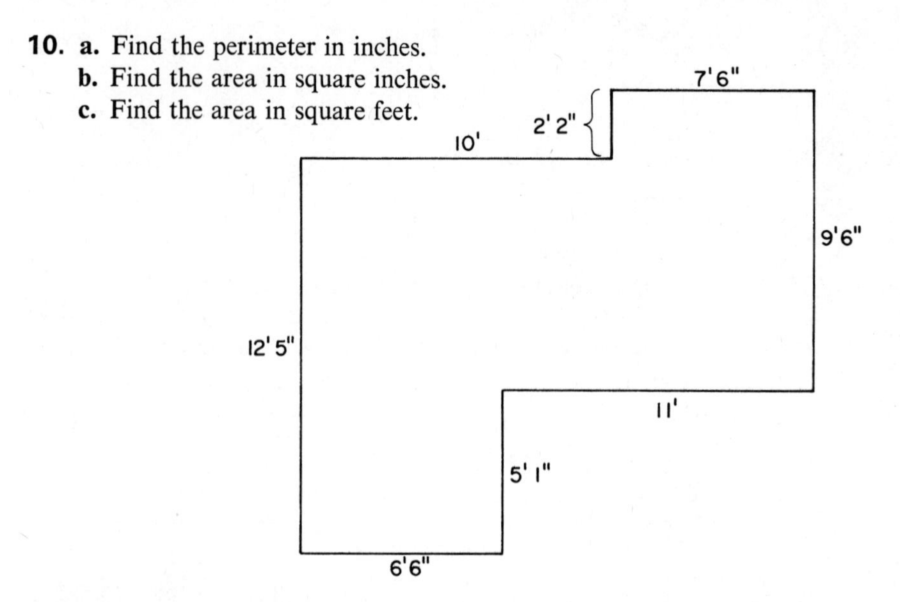

SELF-ANALYSIS TEST I

Time: 10 minutes

1. How many inches are there in 4 yd.?
2. How many yards are there in 7 ft.?
3. How many feet are there in 132 in.?
4. How many square feet are there in 12 sq. yd.?
5. How many square yards are there in 3600 sq. ft.?
6. How many square inches are there in 6 sq. ft.?
7. What is the total area, in square inches, of the rectangular prism shown?

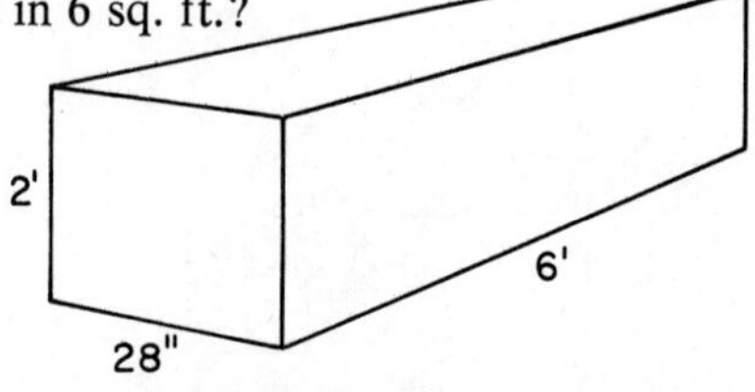

8. Find the lateral area of the cylinder, in square yards, if the radius is 60″ and the height is 10′.

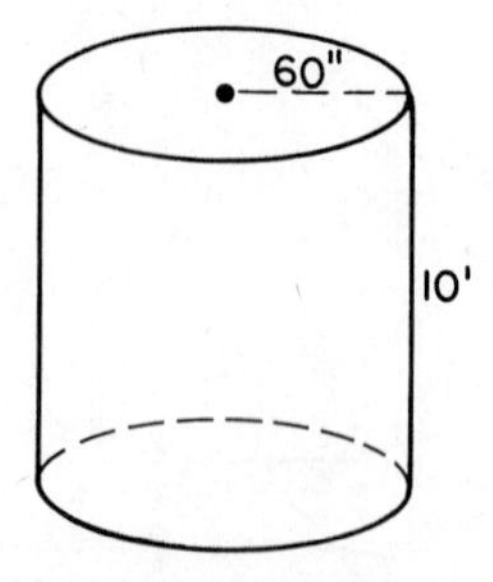

9. What is the lateral area (L), in square feet, if the radius of the cone is 24″ and the slant height is 3′?

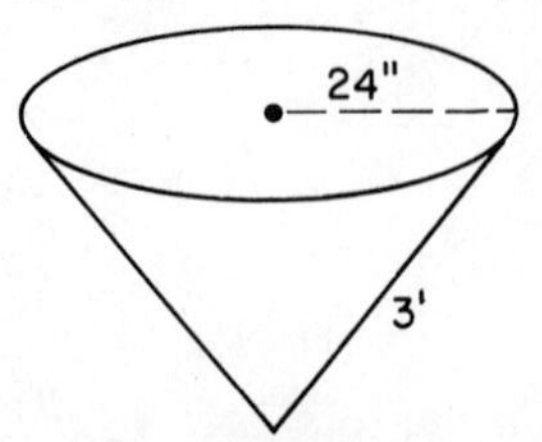

10. Determine the cost of painting the cylinder in Exercise 8, if the cost of the paint is $5.00 per gallon and a gallon covers 110 sq. ft.

6–3 Cubic Measure

Suppose you were trying to build a patio for your home. How would you go about buying the cement necessary to pour the patio?

In most cases, cement is purchased by the cubic yard. The drawing shows the dimensions of the patio as 16′ × 24′. Assuming an average depth of 4″, we can calculate the number of cubic yards of cement needed.

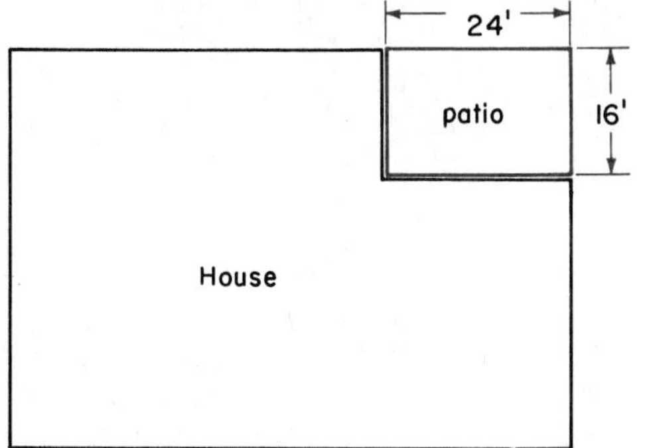

The patio can be thought of as a rectangular prism.

Volume = area of base × height
Height $= 4 \times \frac{1}{12} = \frac{4}{12}$ (ft.)
$V = Bh$
$V = (16 \times 24)(\frac{4}{12})$
$V = 128$ (cu. ft.)

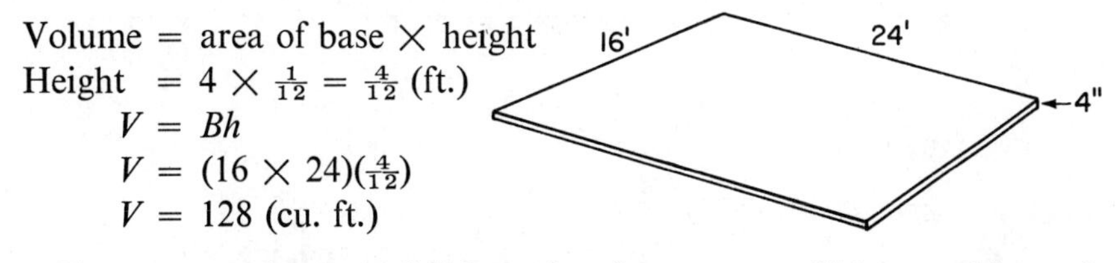

To compute the cost of 128 cu. ft. of concrete at $15 per cubic yard, we first need to find the number of cubic yards in 128 cu. ft. Since one cubic yard contains 27 cu. ft., we divide 128 by 27.

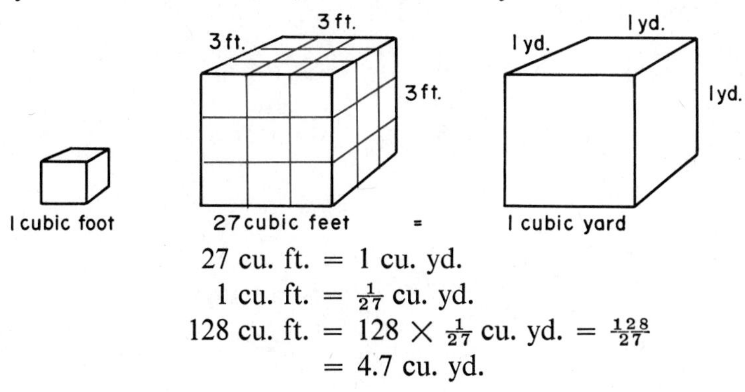

27 cu. ft. = 1 cu. yd.
1 cu. ft. = $\frac{1}{27}$ cu. yd.
128 cu. ft. = $128 \times \frac{1}{27}$ cu. yd. = $\frac{128}{27}$
= 4.7 cu. yd.

This is approximately 5 cu. yd., and in fact we would order 5 cu. yd. in order to guarantee having enough concrete. At $15 per cubic yard, the cost would be 5 × $15, or **$75.**

The conversion of cubic inches to cubic feet, and cubic feet to cubic inches, is based on the fact that 1 cu. ft. contains 1728 cu. in., as suggested by the following drawing.

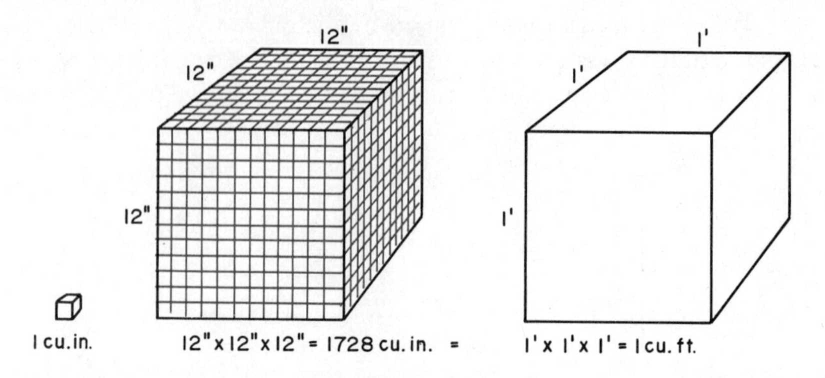

CUBIC MEASURE

1728 cubic inches (cu. in.) = 1 cubic foot (cu. ft.)
27 cubic feet = 1 cubic yard (cu. yd.)

EXAMPLE 1

How many cubic inches in 10 cu. ft.?

Solution. 1 cu. ft. = 1728 cu. in.
10 cu. ft. = 10 × 1728 cu. in. = **17,280 cu. in.**

EXAMPLE 2

How many cubic feet in 34,560 cu. in.?

Solution. 1728 cu. in. = 1 cu. ft.

1 cu. in. = $\frac{1}{1728}$ cu. ft.

34,560 cu. in. = 34,560 × $\frac{1}{1728}$ cu. ft.

$\frac{34,560}{1728}$ cu. ft. = **20 cu. ft.**

EXERCISES

A

1. How many cubic feet in 3 cu. yd.?
2. How many cubic inches in $2\frac{1}{2}$ cu. ft.?
3. How many cubic inches in 5 cu. yd.?

4. How many cubic feet in the rectangular prism shown?

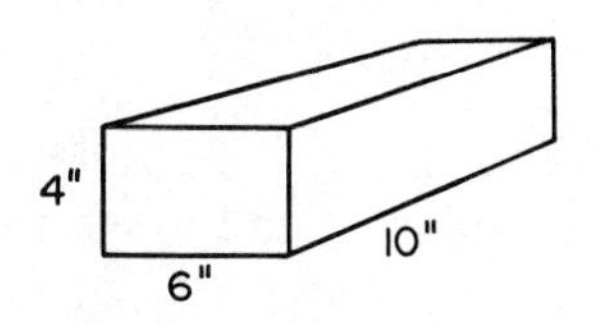

5. How many cubic yards in this cylinder?

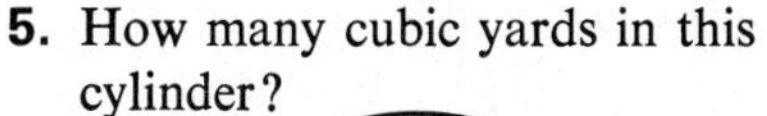

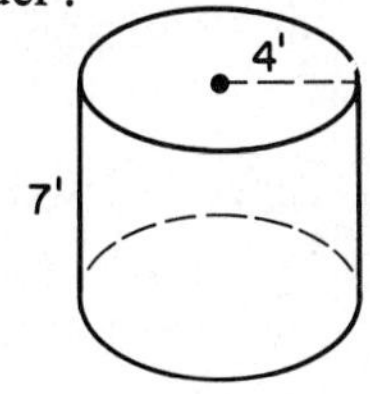

B

6. a. How many cubic feet in this cone?

b. What is the cost of the contents of the cone if a cubic foot of the material costs 75¢?

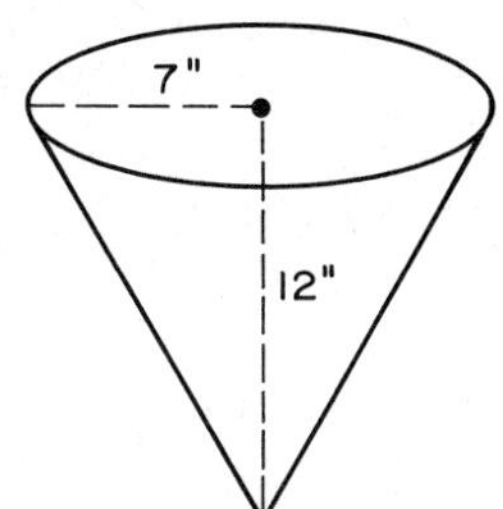

7. a. How many cubic yards of cement are needed to pour a rectangular patio 15 ft. by 18 ft. to a depth of 3 in.?

b. If the cement costs $15 a cubic yard, find the cost of pouring the patio.

6–4 Capacity and Weight

The volume of a container is often expressed in units such as pints or gallons. We then refer to the **capacity** of the container. Two systems, one for dry and one for liquid measure, are in common use.

CAPACITY	
Dry Measure	**Liquid Measure**
2 pints (pt.) = 1 quart (qt.)	16 fluid ounces (fl. oz.) = 1 pt.
8 qt. = 1 peck (pk.)	2 pt. = 1 qt.
4 pk. = 1 bushel (bu.)	4 qt. = 1 gallon (gal.)
	231 cu. in. = 1 gal.

The volumes of one pint dry measure and one pint liquid measure are not equal.

EXAMPLE 1

How many one-pint cartons are needed to hold 5 pecks of strawberries?

Solution. Since we want to find the number of pints in 5 pecks, we must first convert the 5 pecks to quarts, and then from quarts to pints.

Step 1. 8 qt. = 1 pk.
5 pk. = 5×8 qt. = 40 qt.

Step 2. 2 pt. = 1 qt.
40 qt. = 40×2 pt. = 80 pt.

Thus, **80 one-pint cartons will be needed.**

EXAMPLE 2

A case of motor oil contains 24 one-quart cans and costs $13.20. How much does a gallon of oil cost?

Solution.

4 qt. = 1 gal.
1 qt. = $\frac{1}{4}$ gal.
24 qt. = $24 \times \frac{1}{4}$ gal.
= $\frac{24}{4}$ gal.
= 6 gal.

Point out that, alternatively, we could calculate the cost of a one-quart can and multiply by 4.

There are 6 gallons of oil in a case of 24 one-quart cans. To determine the cost of one gallon, we divide the cost of the case by 6.

$$\$13.20 \div 6 = \$2.20$$

Thus, **a gallon of oil costs $2.20.**

You also need to be familiar with the common units of weight.

WEIGHT
16 ounces (oz.) = 1 pound (lb.)
2000 lb. = 1 (short) ton (T.)

EXAMPLE 3

An automobile weighs 4500 lb. How many tons does it weigh?

Solution.

2000 lb. = 1 T.
1 lb. = $\frac{1}{2000}$ T.
4500 lb. = $4500 \times \frac{1}{2000}$ T. = $\frac{4500}{2000}$ T. = **$2\frac{1}{4}$ T.**

Discuss some of the applications suggested by these exercises.

EXERCISES

A

1. How many quarts in 7 bu.?
2. How many fluid ounces in 2 qt.?
3. 96 pt. is equivalent to how many pecks?
4. 108 pt. of fluid is equivalent to how many gallons?
5. What fractional part of a ton is 32 oz.?
6. How many quart containers are needed to package 117 bu. of beans?
7. The inside of a rectangular plastic container for fluids measures 11″ long, 7″ wide, and $10\frac{1}{2}$″ deep. How many gallons of fluid will it hold?
8. If a ton of coal costs $53.20, what is the cost of 250 lb.?

B

9. Which is the better buy on oranges: 1 bu. for $5.76 or 1 qt. for 19¢?
10. Which is the better buy on chocolate sauce: a one-pint can for 59¢ or a 24-ounce can for 87¢?

Stress the necessity of converting each quantity into the same unit in order to compare prices.

SELF-ANALYSIS TEST II

Time: 15 minutes

1. How many cubic feet are in 9 cu. yd.?
2. How many cubic inches are in 5 cu. ft.?
3. How many cubic inches are in 10 cu. yd.?
4. How many quarts in 9 pk.?
5. How many pints in 2 gal.?
6. How many ounces in 27 lb.?
7. How many cubic feet are there in the cylinder?

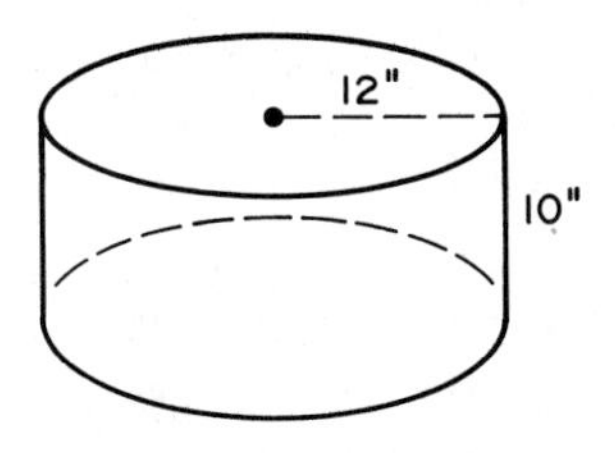

8. Find the number of square inches in the triangle.

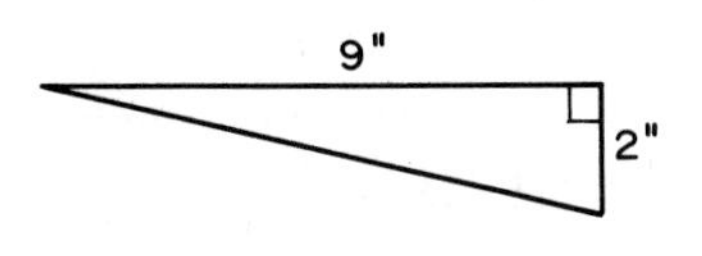

9. Find the number of cubic inches in the rectangular box.

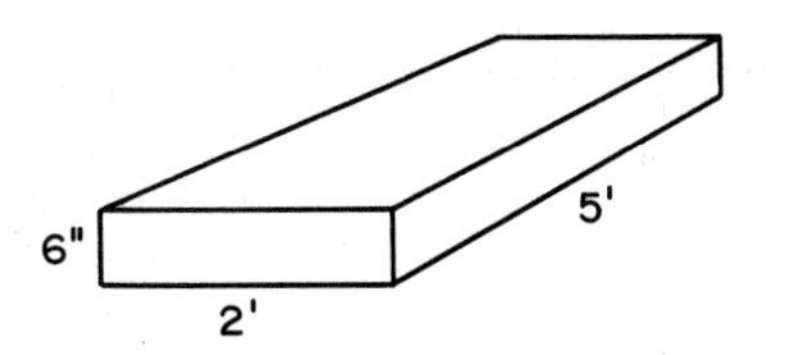

10. Find the number of square inches in the figure.

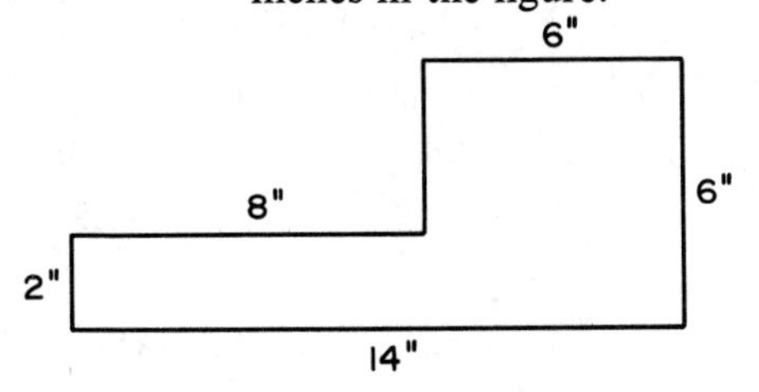

TM p. 15 , 6-5(1)

Metric System of Measurement

6–5 Linear Measure

Do you have trouble remembering the tables of measurement in our common system of measures? You will not have this difficulty with the metric system because it is a decimal system; that is, units are always $\frac{1}{10}$ the next larger unit.

Nearly every country except the United States uses the metric system as its official system of measurement. It is legal in the United States, but is used mainly in scientific work.

The basic unit of linear measurement in the United States system is the yard. In the metric system it is the **meter.** Officially, a yard is *defined* as 0.9144 meter. The following table shows the linear units of

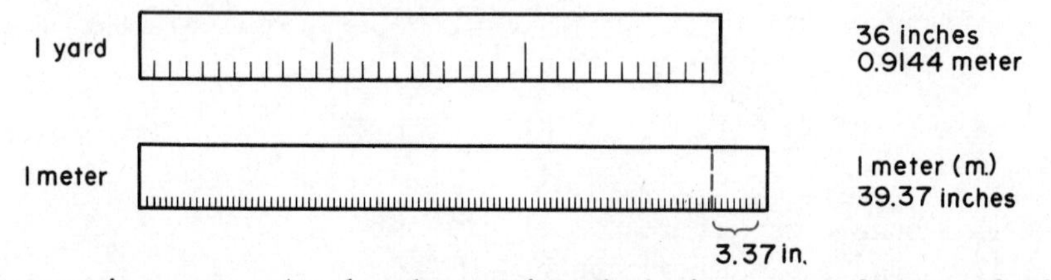

the metric system. As already mentioned, the important feature of this system is that each unit is $\frac{1}{10}$ the next larger unit. Thus, the decimeter is $\frac{1}{10}$ of a meter, a centimeter is $\frac{1}{10}$ of a decimeter, and a millimeter is $\frac{1}{10}$ of a centimeter. The most commonly used units are the millimeter, centimeter, meter, and kilometer. TM p. 15 , 6-5(2)

METRIC UNITS OF LENGTH

10 millimeters (mm.)	=	1 centimeter (cm.)	=	$\frac{1}{100}$ meter
10 centimeters	=	1 decimeter (dm.)	=	$\frac{1}{10}$ meter
10 decimeters	=	1 *meter* (m.)		
10 meters	=	1 decameter (dkm.)	=	10 meters
10 decameters	=	1 hectometer (hm.)	=	100 meters
10 hectometers	=	1 kilometer (km.)	=	1000 meters

EXAMPLE 1

Express 2.65 meters (m.) as centimeters (cm.).

Solution. The conversion consists of multiplying by 100, since one meter is equivalent to 100 centimeters.

$$1 \text{ m.} = 100 \text{ cm.}$$
$$2.65 \text{ m.} = 2.65 \times 100 \text{ cm.} = \mathbf{265 \text{ cm.}}$$

EXAMPLE 2

Complete the blank to make the sentence true:

756 mm. = _?_ cm.

Solution. 1 mm. = $\frac{1}{10}$ cm.
756 mm. = 756 × $\frac{1}{10}$ cm.
= $\frac{756}{10}$ cm. = **75.6 cm.**

EXAMPLE 3

6.5 m. = _?_ km.

Solution. Is a meter smaller or larger than a kilometer?
Will the number of kilometers be more or less than the number of meters?

These are good questions for the student to ask as a check.

1000 m. = 1 km.
1 m. = $\frac{1}{1000}$ km.
6.5 m. = 6.5 × $\frac{1}{1000}$ km. = **.0065 km.**

EXERCISES

Complete each of the following with the number which makes the sentence true.

A

1. 250 mm. = _?_ dm.
2. 5000 m. = _?_ cm.
3. 100 km. = _?_ mm.
4. 2 hm. = _?_ dm.
5. 450 mm. = _?_ cm.
6. 70 m. = _?_ mm.
7. 320 dkm. = _?_ km.
8. 5 mm. = _?_ dm.
9. 15 hm. = _?_ m.
10. 950 dkm. = _?_ dm.
11. 4800 cm. = _?_ km.
12. 325 hm. = _?_ cm.
13. .2 m. = _?_ cm.
14. .085 km. = _?_ m.
15. 10.5 km. = _?_ dkm.
16. 4.5 mm. = _?_ m.

6–6 Conversion of Linear Units

Using the relationships TM p. 15 , 6-6

1 yd. = 0.9144 m.

and

1 m. = 39.37 in.

you can easily make conversions from one system to the other. For example, to change 3 yards to meters, multiply 3 by .9144. A number, such as .9144, used in changing from one system to another is called a **conversion factor.**

EXAMPLE 1

Convert 40 m. to inches.

Solution.
$$1 \text{ m.} = 39.37 \text{ in.}$$
$$40 \text{ m.} = 40 \times 39.37 \text{ in.}$$
$$= \mathbf{1574.8\ in.}$$

EXAMPLE 2

Convert 50 m. to yards.

Solution.
$$1 \text{ m.} = 39.37 \text{ in.}$$
$$50 \times 39.37 = 1968.5 \text{ in.}$$
$$\frac{1968.5}{36} = \mathbf{54.7\ yd.}$$

EXAMPLE 3

Convert 9 ft. to meters.

Solution.
$$9 \text{ ft.} = 3 \text{ yd.}$$
$$1 \text{ yd.} = 0.9144 \text{ m.}$$
$$3 \text{ yd.} = 3 \times 0.9144 \text{ m.} = 2.7432 \text{ m., or approximately } \mathbf{2.7\ m.}$$

This ruler shows the relationship between inches, centimeters, and millimeters. You can see that 1 in. = 2.54 cm. = 25.4 mm.

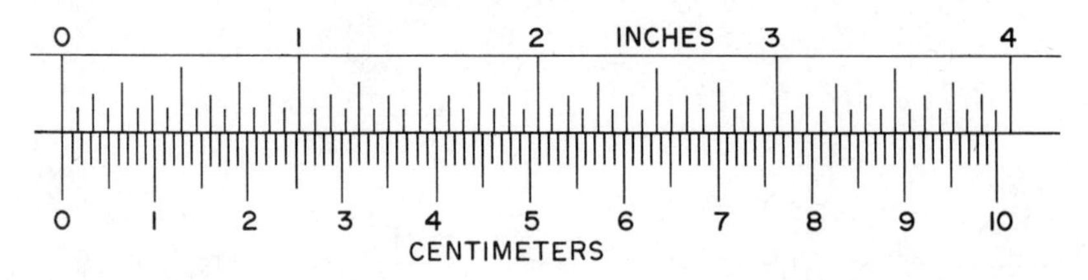

The table below lists some conversion factors between various units of the metric system and the United States system. It is not important to memorize such conversion factors. It is more important to understand how to use them. You should try to remember, however, that one inch is about $2\frac{1}{2}$ cm., one meter is about 39 in., and one kilometer is about $\frac{2}{3}$ mi. Exact conversion factors are always available from tables.

This is useful information.

This table is for reference, and not to be committed to memory.

APPROXIMATELY EQUIVALENT LINEAR UNITS

Metric Unit	U.S. Unit
1 mm.	0.04 in.
1 cm.	0.39 in.
1 m.	39.37 in.
1 km.	0.62 mi.
2.54 cm. (exact)	1 in.
0.30 m.	1 ft.
0.91 m.	1 yd.
1.61 km.	1 mi.

EXAMPLE 4

Convert 20 in. to centimeters.

Solution. $1 \text{ in.} = 2.54 \text{ cm.}$
$20 \text{ in.} = 20 \times 2.54 \text{ cm.}$
$= \mathbf{50.8 \text{ cm.}}$

EXAMPLE 5

Convert 508 cm. to inches.

Solution. $1 \text{ cm.} = 0.39 \text{ in.}$
$508 \text{ cm.} = 508 \times 0.39 \text{ in.}$
$= \mathbf{198.12 \text{ in.}}$

EXAMPLE 6

Convert 200 km. to miles.

Solution. $1 \text{ km.} = 0.62 \text{ mi.}$
$200 \text{ km.} = 200 \times 0.62 \text{ mi.} = \mathbf{124 \text{ mi.}}$

EXAMPLE 7

Convert 984.24 ft. to meters.

Solution. $1 \text{ ft.} = 0.30 \text{ m.}$
$984.24 \text{ ft.} = 984.24 \times 0.30 \text{ m.} = 295.272$, or **295.3 m.**

EXERCISES

Complete each of the following with the number which makes the sentence true

A

1. 20 ft. = __?__ cm.
2. 5280 ft. = __?__ m.
3. 20 mi. = __?__ km.
4. 5000 km. = __?__ mi.
5. 200 cm. = __?__ yd.
6. Convert 20 m. to inches.
7. Convert 12 ft. to meters.
8. Convert 35 m. to yards.
9. Convert 12 m. to inches.
10. Convert 15 ft. to meters.
11. Convert 27 m. to yards.
12. Convert 14 m. to feet.
13. Convert 10 yd. to meters.

B

14. In the Olympics how high is the 10-meter diving board in feet?
15. The 200-meter dash is how many yards?
16. The 800-meter run is how many feet?
17. If a man does 8.7 m. in the long jump, how many feet is this?
18. If a swimmer goes 400 m., how many yards is this?

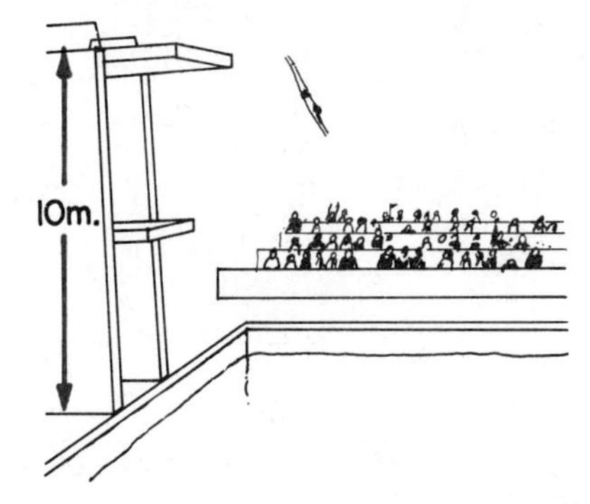

19. Find the perimeter in meters.

20. Find the perimeter in inches.

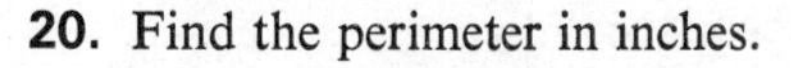

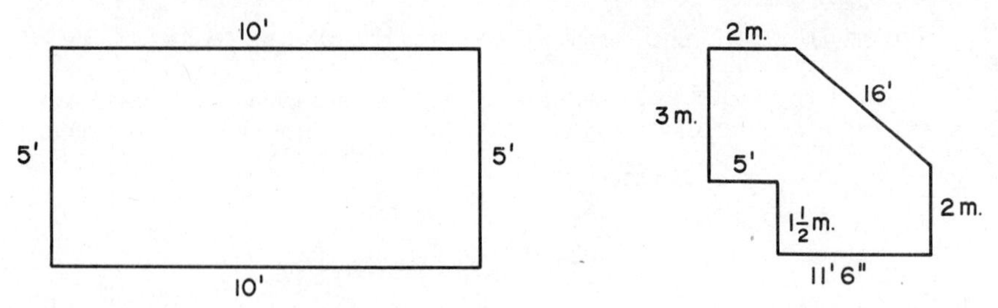

6–7 Square Measure

In measuring area in the metric system, the basic unit is the **square meter.** As in the United States system, other units of area can be obtained by using other units of linear measure. Thus, area can be measured in square millimeters, square centimeters, square meters, and so on. TM p. 15 , 6-7

Some common conversion factors are given in this table for units of area in the United States and metric systems.

This table is for reference, and not to be committed to memory.

APPROXIMATELY EQUIVALENT UNITS OF AREA	
Metric Unit of Area	**U.S. Unit of Area**
1 sq. mm.	0.002 sq. in.
1 sq. cm.	0.16 sq. in.
1 sq. m.	10.76 sq. ft.
1 sq. km.	0.39 sq. mi.
6.45 sq. cm.	1 sq. in.
0.09 sq. m.	1 sq. ft.
0.84 sq. m.	1 sq. yd.
2.59 sq. km.	1 sq. mi.

EXAMPLE 1

How many square millimeters in 1 sq. cm.?

Solution.

1 cm. = 10 mm. Therefore 1 sq. cm. = 10 × 10 = **100 sq. mm.**

EXAMPLE 2

Convert 100 sq. mm. to square inches.

Solution. 1 sq. mm. = .002 sq. in.

100 sq. mm. = 100 × .002 = **.20 sq. in.**

EXAMPLE 3

Convert 50 sq. m. to square feet.

Solution. 1 sq. m. = 10.76 sq. ft.
50 sq. m. = 50 × 10.76 = **538 sq. ft.**

EXAMPLE 4

Convert 30 sq. ft. to square meters.

Solution. 1 sq. ft. = 0.09 sq. m.
30 sq. ft. = 30 × .09 = **2.70 sq. m.**

EXERCISES

A

1. 3 sq. cm. = _?_ sq. mm.
2. 1 sq. m. = _?_ sq. cm.
3. 5 sq. m. = _?_ sq. cm.
4. 1 sq. km. = _?_ sq. m.
5. 4 sq. km. = _?_ sq. m.
6. Convert 500 sq. mm. to square inches.
7. Convert 75 sq. m. to square feet.
8. Convert 45 sq. ft. to square meters.
9. Convert 10 sq. mi. to square kilometers.
10. Convert 300 sq. km. to square miles.

EXAMPLE 5

Find the number of square inches in the following figure.

Solution.

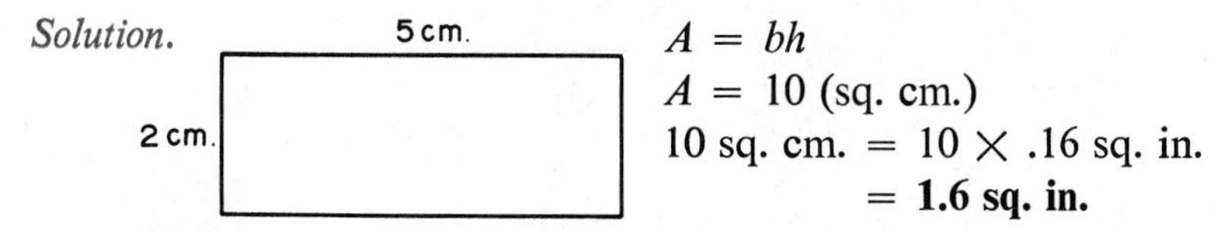

$A = bh$
$A = 10$ (sq. cm.)
10 sq. cm. = 10 × .16 sq. in.
= **1.6 sq. in.**

EXAMPLE 6

Find the number of square centimeters in the following figure.

Solution.

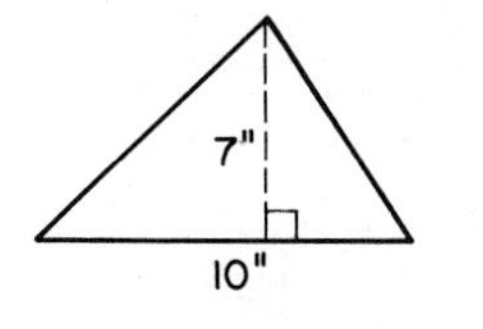

$A = \frac{1}{2}bh$
$A = \frac{1}{2}(7)(10)$
$A = 35$ (sq. in.)
1 sq. in. = 6.45 sq. cm.
35 sq. in. = 35 × 6.45 sq. cm.
= **225.75 sq. cm.**

EXERCISES

A

1. Find the area in square inches.

2. Find the area in square inches.

3. Find the area in square feet.

4. Find the area in square meters.

5. Find the area in square meters.

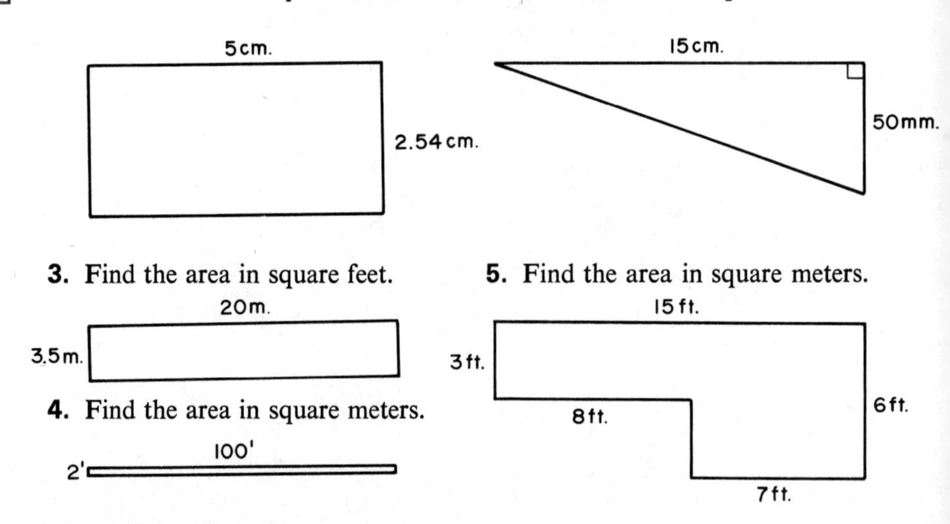

6–8 Cubic Measure

Volume in both the United States and metric systems is measured in cubic units. The basic unit of volume for the metric system is the **cubic meter.** A cube with each edge measuring 1 meter contains 1 cubic meter.

The following table gives conversion factors for different units of volume in the two systems.

This table is for reference, not for memorization.

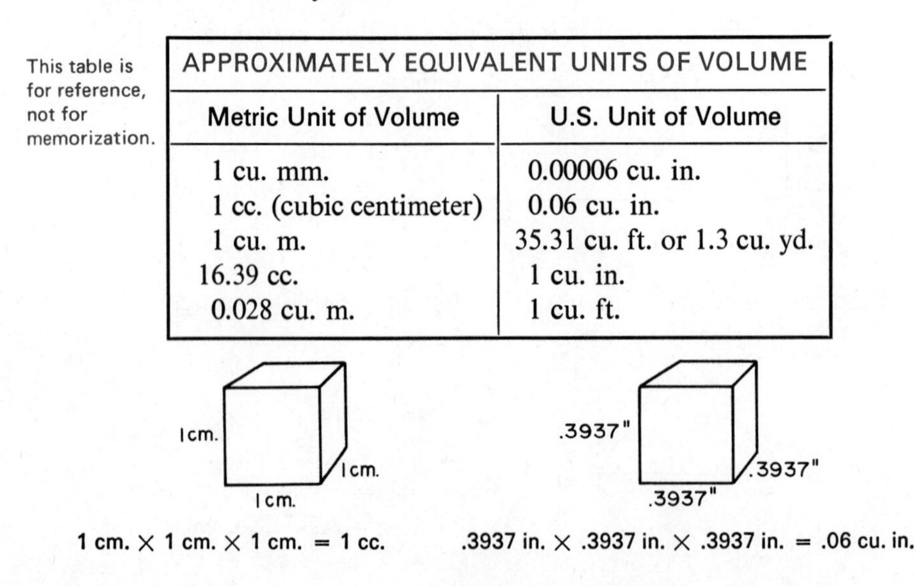

APPROXIMATELY EQUIVALENT UNITS OF VOLUME	
Metric Unit of Volume	**U.S. Unit of Volume**
1 cu. mm.	0.00006 cu. in.
1 cc. (cubic centimeter)	0.06 cu. in.
1 cu. m.	35.31 cu. ft. or 1.3 cu. yd.
16.39 cc.	1 cu. in.
0.028 cu. m.	1 cu. ft.

1 cm. × 1 cm. × 1 cm. = 1 cc.   .3937 in. × .3937 in. × .3937 in. = .06 cu. in.

EXAMPLE 1

How many cubic inches in 100 cc.?

Solution. 1 cc. = .06 cu. in.
100 cc. = 100 × .06 cu. in.
= **6 cu. in.**

EXAMPLE 2

How many cubic centimeters in 10 cu. in.?

Solution. 1 cu. in. = 16.39 cc.
10 cu. in. = 10 × 16.39 cc.
= **163.9 cc.**

EXAMPLE 3

Find the volume of the cylinder below in cubic centimeters.

Solution.

$$V = \pi r^2 h$$
$$V = \tfrac{22}{7}(7'')(7'')(10'')$$
$$V = 1540 \text{ cu. in.}$$

1 cu. in. = 16.39 cc.
1540 cu. in. = 1540 × 16.39 cc.
= **25,240.6 cc.**

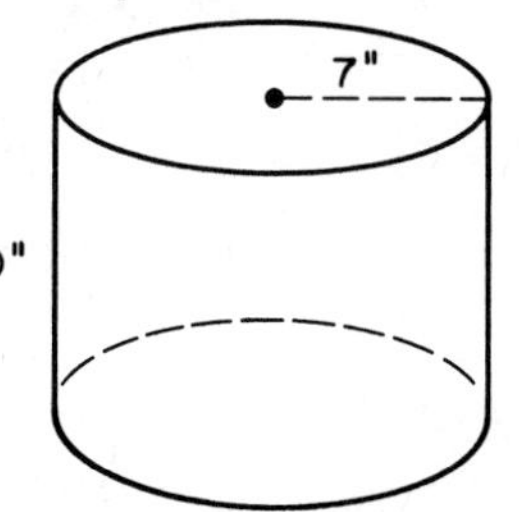

A

1. How many cubic inches in 27 cc.?
2. How many cubic meters in 10 cu. ft.?
3. How many cubic yards in 50 cu. m.?
4. Find the volume of this rectangular prism in cubic meters.

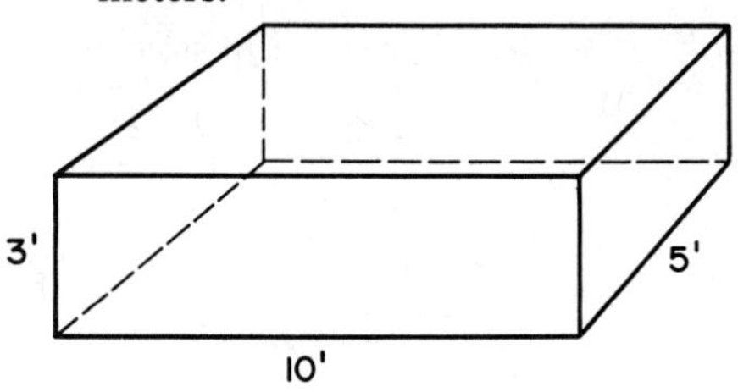

5. Find the volume of this cylinder in cubic inches.

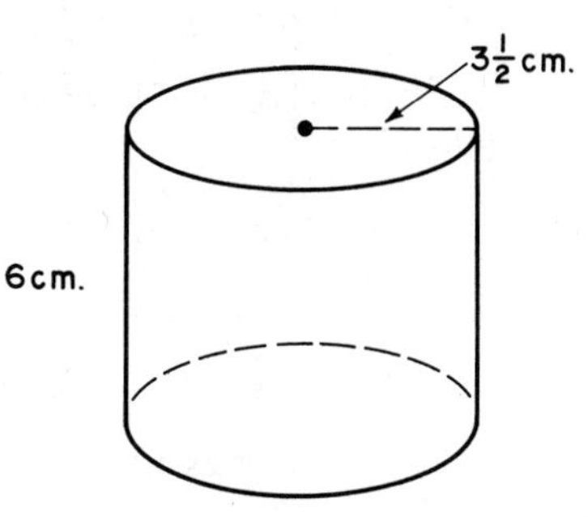

6–9 Units of Capacity

The unit of capacity in the metric system is the **liter.** A cubical container with an edge of 10 cm. holds exactly 1 liter; that is, 1 liter = 1000 cc.

The following table gives conversion factors for converting units of capacity from one system to the other. Notice that a liter is a little more than a quart. This is useful to remember.

This table is intended for reference only.

APPROXIMATELY EQUIVALENT UNITS OF CAPACITY	
Metric Unit of Capacity	U.S. Unit of Capacity
1 liter (l.)	2.1134 pt.
1 liter	1.0567 qt.
1 liter	0.2642 gal.
3.785 liters	1 gal.

EXAMPLE 1

How many gallons of paint in 10 liters?

Solution. 1 liter = .2642 gal.
10 liters = 10 × .2642
= **2.64 gal.**

In the United States we buy gasoline by the gallon. If you were visiting in Europe, which uses the metric system, you would have to think in terms of the liter.

EXAMPLE 2

a. Find the cost of 20 gal. of gasoline in the United States at 36¢ a gallon.

Solution. 20 × .36 = **$7.20**

b. 20 gal. of gasoline = __?__ liters.

Solution. 1 gal. = 3.785 liters

20 × 3.785 liters = **75.70 liters**

c. When 20 gal. cost \$7.20, what is the cost of one liter?

Solution. Cost of liter $= \dfrac{\text{Total cost}}{\text{no. of liters}}$

$$= \frac{\$7.20}{75.7} = \$.095, \text{ or about } \mathbf{10¢}.$$

EXAMPLE 3

If a car has a 427-cubic-inch engine, what is its capacity in liters?

Solution.

$$1 \text{ cu. in.} = 16.4 \text{ cc.}$$
$$427 \times 16.4 = 7002.8 \text{ cc.}$$
$$1000 \text{ cc.} = 1 \text{ liter}$$
$$\frac{7002.8}{1000} = \mathbf{7 \text{ liters, approximately}}$$

EXERCISES

Find the number that makes each sentence true.

A

1. 1 liter = ? cc.
2. 50 liters = ? qt.
3. 25 liters = ? gal.
4. Find the cost of 35 gal. of gasoline at 37.6 cents per gallon. What is the approximate cost per liter?
5. If a car has a 327-cubic-inch engine, what is its capacity in liters?

6–10 Units of Weight TM p. 15 , 6-10(1)

In everyday talk the terms weight and mass are often used interchangeably. However, weight and mass are not the same, though they are very closely related. The **mass** of an object is the amount of matter present, and does not change at different locations. The **weight** of an object is the measure of the force of gravity acting upon the object. The weight of an object varies at different places. (Note. In this book we will always assume that all objects referred to are subject to the earth's gravitational force, thereby allowing us to make direct comparisons between mass and weight.)

The unit of mass in the metric system is defined to be 1 cc. of water at its maximum density, called the **gram.** Since the gram is quite small, we often use the **kilogram** (1000 grams) as a unit of mass. A **metric ton** is equivalent in mass to a cubic meter of water. TM p. 16 , 6-10(2)

The following table shows the relationships between various metric measures and conversion factors for the corresponding units in the United States system.

It is recommended that ~~not~~ be required.

APPROXIMATELY EQUIVALENT UNITS OF WEIGHT	
Metric Unit of Mass	U.S. Unit of Weight
1 gram (gm.)	0.0353 oz.
1 kilogram (kg.)	2.2046 lb.
1 kg.	0.0011 ton (short)
28.3495 gm.	1 oz.
0.4536 kg.	1 lb.
907.1848 kg.	1 ton (short)

EXAMPLE

Convert 2000 lb. to kilograms.

Solution. 1 lb. = .4536 kg.
2000 lb. = 2000 × .4536 kg. = **907.2 kg.**

EXERCISES

Copy and complete the chart.

	MASS		CAPACITY	
	Gram	Milligram	Milliliter	Liter
	1	1000	1	.001
A 1.	30	?	20	?
2.	100	?	?	3
3.	250	?	200	?
4.	?	625	?	5

5. 6000 lb. = __?__ kg.
6. 50 tons = __?__ kg.
7. If the pool in the picture holds 10,000 gal. of water, how many cubic inches does it contain? (1 gal. = 231 cu. in.)

B

8. How many pounds does the water in Exercise 7 weigh? (A gallon of water weighs approximately 62.4 lb.)
9. If the tank on top of a 30-story building is 6 meters high, find the number of grams of water at maximum density it will hold?

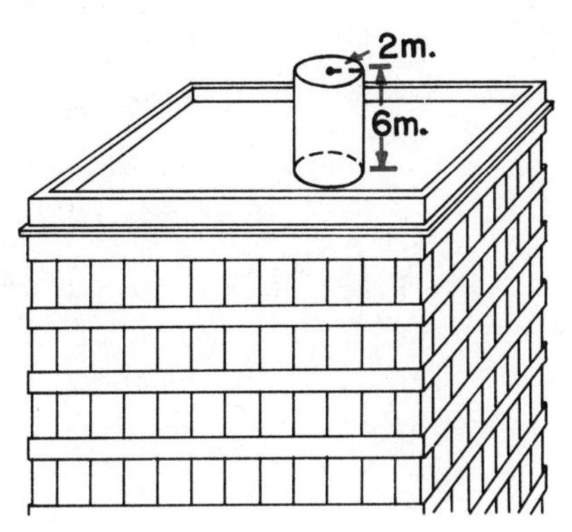

SELF-ANALYSIS TEST III

Time: 10 minutes

Students should be allowed to use tables to obtain conversion factors.

1. 12 in. = _?_ cm.
2. 2000 cm. = _?_ in.
3. 10 milliliters = _?_ liter.
4. 800 mm. = _?_ cm.
5. 25 ft. = _?_ cm.
6. 100 sq. m. = _?_ sq. ft.
7. 100 sq. km. = _?_ sq. mi.
8. 1 pt. = _?_ liters.
9. Find the cost of 10 gal. of gasoline at 40 cents a gallon.
10. In Exercise 9, how much per liter is the gasoline?

■ Other Conversions

6–11 Temperature

As you recall from page 88, two scales are commonly used to measure temperature, Fahrenheit and centigrade. On the Fahrenheit scale, the scale you are familiar with, water freezes at 32° and boils at 212°. On the centigrade scale, however, the corresponding readings are 0° and 100°. Most scientific calculations involving temperature use degrees centigrade.

	Boiling point	Freezing point	Difference
Fahrenheit scale	212°	32°	180°
Centigrade scale	100°	0°	100°

The diagram shows that a degree on the Fahrenheit scale is a smaller unit than on the centigrade scale. Thus, for temperatures above −40°F, the reading on the Fahrenheit scale will always be a larger number than its equivalent on the centigrade scale.

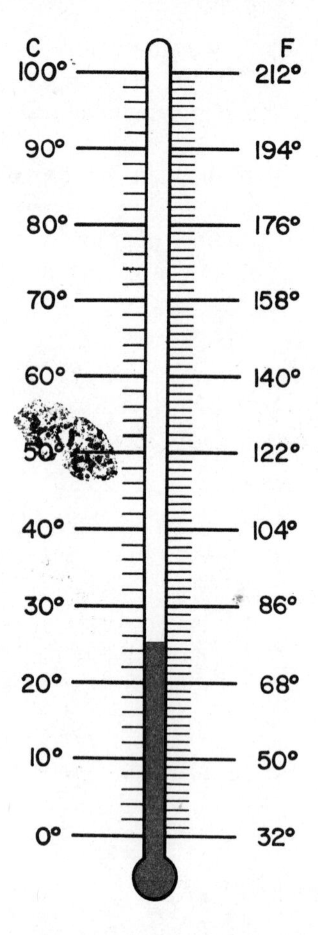

Two useful formulas for conversion from one scale to the other are

Stress the order of operations for each formula.

$$C = \tfrac{5}{9}(F - 32)$$
$$F = \tfrac{9}{5}C + 32$$

Note. The man who devised the centigrade scale was Anders Celsius, and the official name of the centigrade scale is the Celsius scale.

EXAMPLE 1

Convert 25°C to a Fahrenheit reading.

Solution.
$$\begin{aligned} F &= \tfrac{9}{5}C + 32 \\ &= \tfrac{9}{5}(25) + 32 \\ &= 45 + 32 = 77^\circ \end{aligned}$$

EXAMPLE 2

Convert 221°F to a centigrade reading.

Solution.
$$\begin{aligned} C &= \tfrac{5}{9}(F - 32) \\ &= \tfrac{5}{9}(221 - 32) \\ &= \tfrac{5}{9}(189) \\ &= 5(21) = \mathbf{105^\circ} \end{aligned}$$

EXAMPLE 3

A thermostat installed in an automobile is to maintain an engine temperature of 185°F. The temperature gauge is calibrated in the centigrade scale. Determine whether or not a reading of 84°C on the gauge is satisfactory.

Solution. Use the formula $F = \tfrac{9}{5}C + 32$.

$$F = (\tfrac{9}{5} \times 84) + 32 = 183\tfrac{1}{5}^\circ$$

Reading is near 185°, so it is satisfactory.

EXERCISES

A

1. 35°C = ___?___ °F
2. 59°F = ___?___ °C
3. 40°C = ___?___ °F

4. $95°F =$ __?__ $°C$.
5. At __?__ $°C$ water freezes.
6. At __?__ $°F$ water freezes.
7. At __?__ $°C$ water boils.
8. At __?__ $°F$ water boils.
9. Is the boiling point of water the same as for alcohol? (Consult reference books.)
10. How accurate do you think a thermometer is?

SELF-ANALYSIS TEST IV

Time: 10 minutes

1. Convert 30°C to a Fahrenheit reading.
2. Convert 200°F to a centigrade reading.
3. Water boils at __?__ °C.
4. Water freezes at __?__ °F.
5. Normal body temperature is 98.6°F. What is this temperature on the centigrade scale?
6. Water reaches its maximum density at 4°C. What is this temperature on the Fahrenheit scale?

CHAPTER SUMMARY

1. The United States Customary System of Measurement and the International (Metric) System of Measurement can both be used to express measurements of distance, area, volume, capacity, and weight.
2. The basic units of the United States system are the yard (distance), the bushel (capacity), the gallon (capacity), and the pound (weight).
3. The metric system is based on the decimal system; each unit in the metric system is always $\frac{1}{10}$ the next larger unit.
4. The basic units of the metric system are the meter (distance), the liter (capacity), and the gram (mass).
5. We can convert from one unit of measure to another by multiplying by the appropriate conversion factor.
6. Two scales are used to measure temperature—the centigrade and the Fahrenheit.

CHAPTER TEST

(You may use tables or charts in the book when necessary.)

1. How many inches are there in 8 ft.?
2. How many feet are there in 7 yd.?
3. How many inches are there in 27 yd.?
4. How many feet are there in 264 in.?
5. How many square feet are in 10 sq. yd.?
6. How many square yards are in 2700 sq. ft.?
7. How many square inches are in 7 sq. ft.?
8. How many cubic feet are in 5 cu. yd.?
9. How many cubic inches are in 10 cu. ft.?
10. 8000 lb. equals how many short tons?
11. 96 oz. equals how many pounds?
12. 100 mm. is equal to how many centimeters?
13. 20 decimeters equals how many meters?
14. 10 ft. equals how many centimeters?
15. 100 m. equals how many yards?
16. 4000 milliliters is equal to how many liters?
17. 2.365 liters is equal to how many pints?
18. Convert 45° centigrade to Fahrenheit.
19. Convert 100°F to centigrade.
20. Find the area in square centimeters.

23 cm.

7cm.

21. Find the area in square inches.

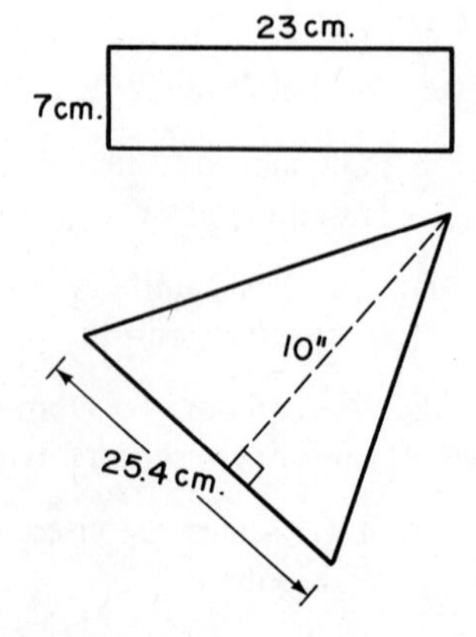

22. Find the area in square millimeters.

23. Find the volume in cubic centimeters.

24. Find the volume in cubic inches.

25. Find the volume in cubic millimeters.

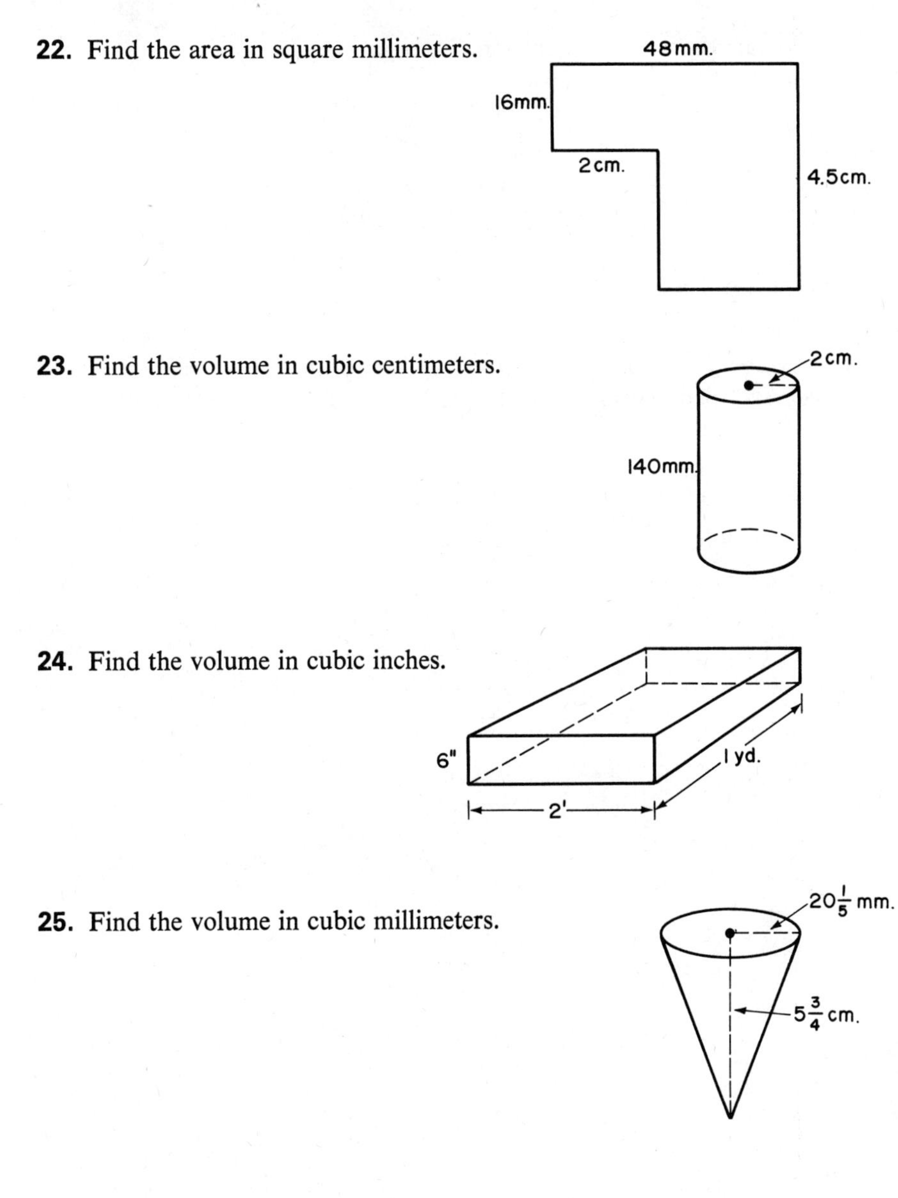

26. Find the perimeter. First estimate the answer.

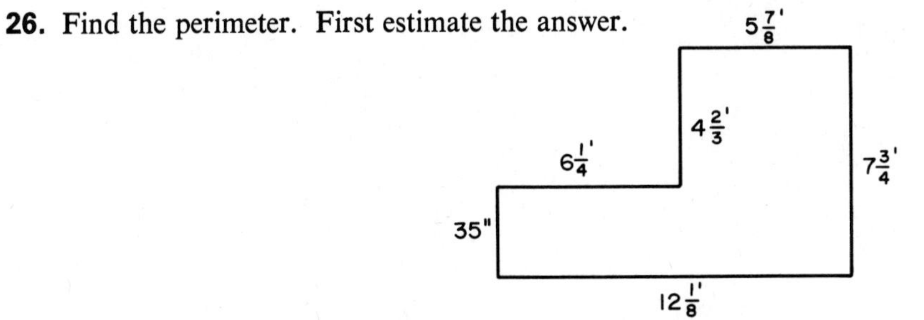

27. Estimate the volume in cubic millimeters. Then calculate it.

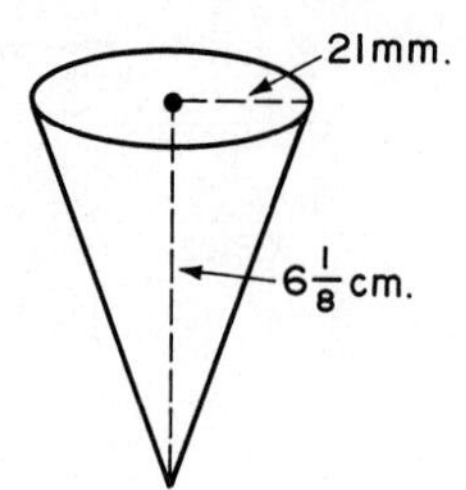

28. Find the cost of painting the top and sides of the cylindrical tank shown below, if paint costs $6 a gallon and covers 130 sq. ft. per gallon. First estimate the answer.

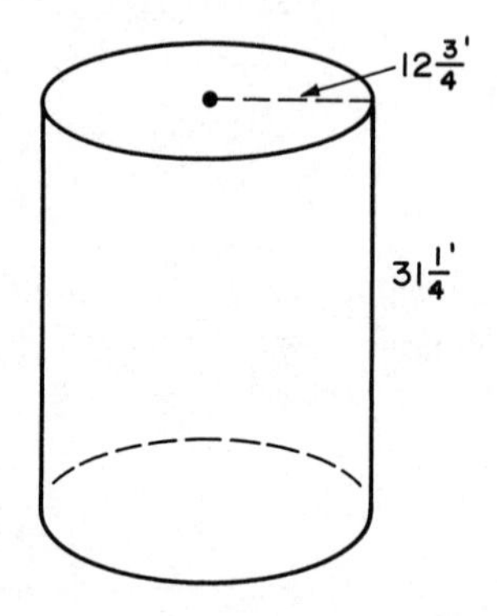

MAINTAINING YOUR SKILLS

Add.

1. $\begin{array}{r} 83 \\ 91 \\ +\ 87 \\ \hline \end{array}$ **2.** $\begin{array}{r} 291 \\ 452 \\ +\ 371 \\ \hline \end{array}$ **3.** $\begin{array}{r} 11{,}650 \\ 9{,}475 \\ 853 \\ +\ \ 85 \\ \hline \end{array}$ **4.** $\begin{array}{r} 29.62 \\ 82.40 \\ 2.93 \\ +\ .27 \\ \hline \end{array}$

5. $1\frac{1}{4} + 11\frac{3}{8}$ **6.** $\frac{5}{8} + \frac{1}{16} + 7\frac{1}{2}$

Subtract.

7. $\begin{array}{r} 92 \\ -\ 71 \\ \hline \end{array}$ **8.** $\begin{array}{r} 422.4 \\ -\ 219.1 \\ \hline \end{array}$ **9.** $\begin{array}{r} 27.23 \\ -\ 9.99 \\ \hline \end{array}$ **10.** $\frac{4}{7} - \frac{3}{14}$

11. $11\frac{3}{5} - 1\frac{2}{15}$ **12.** $(27\frac{3}{16} + 1\frac{3}{4}) - \frac{5}{16}$

Multiply.

13. 44×23 **14.** 155×44 **15.** $19.62 \times .72$ **16.** $.678 \times .456$

17. $\frac{6}{7} \times \frac{7}{11} \times \frac{5}{12}$ **18.** $1\frac{1}{2} \times \frac{5}{9} \times 7\frac{7}{8}$

Divide.

19. $7\overline{)294}$ **20.** $11\overline{)2530}$ **21.** $25\overline{)93.75}$ **22.** $.27\overline{)1.2150}$

23. $3.8\overline{)9.972}$ **24.** $.25\overline{)24973}$

25. $\frac{1}{2} \div \frac{1}{4}$ **26.** $\frac{3}{16} \div \frac{1}{8}$ **27.** $\frac{2}{7} \div \frac{4}{9}$

28. $2\frac{7}{8} \div 3\frac{5}{16}$ **29.** $11\frac{1}{3} \div 6\frac{2}{3}$ **30.** $5\frac{3}{10} \div 2\frac{1}{5}$

Many industries require the services of skilled draftsmen, whose training begins with the study of geometric constructions.

Geometric Constructions

OBJECTIVES

1. To learn the use of the compass and straightedge in making the basic geometric constructions.
2. To learn to use the basic constructions in more involved construction problems.
3. To discover some facts about triangles.
4. To study the construction of designs.

The highly skilled draftsman bases most of his work on the fundamental constructions of geometry. In this chapter you will learn these fundamental constructions and how to use them in more complicated situations. Accurate drawings require the careful use of drawing instruments and attention to detail.

Lines and Angles

7–1 Bisection of a Line Segment

In an earlier section (page 52) you learned how to use the compass to copy a line segment of given length. Draftsmen often need to find the **midpoint** of a line segment. To do so, they **bisect** the segment, as shown below.

CONSTRUCTION: *Bisecting a line segment.*

Procedure:

1. Set the compass with a radius greater than half the length of $\overline{AB}$.
2. With the compass point at A, draw an arc on each side of $\overline{AB}$.

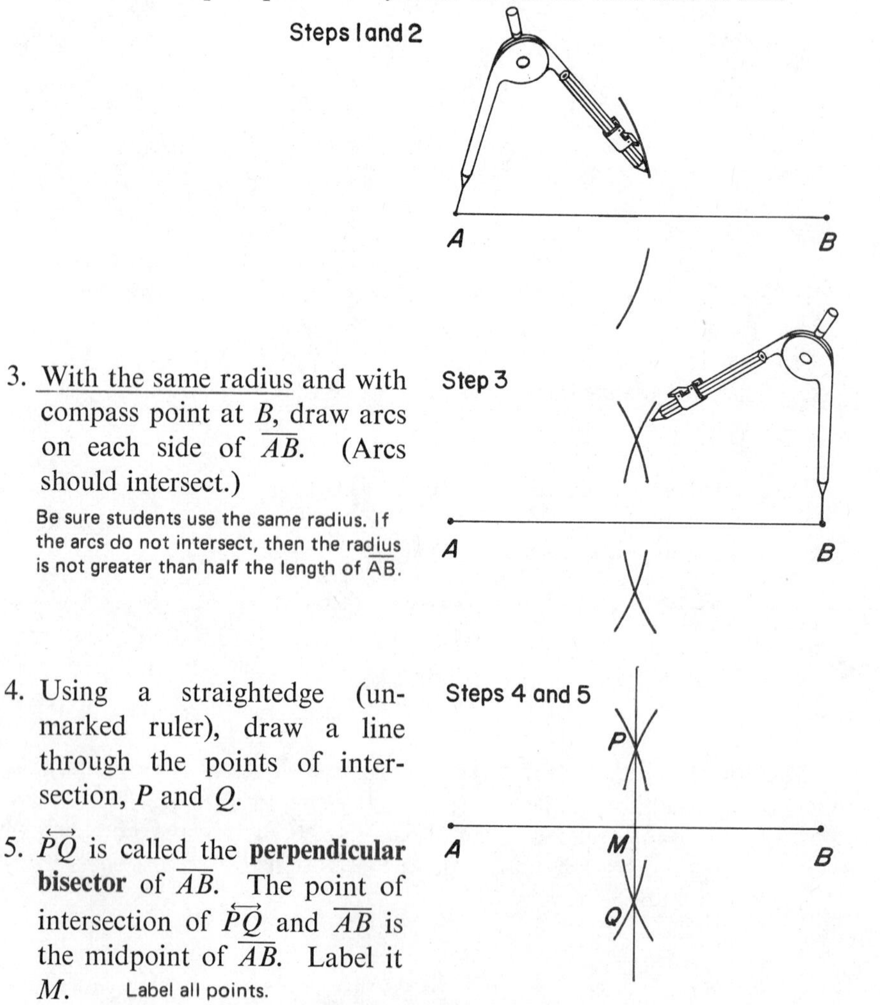

3. With the same radius and with compass point at B, draw arcs on each side of $\overline{AB}$. (Arcs should intersect.)

   Be sure students use the same radius. If the arcs do not intersect, then the radius is not greater than half the length of $\overline{AB}$.

4. Using a straightedge (unmarked ruler), draw a line through the points of intersection, P and Q.
5. $\overleftrightarrow{PQ}$ is called the **perpendicular bisector** of $\overline{AB}$. The point of intersection of $\overleftrightarrow{PQ}$ and $\overline{AB}$ is the midpoint of $\overline{AB}$. Label it M. Label all points.

Remind the students not to erase construction lines.

EXERCISES

Show all construction lines.

A

1. Draw a line segment 5 in. long and find its midpoint. Check your construction with a ruler.
2. Draw a 3-inch segment and construct its perpendicular bisector. Check the lengths with a ruler and check the right angle with a protractor.
3. Divide a 7-inch segment into 4 equal parts by using the bisector technique. (Hint: Bisect the line. Then bisect each half of the line.)
4. Using the same line segment from Exercise 3, divide it into 8 equal parts.

7–2 Construction of Perpendicular Lines

There are two constructions to consider under this heading. In one you are given a point *on* a line. In the other, the given point is *not* on the line. You should work on separate paper as you study each step. Use only your compass and a straightedge.

CONSTRUCTION: *Constructing a line perpendicular to a given line through a given point on the line.*

Procedure:

1. Draw a line l and show P, any point on the line. (This is what we are *given*.)

Step I

ℓ

P

2. Using any convenient radius, and P as center, draw arcs intersecting line l on both sides of P, at M and N.

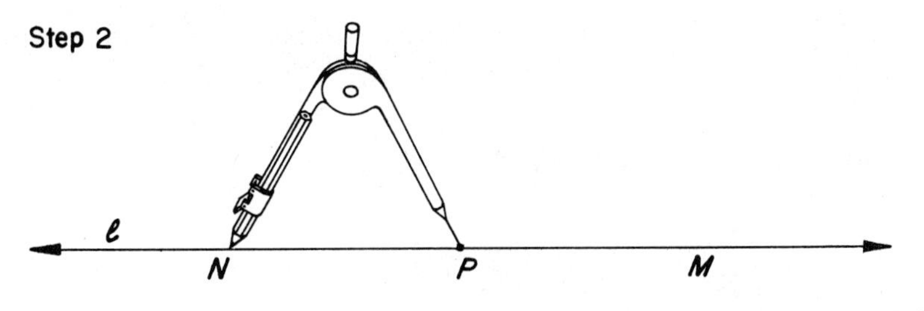

(Continued on p. 258.)

3. With the compass point at M and a radius greater than $\overline{MP}$, draw an arc above line l.

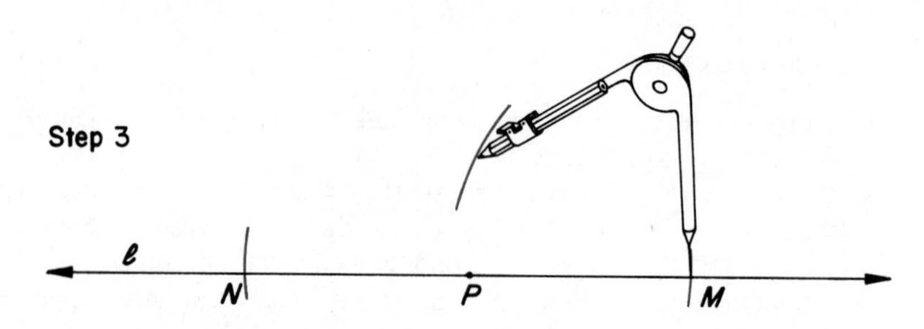

4. Using the same radius and point N, draw an arc which intersects the first arc at C.

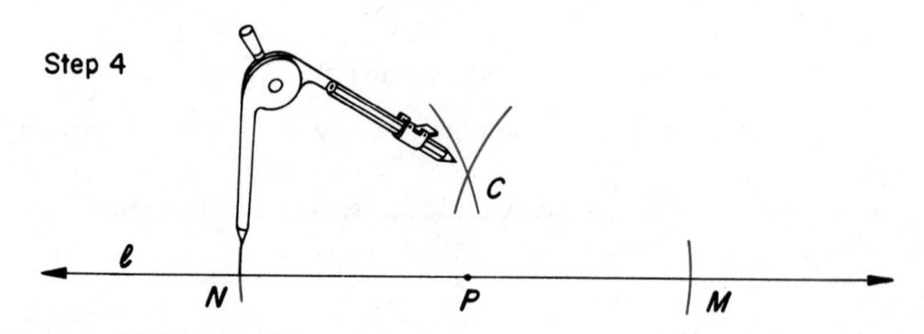

5. Using your straightedge draw a line through C and P. Line $\overleftrightarrow{CP}$ is perpendicular to line l at P.

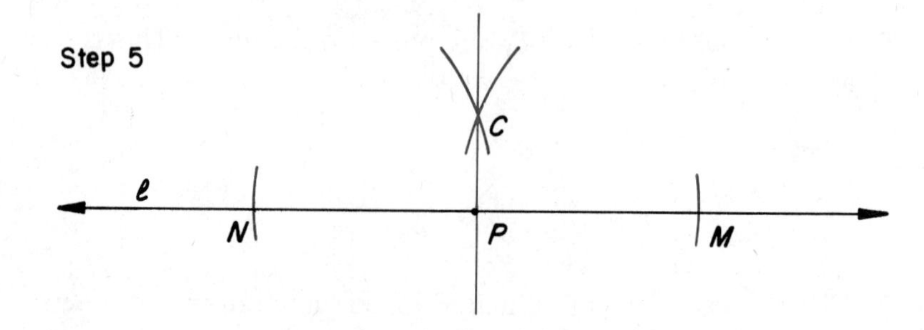

CONSTRUCTION: ***Constructing a perpendicular to a given line from a point not on the line.*** Emphasize how this construction differs from the previous one.

Procedure:

1. You are given line l and a point P not on l.

Step I

P·

ℓ

2. Set the compass with a radius greater than the perpendicular distance from P to the line.
3. Draw an arc which intersects the line l at points M and N.

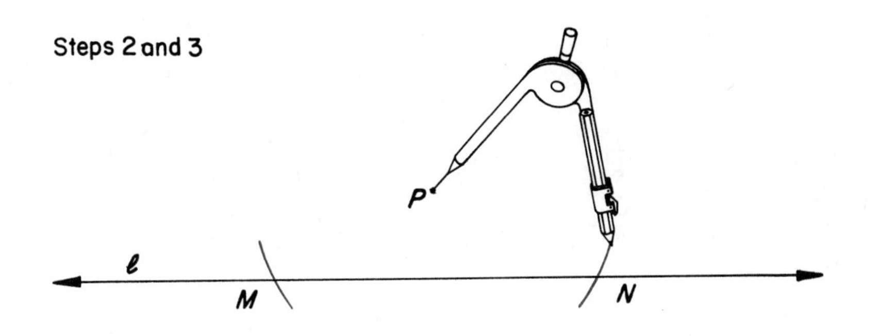

4. Place the compass point at M, and with a radius greater than $\frac{1}{2}$ the line segment $\overline{MN}$, draw an arc below line l.
5. Using the same radius, repeat Step 4 with compass point on N. Call the intersection of the two arcs point C.
6. Draw a line through P and C. Line $\overleftrightarrow{CP}$ is perpendicular to line l.

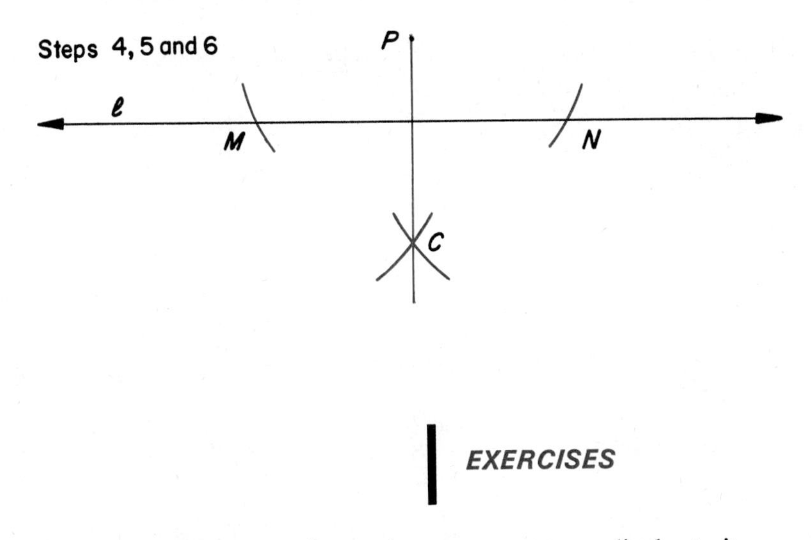

EXERCISES

A

1. Locate a point P on a line and construct a perpendicular to it.
2. Locate a point C above a line and construct a perpendicular to the line.
3. On a line $\overleftrightarrow{AB}$ locate a point X. Above the line and to the right of X locate a point Y. At X construct line l perpendicular to $\overleftrightarrow{AB}$. From Y construct line m perpendicular to $\overleftrightarrow{AB}$. What kind of lines are l and m? (Recall page 105.) Parallel

7–3 Construction of An Angle Equal to a Given Angle

You have used your protractor many times to copy angles. Now you will find an even more accurate way to do this. Keep your pencil sharp and work carefully. TM p. 16 , 7-3(1)

CONSTRUCTION: *Copying a given angle.*

Procedure:

1. Draw an acute angle. This is the angle you will copy.
2. Draw a ray $\overrightarrow{AB}$.
3. Draw an arc which intersects both sides of the *given* angle. Call the points P and Q.

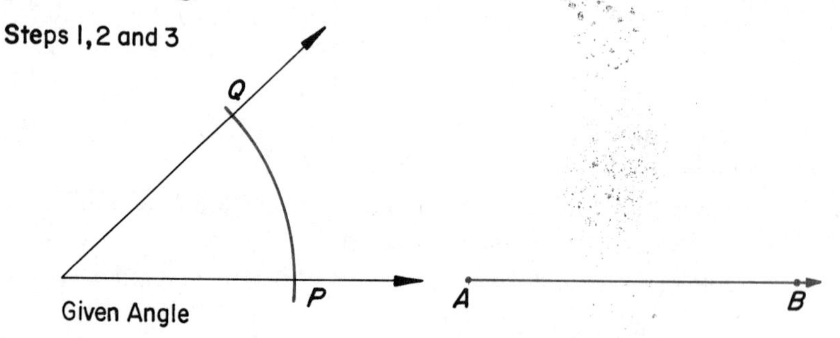

4. Using the same radius, place the compass point at A and draw an arc which cuts $\overrightarrow{AB}$ at P'. This arc must be as long as arc $\widehat{PQ}$.

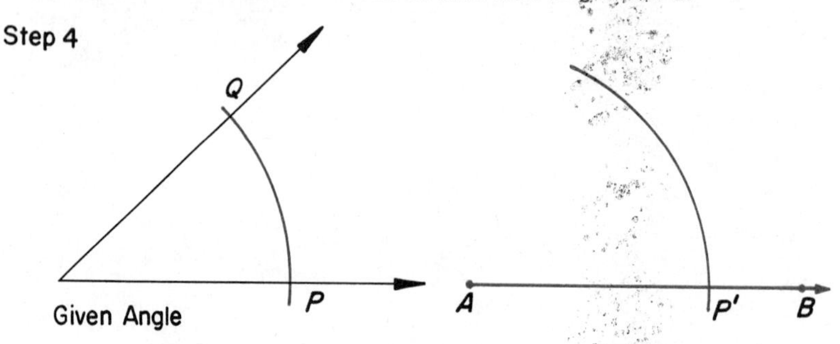

5. Place the compass point at P and measure to point Q.

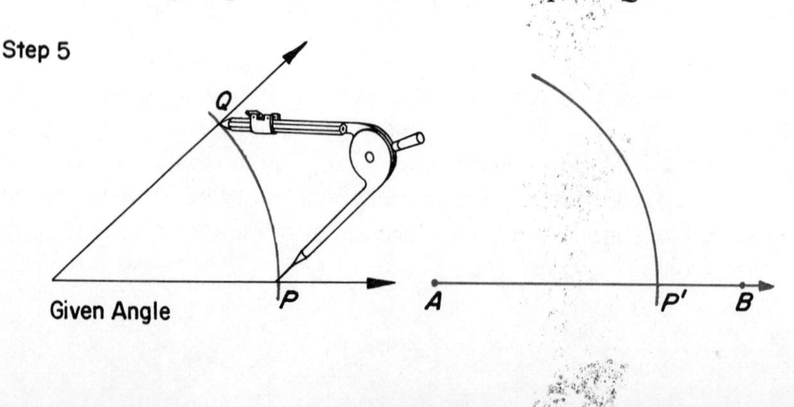

6. Place the compass point at P' and using the distance $\overline{PQ}$ as radius, draw an arc intersecting the first arc at Q'. TM p. 16 , 7-3(2)
7. Draw a ray from point A through point Q'. Then $\angle BAQ'$ equals the given angle.

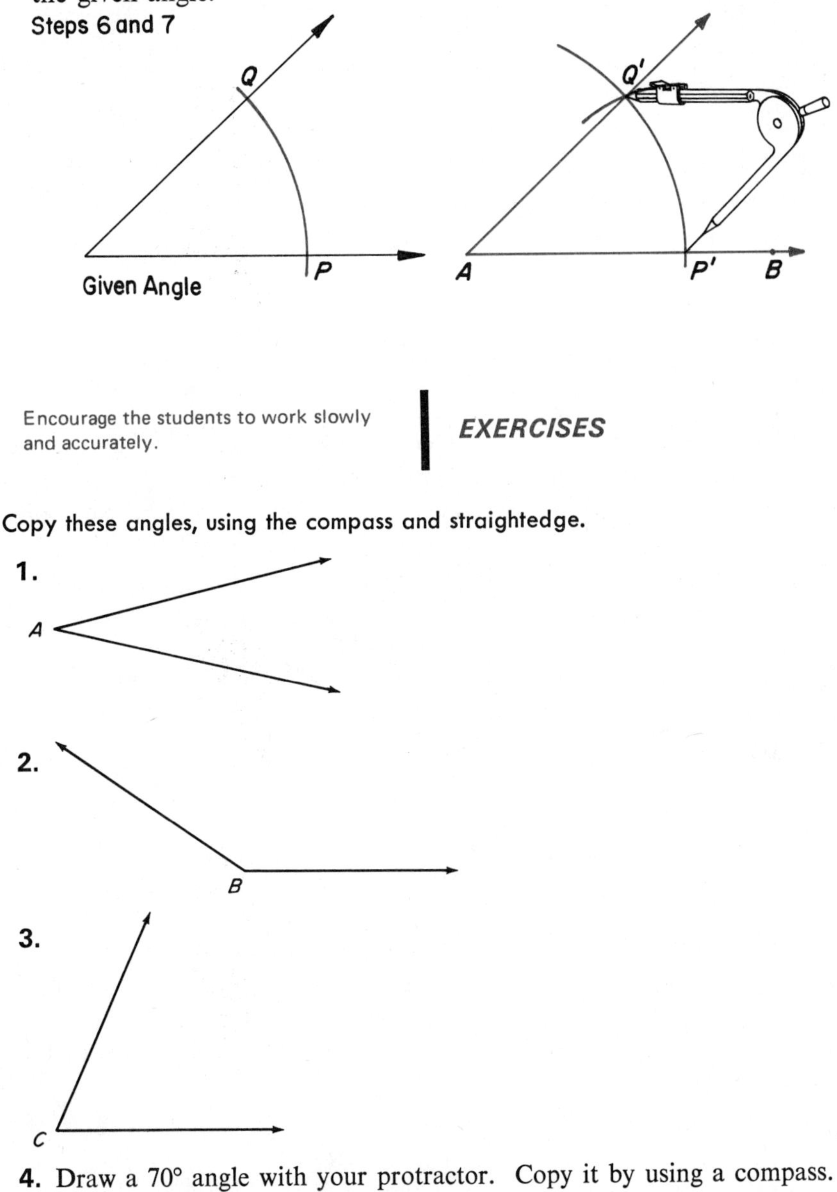

Encourage the students to work slowly and accurately.

EXERCISES

Copy these angles, using the compass and straightedge.

A

1. A

2. B

3. C

4. Draw a 70° angle with your protractor. Copy it by using a compass.

5. On a line $\overleftrightarrow{PQ}$ locate points A, B, and C. At A draw a right angle with your protractor. At B copy the right angle using the construction above. At C construct a line perpendicular to $\overleftrightarrow{PQ}$. Check your work at B and C with your protractor.

7–4 Bisection of an Angle

Draftsmen often need to divide an angle into two equal parts, that is, to bisect it. Take all the steps yourself on a separate piece of paper.

CONSTRUCTION: *Bisecting a given angle.*

Procedure:

1. Draw an acute angle and label it ABC. This is your *given* angle.
2. With any convenient radius and B as center, draw an arc which intersects the two rays, $\overrightarrow{BA}$ and $\overrightarrow{BC}$, at Q and P.

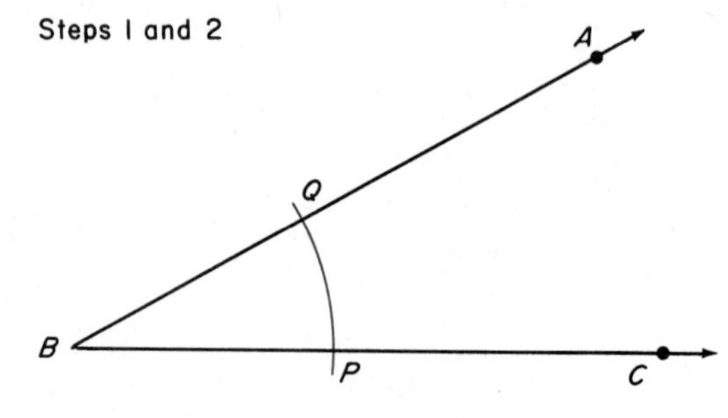

3. Place the compass at point P and draw an arc. (Make sure the arc radius is greater than $\frac{1}{2}$ the distance $\overline{PQ}$.) Emphasize this.
4. Using the same arc radius as in Step 3, place the compass at point Q and draw an arc. It will intersect the first arc at R.
5. From point B draw the ray $\overrightarrow{BR}$. This is the bisector of $\angle ABC$.

Steps 3, 4 and 5

EXERCISES

Draw angles like these and construct angles equal to them. Then bisect the angles you have constructed.

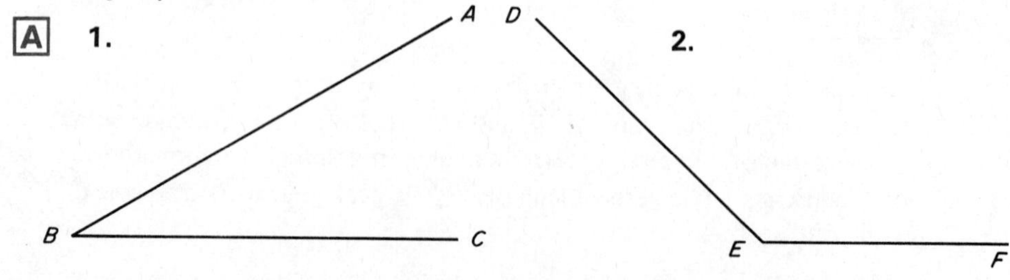

3.

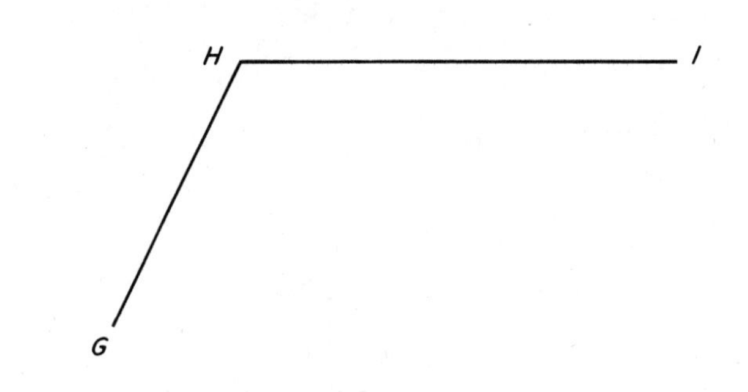

4. Draw an obtuse $\angle DEF$ like the one in Exercise 2. Divide it into 4 equal angles. (Hint. Bisect the angle. Then bisect each half of the angle.)

5. Divide an obtuse $\angle DEF$ into 8 equal angles.

7–5 Construction of Parallel Lines

Two methods for constructing parallel lines are shown below. In both you use only compass and straightedge.

Each method utilizes constructions studied previously.

CONSTRUCTION: ***Constructing a line parallel to a given line.***

Method 1. Using perpendicular lines.

Procedure:

1. Choose a point P on a given line l_1.
2. Construct a line perpendicular to line l_1 at P.

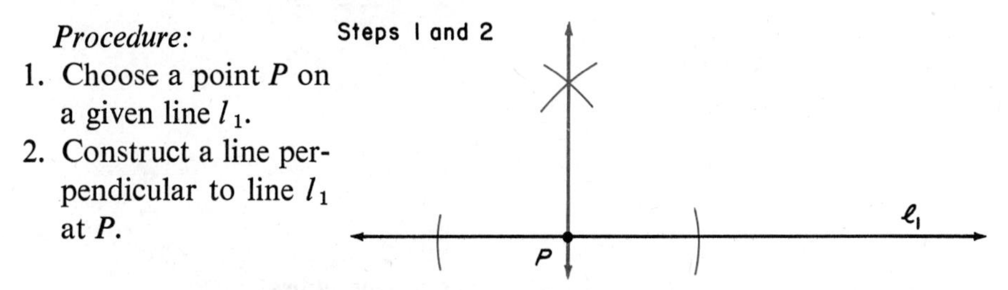

3. Choose a point Q on the perpendicular.
4. Construct a perpendicular to $\overleftrightarrow{PQ}$ at Q. Call it l_2.
5. Line l_2 is parallel to line l_1.

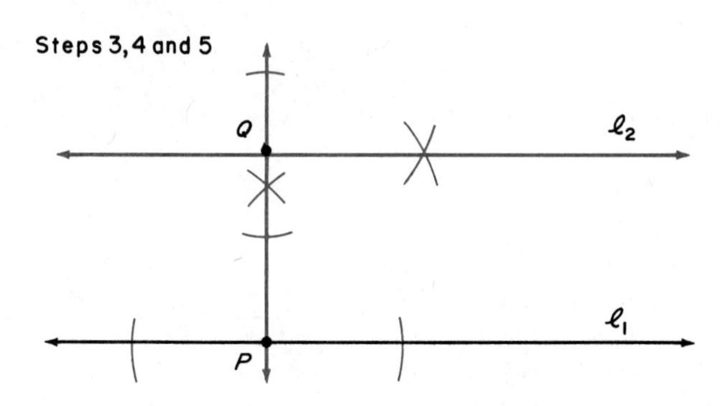

Method 2. Copying an angle. TM p. 16 , 7-5

Procedure:

1. Draw a line n intersecting line l_1 at X.

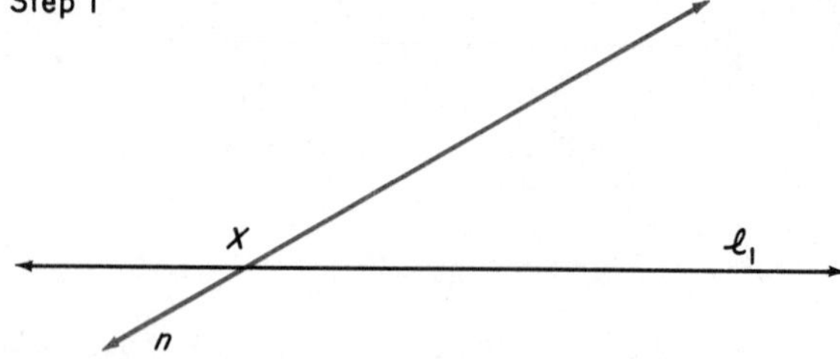

2. Choose a point Y anywhere on line n.
3. Construct an angle at Y equal to the one at X, as shown.
4. The new line, l_2, is parallel to l_1.

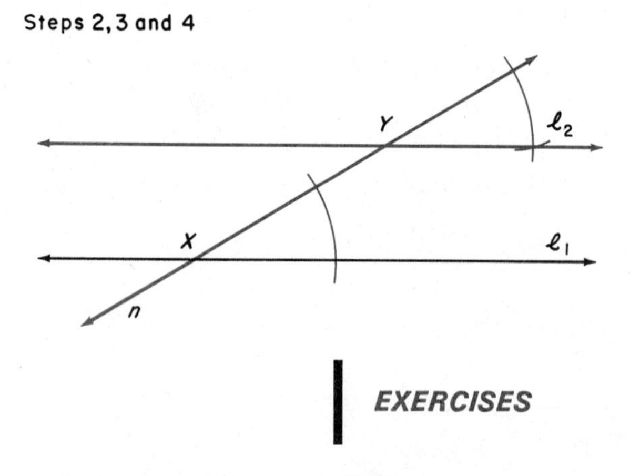

EXERCISES

A

1. Construct a line parallel to another line, using two techniques.

2. Construct three parallel lines, using two techniques.

The ability to follow instructions is essential in all fields of industry. Here is a chance to demonstrate how effective you can be in following instructions.

3. Template problem. Accuracy is important in this exercise.

Instructions:

1. Draw an isosceles trapezoid $ABCD$ as shown at the top of the next page. ($\overline{AD} = \overline{BC}$)
2. Bisect ∡ A, B, C, and D.
3. Connect the points E and F.
4. Construct the perpendicular bisector of $\overline{EF}$.
5. Bisect the four angles at point O.
6. Construct the perpendicular bisectors of $\overline{ON}$ and $\overline{OP}$.
7. Draw line segments $\overline{HJ}$, $\overline{JK}$, $\overline{KM}$, and $\overline{MH}$.
8. What type of figure is $HJKM$?

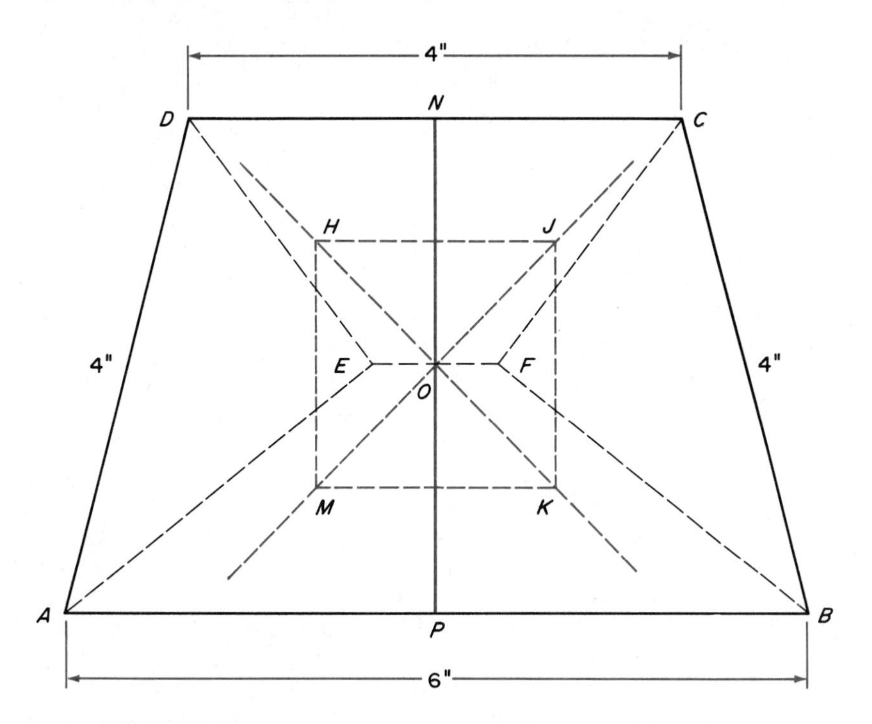

7–6 Division of a Line Segment

The interesting construction below calls for very careful use of the compass and straightedge.

CONSTRUCTION: ***Dividing a line segment into any number of equal parts, here 6.***

Procedure:

1. Given segment $\overline{AB}$. Draw ray $\overrightarrow{AN}$ any convenient length. Using your compass, mark off 6 equal units on ray $\overrightarrow{AN}$, ending at H. Extend the ray if necessary. TM p. 16 , 7-6
2. Connect points H and B. (Continued on next page)

Steps 2 and 3

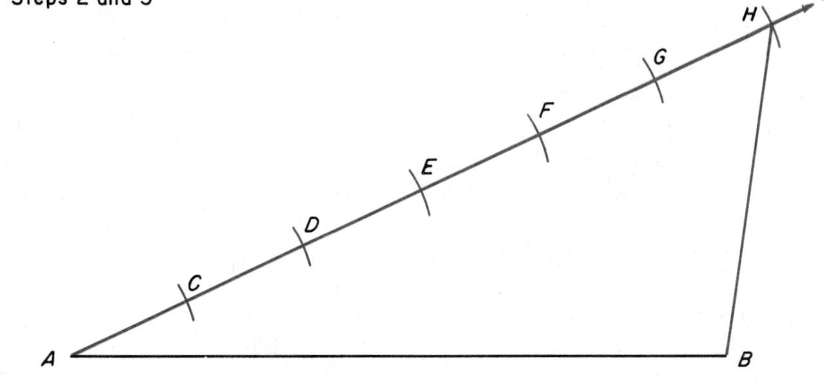

3. Copy $\angle H$ at C, D, E, F, and G.
4. Extend the sides of the angles to intersect the line segment $\overline{AB}$.
5. Line segment $\overline{AB}$ is now divided into 6 equal parts.

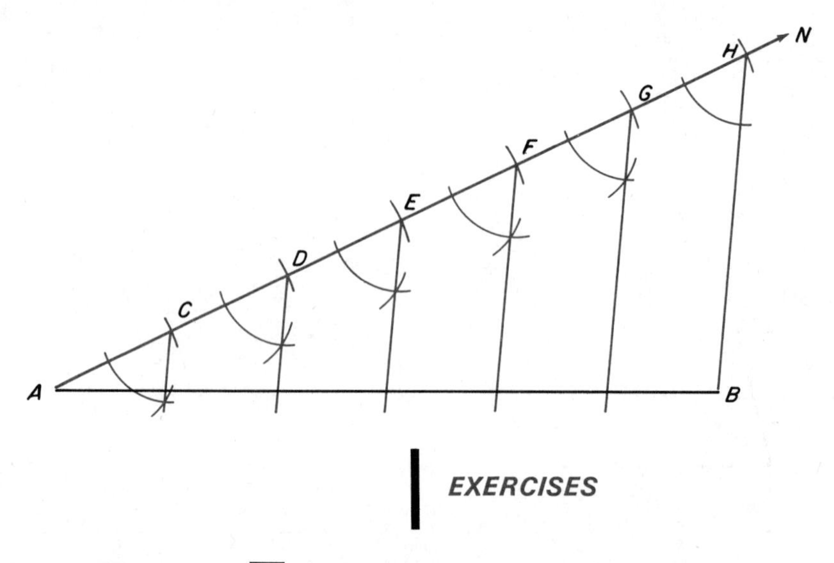

EXERCISES

A

1. Draw line segment $\overline{AB} = 6''$, and divide it into 4 equal parts. Use the method shown above.
2. Divide a line segment 7″ long into 5 equal parts.
3. Divide the sketch of the 28′ beam below into 7 equal units, for locating beams in the proper places.

28'

SELF-ANALYSIS TEST I

Time: 25 minutes

In all your constructions, do *not* erase your arcs.

1. Construct the perpendicular bisector of a 4″ line segment.
2. Draw a line segment. Locate a point P on the segment and construct a perpendicular to the segment at P.
3. Draw a line segment. Locate a point P not on the line and construct a perpendicular from P to the given segment.
4. Draw a 40° angle with your protractor. Copy it by using a compass.
5. Draw any acute angle. Copy the angle.
6. Draw any obtuse angle. Bisect the angle.
7. Draw a line. Construct a line parallel to it.
8. Draw a 5″ line segment. Divide it into 7 equal parts.
9. Using your protractor, make a 155° angle. Copy it and use your compass to divide the constructed angle into 4 equal parts.

■ Triangles

7–7 Construction of Triangles

In Chapter 3, on page 116, you constructed triangles, given the lengths of the three sides. Now you are ready for two other triangle constructions.

It is possible to construct a triangle if we know the lengths of two sides and the size of the angle *included* between them. By "included angle" we mean that the two sides are parts of the sides of the given angle. For example, in a triangle ABC, $\angle A$ is included between side $\overline{AB}$ and side $\overline{AC}$. Illustrate the "included angle."

CONSTRUCTION: ***Constructing a triangle, given two sides and the included angle.***

Procedure:

1. Given sides $\overline{AB}$ and $\overline{AC}$, and $\angle A$.

Step I

A B A C A

2. Draw a line l, longer than $\overline{AB}$.
3. Using your compass, copy $\overline{AB}$ on line l.
4. Starting at point A on $\overline{AB}$, copy $\angle A$, calling it $\angle BAX$.

Steps 2,3 and 4

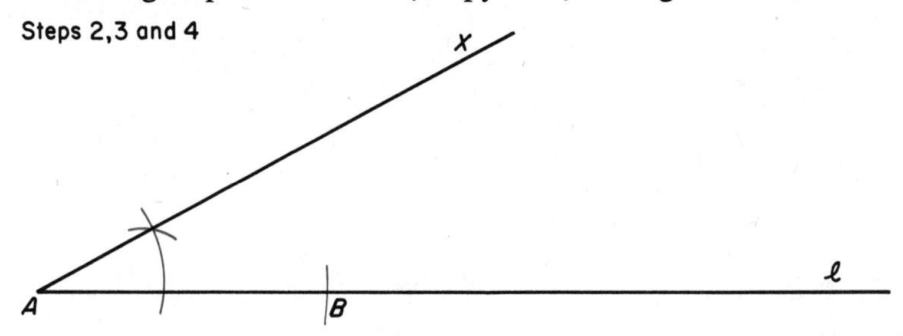

5. Using your compass, measure $\overline{AC}$. Copy $\overline{AC}$ on $\overrightarrow{AX}$. If $\overrightarrow{AX}$ is not drawn long enough, extend it until it intersects the arc.
6. Draw $\overline{BC}$. $\triangle ABC$ is the required triangle.

Steps 5 and 6

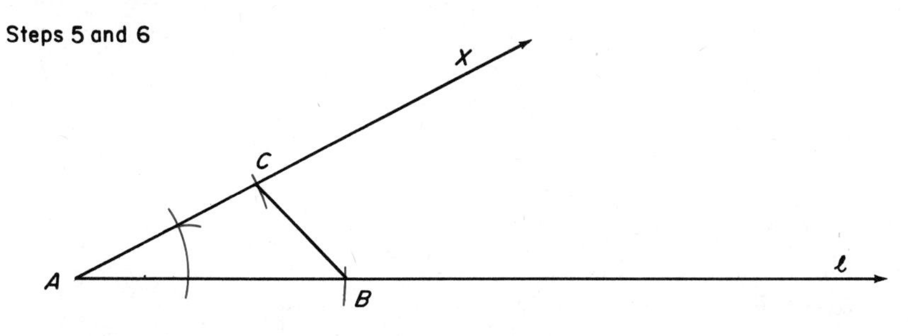

It is also possible to construct a triangle if you know the size of two angles and the length of the side included between them. By "included side" we mean that the side is part of one of the sides of each angle. For example, in a triangle ABC, side $\overline{AB}$ is included between $\angle A$ and $\angle B$. Illustrate the "included side."

CONSTRUCTION: ***Constructing a triangle, given two angles and the included side.***

Procedure:

1. Given $\angle A$, $\angle B$, and side $\overline{AB}$.

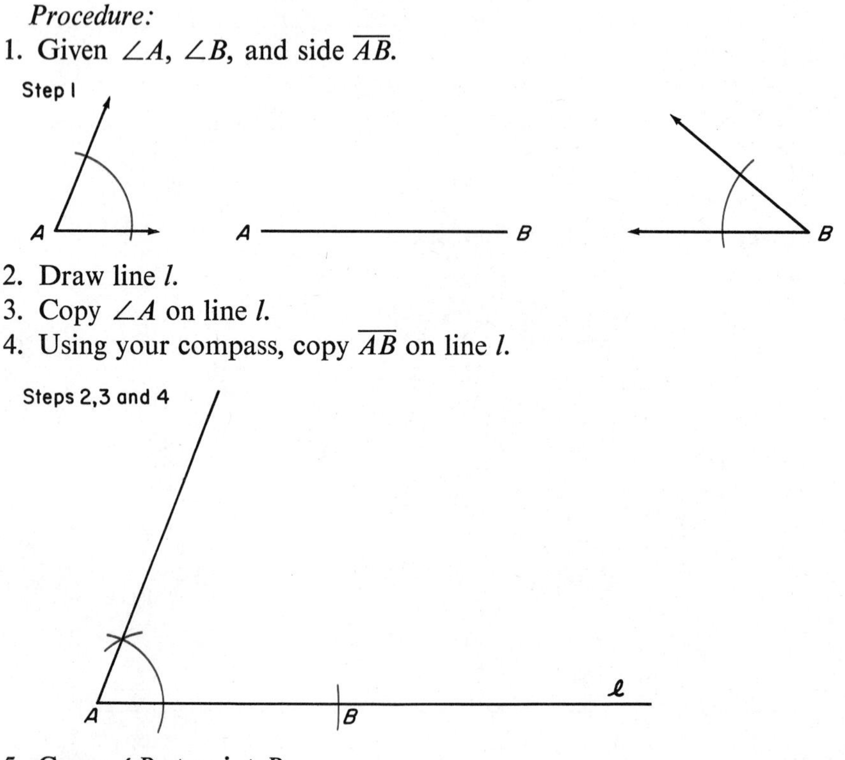

2. Draw line l.
3. Copy $\angle A$ on line l.
4. Using your compass, copy $\overline{AB}$ on line l.

5. Copy $\angle B$ at point B.
6. Extend the sides of $\angle A$ and $\angle B$ until they intersect, as at C.

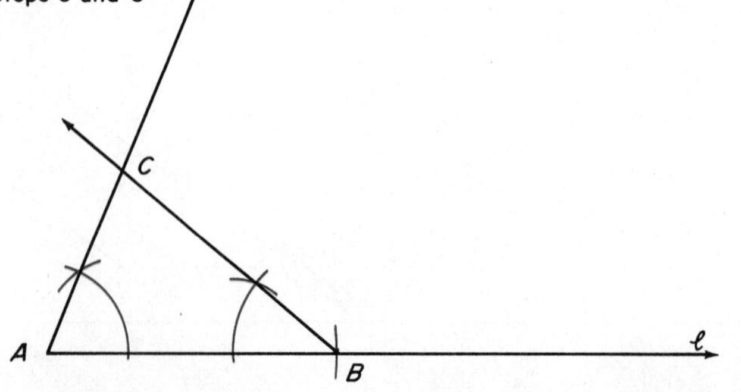

EXERCISES

A protractor may be used to draw the given angles.

A

1. Construct $\triangle ABC$ with the two sides and angle given.

2. Construct $\triangle ABC$, using your compass and protractor: $\overline{AB} = 3''$, $\overline{AC} = 1\frac{3}{4}''$, $\angle A = 60°$.

3. Construct $\triangle ABC$: $\overline{AB} = 5''$, $\overline{AC} = 4''$, $\angle A = 30°$.

4. Construct $\triangle ABC$ with the two angles and side shown.

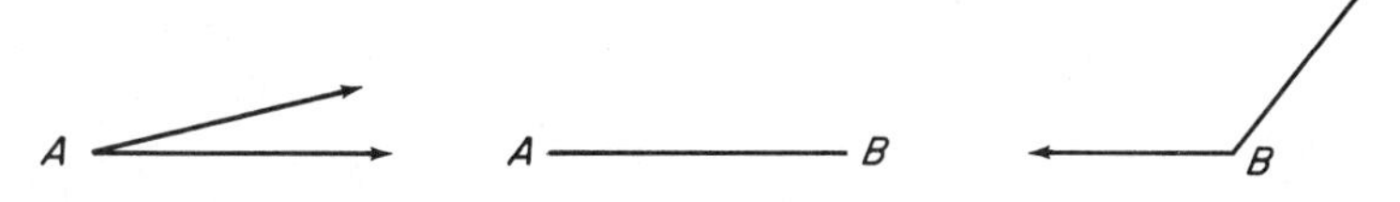

5. Construct $\triangle ABC$, using compass and protractor: $\angle A = 45°$, $\angle B = 26°$, $\overline{AB} = 3\frac{3}{16}''$.

6. Construct $\triangle ABC$: $\angle A = 30°$, $\angle B = 60°$, $\overline{AB} = 4''$.

a. What kind of triangle is this? **b.** What is the length of side $\overline{BC}$?

7–8 Altitudes of a Triangle

You will recall that every triangle has three altitudes (see page 115). Since an altitude is a perpendicular, you now know how to construct altitudes with your compass and straightedge. Perform the following steps on a separate piece of paper.

Acute Triangle

Procedure:

1. Draw an acute $\triangle ABC$, as shown.
2. From point A construct the line segment $\overline{AX}$ perpendicular to $\overline{BC}$. TM p. 16 , 7-8
3. Construct the line segment $\overline{BY}$ from B perpendicular to $\overline{AC}$.
4. Construct the line segment $\overline{CZ}$ from C perpendicular to $\overline{AB}$.

Check constructions of other students to see if the altitudes intersect at one point. What is your conclusion?

Obtuse Triangle (Altitudes) This construction may give the student more difficulty since the sides of the triangle must be extended.

Procedure:

1. Draw an obtuse $\triangle DEF$, as shown in the figure below.
2. From point D construct $\overline{DX}$, the altitude to $\overline{EF}$.
3. From point E construct the altitude $\overline{EY}$ to $\overline{DF}$. Notice that it is necessary to extend the line $\overleftrightarrow{FD}$ through point D.

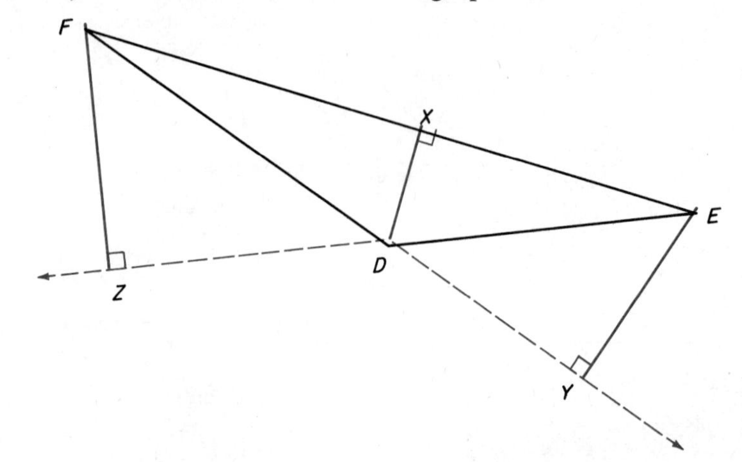

4. From point F construct the altitude $\overline{FZ}$ to $\overline{DE}$. (Extend the line $\overleftrightarrow{ED}$ through point D.) Will the three altitudes, if extended, intersect at one point? Yes

EXERCISES

A

1. Construct $\triangle ABC$, given sides $\overline{AB}$ and $\overline{AC}$, and $\angle A$. Then construct its three altitudes.

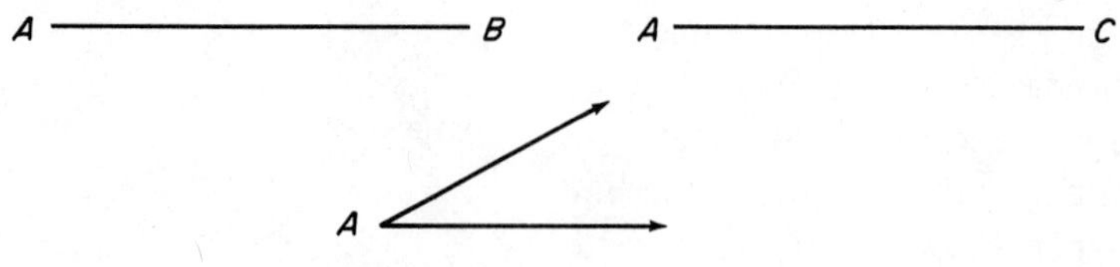

2. Construct $\triangle DEF$ and its three altitudes.

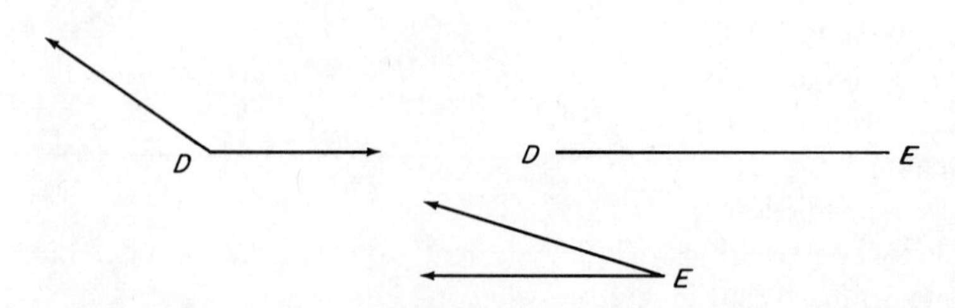

7–9 Medians of a Triangle

A **median** of a triangle is a segment from a vertex to the midpoint of the opposite side. As you can see, every triangle has three medians.

CONSTRUCTION: *Constructing the medians of a triangle.* TM p. 16 , 7-9

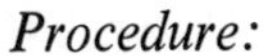

Procedure:

1. Draw an acute $\triangle ABC$.
2. Bisect $\overline{AB}$, $\overline{BC}$, and $\overline{CA}$. (Show all construction marks.)
3. Connect point C to point E, the midpoint of $\overline{AB}$.
4. Connect point B to point D, the midpoint of $\overline{AC}$.
5. Connect point A to point F, the midpoint of $\overline{BC}$.

Do the three medians intersect at one point? Yes

EXERCISES

A

1. Draw an obtuse triangle. Using your ruler, find the midpoints of the three sides. Draw line segments from each vertex to the midpoint of the opposite side. Do the three medians intersect at one point?
2. Construct $\triangle ABC$ and its three medians, given the three sides.

   A ——— B   B ——— C

   A ——— C

3. Construct $\triangle ABC$ given two sides and an included angle, as shown. Using a compass, bisect the three sides of the triangle. Draw its medians.

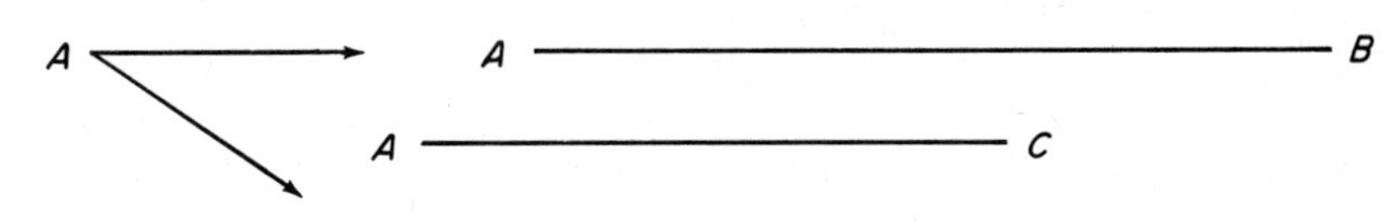

4. Construct $\triangle ABC$ given two angles and the included side. Construct its medians.

   A   A ——— B   B

ACTIVITY: *To locate the centroid of a triangle.*

Did you notice in each of the four preceding constructions that the three medians of each triangle intersect at a point inside the triangle? We call this point the **centroid** of the triangle. When we are speaking about a physical triangle made of a material we usually refer to the centroid as the *center of gravity.*

Problem: To locate the centroid of a triangle and study its properties.

Materials: Pencil, compass, straightedge, scissors, straight pin, flat sheet of cardboard. Accuracy is essential in this activity.

Plan: Draw the three medians of the triangle.

1. Draw a triangle on the cardboard.
2. Determine the midpoint of each side and draw the three medians.
3. Using the scissors, cut out the triangle.
4. Hold the pin with the point upward. Position the triangle on the pin so that the point is at the centroid of the triangle. Do *not* push the pin into the triangle. The triangle should balance.

EXERCISES

A

1. Remove your hand from the triangle. Does the triangle tilt or remain level with respect to the pin? Check with others in the class.
2. Push the triangle gently to start it spinning. Does it tilt or remain level while spinning? Check with others in your class.
3. What reason can you give for calling the centroid the center of gravity?
4. List some reasons to explain why some of the triangles in your class may have tilted in doing Exercises 1 and 2.

7–10 Angle Bisectors of a Triangle

You have seen that the altitudes of a triangle intersect in a point and that the medians do also. Here is one more interesting construction closely related to the other two.

CONSTRUCTION: *Bisecting the angles of a triangle.*

Procedure:

1. Draw any triangle ABC.
2. Bisect $\measuredangle A$, B, and C.
3. Draw $\overline{AF}$, $\overline{CE}$, $\overline{BD}$.

Do the bisectors meet in a point? Yes

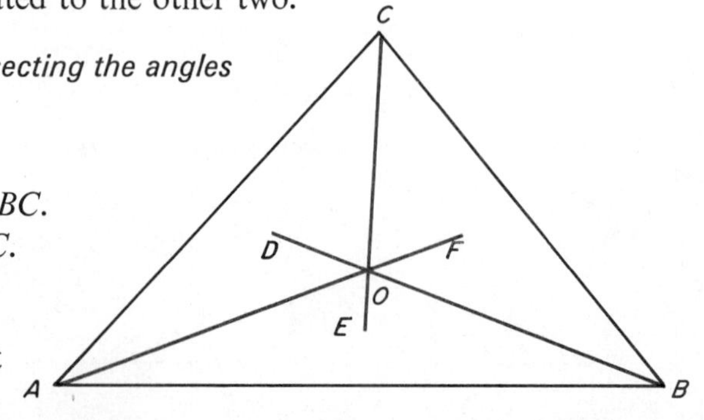

EXERCISES

A

1. Construct $\triangle ABC$ with sides 3″, 4″, and 6″. Construct the bisectors of $\angle$s A, B, C.
2. Construct $\triangle ABC$ with sides $2\frac{3}{4}''$, 3″ and $5\frac{1}{4}''$. Construct the bisectors of $\angle$s A, B, and C.

Triangles and Circles

7–11 Inscribed and Circumscribed Circles

As you recall from page 131, a tangent is a line which intersects a circle at one and only one point. Now you will learn how to construct a tangent to a circle, given a point on the circle.

CONSTRUCTION: *Constructing a tangent to a circle at a given point on the circle.*

Procedure:

1. Draw a circle O.
2. Locate a point P on the circle.
3. Draw the radius $\overline{OP}$ and extend the line beyond P.
4. Construct a line l perpendicular to $\overleftrightarrow{OP}$ at P.
5. Line l is tangent to circle O at point P.

Can you guess from the figures below what is meant by the terms **inscribed** and **circumscribed?**

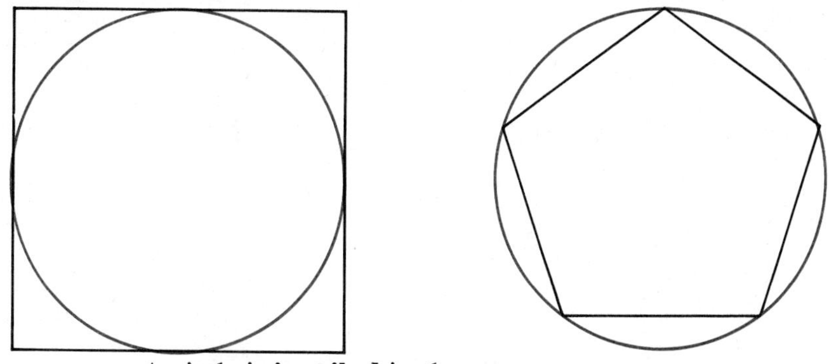

A circle is **inscribed** in the square.
A circle is **circumscribed** about the pentagon.

Below are two constructions you will wish to try. Perform each step carefully. Stress that accuracy is essential in the following constructions.

CONSTRUCTION: ***Inscribing a circle in a triangle.***

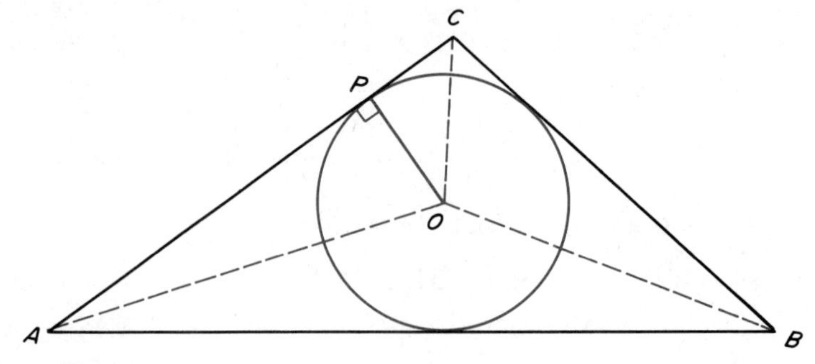

Procedure:

1. Draw any $\triangle ABC$.
2. Bisect $\measuredangle$s A, B, C.
3. From the point O, where the bisectors intersect, construct the perpendicular to any one side of the triangle, here side $\overline{AC}$. Call the point of intersection P.
4. Using O as the center, and $\overline{OP}$ as the radius, draw a circle. Then each side of $\triangle ABC$ should be tangent to the circle. The circle is *inscribed* in the triangle.

CONSTRUCTION: ***Circumscribing a circle about a triangle.***

Procedure:

1. Draw any $\triangle ABC$.
2. Construct the perpendicular bisectors of $\overline{AB}$, $\overline{BC}$, and $\overline{AC}$.
3. Using the intersection of these bisectors, point O, as center and $\overline{OA}$ as radius, draw a circle. This circle should pass through each vertex of the triangle. The circle is *circumscribed* about the triangle.

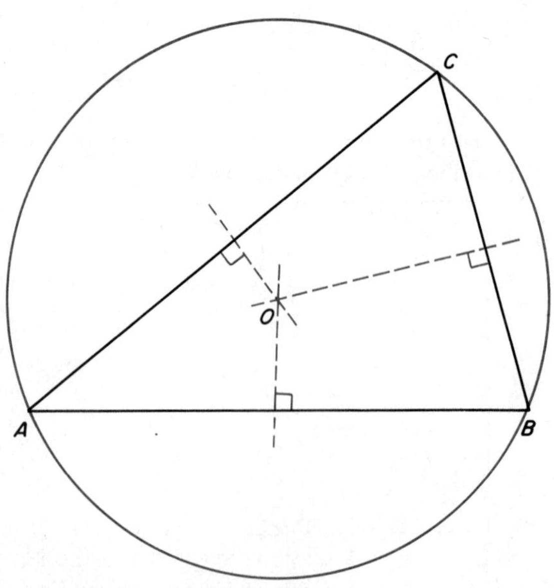

EXERCISES

A

1. Draw a circle of radius $1\frac{5}{8}''$. Construct a tangent to the circle at a point P on the circle. Verify that the radius and tangent meet at right angles by using your protractor.
2. Draw an acute triangle and construct the inscribed circle.
3. Draw an acute triangle and construct the circumscribed circle.

B

4. Draw an obtuse triangle and construct the inscribed circle.
5. Draw an obtuse triangle and construct the circumscribed circle.

ACTIVITY: ***To locate the center of a circle.***

Problem: To find the center of a circle.

Plan: Draw two chords and construct their perpendicular bisectors.

Materials: Pencil, compass, straightedge, circular object (a coin, for instance), or object with circular base.

1. Trace a circular object on your paper.
2. Draw any two chords of the circle.
3. Construct the perpendicular bisector of each chord, extending the lines to intersect.
4. The point of intersection is the center of the circle.
5. Check your result with a compass, using this point as center.

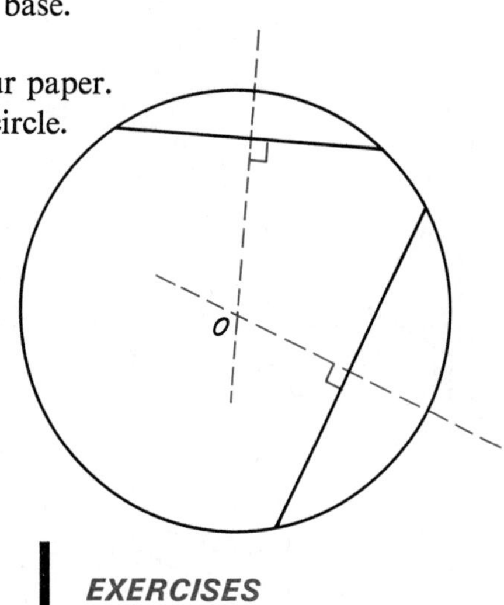

EXERCISES

A

1. Draw a large circle. By the method above verify that the perpendicular bisectors of any two chords of your circle intersect at the center.
2. Select any object with a round base (can, cup, vase, etc.) and find the center of the base.

7–12 Regular Polygons

Some regular polygons are easy to construct. The following drawings show you how to draw regular polygons of three sides (equilateral triangle), four sides (square), six sides (hexagon), and eight sides (octagon).

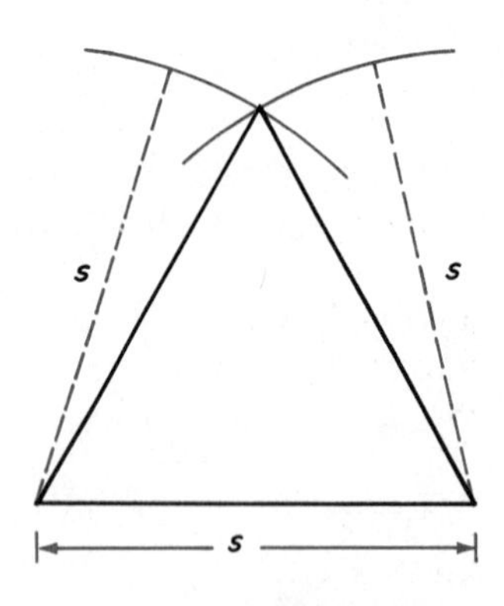

Equilateral Triangle

Using the distance s as radius, draw intersecting arcs to locate the third vertex.

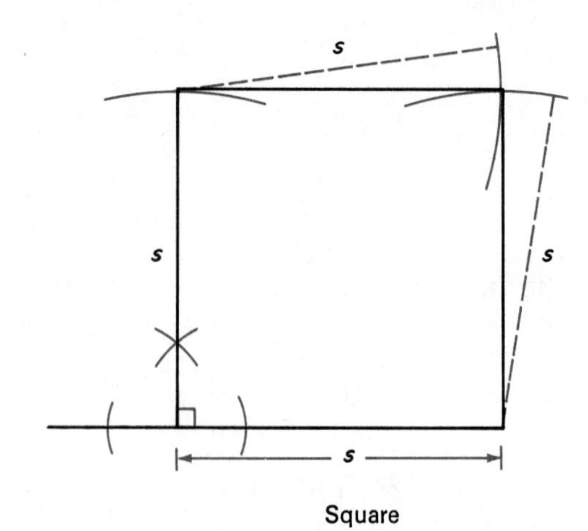

Square

At one end of the base s, construct a perpendicular.
Mark off the distance s on the perpendicular.
Using the distance s as radius, draw intersecting arcs as shown to find the fourth vertex.

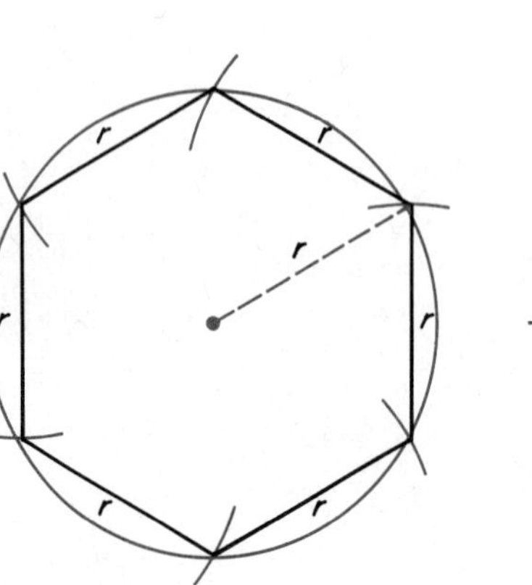

Hexagon

Using the distance r as radius, mark off six arcs in succession around the circle.
Join the points on the circle.

The 6th arc should include the first point.

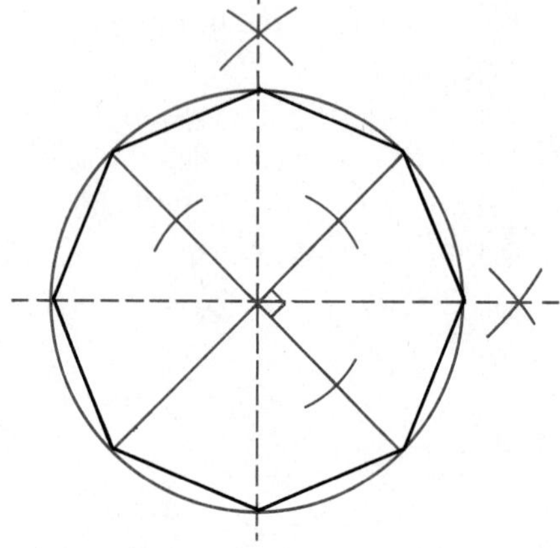

Octagon

Construct perpendicular diameters.
Bisect the right angles.
Join the points on the circle as shown.

Constructing a pentagon is a little more difficult. The following outline shows the steps to be taken.

CONSTRUCTION: ***Constructing a regular pentagon.***

Procedure:

1. Draw a circle with any convenient radius.
2. Construct $\overline{CD}$, the perpendicular bisector of diameter $\overline{AB}$.

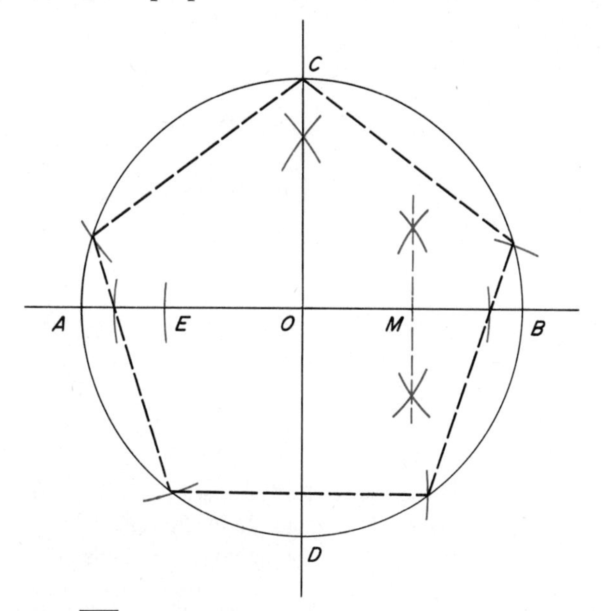

3. Bisect radius $\overline{OB}$, calling the midpoint M.
4. With M as center and $\overline{MC}$ as radius, draw an arc which intersects $\overline{AB}$ at E.
5. Starting at C, lay off $\overline{CE}$ five times around the circle to locate the vertices of a regular pentagon. Then connect the points in order.

EXERCISES

Construct the following polygons. Show all construction lines.

A

1. Equilateral triangle
2. Square
3. Hexagon
4. Octagon

B

5. Construct a regular pentagon.
6. Draw a circle with a radius 2″. Use the pentagon construction above to locate the five vertices of a regular pentagon on the circle. Label the vertices in order A, B, C, D, and E. Draw the following line segments: $\overline{AC}$, $\overline{AD}$, $\overline{BE}$, $\overline{BD}$, $\overline{CE}$. What figure is formed?

SELF-ANALYSIS TEST II

Time: 25 minutes

In Exercises 1–4 use only a compass and straightedge to construct triangle *ABC* having parts like those shown. Do not erase any arcs used in your constructions.

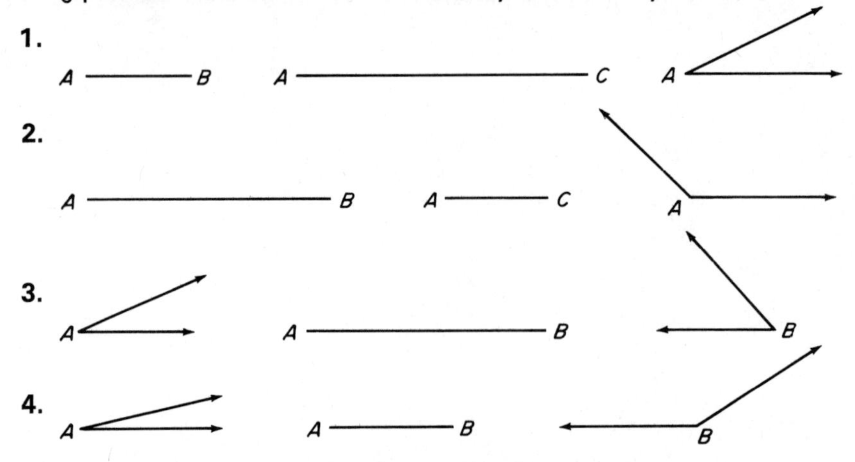

5. Construct a triangle with sides of 3″, 4″, and $4\frac{1}{2}$″.
6. Construct the 3 altitudes of the triangle in Exercise 5.
7. Draw an obtuse triangle. Using your compass, construct the medians to the three sides.
8. Draw an acute triangle and construct the bisectors of the three angles.
9. Draw any triangle and construct the inscribed circle.
10. Draw any triangle and construct the circumscribed circle.

ACTIVITY: *To construct geometric designs.*

Problem: To construct the three-pointed star shown here.

Plan:
1. Draw an equilateral triangle.
2. Bisect the three angles.
3. Bisect the angles again, as shown.

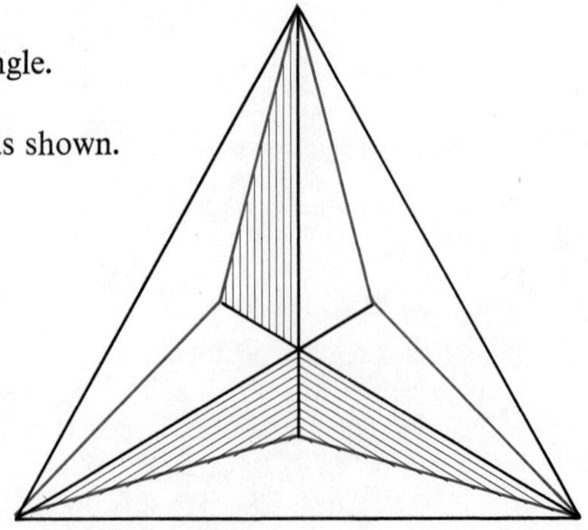

Students will find these exercises interesting and challenging. They may enjoy making their own patterns.

EXERCISES

Construct the figures below and make up a construction plan as was done for the three-pointed star.

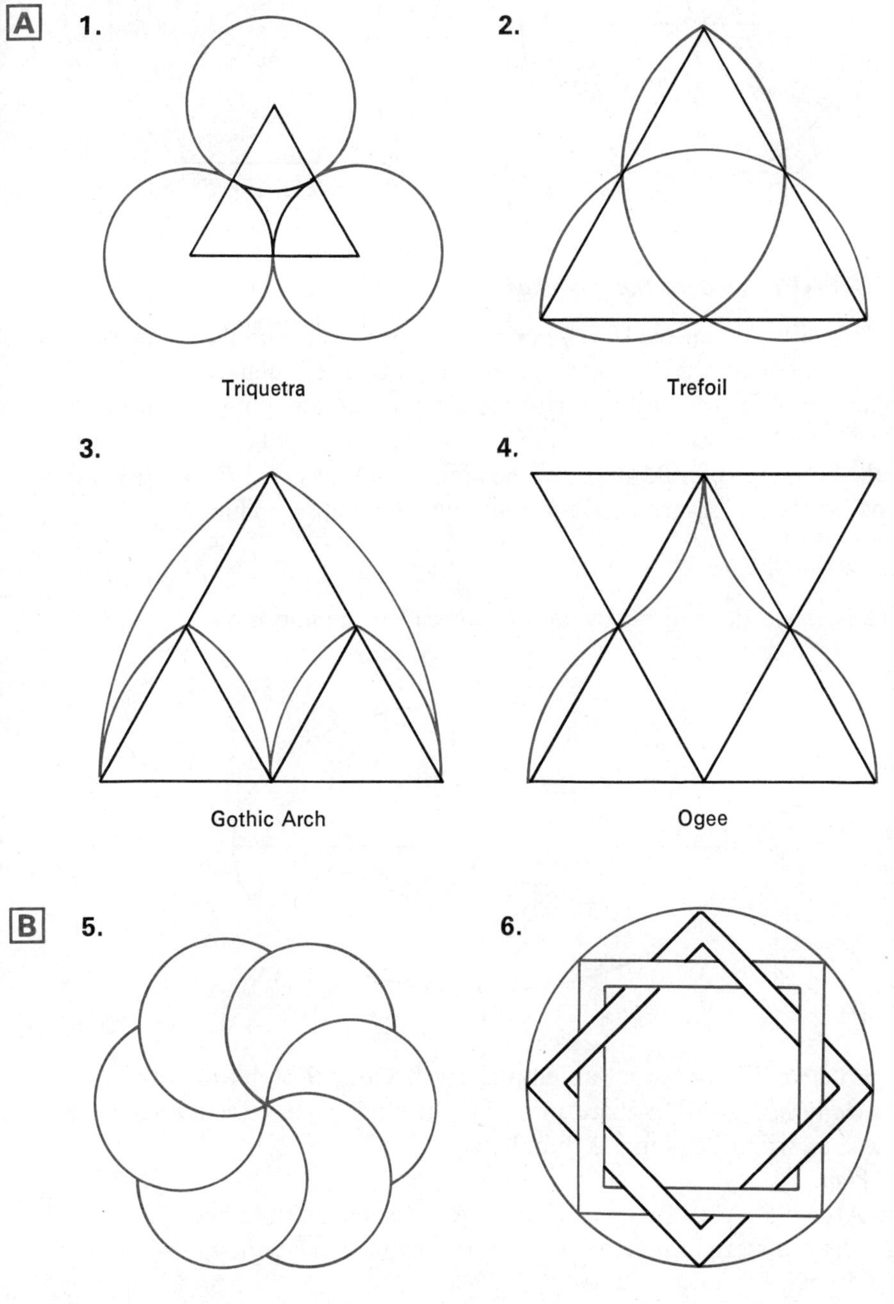

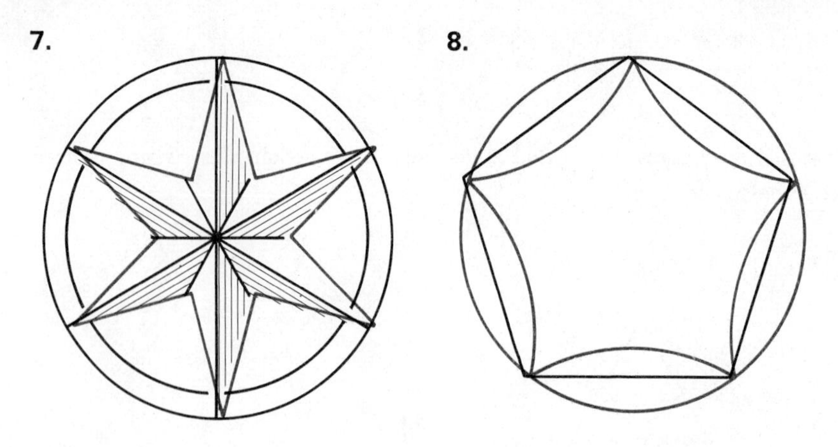

ACTIVITY: *To construct an ellipse.*

An **ellipse** is an oval. The orbits of satellites around the earth are examples of ellipses. In plane geometry an ellipse is defined as a closed plane curve such that the sum of the distances to any point on the curve from two fixed points inside the curve is constant. Each fixed point is called a *focus* (plural, *foci*). In the figure below, F_1 and F_2 are the foci and X, Y, and Z are random points on the ellipse. Thus,

$$\overline{F_1X} + \overline{F_2X} = \overline{F_1Y} + \overline{F_2Y} = \overline{F_1Z} + \overline{F_2Z}$$

$\overline{AB}$ is called the major axis, and $\overline{CD}$ is called the minor axis.

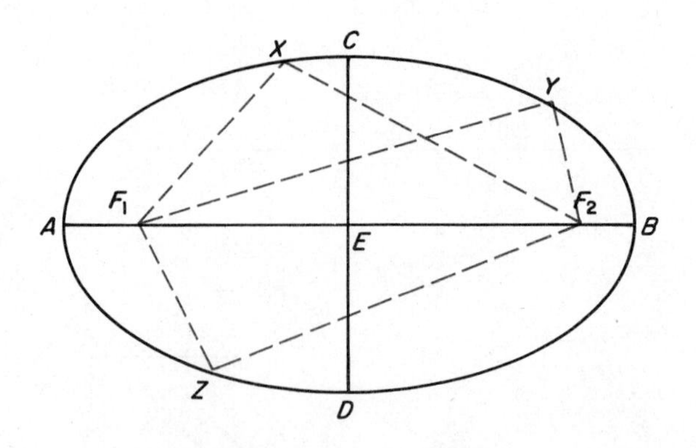

Problem: To construct an ellipse, given the major and minor axes.

Materials: A 10″ square piece of plywood, tape, compass, ruler, a piece of string 12″ long, 2 thumbtacks.

Plan:

1. Attach a piece of paper to the plywood square with tape.
2. Draw a straight line and mark off a segment $\overline{AB}$ 6″ long.

3. Construct the perpendicular bisector of $\overline{AB}$, and on it mark off segments $\overline{CE}$ and $\overline{DE}$, each 2″ long.

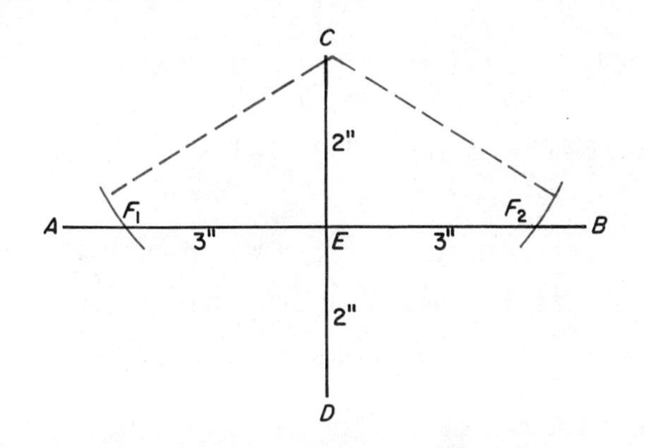

4. Use your compass to measure distance $\overline{AE}$. With C as center and $\overline{AE}$ as radius, draw an arc which intersects $\overline{AB}$ at points F_1 and F_2.
5. At points F_1 and F_2 push thumbtacks in firmly.

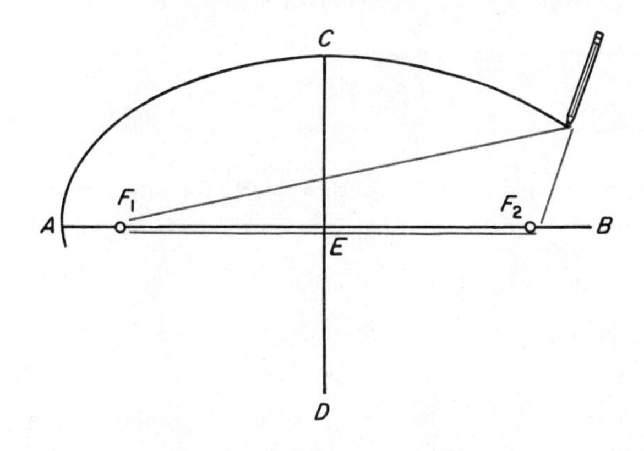

6. Loop the string over the thumbtacks and knot it securely so that its total length is twice the distance $\overline{AF_2}$.
7. Put your pencil inside the loop, and while keeping the string as taut as possible, draw the ellipse. Do not allow the string to bind around the tacks.

EXERCISES

A

1. Draw an ellipse with the foci 2″ apart and the string loop 5″ across (when taut). Measure the length of the major axis.
2. Draw an ellipse with the foci 4″ apart and the string loop $5\frac{1}{2}$″ across (when taut). Measure the length of the minor axis. TM p. 16 , 7-12

CHAPTER SUMMARY

1. Basic geometric constructions are done by using a compass and straightedge.
2. Line segments and angles can be bisected.
3. An angle can be copied.
4. A line can be constructed perpendicular or parallel to another line.
5. A line segment can be divided into any number of equal parts.
6. A triangle can be constructed when given
   a. the lengths of the three sides;
   b. the lengths of two sides and the size of the included angle;
   c. the size of two angles and the length of the included side.
7. A circle can be inscribed in or circumscribed about any triangle.
8. Some regular polygons can be constructed.

CHAPTER TEST

Use only a compass and a straightedge or ruler for the following constructions, unless stated otherwise. Do *not* erase any arcs used in your constructions.

1. Construct the perpendicular bisector of a 5″ line segment.
2. Draw a line segment $\overline{AB}$ 4″ long. Place a point P at least 1″ above $\overline{AB}$. From P construct a perpendicular to $\overline{AB}$.
3. Using your protractor, draw a 45° angle. Copy it, using a compass and straightedge.
4. Bisect the 45° angle which you constructed in Exercise 3.
5. Draw a 4″ line segment. Divide it into 5 equal parts.
6. Construct triangle ABC, given two angles and the side included between them.

A A B B

7. Construct a triangle with sides 4″, 5″, and 6″.
8. Construct the 3 altitudes of the triangle in Exercise 7.
9. Draw an acute triangle and, using your compass and straightedge, draw its three medians.

MAINTAINING YOUR SKILLS

Add.

1. $\begin{array}{r} 53 \\ 27 \\ +\ 35 \\ \hline \end{array}$ **2.** $\begin{array}{r} 47 \\ 29 \\ 35 \\ +\ 71 \\ \hline \end{array}$ **3.** $\begin{array}{r} 125 \\ 377 \\ +\ 288 \\ \hline \end{array}$ **4.** $\begin{array}{r} 10{,}005 \\ 7{,}225 \\ +\ 23{,}175 \\ \hline \end{array}$

5. 23.4 + 744.3 **6.** 944.25 + 125.75

Subtract.

7. $\begin{array}{r} 639 \\ -\ 257 \\ \hline \end{array}$ **8.** $\begin{array}{r} 755 \\ -\ 477 \\ \hline \end{array}$ **9.** $\begin{array}{r} 1{,}468 \\ -\ 925 \\ \hline \end{array}$ **10.** $\begin{array}{r} 253{,}576 \\ -\ 16{,}767 \\ \hline \end{array}$

11. 273.67 − 49.53 **12.** 627.56 − 46.75

Multiply.

13. 65 × 27 **14.** 95 × 25 **15.** 135 × 26 **16.** 247 × 179

17. 3.56 × 27.8 **18.** 2.753 × .279

Divide.

19. $95\overline{)2090}$ **20.** $73\overline{)3869}$ **21.** $36\overline{).8100}$

22. $\frac{1}{16} \div 4$ **23.** $\frac{5}{7} \div \frac{3}{14}$ **24.** $5\frac{1}{2} \div 2\frac{1}{4}$

Simplify.

25. 36 inches = __?__ feet **26.** 12 feet = __?__ yards

27. 118 inches = __?__ feet __?__ inches

Add or subtract.

28. $\begin{array}{r} 5\text{ ft. } 9\text{ in.} \\ +\ 4\text{ ft. } 10\text{ in.} \\ \hline \end{array}$ **29.** $\begin{array}{r} 27\text{ ft. } 6\text{ in.} \\ +\ 37\text{ ft. } 7\text{ in.} \\ \hline \end{array}$

30. $\begin{array}{r} 19\text{ ft. } 10\text{ in.} \\ -\ 5\text{ ft. } 11\text{ in.} \\ \hline \end{array}$

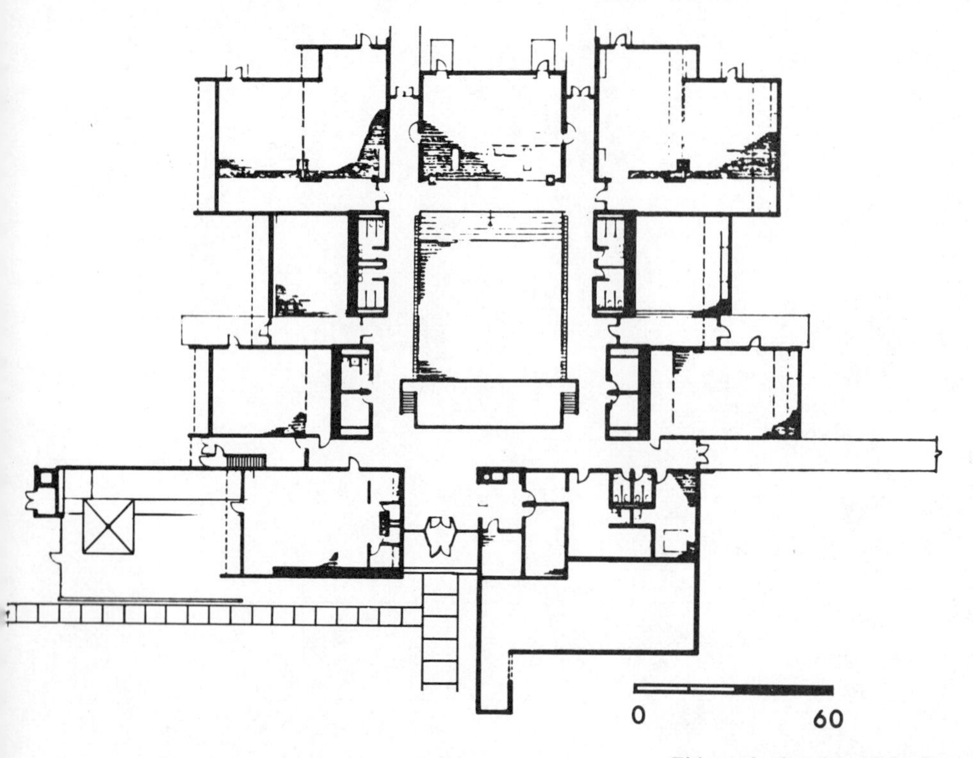

This scale drawing of the floor plan of the school building shown illustrates one important application of ratio and proportion.

Ratio and Proportion

OBJECTIVES

1. To learn about ratios and some of their applications.
2. To learn about proportions and some of their applications.
3. To learn about the relationships in similar triangles and other similar polygons.
4. To learn to read and use scale drawings.

In many applications of mathematics we need to know how two numbers compare with one another. One way of comparing two numbers is by division. This leads to the idea of ratio and its use in proportions, the subject of this chapter.

Ratio and Proportion

8–1 The Meaning of Ratio

When we compare two numbers by division, we are using the idea of **ratio.**

> The ratio of one number to another is the quotient when the first is divided by the second.

We often write a ratio as a fraction. The ratio of 5 to 9 is written $\frac{5}{9}$ and means that 5 is $\frac{5}{9}$ of 9. Ratios are also written in the form 5:9.

From your work with formulas you will recall that $\pi = \dfrac{C}{d}$ and that $r = \dfrac{d}{t}$. We can say that π is the ratio of the circumference of a circle to its diameter, and that the rate of speed is the ratio of the distance to the time. Ask students to recall other examples of ratio, such as rear-axle ratios (page 210).

EXAMPLE 1

What is the ratio of 16 to 48?

Solution. **The ratio is 16:48, or $\frac{16}{48}$, or $\frac{1}{3}$,** since both $\frac{16}{48}$ and $\frac{1}{3}$ have the same value. Either form shows that the first number (16) is $\frac{1}{3}$ as large as the second (48).

EXAMPLE 2

What is the ratio of $2\frac{1}{2}$ to 4?

Review division of fractions, page 28.

Solution. $\dfrac{2\frac{1}{2}}{4} = 2\frac{1}{2} \div 4 = \frac{5}{2} \times \frac{1}{4} = \frac{5}{8}$

EXERCISES

Express the following ratios in simpler form. TM p. 17, 8-1

A

1. $\dfrac{3}{6} = \dfrac{?}{?}$ **4.** $\dfrac{15}{35} = \dfrac{?}{?}$ **7.** $\dfrac{6\frac{3}{4}}{2} = \dfrac{?}{?}$

2. $\dfrac{9}{27} = \dfrac{?}{?}$ **5.** $\dfrac{24}{32} = \dfrac{?}{?}$ **8.** $\dfrac{5\frac{1}{2}}{\frac{3}{4}} = \dfrac{?}{?}$

3. $\dfrac{10}{12} = \dfrac{?}{?}$ **6.** $\dfrac{42}{7} = \dfrac{?}{?}$ **9.** $\dfrac{2.1}{.3} = \dfrac{?}{?}$

10. If you travel 350 mi. in 6 hr., what is the ratio of the distance to the time? What is the average rate of speed?

11. Find the ratio of the lengths of these two segments.

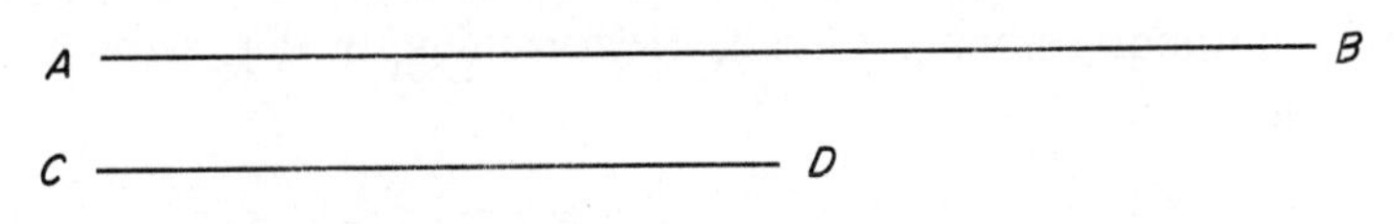

12. John is 16 yr. old. His sister's age is 14 yr.
  a. What is the ratio of John's age to his sister's?
  b. What is the ratio of his sister's age to his?

8–2 Screw Threads

There are several different kinds of screw threads used in the United States today. The drawings below show three common threads and give the formulas relating the depth of the thread, *D*, and the number of threads per inch, *N*. Notice that a ratio is involved in each formula.

American National Standard thread

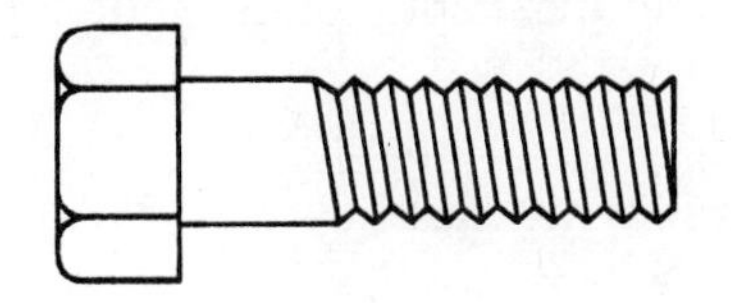

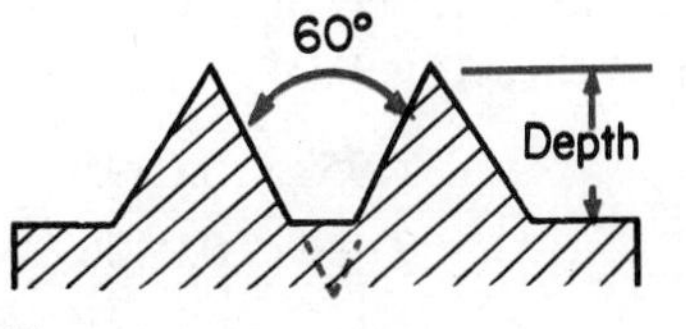

$$D = \frac{0.6495}{N}$$

Acme thread

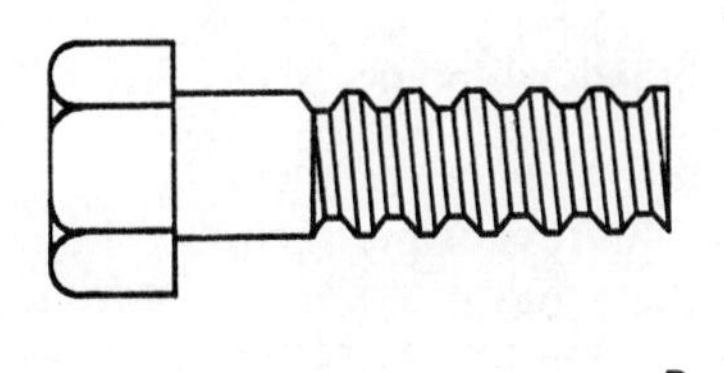

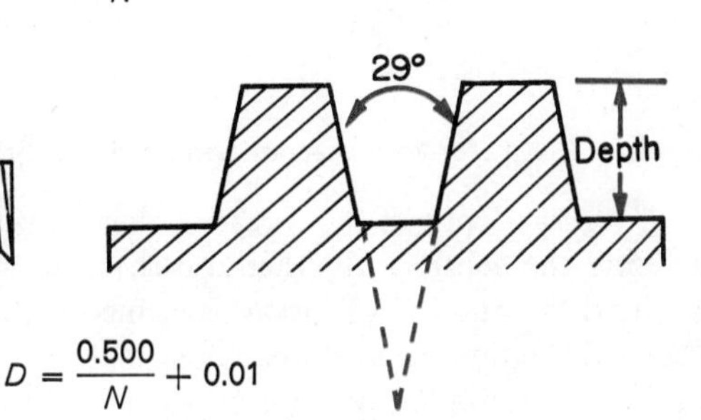

$$D = \frac{0.500}{N} + 0.01$$

Square thread

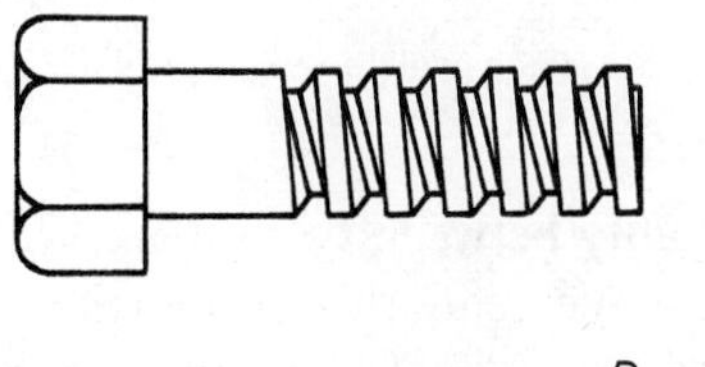

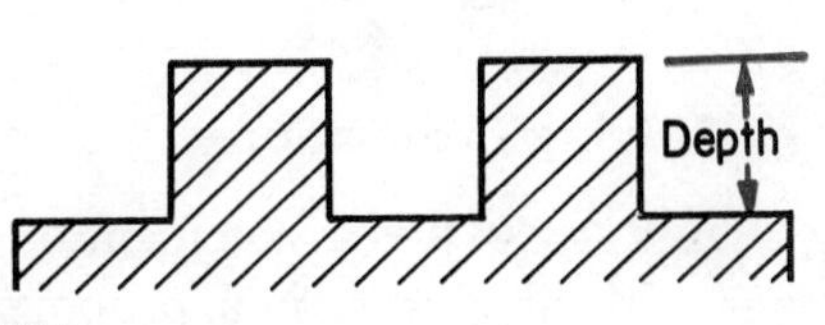

$$D = \frac{0.5000}{N}$$

The depth of a thread is used to set the controls on a thread-cutting machine. These figures are found in tables, but if tables are not available, the thread depth may be computed from the formula. For the American National Standard thread, the formulas for depth and number of threads are:

$$\mathbf{D = \frac{0.6495}{N}} \qquad D = \text{depth of threads in inches}$$

$$\mathbf{N = \frac{0.6495}{D}} \qquad N = \text{number of threads per inch}$$

EXAMPLE 1 The answers to the following examples are approximations.

What is the depth of an American National Standard thread having 8 threads per inch?

Solution. $D = \frac{0.6495}{N} = \frac{0.6495}{8} = \mathbf{0.081''}$

EXAMPLE 2

Find the number of threads per inch if the depth of a National Standard thread is 0.0406″.

Solution. $N = \frac{0.6495}{D} = \frac{0.6495}{0.0406} =$ **16 threads per inch**

EXERCISES

Exercises 1–5 refer to the American National Standard thread.

A

1. Find the depth of the thread if there are 13 threads per inch.
2. Find the depth of the thread if there are 40 threads per inch.
3. Find the number of threads per inch if the depth is 0.027″.
4. Find the number of threads per inch if the depth is 0.059″.
5. Find the number of threads per inch if the depth is 0.0203″.

B

6. In an Acme screw, the number of threads per inch is 25. Find the depth.
7. In a square thread, the number of threads per inch is 36. Find the depth.

8–3 Solving Proportions

A **proportion** is a statement of equality between two ratios. Thus $3:4 = 6:8$, or $\frac{3}{4} = \frac{6}{8}$, is a proportion. We read this proportion as "3 is to 4 as 6 is to 8" or as "3 divided by 4 equals 6 divided by 8."

The four numbers in a proportion are called **terms,** and they are named in order, as follows:

$$\begin{matrix}\textbf{1st term} \rightarrow \\ \textbf{2nd term} \rightarrow\end{matrix} \frac{3}{4} = \frac{6}{8} \begin{matrix}\leftarrow \textbf{3rd term} \\ \leftarrow \textbf{4th term}\end{matrix}$$

The first and fourth terms are also called the **extremes,** while the second and third terms are called the **means.** In the proportion above, if you multiply the *extremes*, you have 3×8, or 24. But notice that the product of the *means* gives the same result, $4 \times 6 = 24$.

A very important property of proportions is the following:

Be sure students understand this property.

> In any proportion, the product of the extremes equals the product of the means.

We are able to use this property to find a missing term in a proportion.

EXAMPLE 1

Find the value of n in $\frac{n}{6} = \frac{7}{42}$.

Solution. $42 \times n = 6 \times 7$	(Product of extremes = product of means.)
$42 \times n = 42$	(Replace 6×7 by its equal, 42.)
$n = \mathbf{1}$	(Divide *each* of the two equal expressions by 42.)

EXAMPLE 2

Find the missing value in the following proportion:

$$\frac{3}{4} = \frac{n}{16}$$

Solution. $3 \times 16 = 4 \times n$	(Product of extremes = product of means.)
$48 = 4n$	(Simplify the products.)
$12 = n$	(Divide each of the two equal expressions by 4.)

The missing value is **12.**

Check. Replace n by 12 in the original proportion.

$\frac{3}{4} = \frac{12}{16}$. This is a true statement, and the answer 12 is correct.

A "check" is always recommended.

Any statement of equality is called an **equation.** An equation often contains a symbol, as n in the Examples on the preceding page, which *stands for* a number. When we have found that number, we say that we have *solved* the equation. Many of the applications in this chapter depend on such equations. First, try the exercises which follow.

EXERCISES

Find the missing term.

A

1. $\frac{2}{5} = \frac{N}{20}$ **4.** $\frac{3}{4} = \frac{7}{N}$ **7.** $6:7 = N:21$

2. $\frac{N}{21} = \frac{18}{63}$ **5.** $\frac{8}{24} = \frac{x}{8}$ **8.** $7:11 = 11:N$

3. $\frac{5}{N} = \frac{20}{12}$ **6.** $21:5 = 6:N$ **9.** $X:5 = 25:5$

10. $9:x = 6:4$

Students may need to review exponents and square roots (page 39) before attempting these exercises.

Solve each equation for x.

B

11. $\frac{27}{x} = \frac{x}{3}$ **13.** $x:2 = 32:x$ **15.** $\frac{35}{5x} = \frac{7x}{49}$

12. $8:x = x:32$ **14.** $6x = \frac{6}{x}$

8–4 Levers

One of the simplest forms of a **lever** is a children's seesaw. Children soon learn that to "balance" the board, the child weighing less must sit farther from the pivot point, or **fulcrum,** than the heavier child.

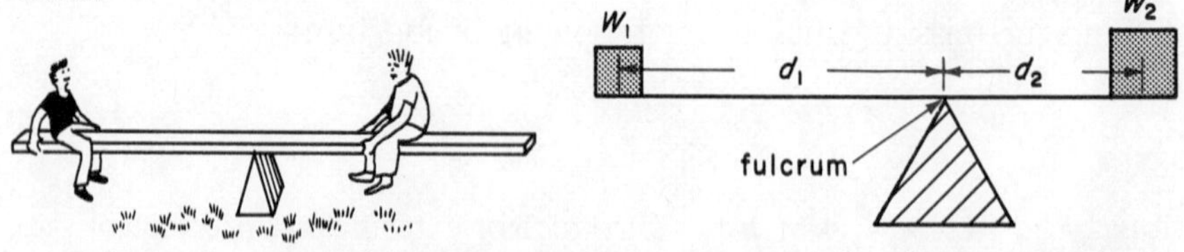

The relationship is expressed concisely in the following proportion:

$$\frac{w_1}{w_2} = \frac{d_2}{d_1}$$

"Cross multiplication" shows that the product of the extremes equals the product of the means (see page 289).

By cross multiplication, $w_1 d_1 = w_2 d_2$.

This simple formula holds for many different types of problems which involve levers.

EXAMPLE 1

Find to the nearest pound the minimum force necessary to lift a 1000-pound machine with a pry bar, if the fulcrum is 6″ from the machine and 54″ from the pushing force.

Solution. By referring to the diagram below, you can see that the machine corresponds to w_1, the shorter arm of the pry bar to d_1, and the longer arm to d_2. We must find w_2.

$$\frac{w_1}{w_2} = \frac{d_2}{d_1}$$

$$\frac{1000}{w} = \frac{54}{6}$$

$$54w = 6000$$

$$w = 111.1 \text{ (lb.)}$$

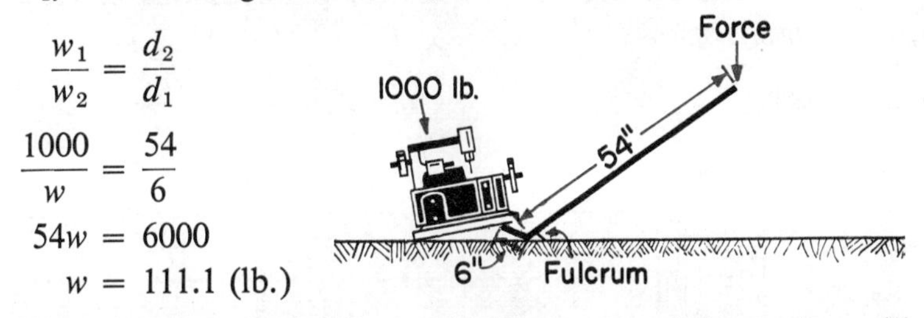

Thus, a force of 111.1 lb. on the longer arm of the pry bar will "balance" the weight of the machine on the shorter arm. In order to lift the machine we must upset the "balance" by applying a force greater than 111.1 lb., here, **a force of 112 lb.**

The hammer is another tool which works on the principle of the lever. We can describe its operation by the following proportion:

$$\frac{\textbf{pulling force on the handle}}{\textbf{resisting force of the wood on the nail}} = \frac{\textbf{distance from the fulcrum to the nail}}{\textbf{length of the handle}}$$

By referring to the figure at the right, we can express this proportion as

$$\frac{P}{w} = \frac{d}{D}$$

EXAMPLE 2

Find the holding force of the wood on the nail if $P = 25$ lb., $D = 14''$, and $d = 2''$.

Solution. $\frac{P}{w} = \frac{d}{D}$ $\qquad \frac{25}{w} = \frac{2}{14}$

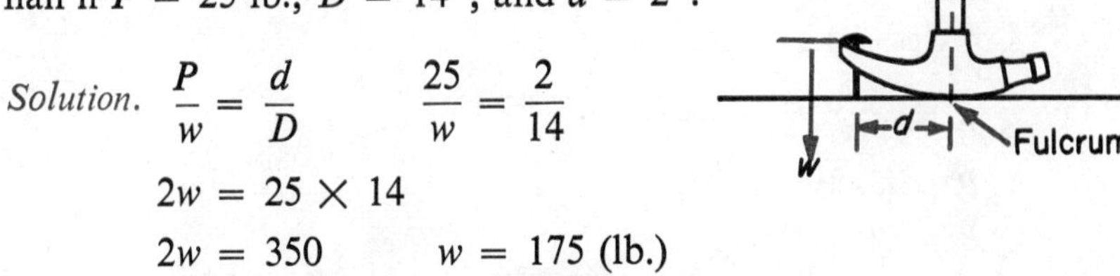

$$2w = 25 \times 14$$

$$2w = 350 \qquad w = 175 \text{ (lb.)}$$

Since the maximum holding force of the wood on the nail is measured when the resisting force and the pulling force are "in balance," **the holding force here is 175 lb.**

A hydraulic jack is another example of a tool which operates according to the lever principle. The following proportion describes its operation:

$$\frac{\textbf{upward force}}{\textbf{weight to be lifted}} = \frac{\textbf{length of the beam}}{\textbf{distance from the fulcrum to the hydraulic rod connection}}$$

Can you write the correct formula for the hydraulic jack by referring to the figure below? $\frac{P}{W} = \frac{d}{D}$

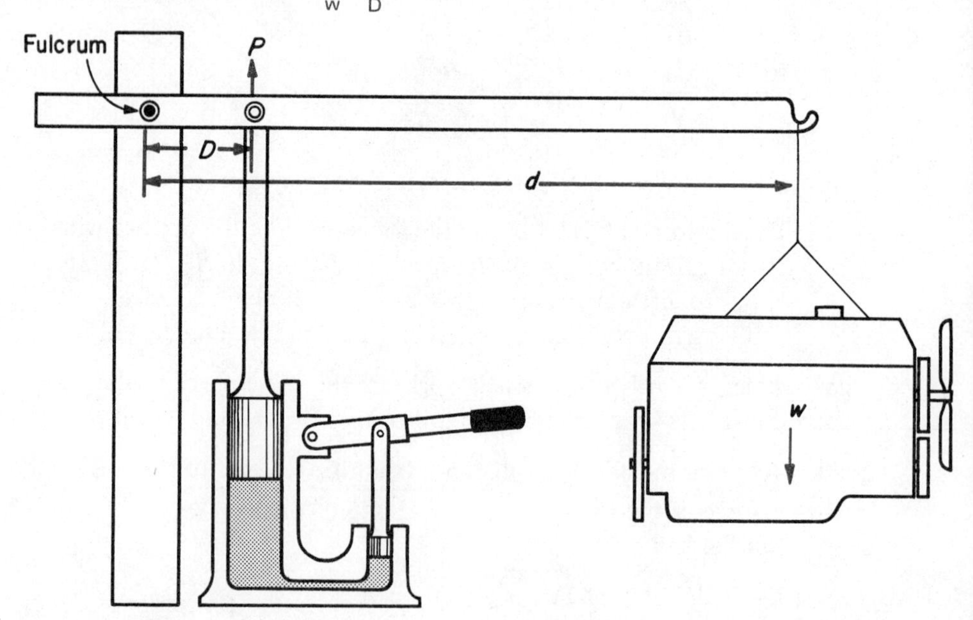

EXAMPLE 3

Find to the nearest pound the minimum upward force needed to lift the engine of a car, if the engine W weighs 500 lb., the distance d is 9 ft., and the distance D is 18 in.

Solution. $\frac{P}{W} = \frac{d}{D}$

$\frac{P}{500} = \frac{9}{1\frac{1}{2}}$ (Since $18'' = 1\frac{1}{2}'$) The distance $\underline{d}$ and $\underline{D}$ must be in the same units.

$1\frac{1}{2}P = 4500$

$P = 3000$ (lb.)

An upward force of 3000 lb. on the beam will "balance" the downward force of the weight of the engine. In order to lift the engine, we need to use an upward force greater than 3000 lb., in this case, **a force of 3001 lb.**

Students should be very careful in setting up the proper proportion. Encourage them to check their results.

EXERCISES

Refer to the preceding examples to aid you in solving these exercises.

A

1. Find to the nearest pound the minimum force necessary to lift a 1500 lb. drill press with a pry bar, if the fulcrum is 5 in. from the machine and 50 in. from the pushing force.
2. Find the distance from the fulcrum to the base of a metal lathe, if the lathe weighs 1200 lb., the pushing force is 90 lb., and the distance from the fulcrum to the pushing force is 72 in. (Assume that the weight of the lathe and the pushing force are "in balance.")
3. Find the resistance (or holding force of the wood on nail), if the pulling force is 32 lb., the length of the handle is 16 in., and the distance from the fulcrum to the nail is 2 in.
4. With the same hammer as in Exercise 3, find to the nearest pound the minimum force necessary to pull a nail, if the resisting force of the wood on the nail is 450 lb.
5. Find to the nearest pound the minimum upward force needed to lift an engine and transmission of a car with a beam hoist, if their total weight is 700 lb., the distance d is 10 ft., and the distance D is 21 in.
6. What is the maximum weight that a beam hoist can lift, if the upward force has a top limit of 6000 lb., while d is 9 ft., and D is 27 in.?

SELF-ANALYSIS TEST I

Time: 15 minutes

1. Express the following ratios in simplest form.

   a. $\frac{7}{21}$　　b. $\frac{9}{81}$　　c. $\frac{1\frac{1}{4}}{5}$

2. Which of the following are true proportions?

   a. $\frac{2}{3} = \frac{10}{15}$　　c. $\frac{10}{7} = \frac{25}{17.5}$

   b. $\frac{5}{16} = \frac{15}{49}$　　d. $18:11 = 80:55$

In Exercises 3–6, find the value represented by N in the proportion.

3. $\frac{7}{13} = \frac{N}{26}$
4. $\frac{5}{25} = \frac{20}{N}$
5. $\frac{31}{N} = \frac{5}{6}$
6. $10:35 = 11:N$

7. Find the depth of an American National Standard thread, if there are 15 threads per inch.
8. In a square thread, the number of threads per inch is 10. Find the depth.
9. Find to the nearest pound the minimum force necessary to lift a 1500 lb. punch press with a pry bar, if the fulcrum is 8 in. from the press and 60 in. from the pushing force.
10. Find to the nearest pound the minimum force needed to remove a nail with a 13 in. hammer, if the resisting force of the wood on the nail is 286 lb. and the distance from the fulcrum to the nail is 3 in.

Similarity

8–5 Similar Triangles

Two triangles with the same shape are called **similar triangles.** Such triangles have special properties which prove to be very useful. This activity is quite instructive.

ACTIVITY: *To construct two similar triangles and study their properties.*

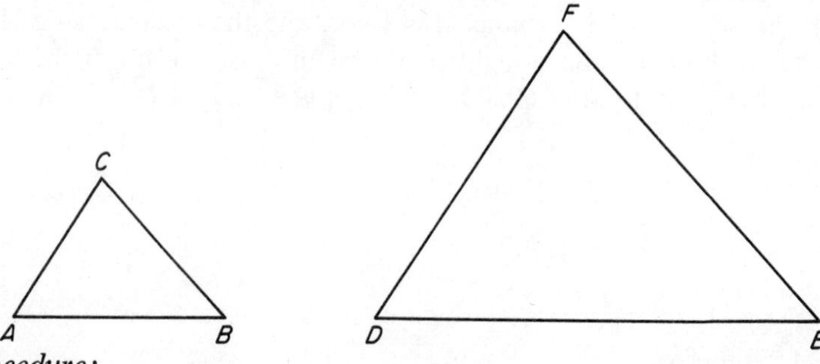

Procedure:

1. Construct two triangles with angles of 57°, 47°, and 76° as shown. Choose any convenient length for side AB and make side DE twice as long. (Use a 6″ ruler calibrated in tenths or in centimeters.)
2. Draw a chart like the one below. Then measure the sides of the triangles and complete the chart.

$\triangle ABC$			$\triangle DEF$			RATIOS		
AB	BC	AC	DE	EF	DF	$AB:DE$	$BC:EF$	$AC:DF$

Exchange triangle drawings with at least three of your classmates and repeat the above measurements on the triangles.

△*ABC*			△*DEF*			RATIOS		
AB	*BC*	*AC*	*DE*	*EF*	*DF*	*AB* : *DE*	*BC* : *EF*	*AC* : *DF*

In comparing the two triangles, you should have found that *each* side of $\triangle DEF$ was twice as long as the corresponding side of $\triangle ABC$. The ratios of corresponding sides were the same in each case, 1:2, or $\frac{1}{2}$.

The above Activity illustrates two important properties of similar triangles. TM p. 17 , 8-5(1)

> 1. The corresponding angles of similar triangles are equal.
> 2. The corresponding sides of similar triangles have equal ratios; that is, the corresponding sides are proportional.

Triangles can be "rotated" and "flipped over." This does not affect the size of the angles or the lengths of the sides.

EXERCISES

A

1. Which triangles are similar? Use a ruler and protractor, and record all proportions.

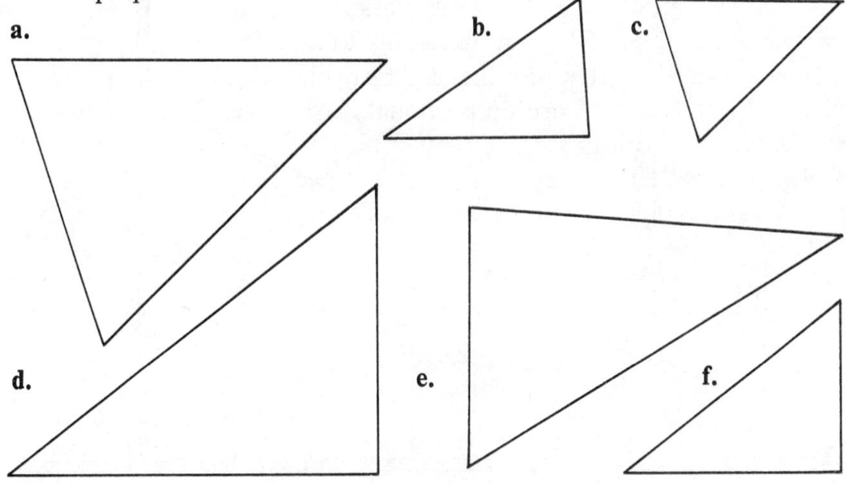

2. Draw three triangles, two of which are similar. The third one should look similar, but not actually be so. Exchange drawings with classmates and test your ability to determine which triangles are similar.

ACTIVITY: ***Constructing similar triangles of wood.***

Purpose: To study the proportions of the sides of similar triangles.

Materials: 4 pieces of $\frac{1}{2}'' \times \frac{1}{2}''$ pine cut to the following lengths: 36″, 36″, 9″, and 32″; a $1'' \times \frac{1}{2}''$ cardboard rectangle, 2 thumbtacks, a ruler.

Procedure:

1. Lay the two 36″ sticks alongside one another. Attach the cardboard rectangle to the end of each stick with thumbtacks. The cardboard will serve as a hinge at the vertex *A*.
2. From *A* measure a distance of 30″ to locate point *B*, and a distance of 18″ to locate point *D*. Mark each point on the stick.
3. Place the 9″ piece (*DE*) perpendicular to *AB* at *D*. Use a protractor to be sure you have a right angle.
4. Adjust the other 36″ stick until it touches *DE* at *E*, as shown in the figure above.
5. We now need a stick *BC*. To find its length, use the proportion $\frac{AD}{DE} = \frac{AB}{BC}$. Substitute the known values and solve for *BC*.
6. Put a mark on the 32″ stick to correspond with the value for *BC* which you have found. Place the stick in position at *B* perpendicular to *AB*. Does the mark fall exactly on the inside edge of the other stick? Accuracy is essential here.

If you have been accurate in your work, the length of stick *BC* will be 15″. You were able to calculate this length in Step 5 because the lengths of the sides of $\triangle ABC$ and $\triangle ADE$ are proportional. $\triangle ABC$ is similar to $\triangle ADE$ because $\angle A$ (in $\triangle ADE$) $= \angle A$ (in $\triangle ABC$) and right $\angle ADE =$ right $\angle ABC$. Why must $\angle AED = \angle ACB$?

TM p. 17 , 8-5(2)

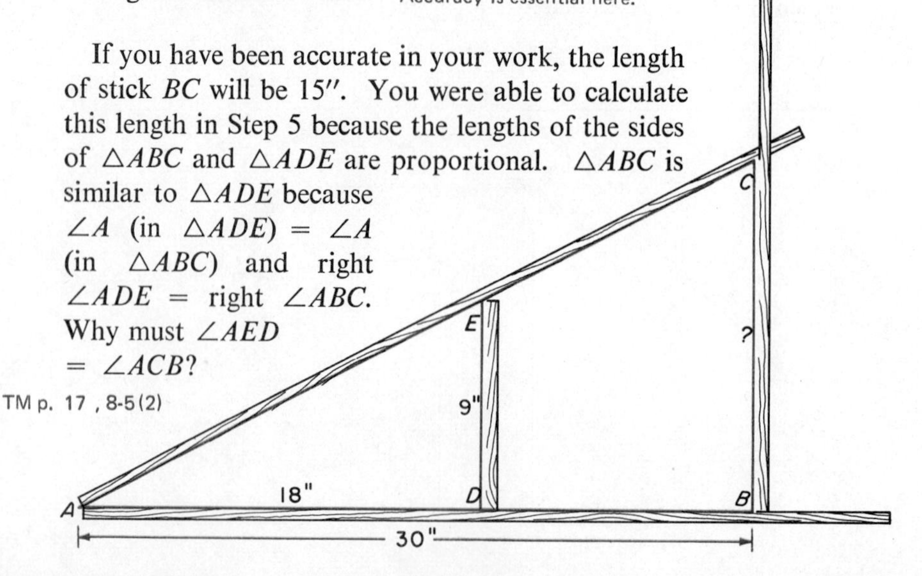

This Activity suggests the following important fact.

Two triangles are similar if two angles of the first equal two angles of the second.

EXERCISES

A

1. Copy and complete this chart, using your triangle sticks to check your calculations.

AD	*AB*	*DE*	*BC*
18″	18″	9″	?
18″	21″	9″	?
18″	24″	9″	?
18″	27″	9″	?
18″	30″	9″	?

$$\frac{AD}{DE} = \frac{AB}{BC}$$

By how much does BC increase each time you lengthen AB by 3″?

2. Copy and complete the chart below for the figures shown. Check your calculations by using your sticks.

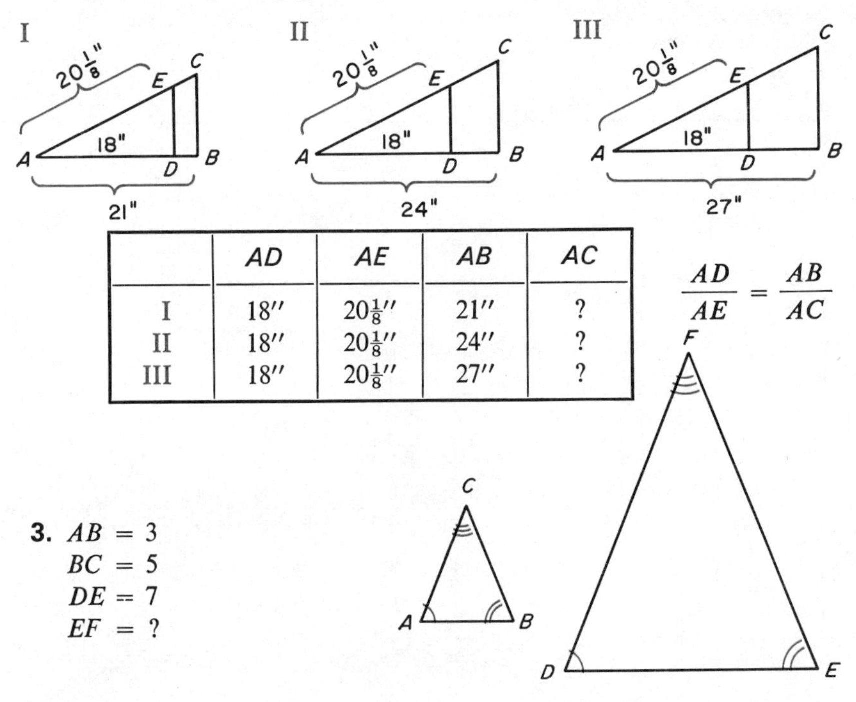

	AD	*AE*	*AB*	*AC*
I	18″	$20\frac{1}{8}$″	21″	?
II	18″	$20\frac{1}{8}$″	24″	?
III	18″	$20\frac{1}{8}$″	27″	?

$$\frac{AD}{AE} = \frac{AB}{AC}$$

3. $AB = 3$
$BC = 5$
$DE = 7$
$EF = ?$

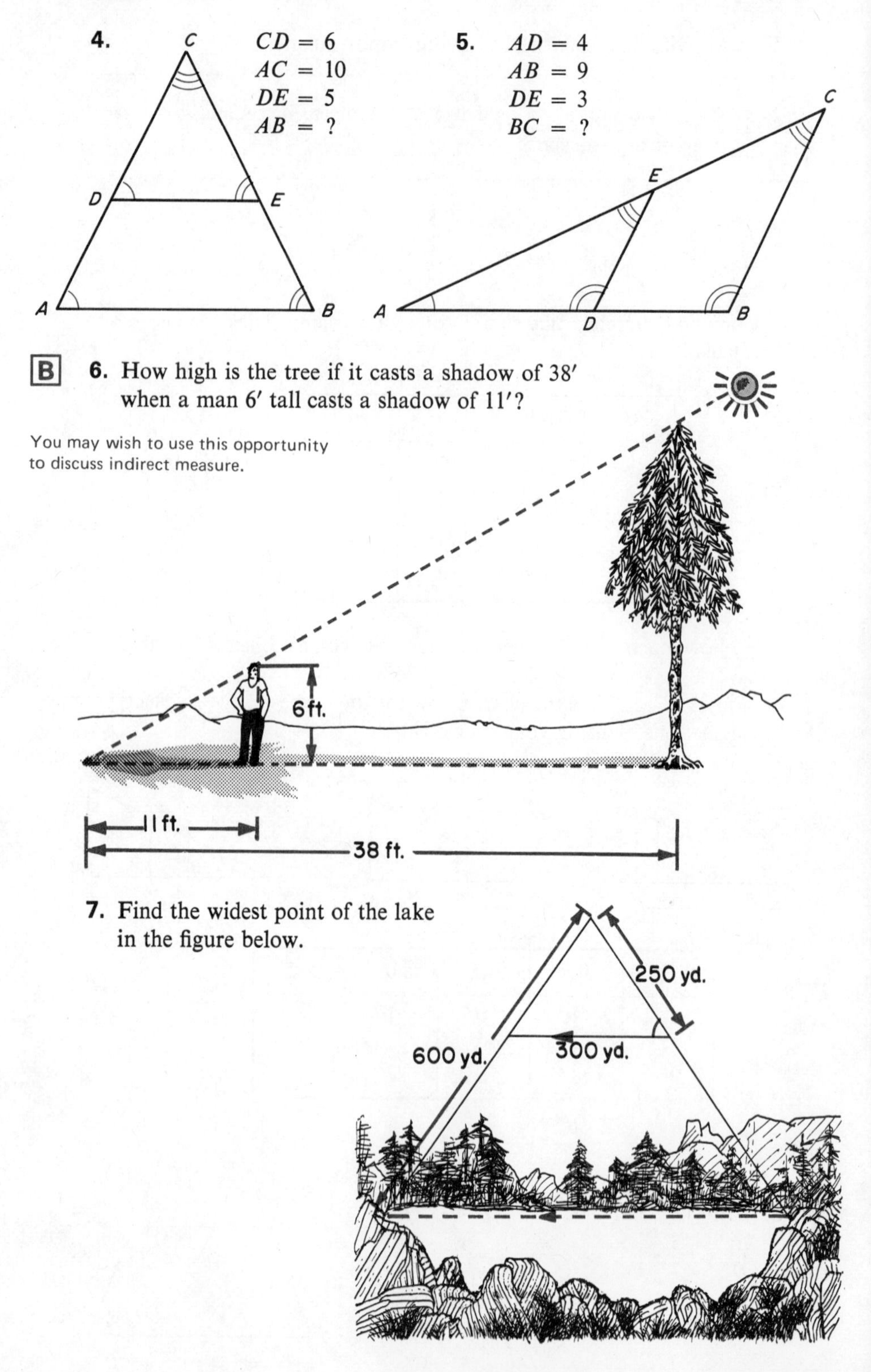

4. $CD = 6$
$AC = 10$
$DE = 5$
$AB = ?$

5. $AD = 4$
$AB = 9$
$DE = 3$
$BC = ?$

B **6.** How high is the tree if it casts a shadow of 38′ when a man 6′ tall casts a shadow of 11′?

You may wish to use this opportunity to discuss indirect measure.

7. Find the widest point of the lake in the figure below.

8–6 Similar Polygons

Polygons other than triangles may also be similar. **Similar polygons,** like similar triangles, have the same shape. We state this in more exact language as follows:

1. The corresponding angles of similar polygons are equal.
2. The corresponding sides of similar polygons have equal ratios; that is, they are proportional.

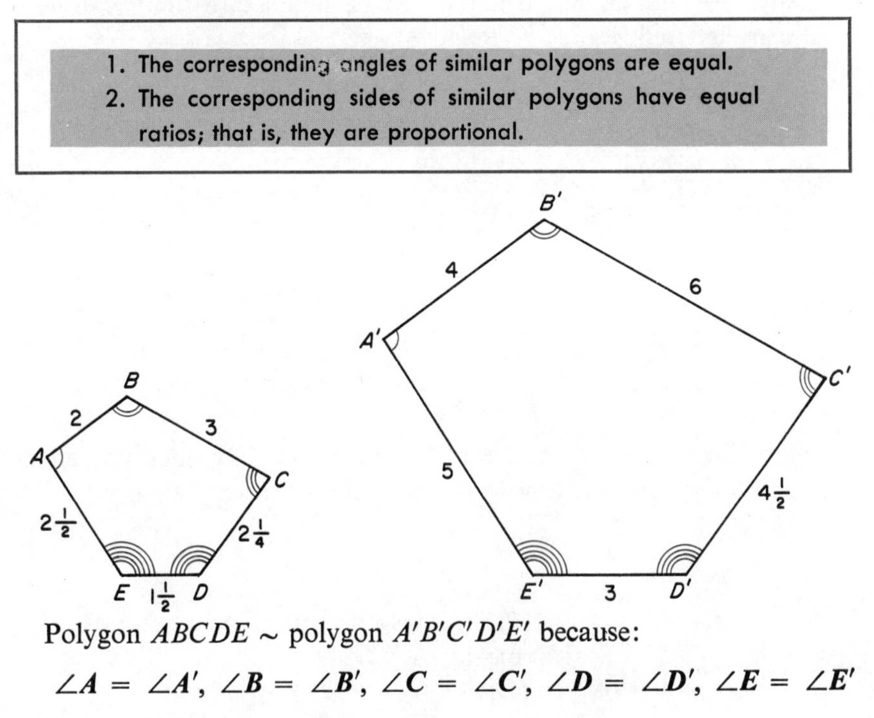

Polygon $ABCDE \sim$ polygon $A'B'C'D'E'$ because:

$$\angle A = \angle A',\ \angle B = \angle B',\ \angle C = \angle C',\ \angle D = \angle D',\ \angle E = \angle E'$$

and
$$\frac{AB}{A'B'} = \frac{BC}{B'C'} = \frac{CD}{C'D'} = \frac{DE}{D'E'} = \frac{EA}{E'A'}.$$

Note. The symbol $\sim$ is read "is similar to." Encourage students to use this notation.

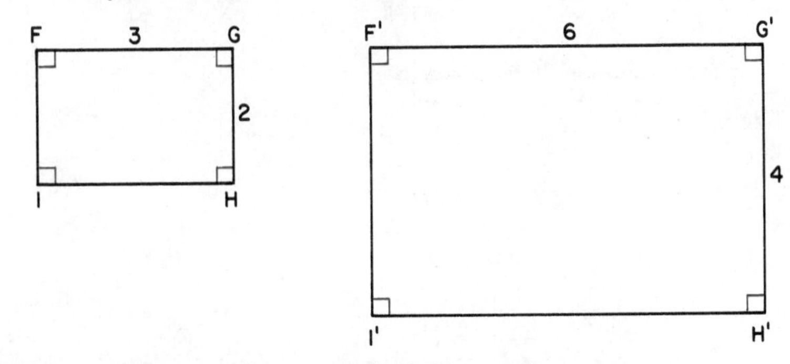

Polygon $FGHI \sim$ polygon $F'G'H'I'$ because:

All angles are right angles and $\dfrac{FG}{F'G'} = \dfrac{GH}{G'H'} = \dfrac{HI}{H'I'} = \dfrac{IF}{I'F'}$.

We can use the equal ratios of the known sides to find the lengths of unknown sides. Students must be able to match the corresponding sides of similar polygons.

EXAMPLE

Find the length of side a if the two pentagons are similar. Equal angles are lettered A and A', B and B', etc.

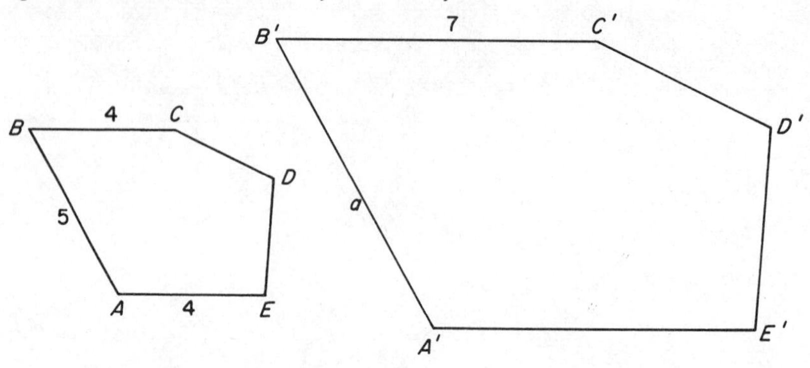

Solution. Since the polygons are similar, corresponding sides have equal ratios, and the following proportion is true.

$$\frac{4}{7} = \frac{5}{a}$$

$4a = 35$ (Product of extremes equals the product of means.)

$a = \frac{35}{4} = \mathbf{8\frac{3}{4}}$ (Divide by 4.)

EXERCISES

Find the missing values in these similar polygons.

A

1. Side m = ?
Side n = ?
Side o = ?

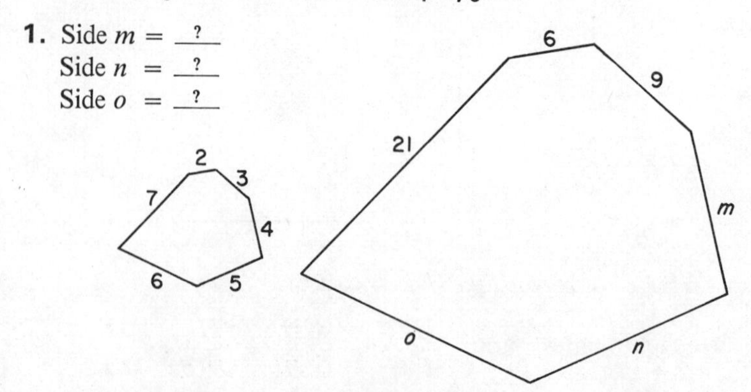

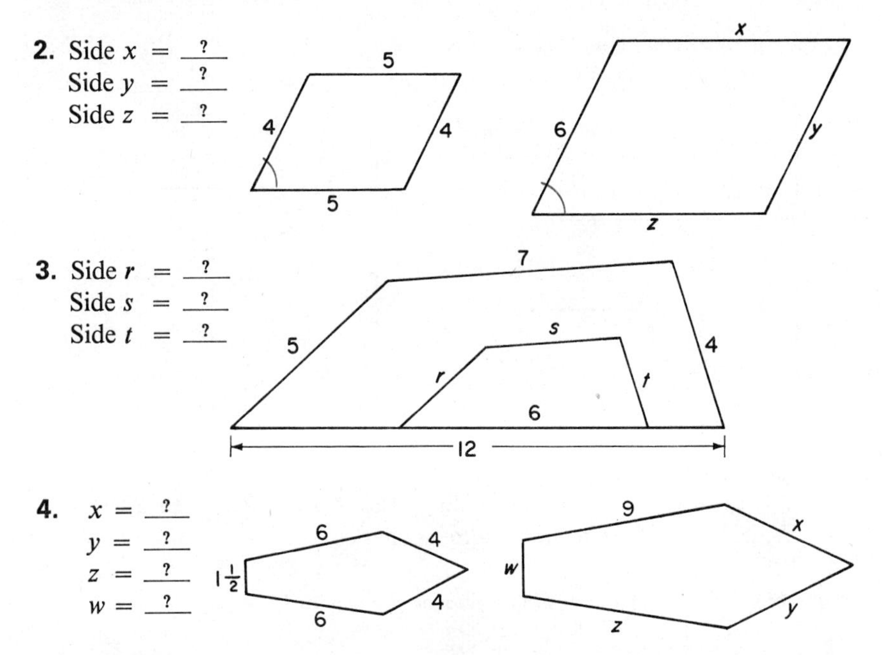

2. Side x = ?
   Side y = ?
   Side z = ?

3. Side r = ?
   Side s = ?
   Side t = ?

4. x = ?
   y = ?
   z = ?
   w = ?

5. **a.** Which rectangles below are similar?
   b. What is the ratio of a side of rectangle A to a corresponding side of B?
   c. What is the ratio of corresponding sides of rectangles C and D? Is there a single answer?
   d. Are all rectangles similar?

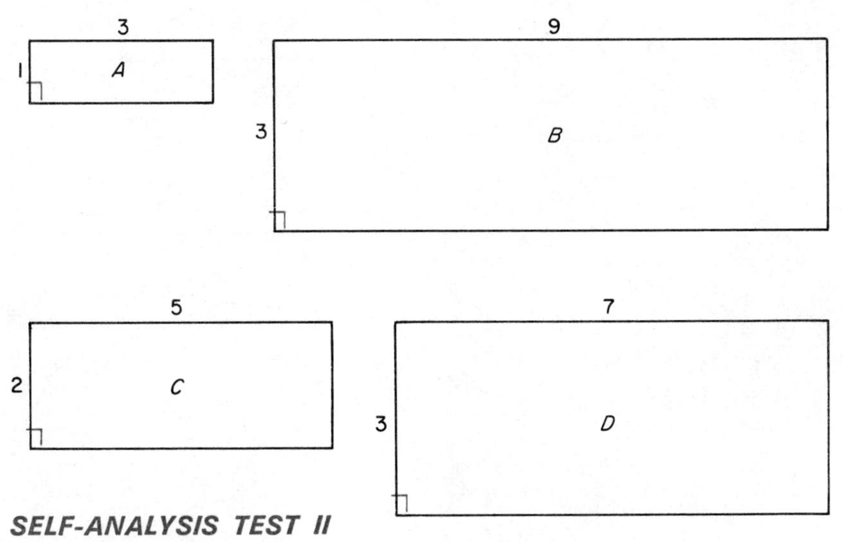

SELF-ANALYSIS TEST II

Time: 25 minutes

1. Two polygons are similar if their corresponding angles are ? and their corresponding sides are ? .

Exercises 2–4 refer to the figures below.

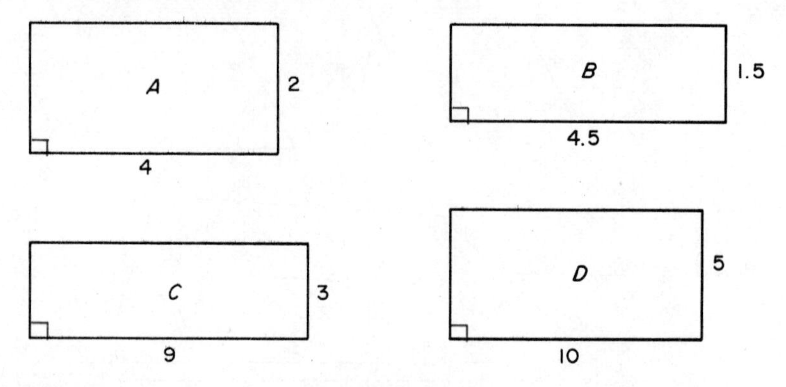

2. Is rectangle A similar to rectangle C?
3. What is the ratio of corresponding sides in rectangles C to B?
4. Which of the four rectangles are similar?

In Exercises 5–8, find the missing values in the similar polygons.

5. $x =$?
$y =$?

6. $x =$?

7. $a =$?
$b =$?
$x =$?
$y =$?
$z =$?

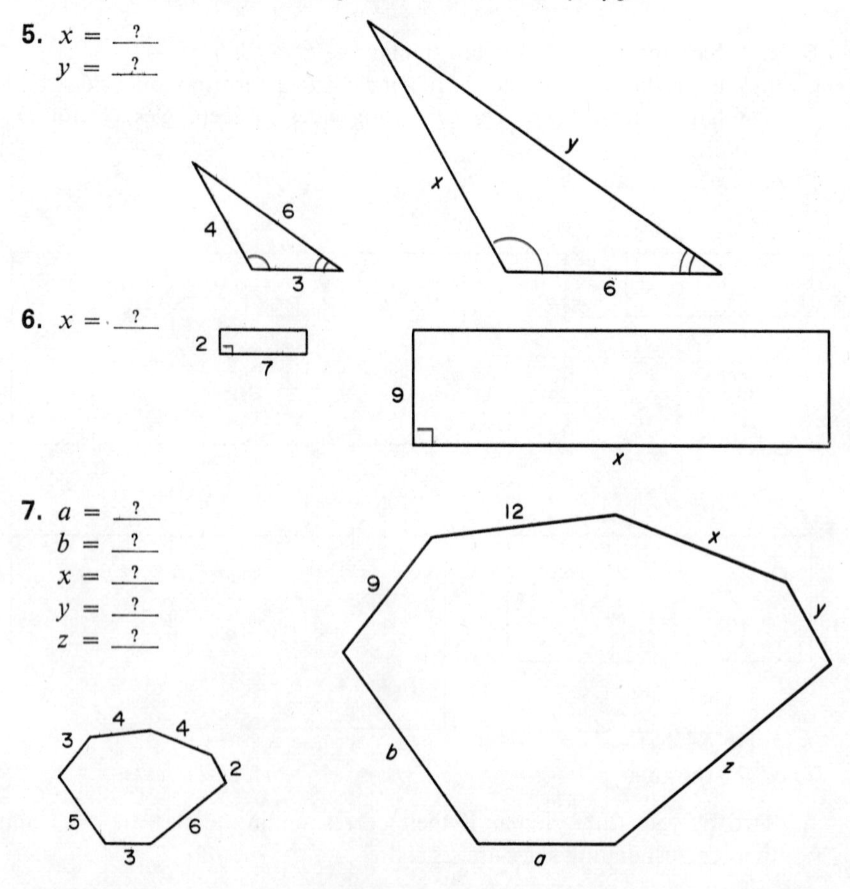

8. $x =$?
$y =$?
$z =$?

9. Find the length of AC.

10. Find the length of BC.

11. Find the widest point of the lake.

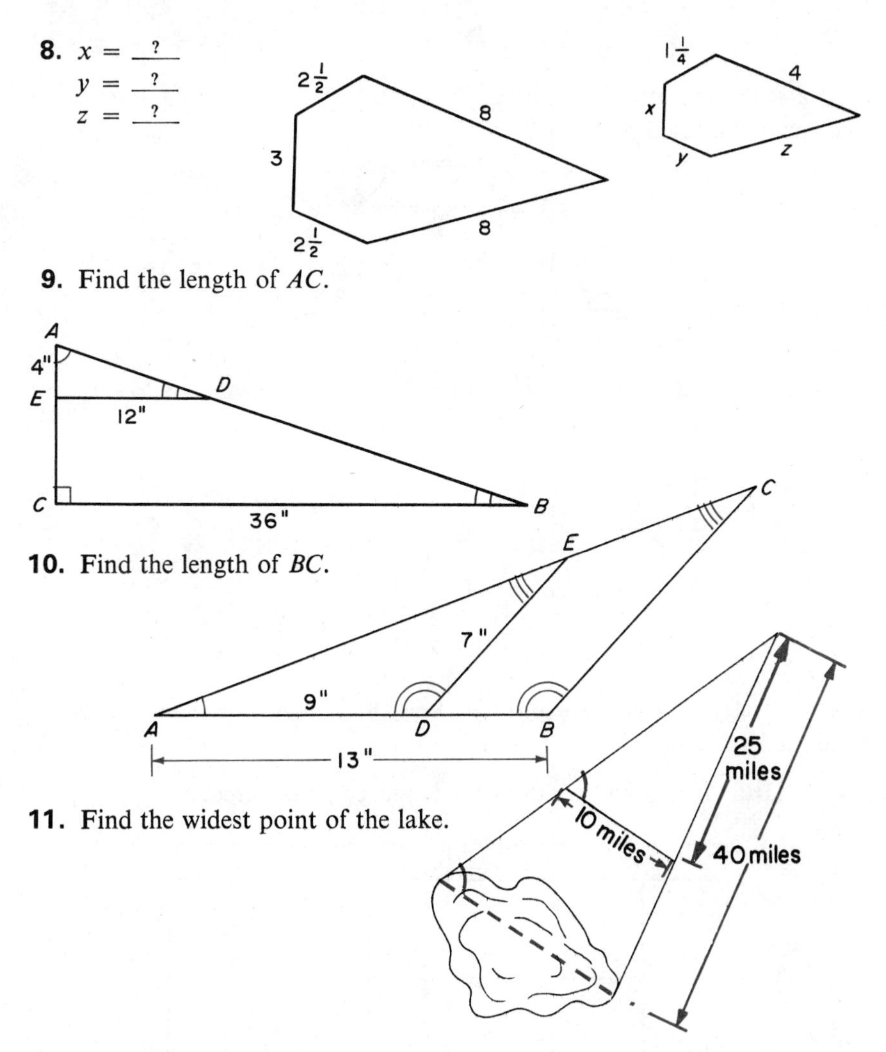

8–7 Scale Drawings

TM p. 17, 8-7

Many times it is not practical to make full-size drawings of objects to be manufactured. Sometimes the objects are too large, other times too small. This requires drawings which describe the object accurately, but in a different size.

The ratio of a length on the drawing to the corresponding length on the object is called the *scale*. Thus a half-size drawing has a scale of 1 : 2. This means that 1″ on the drawing represents 2″ on the object.

Sometimes the scale is given in the form 1″ to 6′ for a scale of 1 : 72 (since 6′ = 72″). On a map you may find a statement similar to the following:

Scale: one inch to 1.6 miles, or 1 : 101,376.

EXAMPLE Model cars, planes, etc., are examples of three-dimensional scale objects.

If a scale drawing shows a car as 3 in. long, find the actual length of the car if the scale is 1″ to 6′, or 1 : 72.

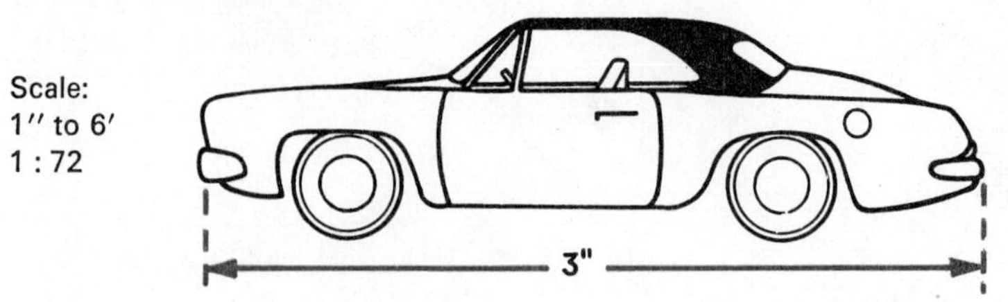

Solution. Since the scale is 1″ to 6′, 3 in. will represent 3 × 6 ft., or **18 ft.** You may use a proportion as follows:

$$\frac{1}{6} = \frac{3}{x} \qquad x = \mathbf{18\ (ft.)}$$

EXERCISES

Use your ruler to measure the distances on the figures. Calculate the actual distances according to the given scale.

A **1.** Find the length and width of the tennis court pictured.

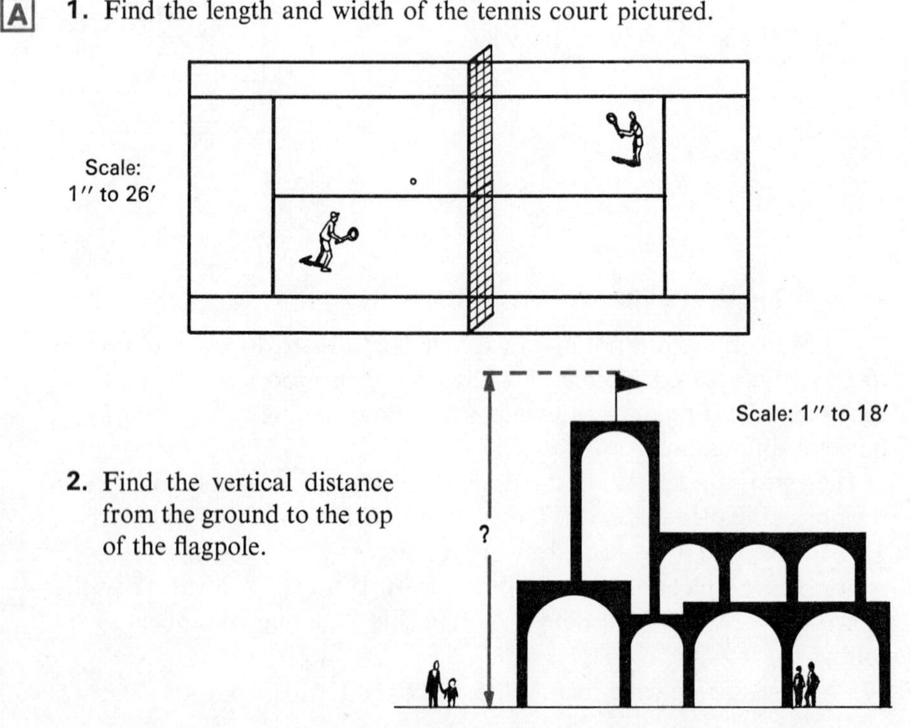

2. Find the vertical distance from the ground to the top of the flagpole.

3. Find the length of the truck bed.

Scale: $\frac{1}{4}''$ to 18″

4. Find the diagonal $\overline{AB}$ of the dresser.

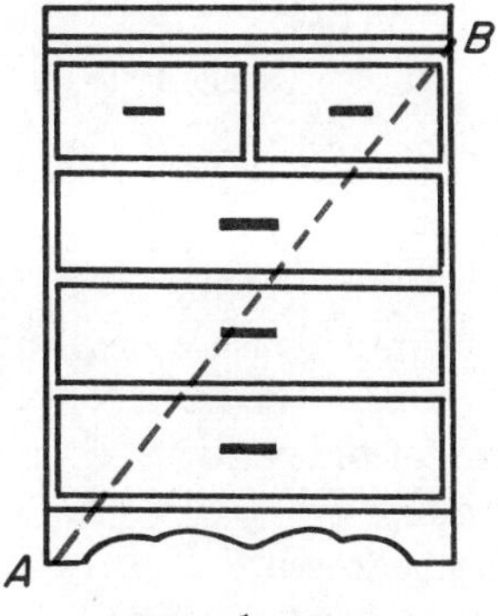

Scale: $\frac{1}{8}''$ to 4″

5. Find the width of each door of the double-door refrigerator.

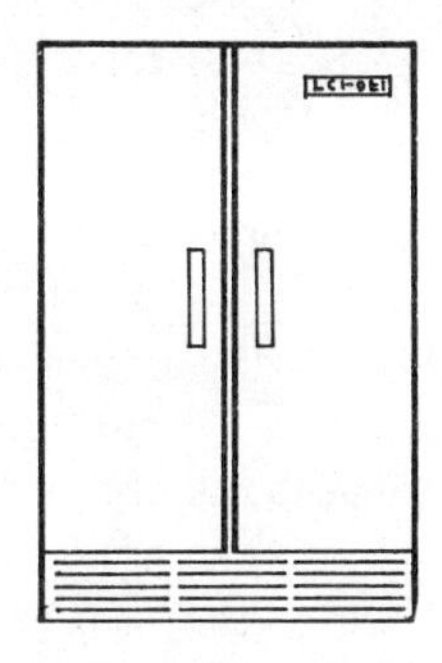

Scale: $\frac{1}{4}''$ to 8″

6. Find the length L of the brick pile.

7. Find the height of the cross bar.

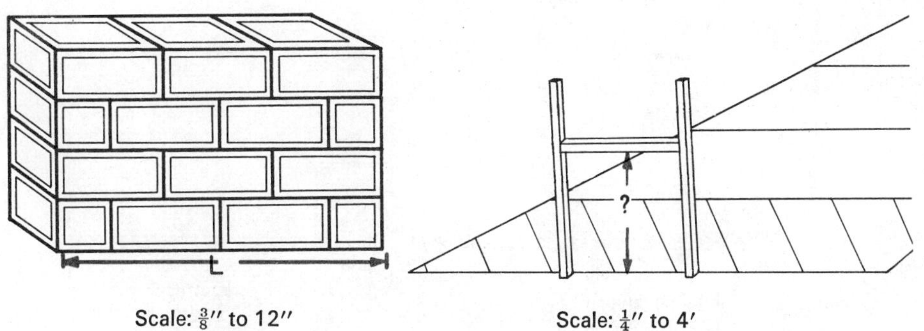

Scale: $\frac{3}{8}''$ to 12″

Scale: $\frac{1}{4}''$ to 4′

8. Find the length of the box car, including the couplers.

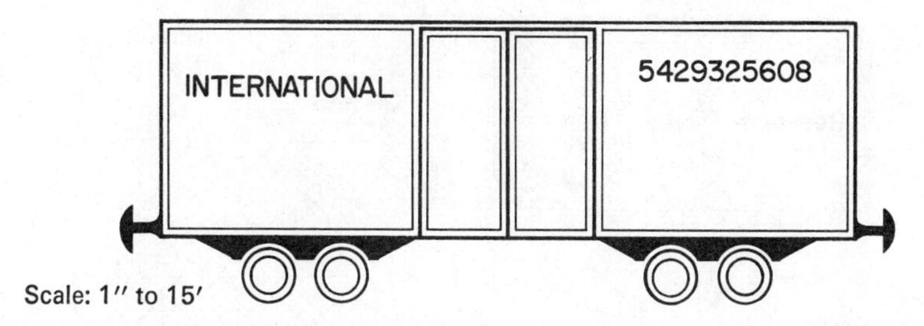

Scale: 1″ to 15′

9. Find the dimensions of the billboard.

10. Find the length L and height h of the gasoline storage tank.

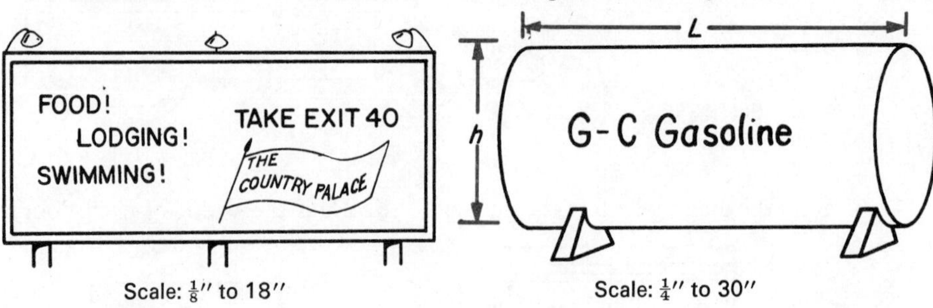

Scale: $\frac{1}{8}''$ to 18″

Scale: $\frac{1}{4}''$ to 30″

Exercises 11–18 refer to the house plan shown. Use your ruler and give all areas in square feet.

11. What is the area of the dining room? Hint. Measure length and width on the plan. Find actual length and width. Then use formula $A = lw$.
12. What is the area of the living room? of the patio?
13. What is the area of the master bedroom?
14. What is the area of each of the other bedrooms?
15. What is the total area of the three bedrooms?
16. What is the open area of the kitchen and pantry?
17. What is the area of the garage?
18. What is the total area of the house, excluding garage?

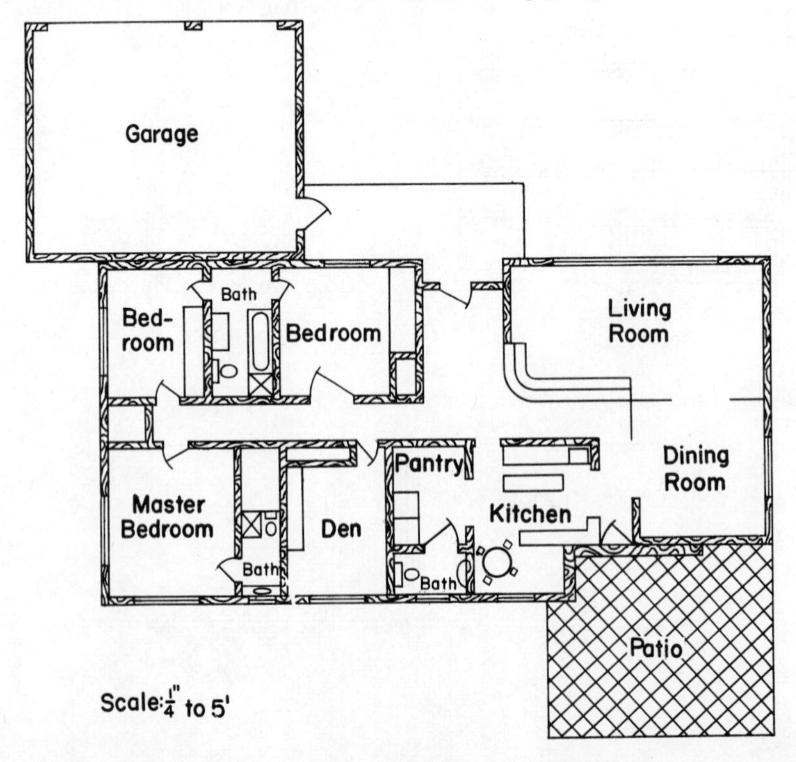

Scale: $\frac{1}{4}''$ to 5′

8–8 Maps

Most of us use maps to plan a trip or to find the route as we travel. The following exercises will give you some practice.

Some students may wish to repeat these exercises by actually using road maps or an atlas.

EXERCISES

On this map some routes are marked between various cities. Air routes are indicated in red and land routes in black. Using this map, your ruler, and the scale given, answer the questions in Exercises 1 and 2.

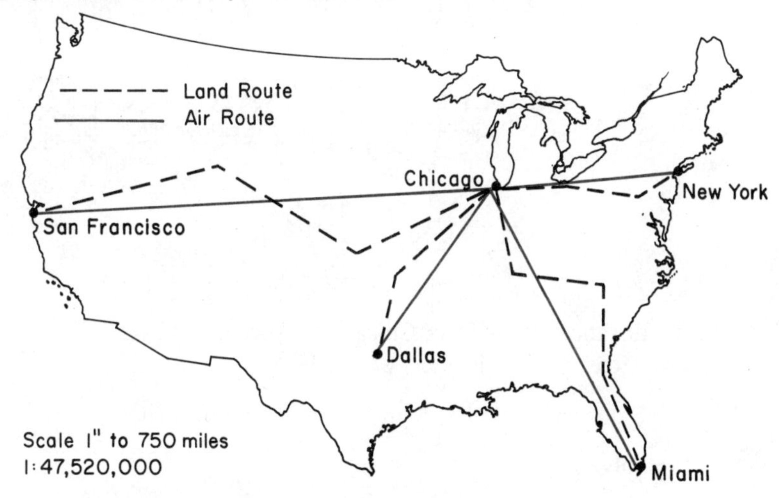

A

1. Using the map, find the flying distance from:
   a. Chicago to San Francisco
   b. Chicago to Dallas
   c. Chicago to Miami
   d. Chicago to New York City

2. Using the map above, find the surface distances in Exercise 1.

The areas circled are shown in detail on the following pages.

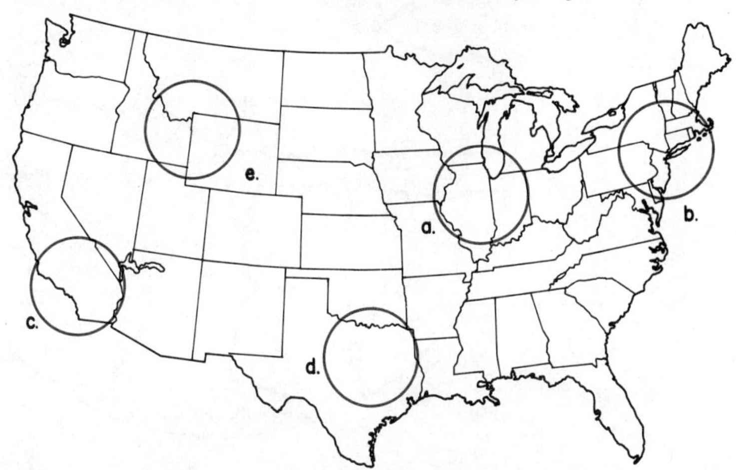

On the maps which follow the scale is 1″ to 120 miles or 1 : 7,603,200.

Chicago Section

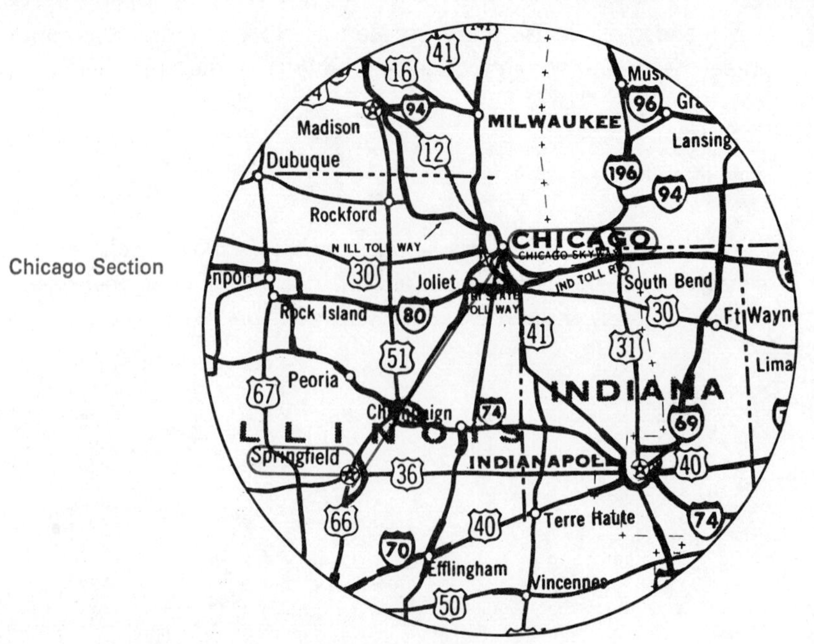

3. Find the distance by air from Chicago to Springfield.
   Hint. 1. Measuring with ruler, we get $1\frac{1}{2}''$.

   2. Since the scale is 120 mi. to the inch, we write $\frac{120}{1} = \frac{x}{1\frac{1}{2}}$ and solve for x.

Find the distance by air from:

4. Dallas to Fort Worth.
5. Dallas to Waco.
6. Chicago to Indianapolis.

Dallas Section

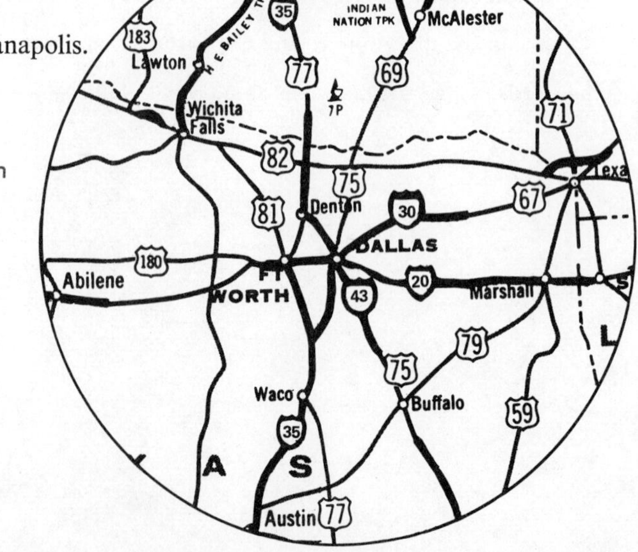

Los Angeles Section

Find the distance by air from:

7. New York City to Philadelphia.
8. Los Angeles to Las Vegas, Nevada.
9. New York to Baltimore.
10. Chicago to Madison, Wisconsin.
11. Los Angeles to Palm Springs.

New York Section

Find the distance by air from:

12. Butte, Montana, to the West Entrance to Yellowstone National Park.
13. Billings, Montana, to Pocatello, Idaho.

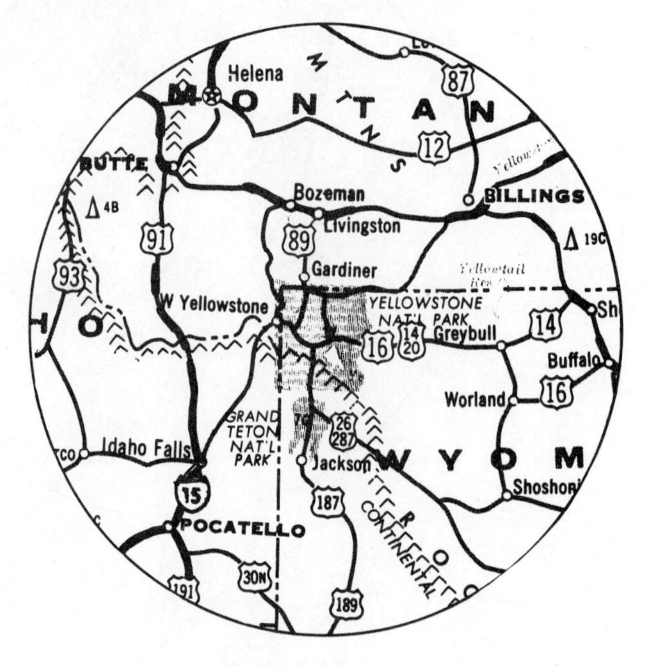

Yellowstone Park Section

SELF-ANALYSIS TEST III

Time: 15 minutes

Use a ruler to measure the distances. Calculate the required distances according to the given scale.

1. Find the height of the car.

Scale: 1″ to 6′

2. Find the diameter of the wheel.

Scale: $\frac{1}{4}$″ to 1′

3. Find the height and length of the bench.

Scale: $\frac{1}{4}''$ to $6''$

4. Find the length and height of the building.

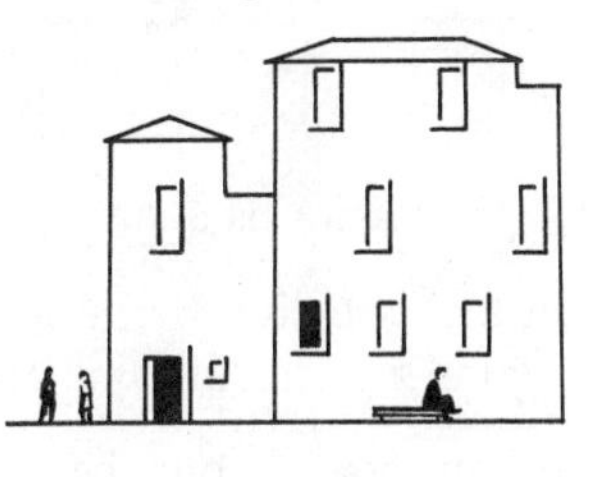

Scale: $\frac{1}{8}''$ to $3'$

5. Find the distance from D to E through S.

6. Find the distance from N to W through S.

Scale: $1''$ to 25 miles

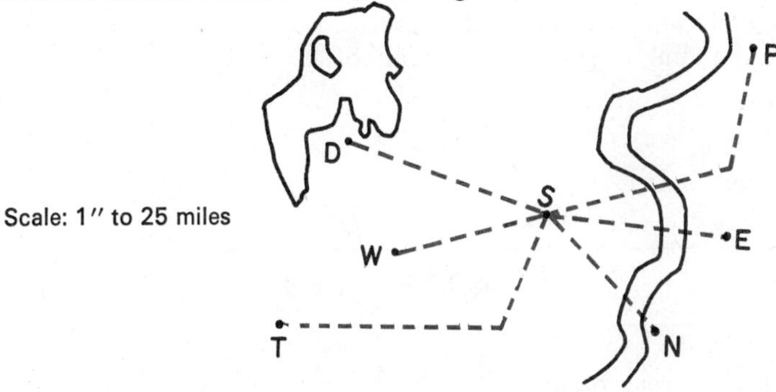

7. Find the cost of traveling from T to P through S, if gasoline costs 37¢ a gallon, and your car gets 13 miles to a gallon.

8. How many square feet are in the living room?

9. What is the total area of the bedrooms?

10. What is the total area of the house, excluding the garage?

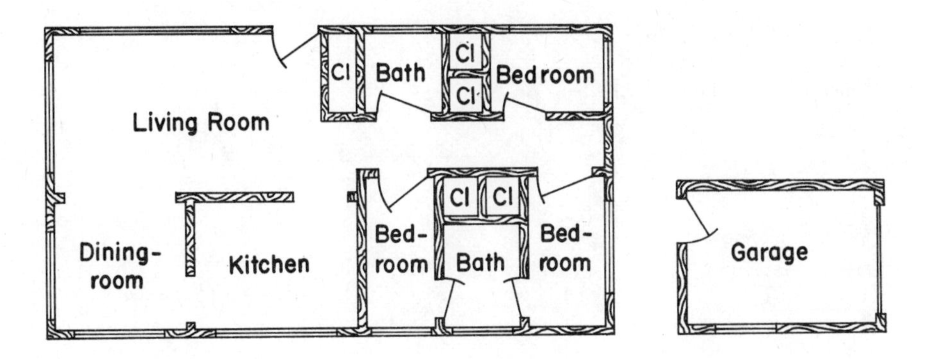

Scale: $\frac{1}{4}''$ to $3'$

CHAPTER SUMMARY

1. A ratio is the quotient of one number divided by another number.
2. A proportion is a statement of equality between two ratios.
3. In a proportion the first and fourth terms are called the extremes; the second and third terms are called the means.
4. In any proportion, the product of the means equals the product of the extremes.
5. Polygons are similar if their corresponding angles are equal and their corresponding sides are proportional.
6. The scale of a drawing is the ratio of a length on the drawing to the corresponding length on the actual object.

CHAPTER TEST

Simplify the following ratios:

1. $\frac{8}{26}$ 2. $\frac{21}{3}$ 3. $\dfrac{1\frac{1}{8}}{2}$ 4. $\dfrac{1\frac{3}{16}}{\frac{1}{2}}$

5. Find the depth of an American National Standard thread if there are 30 threads per inch. (Depth $= \dfrac{0.6495}{N}$; N = number of threads per inch.)

Which of the following are true proportions?

6. $\frac{4}{5} = \frac{12}{15}$ 7. $\frac{3}{9} = \frac{21}{62}$ 8. $\frac{35}{25} = 5{:}7$ 9. $\frac{12}{5} = \frac{6}{2\frac{1}{2}}$

Find the missing value.

10. $\frac{3}{5} = \frac{N}{10}$ 11. $3{:}N = \frac{25}{26}$ 12. $12N = 8 \times 6$

13. Find to the nearest pound the maximum weight of an engine, if the upward pressure P needed to lift the engine of a car is 2400 lb., the distance d from the fulcrum is 8 ft., and the distance D from fulcrum is 16 in. (Refer to Example 3, p. 292.)

14.

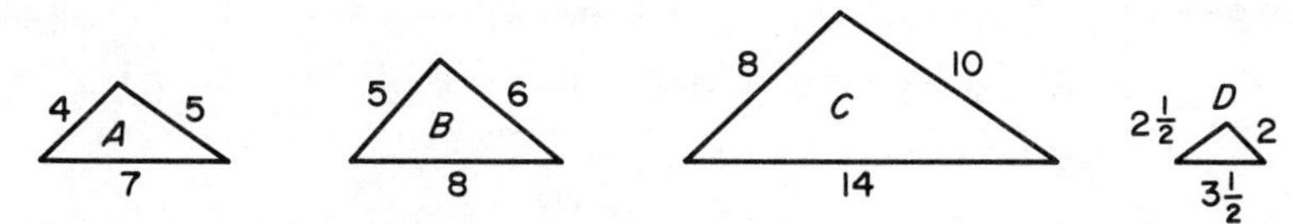

a. Which of the triangles are similar?
b. What is one of the possible ratios of the sides of the similar triangles?

15.

Find the value of X.

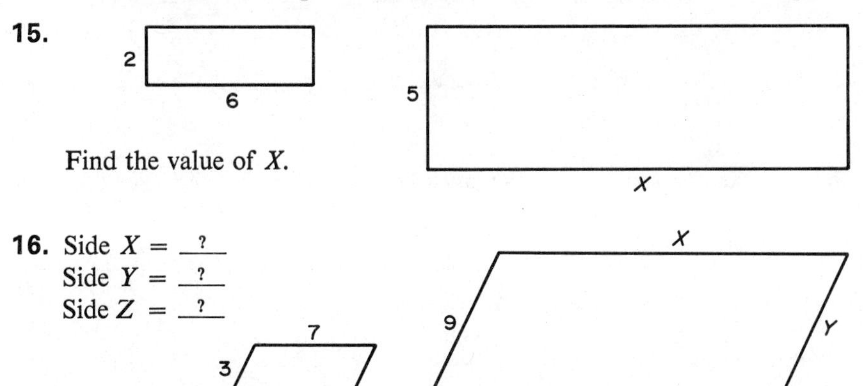

16. Side X = ___?___
Side Y = ___?___
Side Z = ___?___

17. How high is the light pole, if it casts a shadow of 42′ when a man 5′9″ tall casts a shadow of 10′?

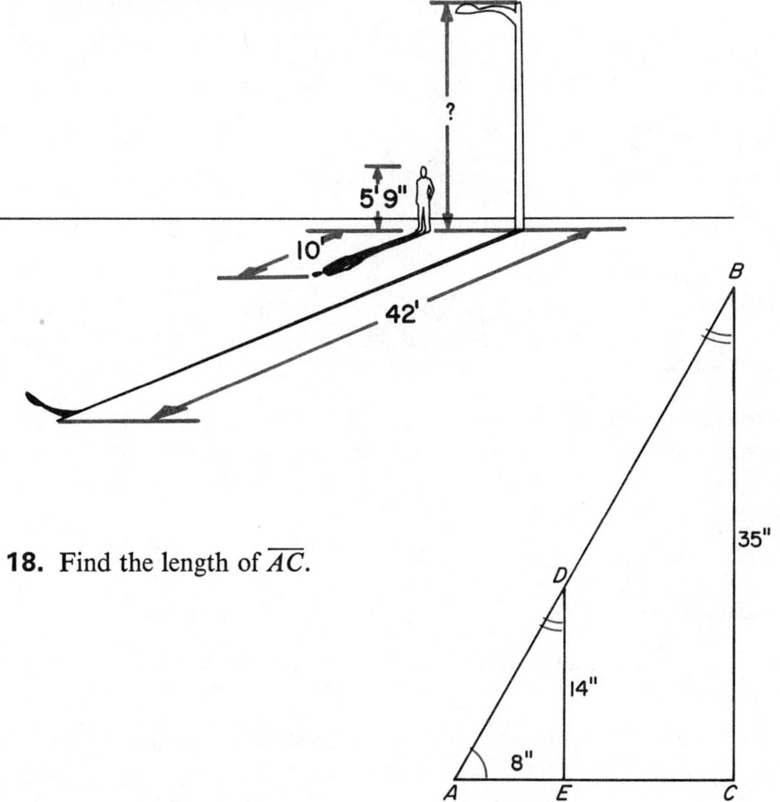

18. Find the length of $\overline{AC}$.

19. Using a ruler, measure the length of the boat as pictured below. Find the length of the full-size boat if the scale of the drawing is $\frac{1}{4}''$ to $1'$.

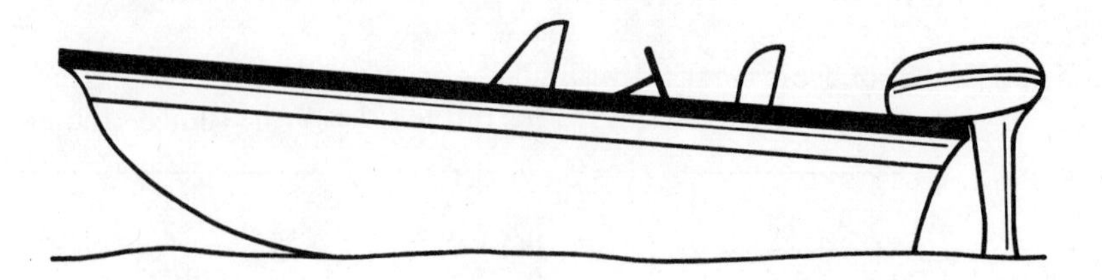

20. A recent World Series was played between the New York Mets and the Baltimore Orioles. What is the air distance between New York City and Baltimore?

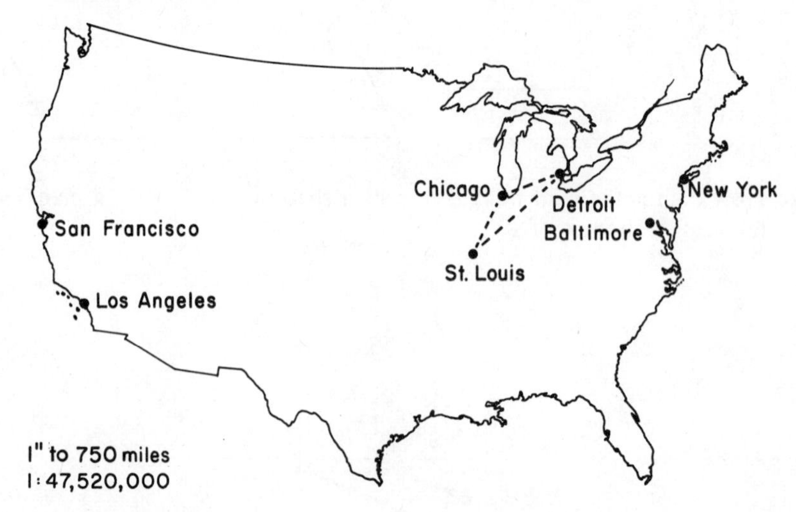

21. What is the air distance between Detroit and St. Louis? What is the approximate land distance between the two cities, if you travel through Chicago?

22. What is the approximate cost of a car trip from San Francisco to Los Angeles, if gasoline costs 37¢ per gallon and the car averages 24 miles per gallon of gasoline? (Use your ruler to estimate the distance from San Francisco to Los Angeles.)

For Exercises 23 and 24 refer to the maps on pages 308 and 309.

23. Find the air distance from Hartford, Connecticut, to Annapolis, Maryland.

24. Find the air distance from Waco, Texas, to Fort Worth, Texas.

MAINTAINING YOUR SKILLS

Add.

1. $\begin{array}{r} 76 \\ 29 \\ +\ 81 \\ \hline \end{array}$

2. $\begin{array}{r} 49 \\ 78 \\ 24 \\ +\ 39 \\ \hline \end{array}$

3. $\begin{array}{r} 341 \\ 862 \\ +\ 939 \\ \hline \end{array}$

4. $\begin{array}{r} 17{,}342 \\ 6{,}483 \\ 33{,}679 \\ +\ \ \ 849 \\ \hline \end{array}$

5. $67.37 + 435.62$

6. $749.83 + 624.87$

Subtract.

7. $\begin{array}{r} 91 \\ -\ 54 \\ \hline \end{array}$

8. $\begin{array}{r} 637 \\ -\ 298 \\ \hline \end{array}$

9. $\begin{array}{r} 36.47 \\ -\ 28.32 \\ \hline \end{array}$

10. $\begin{array}{r} 62{,}341 \\ -\ 39{,}675 \\ \hline \end{array}$

11. $\begin{array}{r} 30.02 \\ -\ 19.67 \\ \hline \end{array}$

12. $\begin{array}{r} 11{,}111 \\ -\ \ 8{,}936 \\ \hline \end{array}$

Multiply.

13. 82×29

14. 324×25

15. 19.02×6.73

16. $.624 \times .537$

17. 405×2.75

18. 93.5×202

Divide.

19. $27\overline{)1512}$

20. $22\overline{)594}$

21. $635\overline{)10{,}795}$

22. $255\overline{)8925}$

23. $1.5\overline{)33.66}$

24. $.15\overline{)45{,}763}$

Simplify.

25. $1\frac{3}{4} + 5\frac{7}{8}$

26. $\frac{1}{2} + 5\frac{3}{16} + 3\frac{7}{8}$

27. $4\frac{7}{9} - 2\frac{1}{3}$

28. $(7\frac{1}{2} + 5\frac{1}{8}) - 11\frac{1}{16}$

29. $1\frac{11}{13} \times \frac{2}{9}$

30. $7\frac{1}{2} \div 3\frac{3}{4}$

Both customer and teller need a knowledge of percentage for an intelligent approach to their business.

Percentage

OBJECTIVES

1. To understand the meaning of percent.
2. To write the equivalents of percents as common fractions and as decimal fractions.
3. To find the percent of a given number.
4. To compare numbers by percent.
5. To use interest formulas and tables.
6. To understand three types of discount problems:
    - **a.** Finding the discount.
    - **b.** Finding the percent of discount.
    - **c.** Finding the original, or marked, price.

In this chapter you will study the meaning of percentage and examine some of its applications, such as interest and discount. You will find that the same methods of solution which you practice here are often used in solving problems of business, industry, and everyday life.

Meaning of Percent

9–1 Three Forms of Fractions

Suppose you pay a meal tax of 4 percent. Can you check the arithmetic on the bill?

You would like to buy a new suit at a 15% markdown sale. Can you figure how much you would save?

To solve such problems, you may first need some review. Recall that "percent" means "hundredths." A **percent** is a *ratio* between two numbers. The first number may be any number, but the second number is always 100. Emphasize this.

4 percent, or 4%, means $\frac{4}{100}$.

Or you may express 4% decimally as .04, because $\frac{4}{100} = .04$.

Other examples are:

$$17\% = \frac{17}{100} = .17$$

and $$90\% = \frac{90}{100} = .90$$

To use percents in computation, first express them as common fractions or decimals. If you need to convert a common fraction to a decimal fraction, remember that you divide the numerator by the denominator.

$$\frac{3}{4} = .75$$

The student may wish to refer to the Table of Equivalents on page 37.

since $$4\overline{)3.00}$$ with quotient .75

EXERCISES

First complete the chart at the top of the next page. Then answer these questions.

What pattern do you notice in the chart? What relationship exists between columns A and B? How do you convert from column A to column B? What relationship exists between columns B and C? How do you convert from column B to column C?

Copy and complete the chart below. All decimals are to be written as hundredths.

	A	B	C
	Common Fraction	Decimal Fraction	Percent
[A] 1.	$\frac{1}{2}$	.50	50%
2.	$\frac{1}{3}$	$.33\frac{1}{3}$	$33\frac{1}{3}\%$
3.	$\frac{2}{3}$	$.66\frac{2}{3}$	?
4.	$\frac{1}{4}$	.25	?
5.	$\frac{3}{4}$	?	?
6.	$\frac{1}{5}$	?	?
7.	$\frac{2}{5}$	?	?
8.	$\frac{3}{5}$	?	?
9.	$\frac{4}{5}$	?	?
10.	$\frac{1}{6}$	?	?

11. Answer the questions at the foot of page 318.

Supply the missing numbers.

	Common Fraction		Decimal Fraction
12.	$\frac{7}{10}$	=	?
13.	$\frac{4}{5}$	=	?
14.	$\frac{3}{8}$	=	?
15.	$\frac{3}{10}$	=	?
16.	$\frac{3}{5}$	=	?

	Decimal Fraction		Common Fraction
17.	.25	=	?
18.	.75	=	?
19.	.10	=	?
20.	.80	=	?
21.	$.62\frac{1}{2}$	=	?

	Percent		Decimal Fraction
22.	20%	=	?
23.	45%	=	?
24.	70%	=	?
25.	$33\frac{1}{3}\%$	=	?
26.	$12\frac{1}{2}\%$	=	?

	Percent		Common Fraction
27.	20%	=	?
28.	17%	=	?
29.	90%	=	?
30.	$12\frac{1}{2}\%$	=	?
31.	$66\frac{2}{3}\%$	=	?

The following table lists the most common equivalents. How many of them do you already know? What arrangement was used in making the table? You may wish to make a second table, arranging the fractions so that those with like denominators are grouped together, for example, $\frac{1}{3}$ and $\frac{2}{3}$.

Urge the students to refer to this table whenever necessary in doing the remaining exercises in this chapter.

TABLE OF EQUIVALENTS

Fractions	Decimals	Percents
$\frac{1}{100}$	.01	1%
$\frac{1}{50}$	.02	2%
$\frac{1}{25}$	.04	4%
$\frac{1}{20}$	.05	5%
$\frac{1}{16}$	$.06\frac{1}{4}$ (or .0625)	$6\frac{1}{4}\%$
$\frac{1}{12}$	$.08\frac{1}{3}$	$8\frac{1}{3}\%$
$\frac{1}{10}$	.10	10%
$\frac{1}{8}$	$.12\frac{1}{2}$ (or .125)	$12\frac{1}{2}\%$
$\frac{1}{6}$	$.16\frac{2}{3}$	$16\frac{2}{3}\%$
$\frac{1}{5}$	.20	20%
$\frac{1}{4}$	.25	25%
$\frac{3}{10}$	.30	30%
$\frac{1}{3}$	$.33\frac{1}{3}$	$33\frac{1}{3}\%$
$\frac{3}{8}$	$.37\frac{1}{2}$ (or .375)	$37\frac{1}{2}\%$
$\frac{2}{5}$	.40	40%
$\frac{1}{2}$	.50	50%
$\frac{3}{5}$	.60	60%
$\frac{5}{8}$	$.62\frac{1}{2}$ (or .625)	$62\frac{1}{2}\%$
$\frac{2}{3}$	$.66\frac{2}{3}$	$66\frac{2}{3}\%$
$\frac{7}{10}$	.70	70%
$\frac{3}{4}$	.75	75%
$\frac{4}{5}$	.80	80%
$\frac{5}{6}$	$.83\frac{1}{3}$	$83\frac{1}{3}\%$
$\frac{7}{8}$	$.87\frac{1}{2}$ (or .875)	$87\frac{1}{2}\%$
$\frac{9}{10}$	.90	90%

SELF-ANALYSIS TEST I

Time: 5 minutes

Copy and complete the chart.

	Common Fraction	Decimal Fraction	Percent
1.	$\frac{1}{2}$		
2.	$\frac{1}{3}$		
3.	$\frac{1}{4}$		
4.	$\frac{1}{5}$		
5.	$\frac{1}{6}$		
6.	$\frac{2}{3}$		
7.	$\frac{3}{4}$		
8.	$\frac{4}{5}$		
9.	$\frac{2}{5}$		
10.	$\frac{5}{6}$		

11. $17\% = \frac{?}{100}$

12. $.90 = \frac{9}{?}$

13. $\frac{3}{10} = \underline{\ ?\ }\%$

14. $.25 = \frac{?}{4}$

15. $55\% = \underline{\ ?\ }$ (Answer in decimal form)

9–2 Percent of a Number

Many applications of percent involve finding a certain percent of a given number.

EXAMPLE 1

Point out that "of" indicates multiplication.

Find 20% of 75.

Solution. Method 1.

$$20\% = .20$$
$$.20 \times 75 = 15.00, \text{ or } \mathbf{15}$$

Method 2.

$$20\% = \tfrac{1}{5}$$
$$\tfrac{1}{5} \times 75 = \mathbf{15}$$

A third method is given on the next page.

Method 3. This method uses a proportion.

$$20\% = \tfrac{20}{100}$$

The number we want to find (n) has the same ratio to 75 as 20 to 100. That is,

$$\frac{n}{75} = \frac{20}{100}$$
$$100n = 75 \times 20$$
$$100n = 1500$$
$$n = \frac{1500}{100} = \mathbf{15}$$

In Example 1, the result 15 is called a **percentage.** It is the number which is a certain percent of another number.

Try working Examples 2–4 by two other methods.

EXAMPLE 2

Find 30% of 15.

Solution. $30\% = .30$
$.30 \times 15 = 4.50 = \mathbf{4.5}$

EXAMPLE 3

Find $33\frac{1}{3}\%$ of 60.

Solution. $33\frac{1}{3}\% = \frac{1}{3}$
$\frac{1}{3} \times 60 = \mathbf{20}$

Ordinarily, choosing a method of solution will depend on the specific details of the problem.

EXAMPLE 4

Find 36% of 200.

Solution. $36\% = \frac{36}{100}$

$$\frac{n}{200} = \frac{36}{100}$$
$$100n = 36 \times 200 = 7200$$
$$n = \mathbf{72}$$

Emphasize this. Common usage tends to refer to percents as fractional values only.

Sometimes percents are greater than 100%. For example, we may say that the retail price is 125% of the cost. Remember that % means "hundredths."

EXAMPLE 5

Find 150% of 12.

Solution. $150\% = \frac{150}{100} = 1.5$

$1.5 \times 12 = 18.0$ or $\mathbf{18}$

EXERCISES

Solve Exercises 1–5 by all three methods.

A

1. 20% of 50 = ?
2. 25% of 80 = ?
3. 30% of 30 = ?
4. 5% of 140 = ?
5. 70% of 60 = ?

Solve Exercises 6–15 by any method you wish.

6. $33\frac{1}{3}$% of 300 = ?
7. 2% of 540 = ?
8. 18% of 2000 = ?
9. $16\frac{2}{3}$% of 600 = ?
10. 24% of 450 = ?
11. 19% of 500 = ?
12. 65% of 400 = ?
13. 75% of 360 = ?

B

14. 150% of 224 = ?
15. $166\frac{2}{3}$% of 66 = ?
16. Many carpenters find that they buy an excess of lumber. If a carpenter bought 700 bd. ft. of lumber and found he had 7% left when he completed the job, how many board feet were not used?
17. If 14% of a copper sheet containing 250 sq. in. remains as scrap after stamping in a punch press, how many square inches are unused?
18. A machine operator sets the control lever on his lathe at 3600 rpm. If the belt slippage is 15%, what is the actual speed of the machine?
19. A certain alloy has a shrinkage rate of 2%. If the cast length of a project is 2.6 inches, what is its cooled length?
20. John earns $25 a week on a part-time job. If 7.2% is deducted for Social Security, what is the amount John receives?

9–3 Comparing Numbers by Percent

The **efficiency** of a machine is defined as the ratio of power produced (output) to the power used (input). For example, the efficiency of a machine with an output of 5600 watts and an input of 7000 watts is

$$\frac{\textbf{output}}{\textbf{input}} = \frac{\mathbf{5600}}{\mathbf{7000}} = \frac{\mathbf{8}}{\mathbf{10}}$$

Usually the efficiency is expressed as a percent. Thus,

$$\frac{\mathbf{8}}{\mathbf{10}} = \frac{\mathbf{80}}{\mathbf{100}} = \mathbf{80\%} \qquad \text{(efficiency of the machine)}$$

We have *compared* the output and input by a percent.

Every percent is therefore an implicit comparison.

EXAMPLE 1

What percent of 30 is 15?

Solution. We are to compare 15 to 30 and express the result as a percent.

$\frac{15}{30} = \frac{1}{2} = \mathbf{50\%}$

EXAMPLE 2

What percent of 15 is 30?

Solution. $\frac{30}{15} = \frac{2}{1}$

$= \frac{200}{100}$

$= \mathbf{200\%}$

EXERCISES

A

1. What percent of 12 is 4?
2. What percent of 6 is 5?
3. What percent of 10 is 13?
4. What percent of 18 is 45?

B

5. The input in a motor is 5000 watts, and the output is 4500 watts.
   a. What is the efficiency in lowest possible ratio?
   b. What is the percent of efficiency?
6. What is the output of a machine if the input is 5400 watts and the efficiency has a ratio of 9:10. (Hint. output = efficiency × input)
7. A certain radio normally sells for $28, but on a special sale it sells for $21. What percent of the old price is the new price?
8. If the Lee Hardware Company has sales of $130,000 for one year, and has operating costs (which include purchasing) of $100,000, what is the percent of profit of total sales?

Interest

9–4 Simple Interest TM p. 18 , 9-4

Interest is sometimes called "rent" on money, since it is what we pay to borrow money for a period of time. It is also the "rent" a bank pays us for the use of our money. The **rate of interest** is usually given as a percent of the amount of money involved for a given period of time, usually a year. The amount on which interest is figured is called the **principal.** Thus if the rate of interest is 4% per year, then the amount of interest on a principal of $500 for one year is 4% of $500, or

$$.04 \times 500 = \$20$$

If the rate remained the same, in a period of 2 years the interest would be twice the interest for one year.

$$.04 \times 500 \times 2 = \$40$$

In cases like this, where the interest is computed on the same principal each time, the interest is called **simple interest.** Stress this.

There is a formula which relates the principal (P), the interest (I), the time (t), and the rate of interest (r). This formula is

$$I = Prt$$

When you know any three of the four values for which the letters stand, you can easily find the fourth.

EXAMPLE 1

Find the interest on an investment of \$5000, at 5% interest for 1 yr.

Solution. $I = Prt$ $\quad P = \$5000;\ r = 5\%$, or $.05$; $t = 1$ (yr.)
$I = \$5000 \times .05 \times 1 = \mathbf{\$250.00}$

Sometimes we want to know the rate of interest, the principal, or the time involved. Again we use the same formula, but in a different form.

To change the form of a formula is simply to solve it for the desired letter. To solve $I = Prt$ for P,

Divide by rt, $$\frac{I}{rt} = \frac{Prt}{rt}$$

Emphasize that both members of the equation must be divided by rt.

or $$\frac{I}{rt} = P$$

or $$P = \frac{I}{rt}$$

Can you show how to find these formulas?

$$r = \frac{I}{Pt}$$

$$t = \frac{I}{Pr}$$

These three formulas, along with the basic formula for interest, are sufficient for completing the exercises which follow.

EXAMPLE 2

Find the rate of interest if the principal is \$4000 and the interest for 2 years is \$400.

Solution. Use $r = \dfrac{I}{Pt}$.

Here $I = \$400$, $P = \$4000$, and $t = 2$ (yr.)

$$r = \frac{400}{4000 \times 2} = \frac{1}{20} = .05 = \mathbf{5\%}$$

EXAMPLE 3

Find the principal if the interest is \$210 and the rate is 7% for 1 year.

Solution. Use the formula $P = \frac{I}{rt}$.

$$P = \frac{210}{.07 \times 1} = \frac{210}{.07} = \$3000$$

EXERCISES

A

1. Find I, if $P = \$550$, $r = 4\%$, $t = 1$ year.
2. Find I, if $P = \$1700$, $r = 8\frac{1}{2}\%$, $t = 5$ years.
3. Find r, if $I = \$700$, $P = \$5000$, $t = 2$ years.
4. Find r, if $I = \$7500$, $P = \$20{,}000$, $t = 5$ years.
5. Find P, if $I = \$350$, $r = 5\%$, $t = 2$ years.

B

6. What is the annual rate of interest if the principal is \$2000 and the annual interest is \$160?
7. What is the annual rate of interest if the principal is \$3200 and the annual interest is \$144?
8. Find the annual rate of interest on a principal of \$1650, if the interest received on it after 4 years is \$462.
9. How many years will it take for a sum of \$280 invested at 5% to earn \$84 in interest?
10. How long must a sum of \$15,000 be invested at $7\frac{1}{2}\%$ in order to yield an interest dividend of \$3375?

SELF-ANALYSIS TEST II

Time: 10 minutes

1. 25% of 16 = ___?___
2. 35% of 60 = ___?___
3. $33\frac{1}{3}\%$ of 90 = ___?___
4. $16\frac{2}{3}\%$ of 36 = ___?___
5. What percent of 16 is 4?
6. What percent of 10 is 120?
7. What percent of 15 is 5?
8. A transistor radio costs \$25.00. Joe purchases it on sale for \$20. What percent is the sale price of the original?
9. What is the interest for one year, if the principal is \$5000, and the annual interest rate is 6%?
10. What is the annual rate of interest, if the principal is \$3600, and the interest for one year is \$108?

9–5 Compound Interest

Be sure the student sees how this differs from simple interest.

Suppose you deposit \$500 in a savings account. Each year the interest is added to the principal so that the next year both the principal and the interest earn more interest. This interest is called **compound interest.** When the interest is computed each year, we say the interest is compounded *annually*. In most cases interest is compounded oftener than once a year. Certain savings institutions may compound interest semiannually, quarterly, monthly, or even daily.

EXAMPLE 1

How much will a deposit of \$500 amount to after 3 yr. if interest of 5% is compounded annually?

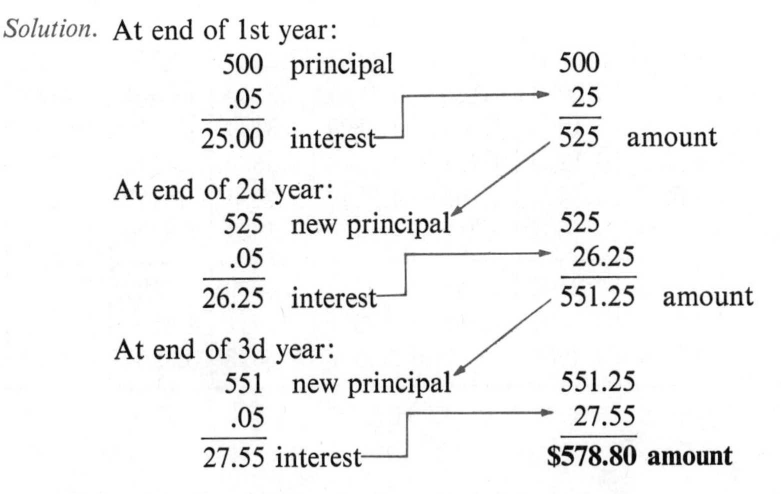

Notice two things about the last row of the solution:

(1) The interest is figured only on whole dollars, \$551. Call attention to these points.

(2) When adding the interest \$27.55 to the account, we include the cents, \$551.25.

Since compound interest requires so much calculation, tables have been prepared to make the work easier. In fact, today large computing machines have been programmed to handle this work for most banks. The table on page 328 shows how much \$1 will amount to after different periods of time at different interest rates when compounded. To use it, you find the value in the table for \$1, for the given length of time at the given rate, and then multiply by the number of dollars. TM p. 18 , 9-5

Using the table to answer the question in the previous example, we find that \$1 at 5% interest in three years will amount to \$1.1576. Multiplying by 500 gives \$578.80.

Although you may never have to use a table like the one shown, it is well to know how to use such a table, should the need arise. Besides, it is interesting to see how fast money "grows."

The table shows how much $1 will amount to at various rates.

COMPOUND INTEREST TABLE

Years or Periods	1%	$1\frac{1}{2}$%	2%	3%	4%	5%	6%
1	1.0100	1.0150	1.0200	1.0300	1.0400	1.0500	1.0600
2	1.0201	1.0302	1.0404	1.0609	1.0816	1.1025	1.1236
3	1.0303	1.0457	1.0612	1.0927	1.1249	1.1576	1.1910
4	1.0406	1.0614	1.0824	1.1255	1.1699	1.2155	1.2625
5	1.0510	1.0773	1.1041	1.1593	1.2167	1.2763	1.3382
6	1.0615	1.0934	1.1262	1.1941	1.2653	1.3401	1.4185
7	1.0721	1.1098	1.1487	1.2299	1.3159	1.4071	1.5036
8	1.0829	1.1265	1.1717	1.2668	1.3686	1.4775	1.5938
9	1.0937	1.1434	1.1951	1.3048	1.4233	1.5513	1.6895
10	1.1046	1.1605	1.2190	1.3439	1.4802	1.6289	1.7908
15	1.1610	1.2502	1.3459	1.5580	1.8009	2.0789	2.3966
20	1.2202	1.3469	1.4859	1.8061	2.1911	2.6533	3.2071
25	1.2824	1.4509	1.6406	2.0938	2.6658	3.3864	4.2919

EXAMPLE 2

a. How much will $750 amount to in 6 years if the interest rate is 4% compounded annually?
b. How much interest will be earned?

Solution. **a.** Start at the top of the 4% columnin the table and go down to row 6. We find $1 will amount to $1.2653 in 6 years. Multiplying by 750 gives $948.975, or **$948.98.**

b. $948.98 − $750 = **$198.98**

EXAMPLE 3

At 6% per year, compounded semiannually, how much will $500 amount to in 4 years?

Solution. Notice the following important facts:

1. The interest will be paid twice each year for 4 years, or a total of 8 interest periods.

2. Since the annual interest rate is 6%, the rate for each period (half year) will be $\frac{1}{2}$ of 6%, or 3%.

Thus, we start at the top of the 3% column in the table and go down to row 8. We see that $1 will amount to $1.2668 after compounding. Multiplying by 500 gives **$633.40.**

EXERCISES

Find (a) the total amount and (b) the amount of compound interest earned. Use the table and assume that interest is added once a year unless otherwise specified.

A

1. $400 for 5 years at 4%
2. $1800 for 4 years at 6%
3. $700 for 3 years at 5%
4. $24,000 for 3 years at 2%
5. $6000 for 25 years at 3%
6. $2000 for 15 years at 3%
7. $30,000 for 2 years at 2%
8. $72,000 for 10 years at 5%
9. $455,000 for 4 years at 6%
10. $1,500,000 for 25 years at 4%

B

11. $200 at 6% for 3 years, compounded semiannually.
    Hint. Interest will be figured 6 times at 3%. Why?
12. $100 at 4% for 3 years, compounded semiannually.
13. $1000 at 6% for 5 years, compounded quarterly.
    Hint. Interest will be figured 20 times at $1\frac{1}{2}$%. Why?
14. $200 at 6% for 2 years, compounded quarterly.
15. Which is the better investment: $275 at 4% simple interest for 6 years, or $200 at 6% for 5 years compounded quarterly?

Exercise 15 is typical of investment situations demanding a clear understanding of interest.

9–6 True Interest Rate TM p. 19 , 9-6

Often the interest rate charged on a loan is more than the rate you determine by comparing the amount of the loan and the amount you must repay. This is the case when the interest is computed as though you had the use of the total amount of the loan for the entire time period. In fact, however, you must often repay the money in monthly payments, rather than all at once at the end of the period.

Consider the bank loan table on the next page.

LOW COST PERSONAL LOANS				
Amount You Receive	12 Months	Total of Payments	24 Months	Total of Payments
$ 500	$ 44.16	$ 529.92	$ 23.33	$ 559.92
1000	88.33	1059.96	46.66	1119.84
2000	176.66	2119.92	93.33	2239.92
3000	265.00	3180.00	140.00	3360.00
3500	309.16	3709.92	163.33	3919.92
Annual Rate	10.90%		11.13%	

A loan of $1000 to be paid back in 12 installments of $88.33 amounts to

$$12 \times \$88.33, \text{ or } \$1059.96.$$

Thus the finance charge is $59.96, which is about 6% of the $1000 borrowed. But, as you see from the table, the true interest rate is 10.90% because the borrower does not have the use of the full $1000 for all 12 months.

Although the Federal Government requires banks and lending institutions to state clearly the true annual interest rate and the total finance charges in all contracts and advertising, you should know how to check thoroughly all details of a loan.

The following formula may be used to find the approximate true interest rate.

The 24 is a constant.

$$r = \frac{24F}{MN(N+1)}$$

Here F = the total finance charge;
M = the amount of the monthly payment;
and N = the number of payments or installments.

EXAMPLE

Find the approximate true interest rate for buying a car "on time" if the finance charges are $228, and the payments are $50 a month for 36 months.

Solution. Substitute \$228 for F, \$50 for M, and 36 for N in the formula. Then

$$r = \frac{24 \times 228}{50 \times 36 \times 37} = .082 = \mathbf{8.2\%}, \text{ approximately}$$

EXERCISES

For Exercises 1–3 use the table on page 330.

A

1. You borrow \$500 and agree to repay the loan in 24 equal payments.
   a. How much is the monthly payment?
   b. What is the total of the 24 payments?
   c. The amount repaid exceeds the amount borrowed by _?_.
   d. The yearly true rate of interest is _?_.
2. You borrow \$2000 and agree to repay the loan in 24 monthly payments.
   a. How much is the monthly payment?
   b. What is the total of the monthly payments?
   c. How much of the loan have you repaid after 21 months?
3. You borrow \$1000 and agree to repay the loan in 12 months.
   a. By how much does your monthly payment exceed the monthly payment for the 24-month repayment plan?
   b. The finance charge on your loan for 12 months is _?_.
   c. The finance charge on a loan like yours for 24 months is _?_.
   d. How much do you save in finance costs by repaying the loan in 12 months instead of 24 months?

In Exercises 4–6 use the formula $r = \frac{24F}{MN(N + 1)}$ to determine the approximate "true" rate of interest.

4. Find the approximate true interest rate on the purchase of a watch, if the finance charge is \$15, and you must make 12 monthly payments of \$15 each.
5. What is the approximate true interest rate on the purchase of an imported camera, if the finance charge is \$20 and you are to make monthly payments of \$30 for 8 months?

B

6. Find the approximate true interest rate on the purchase of a de luxe 4-passenger airplane, if it costs \$16,700, the down payment is \$4700, and the monthly installments are \$300 for 46 months.
   Hint: 1. Find the amount being financed by subtracting the down payment from the original price.
   2. Find the total of payments by multiplying the monthly payment by the number of months.
   3. Find the finance charge by subtracting the result of Step 1 from the result of Step 2.
   4. Use this information to substitute for F in the formula.

Discount

9–7 Three Kinds of Discount Problems TM p. 19 , 9-7

Consider the following case of a television set being sold at a discount. Three different questions might come up.

1. If the set is marked \$400 and you are offered a 20% discount (reduction), how much would you save? Here we want 20% of \$400, or $.20 \times 400 = \$80$. The discount from the marked price is \$80.

2. If the set is marked \$400 and an \$80 discount is available, what percent could be saved? Here we want to know what percent \$80 is of \$400. $\frac{80}{400} = \frac{20}{100} = 20\%$. You could save 20% of the marked price.

3. If a store offers 20% off on a TV set and you save \$80, what is the marked price? In this case we are asked to find the amount, b, such that 20% of $b = 80$, or $.20 \times b = 80$. You know how to solve an equation by dividing the expressions on each side of the equals sign **members** by the same number. Dividing by .20 gives

$$\frac{.20 \times b}{.20} = \frac{80}{.20}$$

or

$$b = \frac{80}{.20} = 400$$

The marked price is \$400.

Stress this.

Each of these questions refers to the same situation, yet each asks for a different number. Every percentage problem involves three items: the **base** (b), the **rate** (r), and the **percentage** (p). In a discount problem, b stands for the marked price, r stands for the rate, or percent, of discount, and p stands for the amount of the discount.

Each of the three problems could be solved by using a proportion.

This is true of any percentage problem.

1. $\frac{20}{100} = \frac{p}{400}$
$\frac{1}{5} = \frac{p}{400}$
$400 = 5p$
$80 = p$
\$80 is the amount of the discount.

2. $\frac{r}{100} = \frac{80}{400}$
$\frac{r}{100} = \frac{1}{5}$
$5r = 100$
$r = 20$
The discount rate is 20%.

3. $\frac{20}{100} = \frac{80}{b}$

$\frac{1}{5} = \frac{80}{b}$

$b = 400$ The marked price is $400.

EXERCISES

A

1. What would be your cost if you were offered a 20% discount on a $600 motorcycle?
2. A coat sells for $23. What is the sale price at a 6% discount?
3. If you were given $40 off on a $320 golf set, what is the percent of discount?
4. Mrs. Lane bought two dresses at a sale and saved $21 of the marked price. The sales slip stated that there was a 30% discount. What was the original price of the two dresses?

B

5. If a new car costs $3300 and its value depreciates approximately 27% in one year, what is its value at the end of one year?
6. I pay $2000 for a used car 1 year old. If its original price was $2800, what percent of the value has been lost?

9–8 Second Discounts

Sometimes an additional discount is available. This might be for prompt payment or for quantity purchase, for instance. The following example shows the method of finding the final, or net, price.

Call attention to this term.

EXAMPLE

At the Acme Tire Company you can get a 15% discount if you buy four tires, and an additional discount of 5% if you pay cash. How much would four tires cost if the list price for each is $27.50?

Solution.

4 tires at $27.50 =	$110.00	110
less discount (15% of 110) =	16.50	.15
	93.50	16.50
less second discount =	4.68	93.50
(5% of 93.50)		.05
net price for cash =	$ 88.82	4.6750

Note that when a second discount applies, the discount is computed on the amount remaining after the first discount has been subtracted.

Important.

EXERCISES

Copy and complete the following purchase order.

A 1.

Center Hardware Co.

Purchase Order No. 36606

Date: August 23, 19--
For: Newton High School **Phone:** 329-4240
Address: 1298 W. Prairie St. **City:** Newton, Illinois 62448

Quantity	Description	Unit Cost	Cost	Discount	Net Cost
3	Soldering guns, 60 watt	9.75		20%	
12	1 lb. Resin core solder	1.10		30%	
6	Pkg., assorted resistors	2.35		40%	
2	Pkg., assorted transistors	5.65		30%	
12	9-volt batteries	.75		25%	

Total ______
3% discount if paid within 30 days ______
Net Total ______

Copy and complete the following invoice. You may wish to review pages 196–197 to recall how to compute board feet.

B 2.

Thompson Lumber Co.
1800 E. Seventh Street
Grand Island, Nebraska 68802

No. 2921
Date: July 13

Sold to: Martin Fleming
243 E. 2nd Street
Grand Island, Nebr. 68805

Quan.	Size	Length	Description	Bd.ft.	Price/Bd.ft.	Cost	Discount	Net Cost
22	2" x 4"	12'	Studding		.09		10%	
16	4" x 6"	8'	Rafter		.11		5%	
2	4" x 6"	12'	Inside header		.11		10%	
2	4" x 8"	15'	Outside header		.12		8%	
4	4" x 6"	10'	Horiz. header		.10		10%	
2	4" x 10"	15'	Beam		.16		5%	
12	1" x 6"	16'	Wind Brace		.13		15%	

Total __________
5% Cash Discount __________
Net Total __________

SELF-ANALYSIS TEST III

Time: 25 minutes

For Exercises 1–3, use the table on page 328 to find (a) the total amount and (b) the amount of compound interest earned.

1. $5000 for 2 years at 5%, compounded annually.
2. $20,000 for 9 years at 6%, compounded annually.
3. $200 for 5 years at 4%, compounded semiannually.
4. Find the approximate true interest rate on the purchase of a portable stereo, if the finance charge is $15, and there are to be 18 monthly payments of $9 each.
5. Find the approximate true interest for buying an electric guitar which costs $750, if the down payment is $100 and the monthly installments are $20 for 36 months.
   Hint. Find the finance charge by following Steps 1–3 for Exercise 6, page 331.

Find the missing items in this purchase order.

6.

Quan.	Item	Unit Cost	Cost	% Discount	Net Cost
5	45° ells	.35	?	20%	?
7	90° ells	.40	?	25%	?
2	valves	1.15	?	30%	?
4	faucets	2.35	?	20%	?
				Total net cost	?

CHAPTER SUMMARY

1. A percent is a ratio having any number as its numerator and 100 as its denominator.

2. Interest is the amount of money which a borrower pays for the use of a sum of money for a specified length of time.

3. Simple interest is computed on the same principal each interest period.

4. Compound interest is computed on the sum of the principal and all previous interest each interest period.

5. The true interest rate on a loan is the annual percentage rate. It can be approximated by the following formula: $r = \dfrac{24F}{MN(N+1)}$, where F = the total finance charge, M = the amount of the monthly payment and N = the number of monthly payments.

6. A discount is a reduction in the marked price of goods. Discount rates are usually expressed as percents.

CHAPTER TEST

Find the numbers needed to complete this chart.

	Proper fraction	Decimal fraction	Percent
1.	$\frac{1}{4}$	?	?
2.	$\frac{2}{5}$	?	?
3.	?	$.66\frac{2}{3}$	?
4.	?	.53	?
5.	?	?	70%
6.	?	?	$12\frac{1}{2}\%$
7.	?	$.87\frac{1}{2}$	?
8.	$\frac{5}{6}$	?	?
9.	?	?	$33\frac{1}{3}\%$
10.	$\frac{1}{12}$	?	?

11. If a man bought a house for $16,000 and it increased in value by 21% in 8 yr., what is the present value of the house?

12. A $450 movie projector is offered at a 12% discount. What is the price reduction?

13. a. What percent of 32 is 8?
    b. What percent of 12 is 18?

14. Find the simple interest on an investment of $8000 at 8% for 3 yr.

15. Find the principal if the interest is $450 and the rate is $4\frac{1}{2}\%$ for one year.

16. Use the table on page 328 to find the interest earned on $600 for 4 yr. at 5%, compounded annually.

17. Find the approximate true interest rate on the purchase of a $2400 airplane, if you pay $400 down, and $66 per month for 36 mo.

Copy and complete this purchase order.

18.

Purchase Order No. 4279

Ace Plumbing Supply Co.

Date: 11/17

For: Miller's Plumbing Phone: 443-2921

Address: 1434 Bridge Blvd. City: Gary, Indiana

QUANTITY	ITEM	UNIT COST	COST	DISCOUNT	NET COST
5	$\frac{3}{4}''$ unions	.75	3.75	20%	3.00
6	$\frac{3}{4}''$ 45° ells	.55		30%	
4	$\frac{3}{4}''$ valves	2.25		25%	
12	$\frac{3}{4}''$ x 6'' nozzles	.80		15%	
5	$\frac{3}{4}''$ faucets	1.75		20%	
10	$\frac{3}{4}''$ 90° ells	.60		30%	
18	$\frac{3}{4}''$ fittings	.20		35%	
6	$\frac{3}{4}''$ T-joints	.45		20%	

Total ________

Less 2%
Cash Discount: ________

Net Total: ________

MAINTAINING YOUR SKILLS

Add.

1. $\begin{array}{r} 45 \\ 56 \\ +\ 67 \\ \hline \end{array}$

2. $\begin{array}{r} 89 \\ 76 \\ 54 \\ +\ 32 \\ \hline \end{array}$

3. $\begin{array}{r} 147 \\ 258 \\ +\ 369 \\ \hline \end{array}$

4. $\begin{array}{r} 16{,}043 \\ 7{,}976 \\ 9{,}437 \\ +\ \ \ 947 \\ \hline \end{array}$

5. $51\frac{1}{2} + 72\frac{3}{4}$

6. $343.45 + 476.73$

Subtract.

7. $\begin{array}{r} 82 \\ -\ 37 \\ \hline \end{array}$

8. $\begin{array}{r} 583 \\ -\ 339 \\ \hline \end{array}$

9. $\begin{array}{r} 63.54 \\ -\ 39.76 \\ \hline \end{array}$

10. $\begin{array}{r} 72{,}720 \\ -\ 64{,}648 \\ \hline \end{array}$

11. $\begin{array}{r} 94.02 \\ -\ 67.54 \\ \hline \end{array}$

12. $\begin{array}{r} 22{,}113 \\ -\ \ 9{,}456 \\ \hline \end{array}$

Multiply.

13. 57×25 **14.** 243×55 **15.** 37.04×1.73

16. $.737 \times .828$ **17.** 505×66.5 **18.** 75.8×303

Divide.

19. $7\overline{)935}$ **20.** $66\overline{)3696}$ **21.** $28\overline{)7532}$

22. $63.\overline{)4.7628}$ **23.** $5\frac{3}{8} \div 9\frac{3}{4}$ **24.** $(4\frac{1}{2} - \frac{3}{4}) \div \frac{1}{2}$

Simplify.

25. 7^2 **26.** 9^2 **27.** 11^2

28. 45^2 **29.** 2^3 **30.** 5^3

These three students in a surveying class are applying their knowledge of trigonometry to a practical problem.

10 *Right Triangles and Trigonometry*

OBJECTIVES

1. To learn the Rule of Pythagoras.
2. To learn to use the Rule of Pythagoras.
3. To learn about special right triangles.
4. To learn about trigonometric ratios and their uses.
5. To learn to use trigonometric tables.

In this chapter you will learn many valuable facts about right triangles. The work includes applications of the Rule of Pythagoras and an introduction to trigonometry.

■ Right Triangles

10–1 The Rule of Pythagoras

Pythagoras (pĭ **thăg** o rŭs) was a Greek mathematician who lived about 500 B.C. His name is given to a very special property of right triangles.

Draw a right triangle as shown here. Then construct a square on

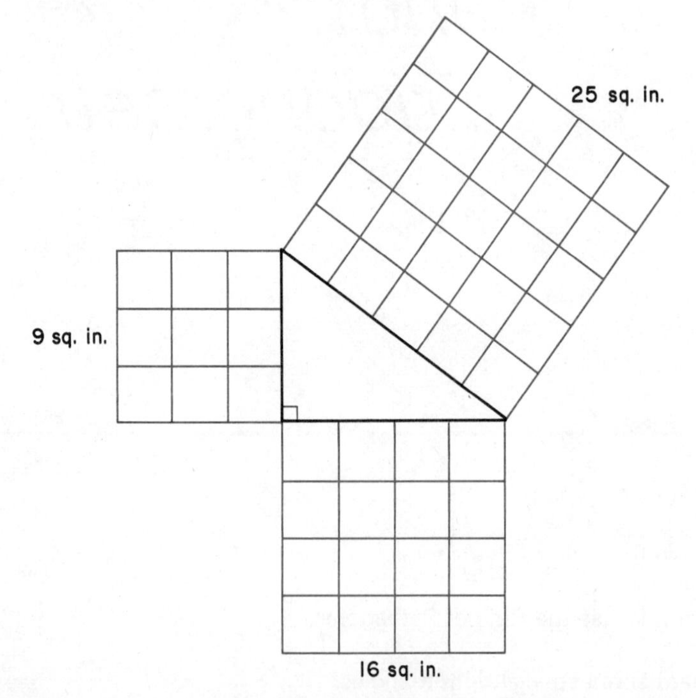

each side of the triangle. Measure the side of each square and find its area, or count the number of small squares in each of the three large squares. Add the two smaller areas. How does their sum compare with the area of the largest square? They are equal.

No matter what size or shape a right triangle has, the following is always true. Be sure students understand this important property.

> **The area of the square on the hypotenuse of a right triangle is equal to the sum of the areas of the squares on the other two sides.**

This fact is called the *Rule of Pythagoras*, or the Pythagorean theorem.

A more useful form of the Pythagorean theorem is in the form of a number relationship involving the lengths of the sides. TM p. 19 , 10-1(1)

> **For any right triangle, the square of the length of the hypotenuse is equal to the sum of the squares of the lengths of the other two sides.**

$$5^2 = 3^2 + 4^2$$
$$25 = 9 + 16$$

Note that this is a numerical relationship instead of one involving area.

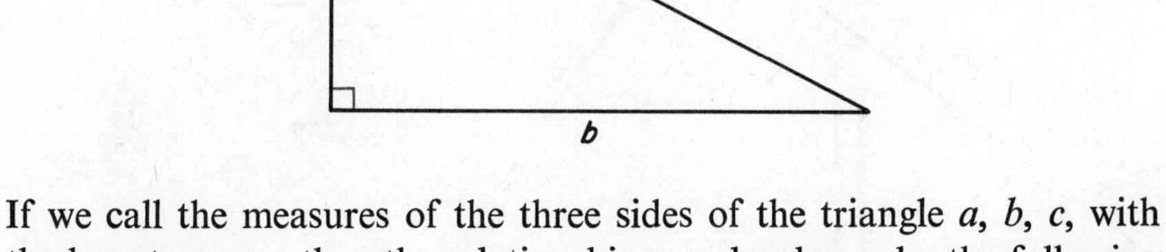

If we call the measures of the three sides of the triangle a, b, c, with the hypotenuse c, then the relationship may be shown by the following formula:

$$c^2 = a^2 + b^2 \qquad \text{or} \qquad c = \sqrt{a^2 + b^2}$$

By using this formula we can find any side of a right triangle if we know the other two.

If we know the two perpendicular sides, the hypotenuse is given by

$$c^2 = a^2 + b^2$$

If we know the hypotenuse and one side, then the other side is given by either

$$a^2 = c^2 - b^2$$

or

$$b^2 = c^2 - a^2$$

Note. In finding the two forms of the formula above, we have used a property of equations which allows us to subtract the same term from each side of the equation $c^2 = a^2 + b^2$. If we subtract b^2, we have $c^2 - b^2 = a^2 + b^2 - b^2$, or $c^2 - b^2 = a^2$. If we subtract a^2, we have $c^2 - a^2 = a^2 + b^2 - a^2$, or $c^2 - a^2 = b^2$. TM p. 19 , 10-1(2)

EXAMPLES

1.

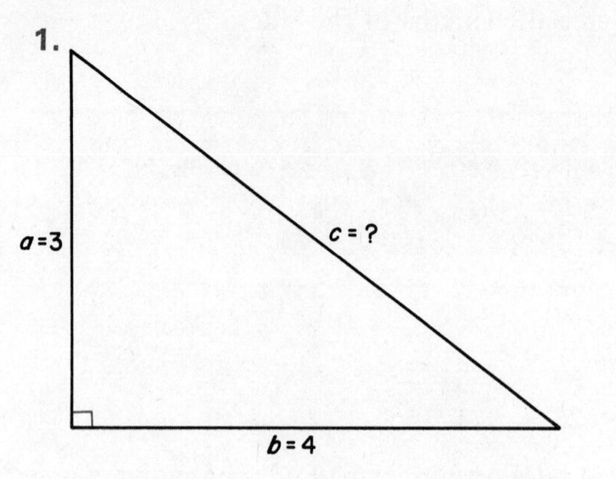

$$c^2 = a^2 + b^2$$
$$c^2 = 3^2 + 4^2$$
$$c^2 = 9 + 16$$
$$c^2 = 25$$
$$c = \sqrt{25}$$
$$\boldsymbol{c = 5}$$

2.

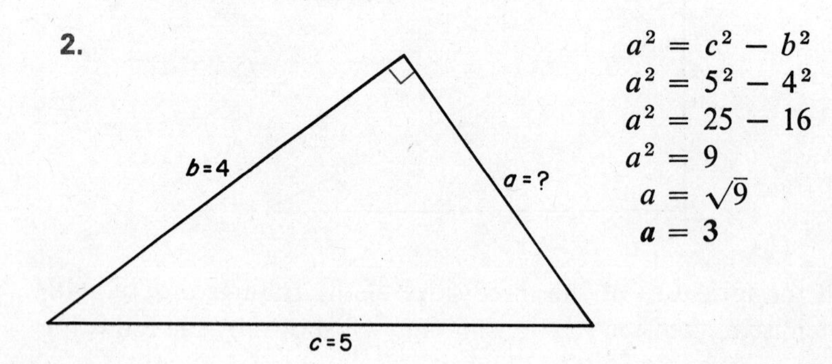

$$a^2 = c^2 - b^2$$
$$a^2 = 5^2 - 4^2$$
$$a^2 = 25 - 16$$
$$a^2 = 9$$
$$a = \sqrt{9}$$
$$\boldsymbol{a = 3}$$

3.

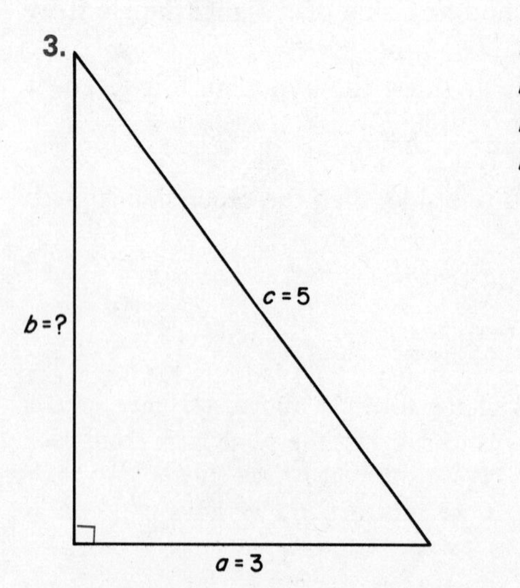

$$b^2 = c^2 - a^2$$
$$b^2 = 5^2 - 3^2$$
$$b^2 = 25 - 9$$
$$b^2 = 16$$
$$b = \sqrt{16}$$
$$\boldsymbol{b = 4}$$

Students may need to review the section on exponents and square roots (page 39) before doing these exercises.

EXERCISES

In the right triangles for Exercises 1–9, compute the length of the third side. Leave answers in radical form where necessary.

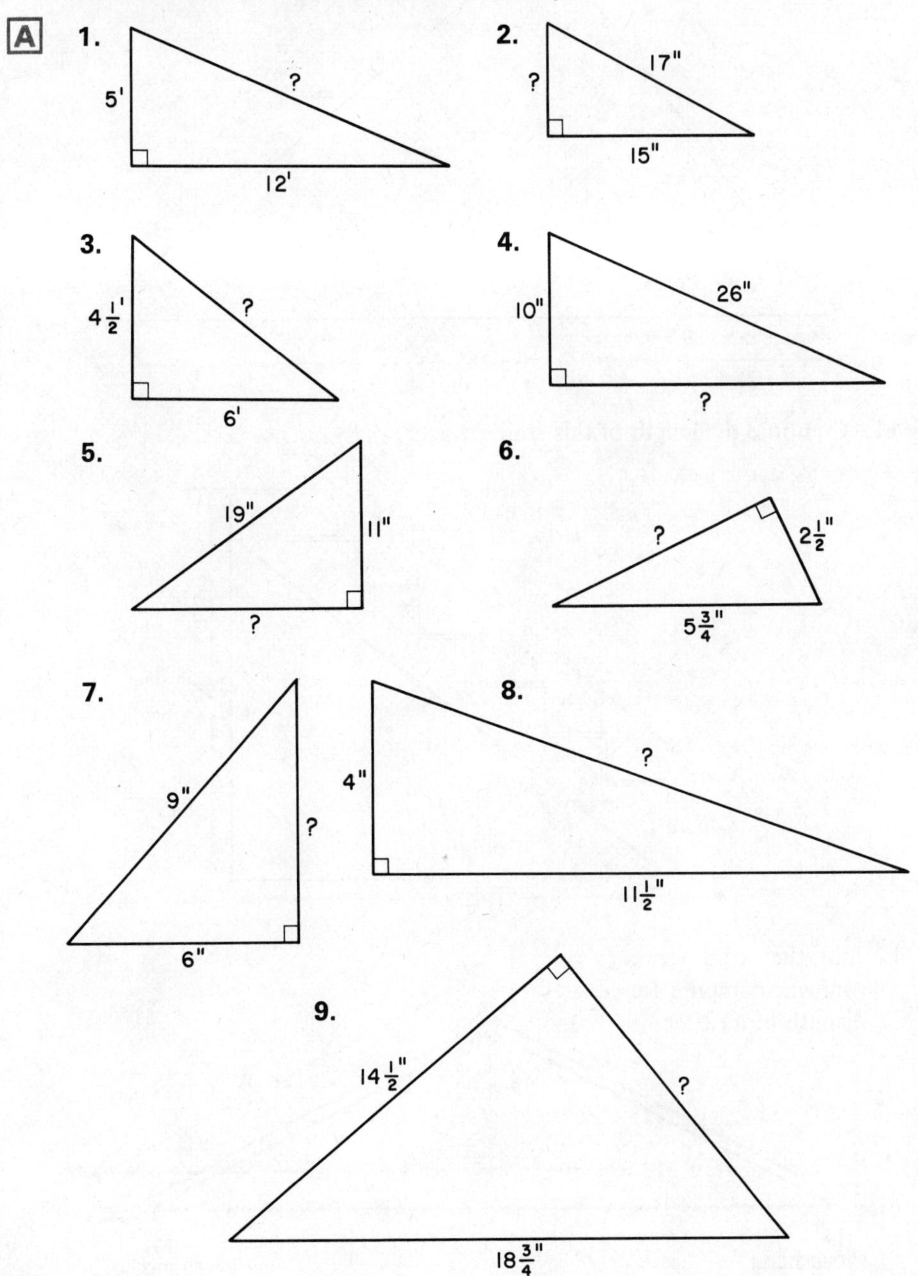

B **10.** Find the length of $\overline{BC}$. Use your result to find the length of $\overline{CD}$.

To find the lengths of $\overline{BC}$ and $\overline{CD}$, use $\triangle ABC$ and $\triangle BCD$, respectively.

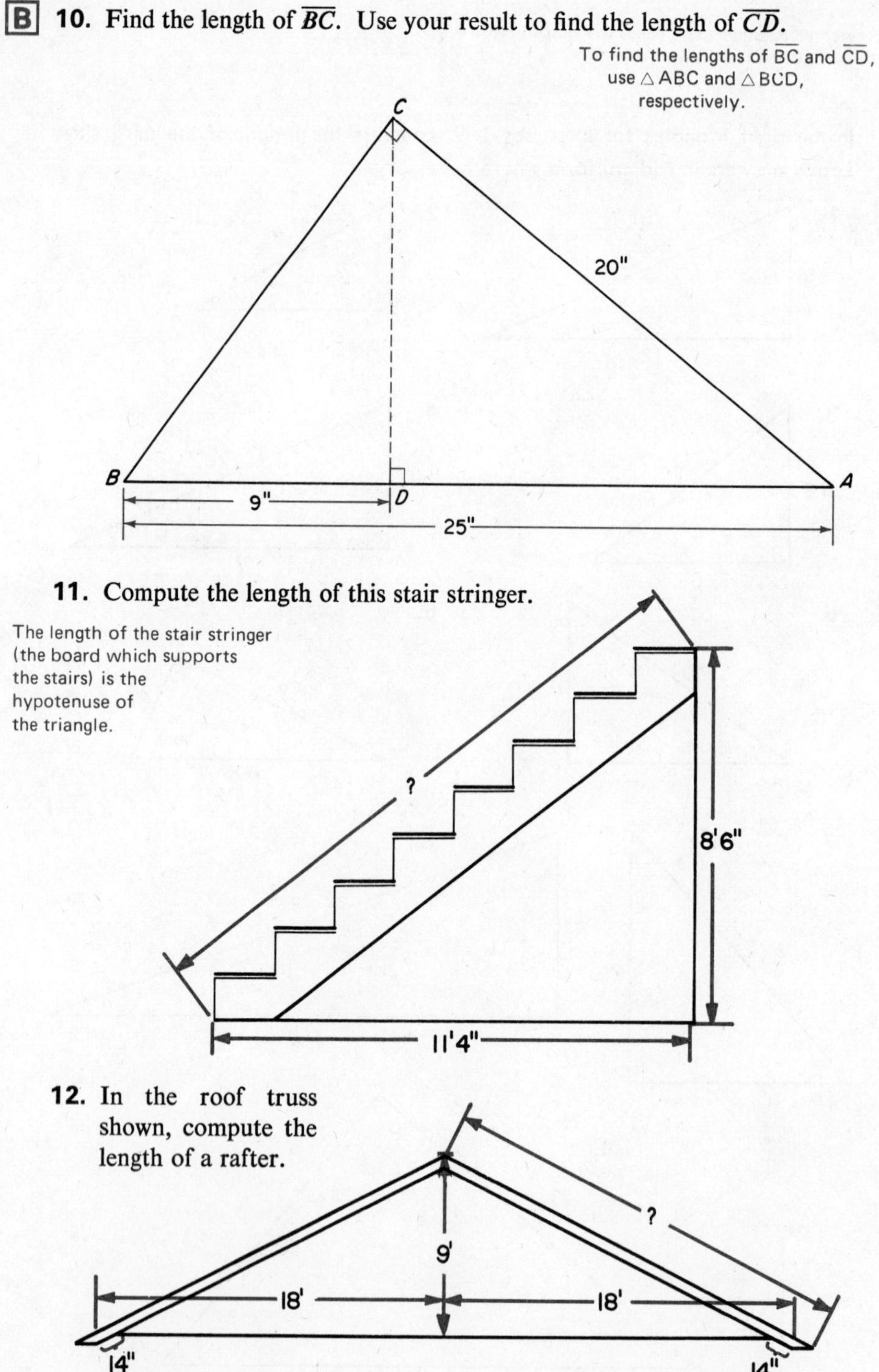

11. Compute the length of this stair stringer.

The length of the stair stringer (the board which supports the stairs) is the hypotenuse of the triangle.

12. In the roof truss shown, compute the length of a rafter.

13. Find the length of the diagonal of a square nut which is 2″ on a side.

14. $BD = 5''$
$AD = 8''$
$AC = 10''$

$CD = \underline{\ ?\ }$
$BC = \underline{\ ?\ }$

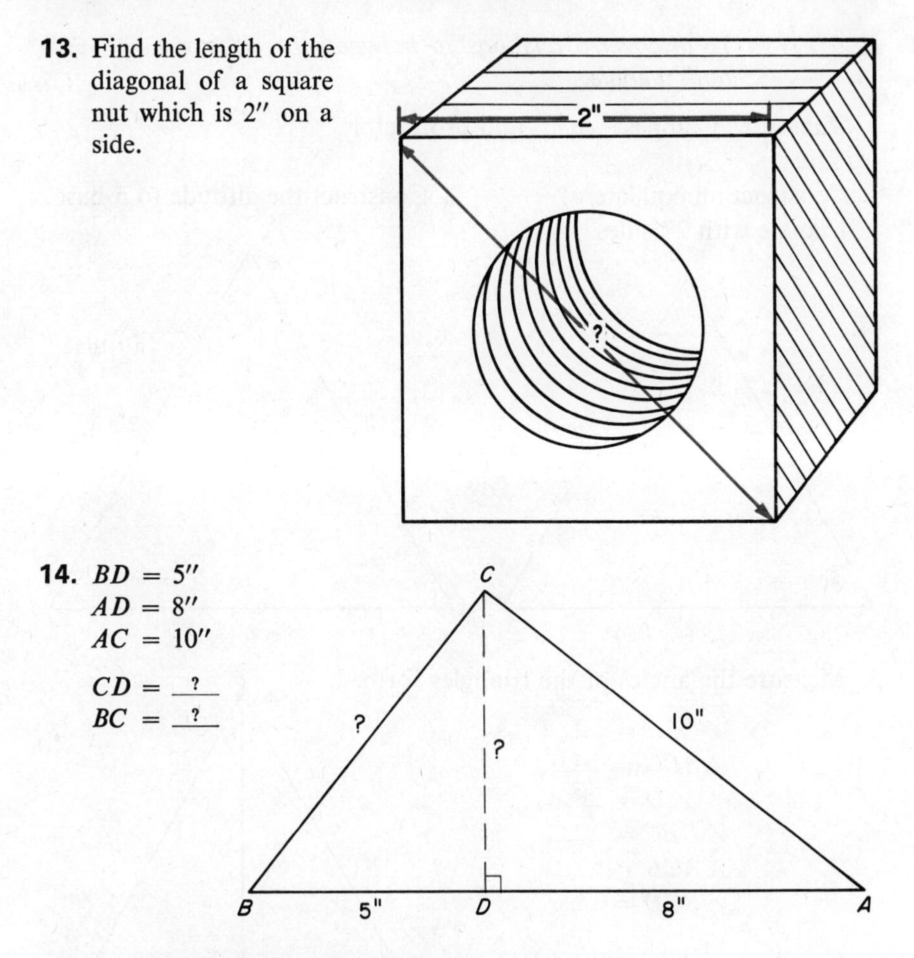

10–2 Special Right Triangles

If you should construct an equilateral triangle *ABD* and then bisect ∠*B*, you would have a figure like the one at the right. Notice that each of triangles *ABC* and *BCD* has angles of 90°, 60°, and 30°. We call them 30°-60° right triangles.

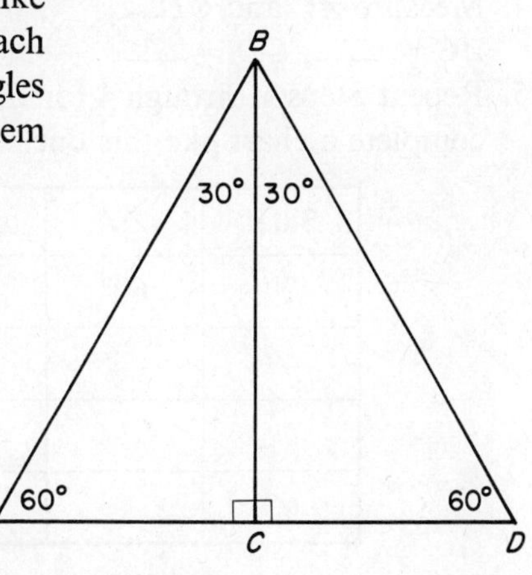

This activity should give each student a good understanding of the properties of a 30°-60° right triangle.

ACTIVITY: ***To discover a relationship between the sides of a 30°-60° right triangle.***

Materials: Compass, ruler, and protractor.

Plan:

1. Construct an equilateral triangle with 2″ sides.
2. Construct the altitude to a base.

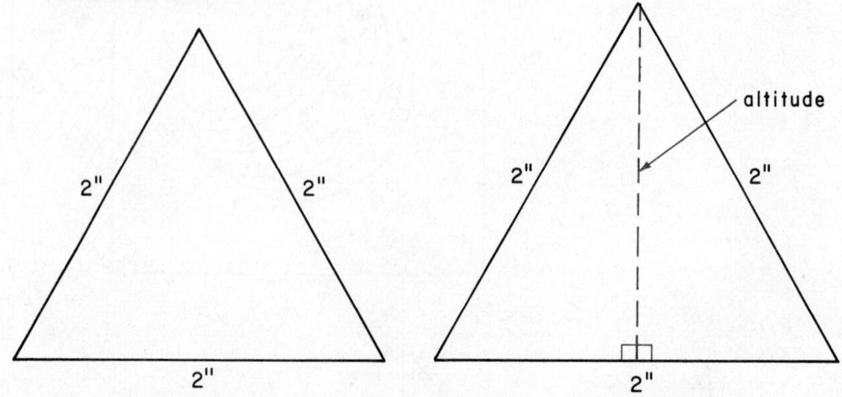

3. Measure the angles of the triangles formed.

$\angle A = \underline{\ ?\ }$
$\angle ABC = \underline{\ ?\ }$
$\angle D = \underline{\ ?\ }$
$\angle DBC = \underline{\ ?\ }$
$\angle ACB = \underline{\ ?\ }$
$\angle BCD = \underline{\ ?\ }$

Compare $\angle ABC$ with $\angle DBC$. What can you say about altitude BC?

4. Measure AC and CD.
$AC = \underline{\ ?\ }$; $CD = \underline{\ ?\ }$

5. Repeat Steps 1 through 4 for the following equilateral triangles and complete a chart like this one.

Sides	$\angle A$	$\angle ABC$	$\angle ACB$	AC
2″	60°	30°	90°	1″
4″				
5″				
6″				

Using your chart, determine the relationship in $\triangle ABC$ between the hypotenuse AB and side AC. Would you conclude that this is always true in a 30°-60° right triangle?

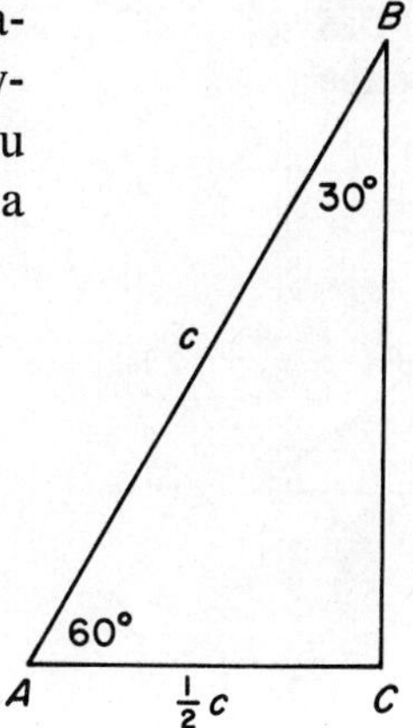

Be sure students understand which is the side opposite the 30° angle. They should be expected to remember this important property.

> **In a 30°-60° right triangle, the length of the side opposite the 30° angle is equal to one half the length of the hypotenuse.**

EXERCISES

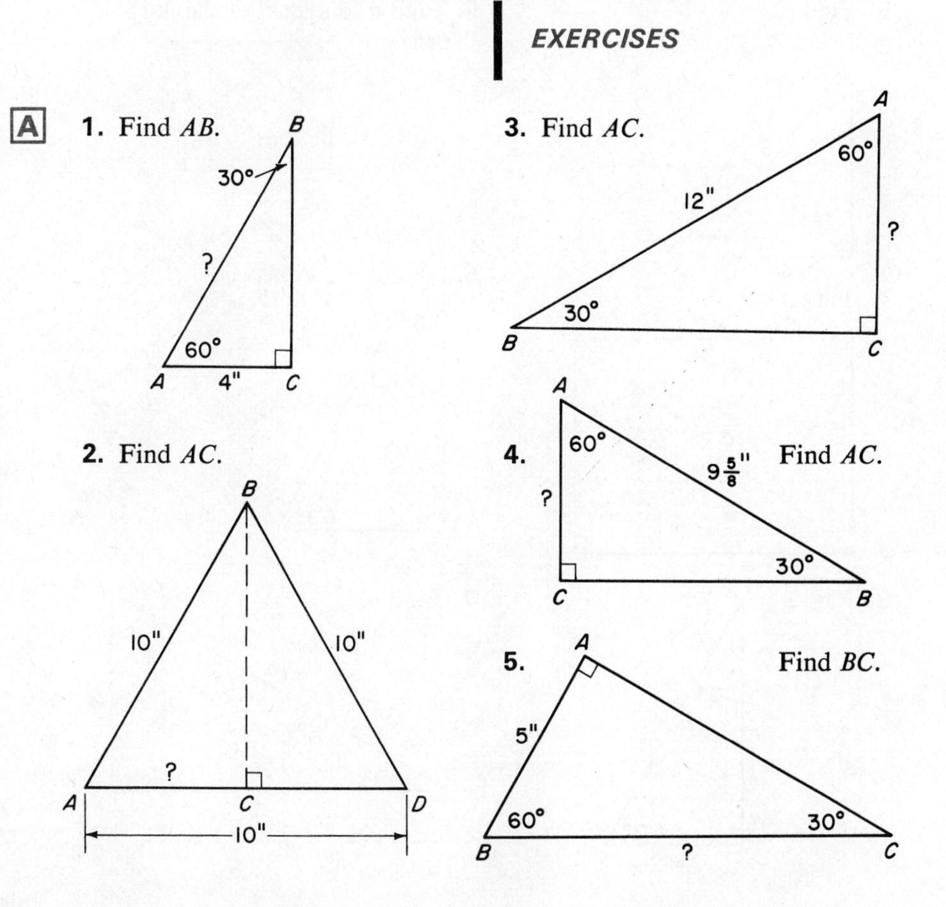

A

1. Find AB.

2. Find AC.

3. Find AC.

4. Find AC.

5. Find BC.

SELF-ANALYSIS TEST I

Time: 10 minutes

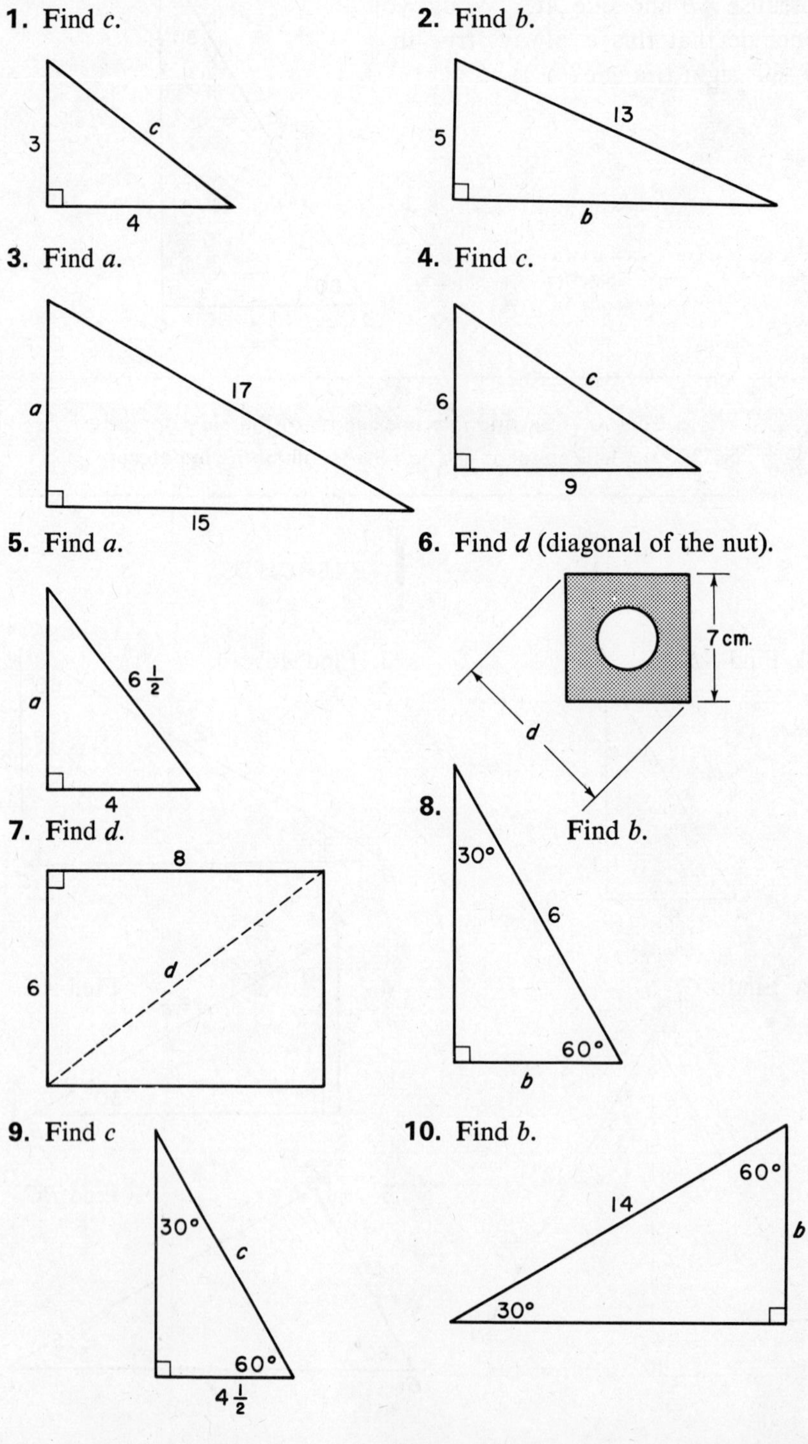

ACTIVITY: *To discover the relationship between the altitude and sides of an equilateral triangle.*

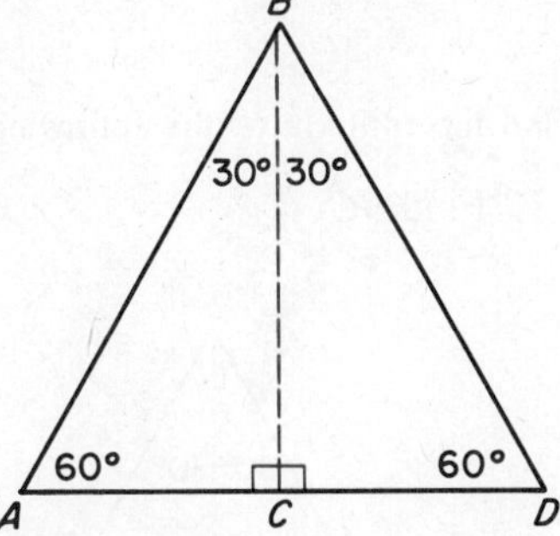

Materials: Compass, protractor, ruler.

Plan:

1. Construct an equilateral triangle with sides of 2 in.

2. Construct the altitude to one of its bases.

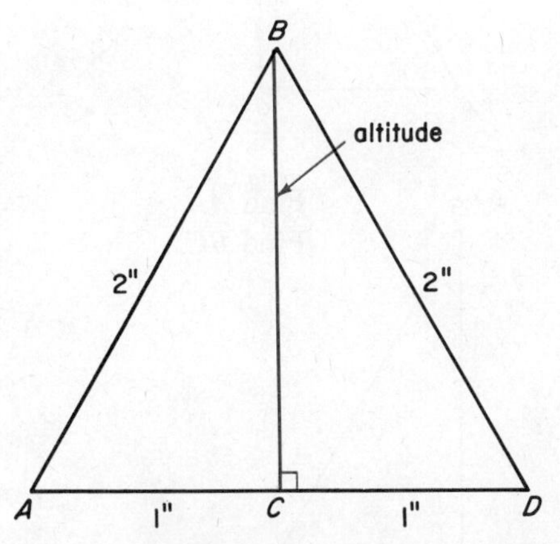

3. Find the altitude BC by using the Rule of Pythagoras.

$$x^2 = 2^2 - 1^2$$
$$x^2 = 4 - 1$$
$$x^2 = 3$$
$$x = \sqrt{3}$$

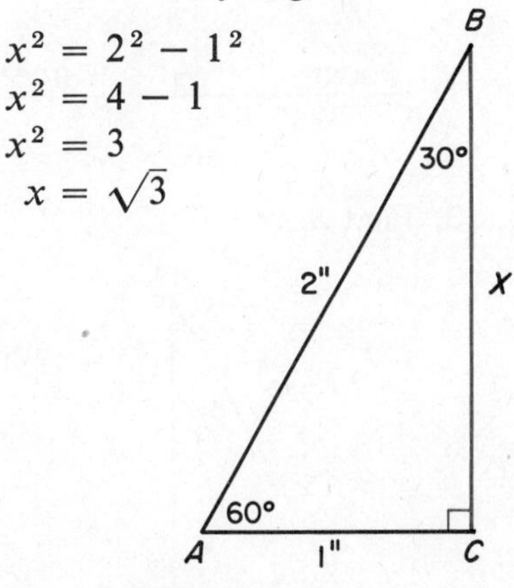

4. Repeat steps 1, 2, 3 for the triangles listed below, all equilateral. Record all information in a chart like the one shown. Use these facts as needed: $\sqrt{12} = 2\sqrt{3}$, $\sqrt{27} = 3\sqrt{3}$, and give the lengths of BC as the product of some number and $\sqrt{3}$.

AB	*AC*	*BC*
2″		
4″		
6″		

What relationship is there between AC and BC? Would you conclude that this is always true in any equilateral triangle? TM p. 20 , 10-2

1. The length of an altitude of an equilateral triangle is equal to one half the length of the base times $\sqrt{3}$.
2. In a 30°-60° right triangle, the length of the side opposite the 60° angle is equal to the length of the side opposite the 30° angle times $\sqrt{3}$.

These exercises use the properties of a 30°-60° right triangle found on pages 349 and 351.

EXERCISES

Find the altitude of the following triangles. Leave answers in square-root form.

A

1. Find BC.

2. Find BC. (Hint. Find AC first.)

3. Find BC.

4. Find AB.
   Find BC.

5. Find AC.
   Find BC.

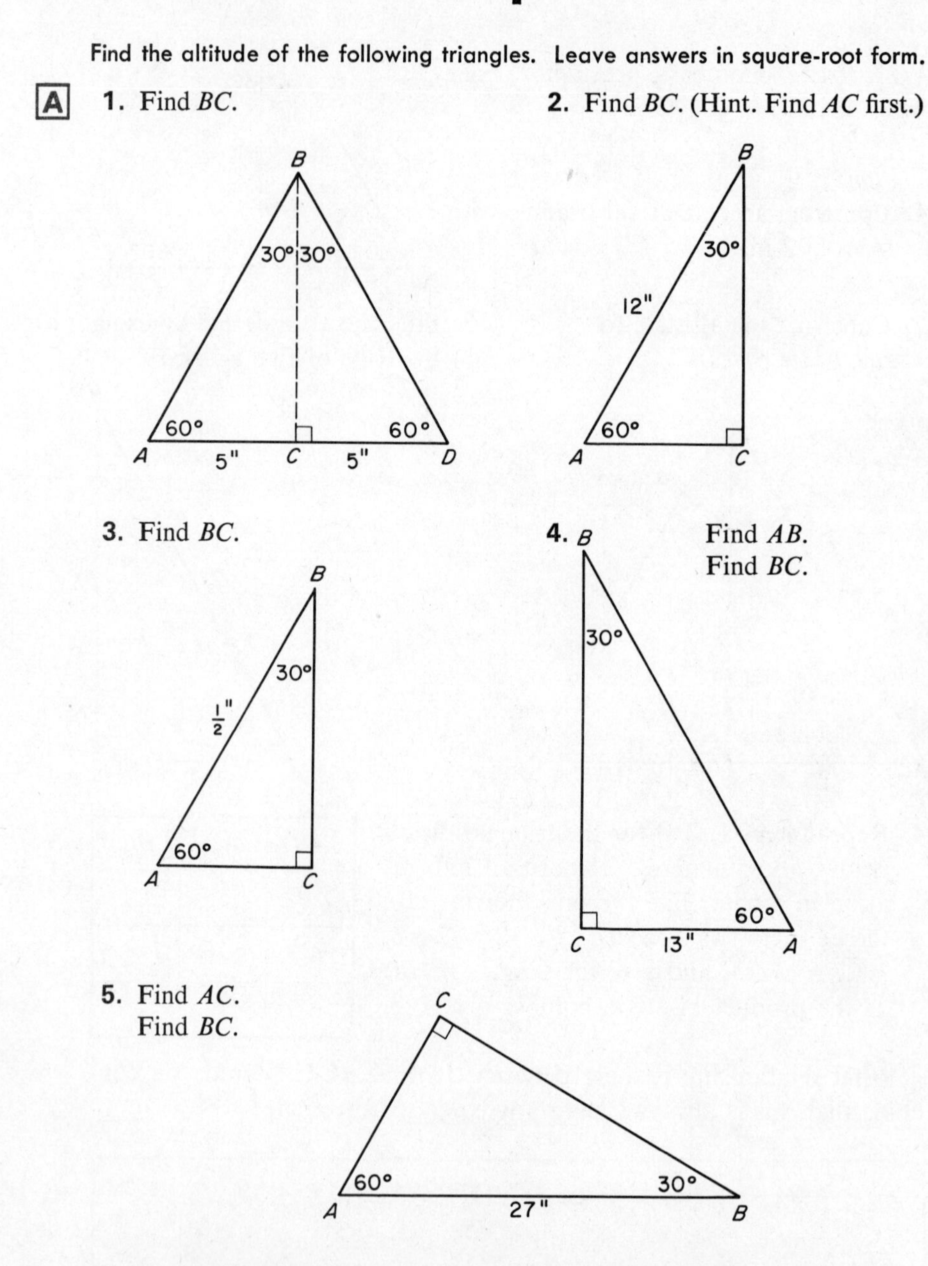

10–3 Applications to Area and Volume Problems

Many problems of area and volume may be solved by using some of the properties of right triangles.

EXAMPLE 1

Find the total area of a regular hexagonal walk surrounding a flower bed.

Encourage student to be alert for ways to simplify problems, as shown in the solution here, for instance. Be sure that students understand the reason for each step.

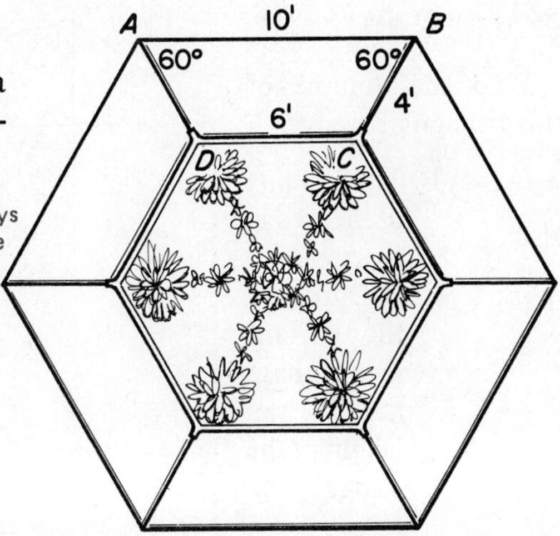

Solution. The walk is made up of 6 trapezoids. Since all 6 trapezoids have equal areas, we will solve for the area of trapezoid $ABCD$ and multiply the result by 6.

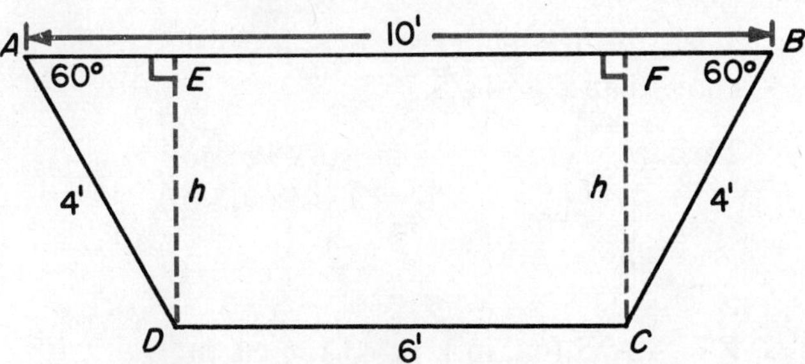

1. $A = \frac{1}{2}h(b_1 + b_2)$ (formula for the area of a trapezoid)
2. $A = \frac{1}{2}h(10 + 6) = \frac{1}{2}h(16) = 8h$

   In order to find the area, we must find h, the altitude of the trapezoid.
3. In right triangle ADE, the side AE opposite the 30° angle equals one half the hypotenuse.

   $AE = \frac{1}{2}(4)$

   $AE = 2$
4. The side DE opposite the 60° angle $= AE \times \sqrt{3}$.

   $$DE, \text{ or } h, = 2\sqrt{3}.$$
5. $A = 8(2\sqrt{3})$ [From Step 2]

   $= 16\sqrt{3}$ (sq. ft.)
6. Total area of the walk $= 6 \times 16\sqrt{3}$ sq. ft.

   $= 96\sqrt{3}$ sq. ft.

   $=$ **166.27 sq. ft.** Approximately

EXAMPLE 2

Find the volume of this triangular wedge.

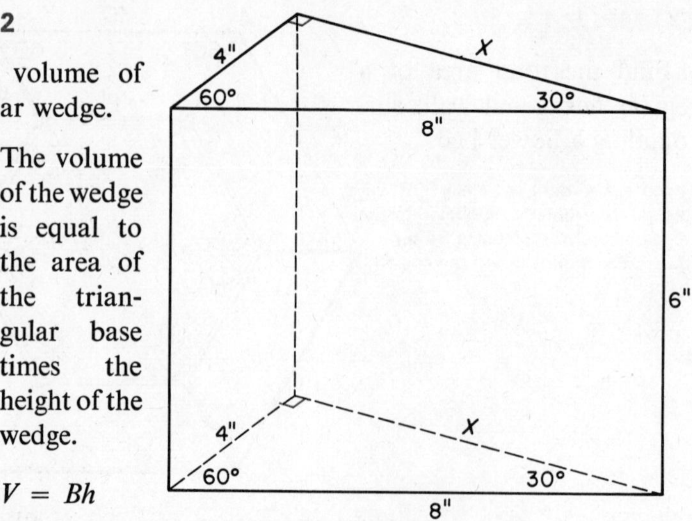

Solution. 1. The volume of the wedge is equal to the area of the triangular base times the height of the wedge.

$V = Bh$

2. First find the area of the triangular base.

$$B = \tfrac{1}{2}(4)x$$

Be sure students understand why $x = 4\sqrt{3}$ (see page 351, Rule 2).

Since the triangular base is a 30°-60° right triangle, we know that $x = 4\sqrt{3}$.

Then
$$B = \tfrac{1}{2}(4)(4\sqrt{3})$$
$$B = 8\sqrt{3} \text{ (sq. in.)}$$

3. $V = Bh$
$V = 8\sqrt{3} \times 6$
$V = 48\sqrt{3}$ (cu. in.), or **83.136 cu. in.** Approximately

EXERCISES

A 1. Find the area of this end view of a house.

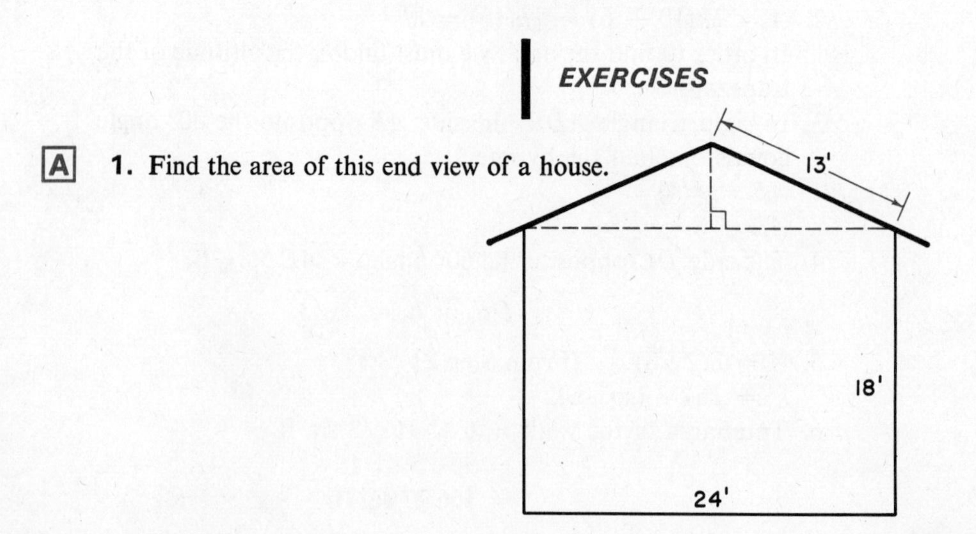

2. Find the length of the diagonal brace on this $3\frac{1}{2}' \times 6'$ rectangular gate.

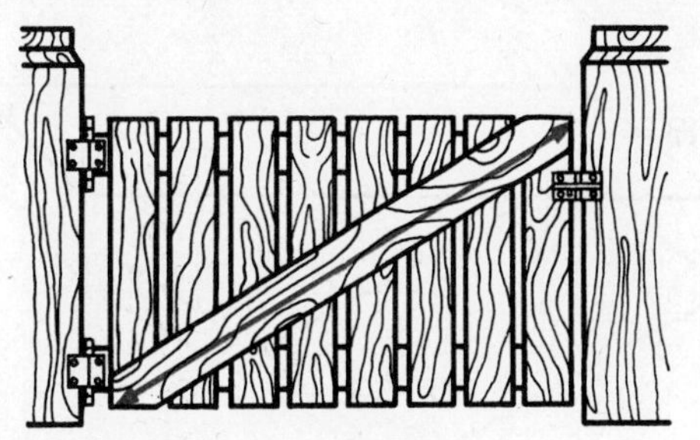

3. Find the volume of the triangular wedge.

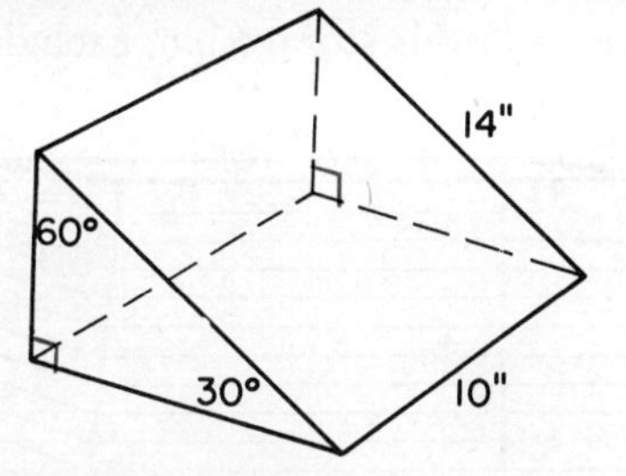

4. Find the amount of roofing paper needed to cover the patio roof pictured. Add 20% to allow for overlapping.

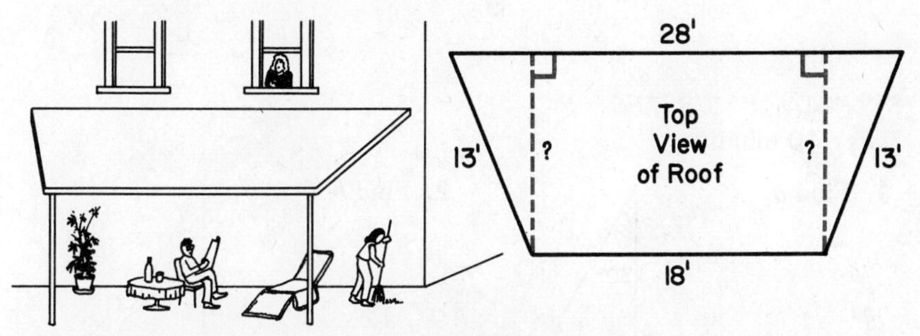

5. Find the volume of concrete needed for the patio pictured, if the depth is 4″. (Hint. First find the area of the trapezoid, then the areas of the 3 semicircles.)

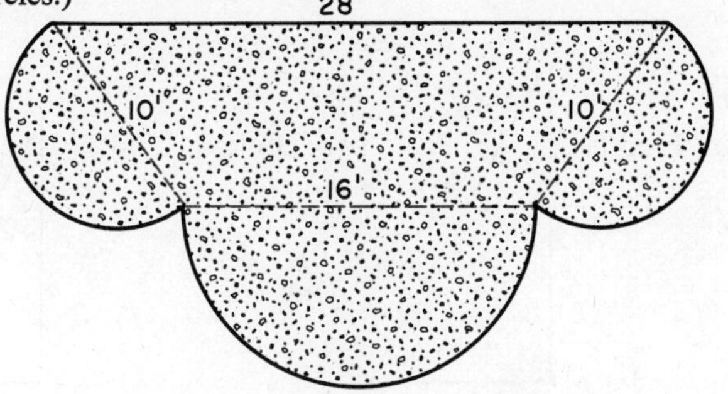

B **6.** Find the volume of this swimming pool in cubic feet.

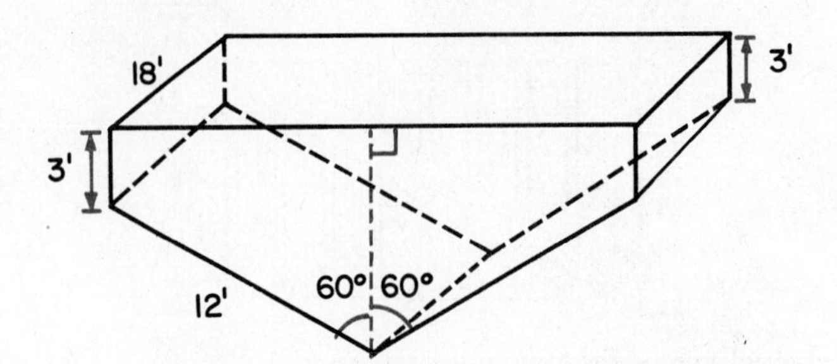

7. Find the surface area of this storage bin, excluding the top.

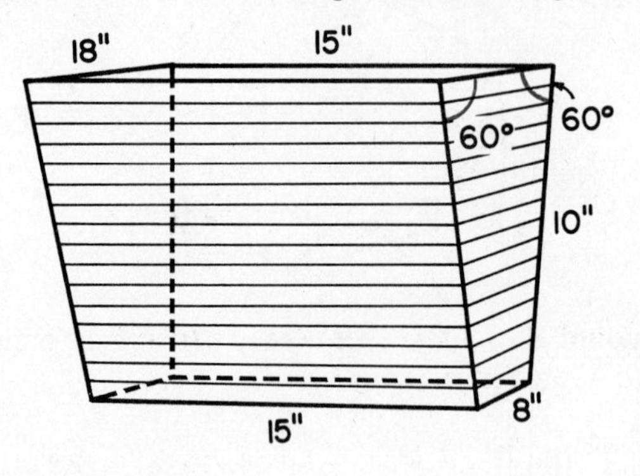

SELF-ANALYSIS TEST II

Time: 10 minutes

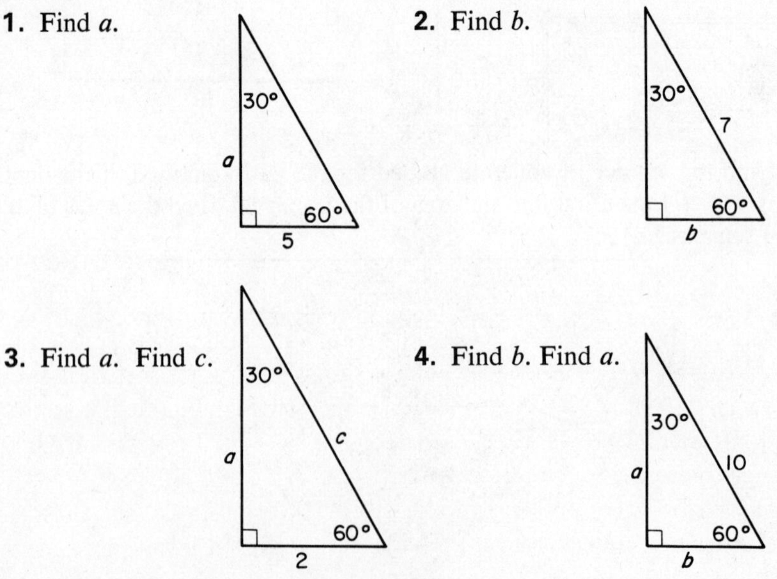

1. Find *a*.

2. Find *b*.

3. Find *a*. Find *c*.

4. Find *b*. Find *a*.

5. Find c. Find a.

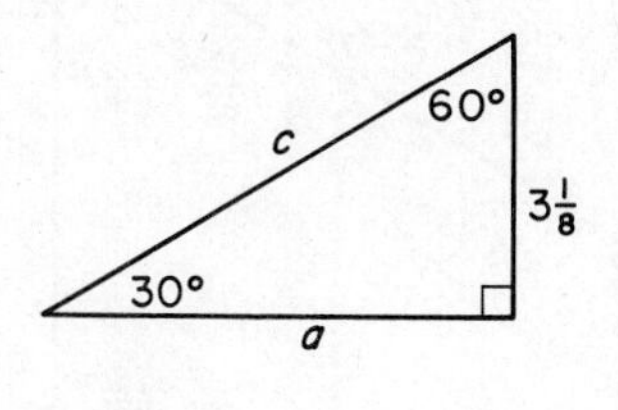

6. Find a. Find $\angle A$. Find $\angle B$.

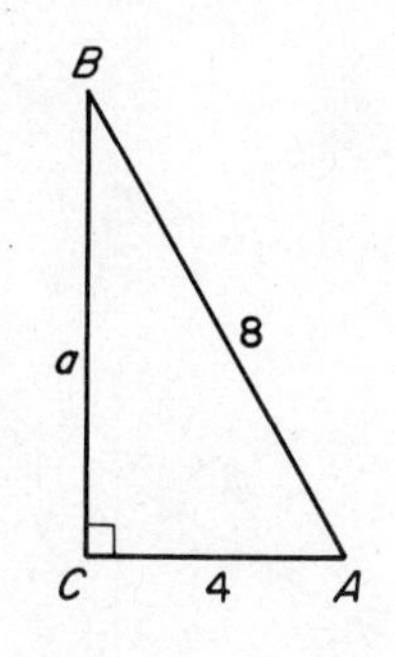

7. Find a. Find $\angle A$. Find $\angle B$.

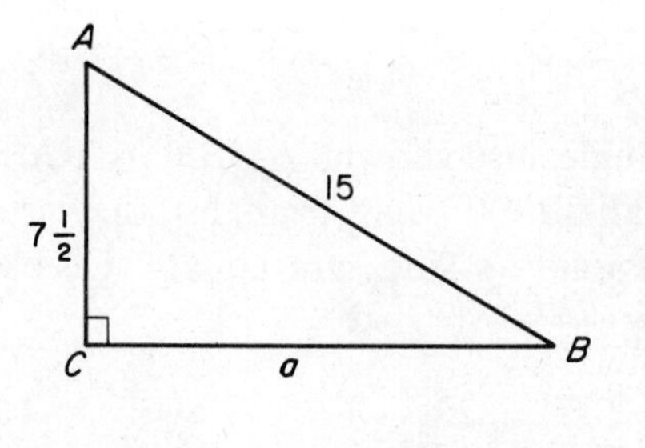

8. Find area of $\triangle ABC$.

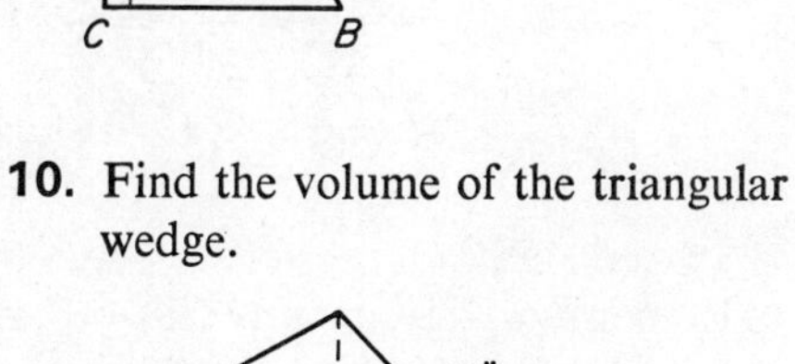

9. Find area of trapezoid $ABCD$.

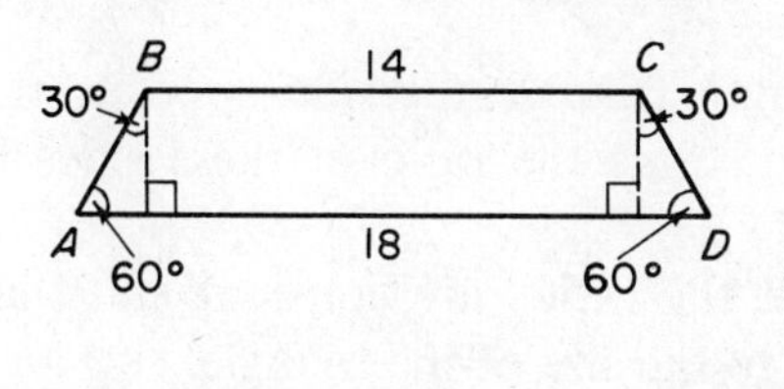

10. Find the volume of the triangular wedge.

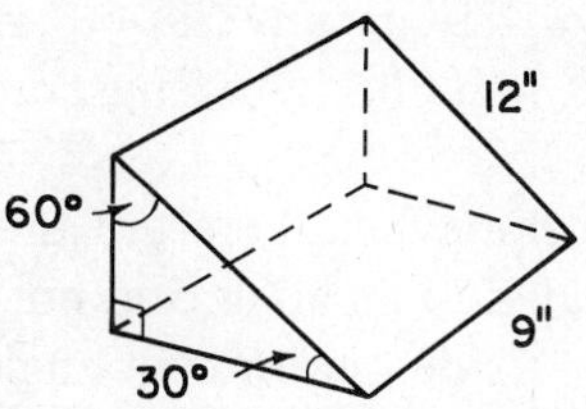

■ Trigonometry

10–4 Trigonometric Ratios

The Rule of Pythagoras gives us a way to find unknown lengths in a right triangle. An even more powerful tool exists in the subject called **trigonometry.** This word came from two Greek words meaning "triangle measure."

The part of trigonometry we will study deals with the measurement of the sides and angles of right triangles.

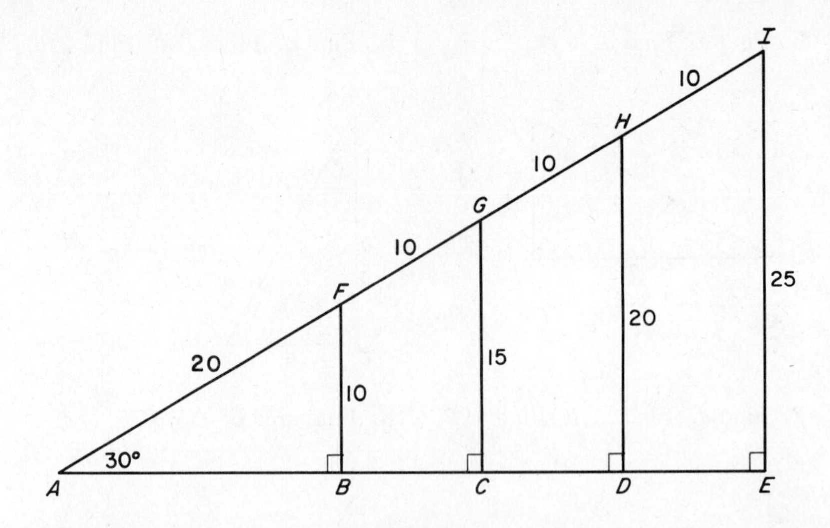

In the figure above, four right triangles are shown, $\triangle ABF$, $\triangle ACG$, $\triangle ADH$, and $\triangle AEI$. Since they are all 30°-60° right triangles, they are similar, so the ratios of their corresponding sides are equal. Check the following by the figure. Recall similar triangles, page 295.

$$\frac{BF}{AF} = \frac{10}{20} = \frac{1}{2} \qquad \frac{DH}{AH} = \frac{20}{40} = \frac{1}{2}$$

$$\frac{CG}{AG} = \frac{15}{30} = \frac{1}{2} \qquad \frac{EI}{AI} = \frac{25}{50} = \frac{1}{2}$$

Remember that in any 30°-60° right triangle the side opposite the 30° angle is half the hypotenuse and thus the ratio of these sides is always $\frac{1}{2}$.

The important facts here are that the ratios are constant and that they are related to an angle and not to the size of the triangle. Stress this.

This ratio, $\dfrac{\text{side opposite an angle}}{\text{hypotenuse}}$, has a special name, the **sine.** We write sine 30° $= \frac{1}{2}$ or, usually, sin 30° $= \frac{1}{2}$. (*Sine* and its abbreviation *sin* are both pronounced like the word *sign.*) The sine ratio varies with the measure of the angle.

There are six possible ratios of sides in any right triangle. The three most useful in practical work are called the sine, cosine, and tangent. They are defined as follows:

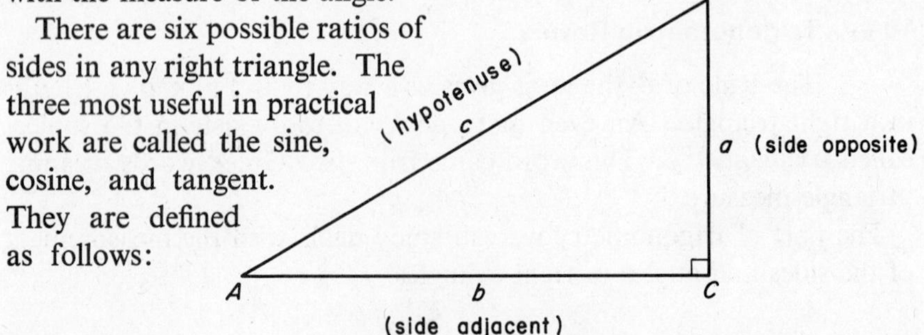

TM p. 20 , 10-4

sine of angle A $= \dfrac{\textbf{side opposite}}{\textbf{hypotenuse}} = \dfrac{a}{c}$ **or** $\sin A = \dfrac{a}{c}$

cosine of angle A $= \dfrac{\textbf{side adjacent}}{\textbf{hypotenuse}} = \dfrac{b}{c}$ **or** $\cos A = \dfrac{b}{c}$

tangent of angle A $= \dfrac{\textbf{side opposite}}{\textbf{side adjacent}} = \dfrac{a}{b}$ **or** $\tan A = \dfrac{a}{b}$

The following examples will illustrate how these are used.

EXAMPLE 1

Find the height of the monument, using the data in the diagram.

Solution. The distance we want to find is h. If we move out from the base of the monument some specific distance, say 100 ft., we can measure the angle to the top of the monument with a transit. This gives us two of the three values involved in the tangent ratio.

h
80°
100'

$$\tan A = \frac{\text{side opposite}}{\text{side adjacent}}$$

$$\tan 80^\circ = \frac{h}{100}$$

If you know that $\tan 80^\circ = 5.67$, then

$$5.67 = \frac{h}{100}$$

$$h = 5.67 \times 100$$

$$h = \mathbf{567\ (ft.)}$$

The angle of 80° in this problem is called the **angle of elevation.**

Finding a height or distance by computation instead of by measuring directly is known as **indirect measurement.** It is the method used by surveyors, who must first find angles and distances which are easy to measure with transit and tape. The optional section on the vertical protractor (pages 81-83), if not covered previously, can be done at this time.

EXAMPLE 2

Write the trigonometric ratio and equation needed to solve this problem.

a. If $\angle A = 30°$ and $c = 20''$, find a.

b. If $a = 4$ in. and $c = 8$ in., how large is $\angle A$?

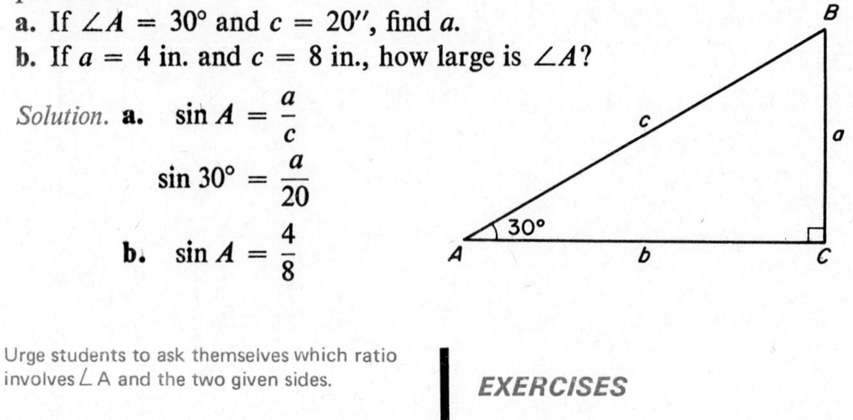

Solution. **a.** $\sin A = \dfrac{a}{c}$

$\sin 30° = \dfrac{a}{20}$

b. $\sin A = \dfrac{4}{8}$

Urge students to ask themselves which ratio involves $\angle$A and the two given sides.

EXERCISES

In the following exercises select the proper trigonometric ratio to solve the problem. Write the equation, but do not solve it.

A

1. Find $\angle A$ if $b = 8$ and $c = 11$.

2. Find $\angle A$ if $a = 3$ and $b = 7$.

3. Find $\angle A$ if $a = 6''$ and $c = 13''$.

4. Find b if $\angle A = 35°$ and $c = 10''$.

5. Find a if $\angle A = 40°$ and $c = 12''$.

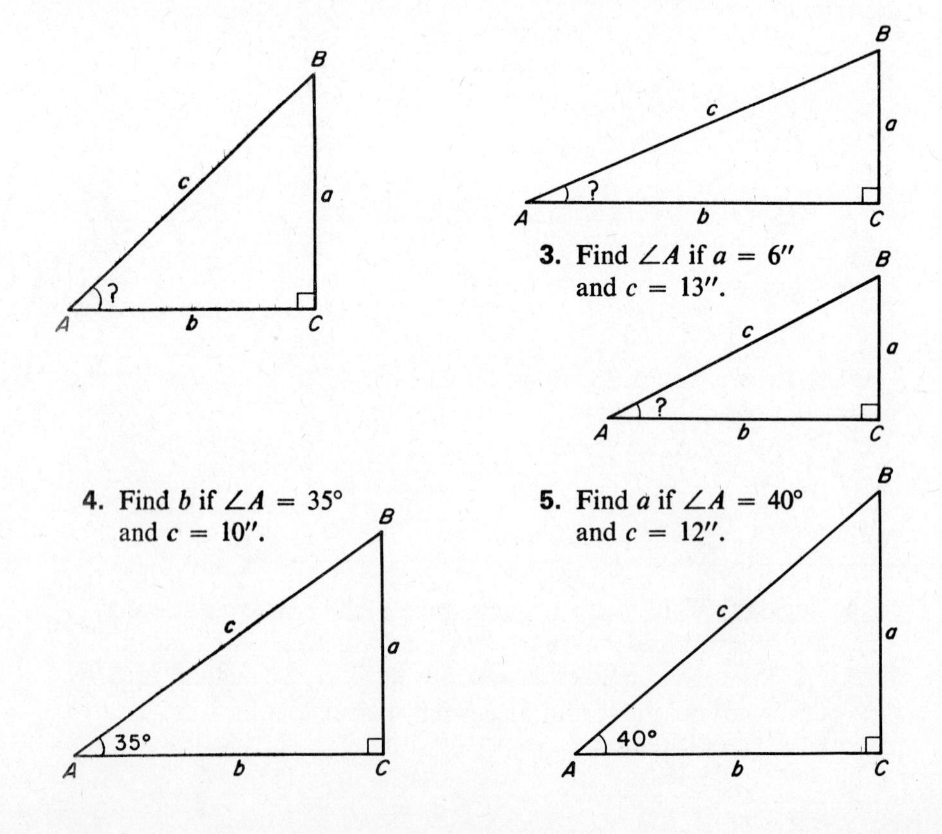

10–5 Trigonometric Tables

The values of the trigonometric ratios of certain angles are easy to find. Use the descriptive definitions of the ratios (page 359) and the diagrams below.

Look at $\triangle ABC$. It is a 30°-60° right triangle, and thus if BC is 1, then AB must be 2, and AC must be $\sqrt{3}$. (Recall these relationships from pages 349 and 351.)

This enables us to find numerical values for the trigonometric ratios of 30° angles.

$$\sin 30° = \frac{1}{2} = .500$$

$$\cos 30° = \frac{\sqrt{3}}{2} = .866$$

$$\tan 30° = \frac{1}{\sqrt{3}} = .577$$

If we look at the triangle below, we can find numerical values of the trigonometric ratios of 60°.

$$\sin 60° = \frac{\sqrt{3}}{2} = .866$$

$$\cos 60° = \frac{1}{2} = .500$$

$$\tan 60° = \sqrt{3} = 1.732$$

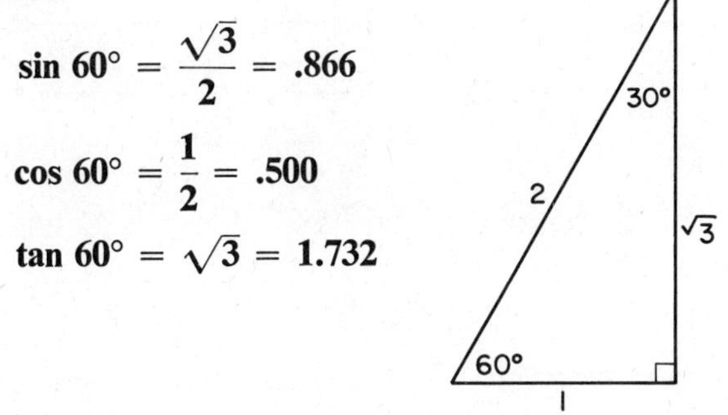

What do you notice about sin 30° and cos 60°? about cos 30° and sin 60°? They are equal.

Using the isosceles right triangle below gives the values for angles of 45°.

$$\sin 45° = \frac{1}{\sqrt{2}} = .707$$

$$\cos 45° = \frac{1}{\sqrt{2}} = .707$$

$$\tan 45° = 1 = 1.000$$

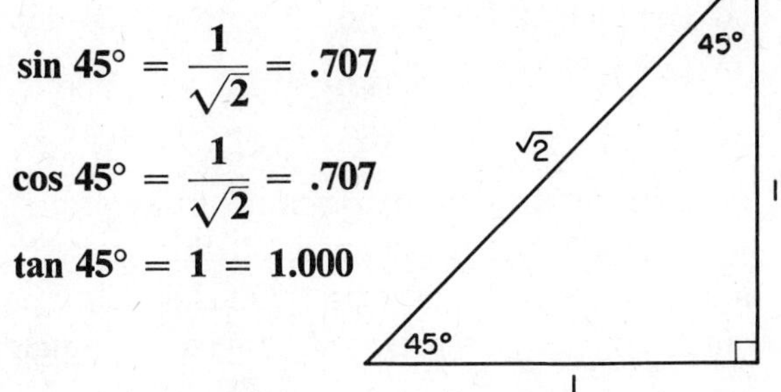

We may summarize the values just given as follows:

Point out that these values are independent of the size of the triangle.

angle	sin	cos	tan
30°	$\frac{1}{2}$	$\frac{\sqrt{3}}{2}$	$\frac{1}{\sqrt{3}}$
45°	$\frac{1}{\sqrt{2}}$	$\frac{1}{\sqrt{2}}$	1
60°	$\frac{\sqrt{3}}{2}$	$\frac{1}{2}$	$\sqrt{3}$

Ordinarily the values in trigonometric tables are given in decimal form.

angle	sin	cos	tan
30°	.500	.866	.577
45°	.707	.707	1.000
60°	.866	.500	1.732

EXAMPLE 1

Find side b of triangle ABC if $AB = 15$ and $\angle A = 30°$.

Solution. $\cos A = \frac{b}{c}$

$$\cos 30° = \frac{b}{15}$$

$$b = 15 \times \cos 30°$$

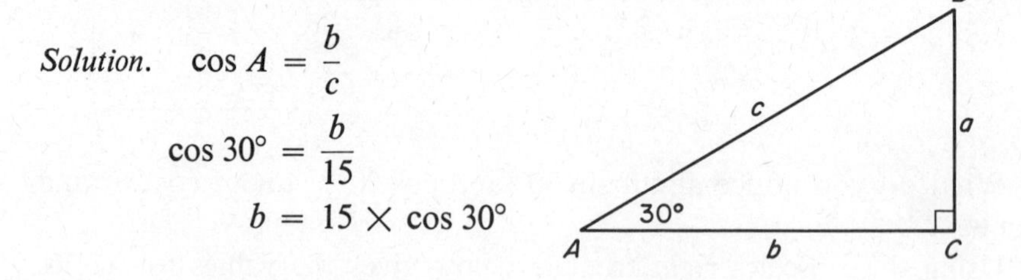

From the second table above, $\cos 30° = .866$

$$b = 15 \times .866$$

$$b = \mathbf{12.99}$$

Values for trigonometric ratios of most angles are not easy to compute. Fortunately, however, all this work has been done by others, and easy-to-use tables exist. On the facing page is a table of decimal values of sines, cosines, and tangents of angles from 1° to 90°.

Sines, Cosines, and Tangents of Angles from 1 to 90 Degrees

Angle	Sine	Cosine	Tangent	Angle	Sine	Cosine	Tangent
1°	.0175	.9998	.0175	**46°**	.7193	.6947	1.0355
2°	.0349	.9994	.0349	**47°**	.7314	.6820	1.0724
3°	.0523	.9986	.0524	**48°**	.7431	.6691	1.1106
4°	.0698	.9976	.0699	**49°**	.7547	.6561	1.1504
5°	.0872	.9962	.0875	**50°**	.7660	.6428	1.1918
6°	.1045	.9945	.1051	**51°**	.7771	.6293	1.2349
7°	.1219	.9925	.1228	**52°**	.7880	.6157	1.2799
8°	.1392	.9903	.1405	**53°**	.7986	.6018	1.3270
9°	.1564	.9877	.1584	**54°**	.8090	.5878	1.3764
10°	.1736	.9848	.1763	**55°**	.8192	.5736	1.4281
11°	.1908	.9816	.1944	**56°**	.8290	.5592	1.4826
12°	.2079	.9781	.2126	**57°**	.8387	.5446	1.5399
13°	.2250	.9744	.2309	**58°**	.8480	.5299	1.6003
14°	.2419	.9703	.2493	**59°**	.8572	.5150	1.6643
15°	.2588	.9659	.2679	**60°**	.8660	.5000	1.7321
16°	.2756	.9613	.2867	**61°**	.8746	.4848	1.8040
17°	.2924	.9563	.3057	**62°**	.8829	.4695	1.8807
18°	.3090	.9511	.3249	**63°**	.8910	.4540	1.9626
19°	.3256	.9455	.3443	**64°**	.8988	.4384	2.0503
20°	.3420	.9397	.3640	**65°**	.9063	.4226	2.1445
21°	.3584	.9336	.3839	**66°**	.9135	.4067	2.2460
22°	.3746	.9272	.4040	**67°**	.9205	.3907	2.3559
23°	.3907	.9205	.4245	**68°**	.9272	.3746	2.4751
24°	.4067	.9135	.4452	**69°**	.9336	.3584	2.6051
25°	.4226	.9063	.4663	**70°**	.9397	.3420	2.7475
26°	.4384	.8988	.4877	**71°**	.9455	.3256	2.9042
27°	.4540	.8910	.5095	**72°**	.9511	.3090	3.0777
28°	.4695	.8829	.5317	**73°**	.9563	.2924	3.2709
29°	.4848	.8746	.5543	**74°**	.9613	.2756	3.4874
30°	.5000	.8660	.5774	**75°**	.9659	.2588	3.7321
31°	.5150	.8572	.6009	**76°**	.9703	.2419	4.0108
32°	.5299	.8480	.6249	**77°**	.9744	.2250	4.3315
33°	.5446	.8387	.6494	**78°**	.9781	.2079	4.7046
34°	.5592	.8290	.6745	**79°**	.9816	.1908	5.1446
35°	.5736	.8192	.7002	**80°**	.9848	.1736	5.6713
36°	.5878	.8090	.7265	**81°**	.9877	.1564	6.3138
37°	.6018	.7986	.7536	**82°**	.9903	.1392	7.1154
38°	.6157	.7880	.7813	**83°**	.9925	.1219	8.1443
39°	.6293	.7771	.8098	**84°**	.9945	.1045	9.5144
40°	.6428	.7660	.8391	**85°**	.9962	.0872	11.4301
41°	.6561	.7547	.8693	**86°**	.9976	.0698	14.3007
42°	.6691	.7431	.9004	**87°**	.9986	.0523	19.0811
43°	.6820	.7314	.9325	**88°**	.9994	.0349	28.6363
44°	.6947	.7193	.9657	**89°**	.9998	.0175	57.2900
45°	.7071	.7071	1.0000	**90°**	1.0000	.0000	

EXAMPLE 2

Use the table on page 363 to find the tangent of 71°.

Solution. Find "71°" in Column 5 of the table. Read across this line to the last column, headed "Tangent," and read the value "2.9042."

$$\tan 71^\circ = 2.9042.$$

The table can be used to find either the trigonometric value of an angle or the angle itself, depending on which is given.

EXAMPLE 3

$\cos A = .8988$. Find $\angle A$.

Solution. Look in the two columns headed "Cosine" until you find ".8988." Read across, to the left, and read "26°" in the column headed "Angle."

$$\angle A = 26^\circ.$$

Notice that as the measure of the angle increases the values of sines and tangents *increase*, whereas the values of cosines *decrease*. This fact will be helpful in using the table.

EXERCISES

Use the table to find the required values.

A

1. $\sin 37^\circ = \underline{\ ?\ }$
2. $\tan 33^\circ = \underline{\ ?\ }$
3. $\cos 52^\circ = \underline{\ ?\ }$
4. $\tan 73^\circ = \underline{\ ?\ }$
5. $\cos 63^\circ = \underline{\ ?\ }$
6. $\cos 23^\circ = \underline{\ ?\ }$
7. $\sin 45^\circ = \underline{\ ?\ }$
8. $\cos 49^\circ = \underline{\ ?\ }$
9. $\tan 29^\circ = \underline{\ ?\ }$
10. $\sin 78^\circ = \underline{\ ?\ }$

11. If $\tan \angle A = .0875$, $\angle A = \underline{\ ?\ }$.
12. If $\cos \angle A = .9816$, $\angle A = \underline{\ ?\ }$.
13. If $\sin \angle A = .6561$, $\angle A = \underline{\ ?\ }$.
14. If $\tan \angle A = .8098$, $\angle A = \underline{\ ?\ }$.
15. If $\sin \angle A = .5446$, $\angle A = \underline{\ ?\ }$.
16. If $\cos \angle A = .4848$, $\angle A = \underline{\ ?\ }$.
17. If $\cos \angle A = .3090$, $\angle A = \underline{\ ?\ }$.
18. If $\tan \angle A = 28.6363$, $\angle A = \underline{\ ?\ }$.
19. If $\sin \angle A = .4226$, $\angle A = \underline{\ ?\ }$.
20. If $\cos \angle A = .9986$, $\angle A = \underline{\ ?\ }$.

SELF-ANALYSIS TEST III

Time: 8 minutes

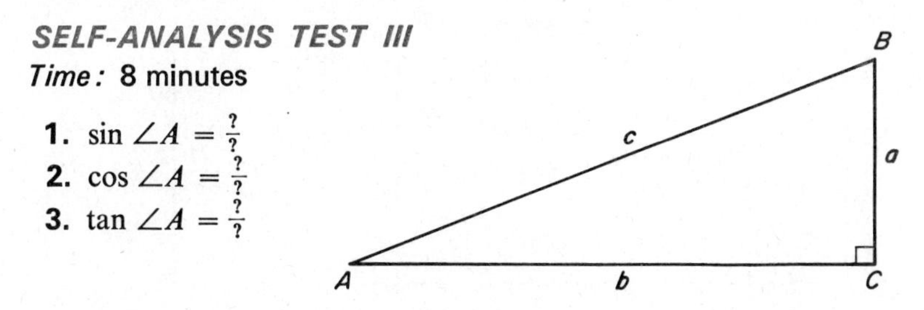

In Exercises 4 and 5, select the proper trigonometric formula, but do not solve.

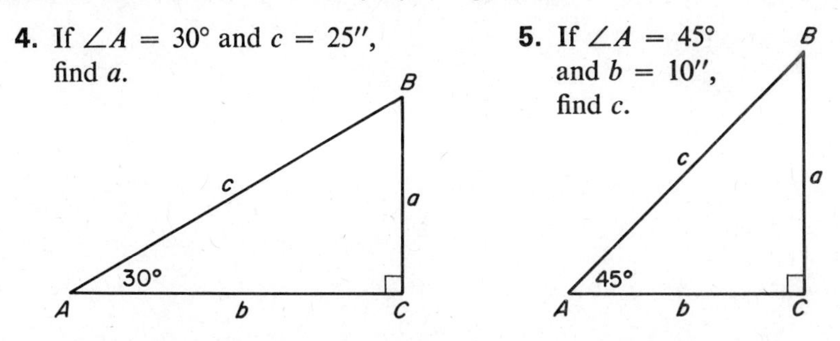

In Exercises 6–10, use the trigonometric table on page 363.

6. sin 27° = _?_. 7. cos 82° = _?_. 8. tan 53° = _?_.
9. cos A = .9962; $\angle A$ = _?_.
10. tan A = 6.3138; $\angle A$ = _?_.

10–6 Trigonometric Formulas

Each of the trigonometric formulas can be solved for any one of the three values involved. The different forms are shown on the next page. Instead of trying to memorize all the different forms, however, it is better to remember the basic form of each formula and then solve for the missing value. Use the same method as you would for solving a simple equation like $3d = 6$. Try to understand how the second and third formulas in each column of the following table are obtained.

Notice the way the triangle is lettered. This is known as a *standard right triangle.*

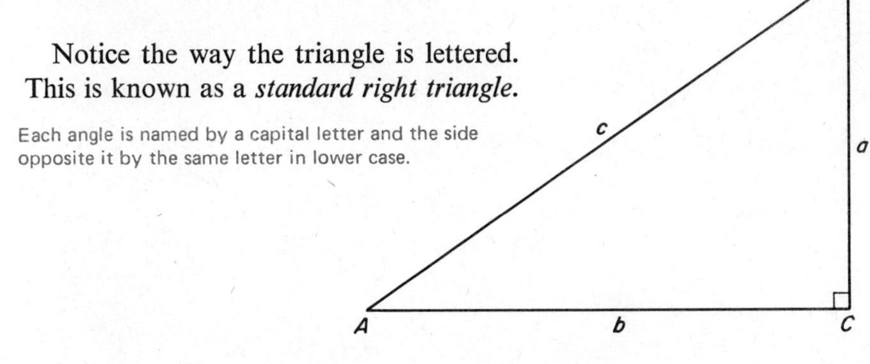

Each angle is named by a capital letter and the side opposite it by the same letter in lower case.

Urge students to learn the basic forms (in boldface) and solve for other values as needed.

$\mathbf{\sin A = \frac{a}{c}}$	$\mathbf{\cos A = \frac{b}{c}}$	$\mathbf{\tan A = \frac{a}{b}}$
$a = c \sin A$ $c = \dfrac{a}{\sin A}$	$b = c \cos A$ $c = \dfrac{b}{\cos A}$	$a = b \tan A$ $b = \dfrac{a}{\tan A}$

EXAMPLE 1

If $\angle A = 30°$ and $a = 10''$, find c.

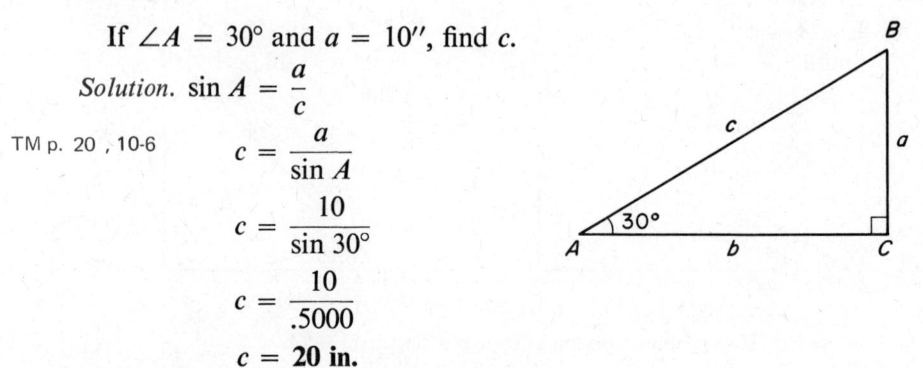

Solution. $\sin A = \dfrac{a}{c}$

TM p. 20 , 10-6

$$c = \frac{a}{\sin A}$$

$$c = \frac{10}{\sin 30°}$$

$$c = \frac{10}{.5000}$$

$$c = \mathbf{20 \text{ in.}}$$

EXAMPLE 2

If $\angle A = 20°$ and $b = 12''$, find c.

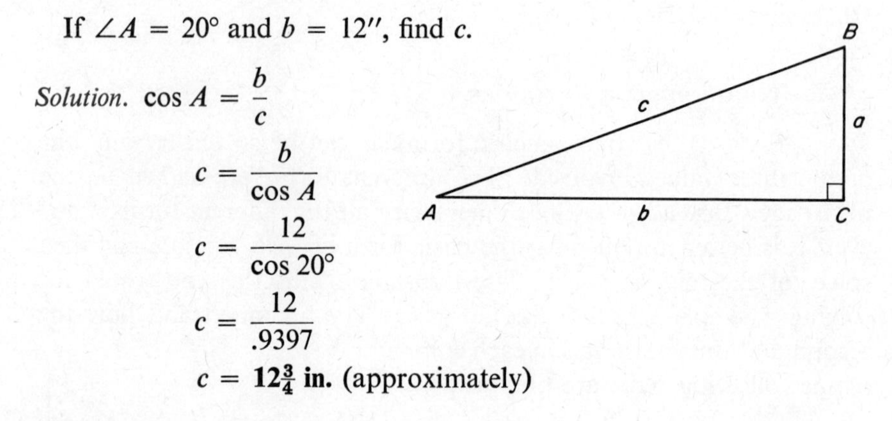

Solution. $\cos A = \dfrac{b}{c}$

$$c = \frac{b}{\cos A}$$

$$c = \frac{12}{\cos 20°}$$

$$c = \frac{12}{.9397}$$

$$c = \mathbf{12\tfrac{3}{4} \text{ in.}} \text{ (approximately)}$$

EXAMPLE 3

If $a = 17.321''$ and $b = 10''$, find $\angle A$.

Solution. $\tan A = \dfrac{a}{b}$

$$\tan A = \frac{17.321}{10}$$

$$\tan A = 1.7321$$

$$\angle A = \mathbf{60°}$$

EXERCISES

Draw a standard right triangle for each exercise.

Use the tables on page 363 to solve these exercises.

A

1. Find a if $\angle A = 27°$ and $c = 30'$.
2. Find b if $\angle A = 45°$ and $a = 10$ cm.
3. Find b if $\angle A = 60°$ and $a = 20$ mi.
4. Find $\angle A$ if $a = 10$ and $c = 20$.
5. Find $\angle A$ if $a = 348.74$ and $b = 100$.
6. Find a if $\angle B = 20°$ and $c = 20'$. (Hint. $\angle B$ is the complement of $\angle A$. $\angle A = 90° - \angle B$.)

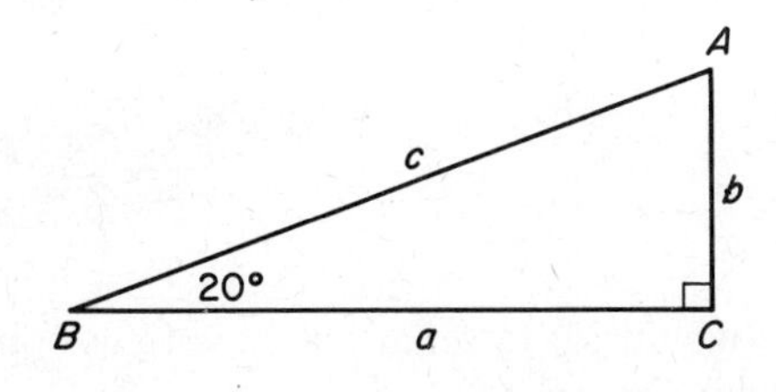

7. Find the height of the school building if the angle of elevation is 24° and the horizontal distance from the building is 100 ft.

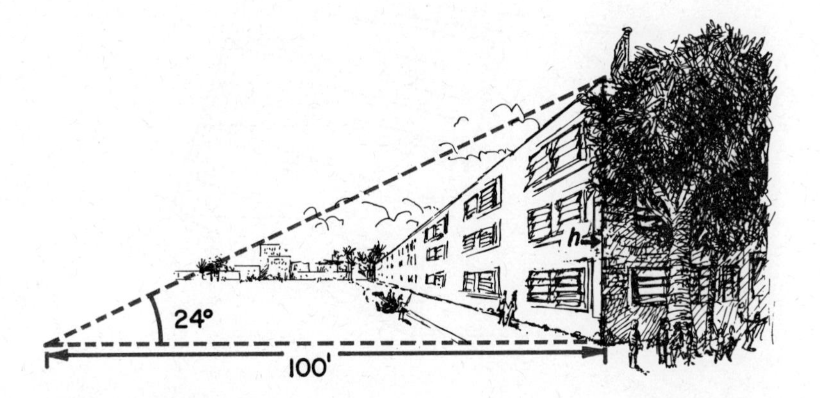

8. Find $\angle ADE$ in this wedge if $AB = 3$ in., $BC = 10$ in., and $DC = .321$ in.

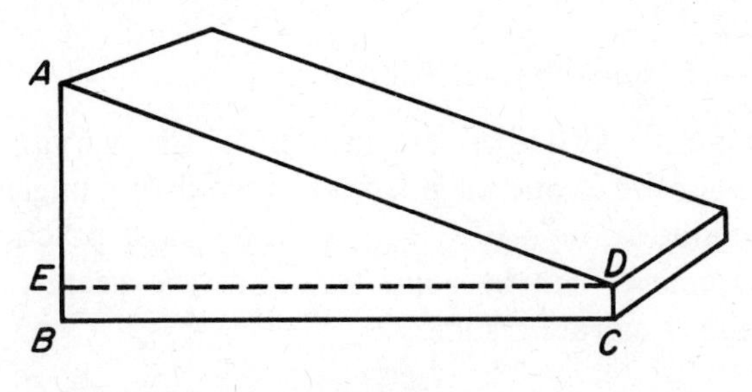

9. From one bank of a river, the angle of elevation to the top of a cliff rising vertically from the opposite bank is 39°. The cliff is known to be 135 ft. high. Find the width of the river.

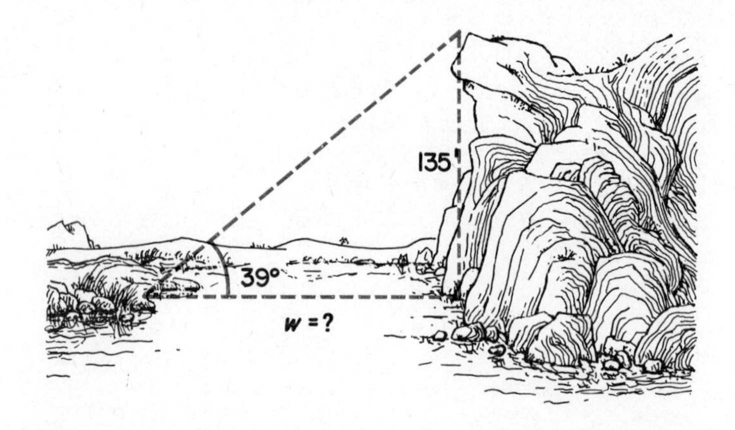

10. Find the angle (within 1°) to set a table saw to cut out the sides of the cabinet in the figure below. Be sure measurements are in the same units.

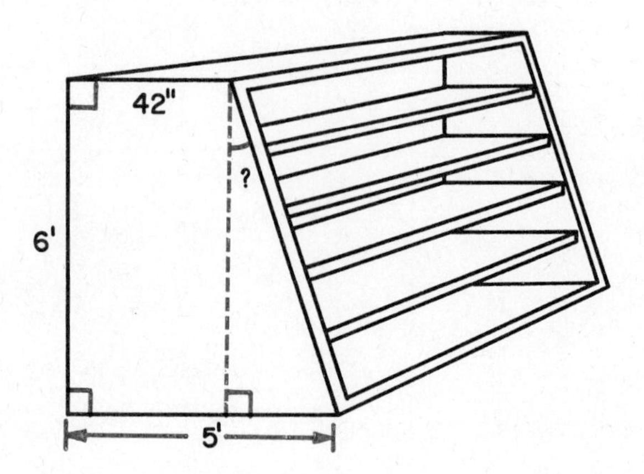

10–7 Other Trigonometric Tables

Trigonometric tables are available for varying degrees of accuracy. Opposite is one page from a table listing angles at intervals of 10′ (10 minutes), or $\frac{1}{6}$ of a degree. For most practical purposes, angle measurements can be rounded off to the nearest 10′ and still give sufficiently accurate results. TM p. 20 , 10-7

Values of Trigonometric Ratios

Angle	Sin	Cos	Tan	
27° 00′	.4540	.8910	.5095	63° 00′
10′	.4566	.8897	.5132	50′
20′	.4592	.8884	.5169	40′
30′	.4617	.8870	.5206	30′
40′	.4643	.8857	.5243	20′
50′	.4669	.8843	.5280	10′
28° 00′	.4695	.8829	.5317	62° 00′
10′	.4720	.8816	.5354	50′
20′	.4746	.8802	.5392	40′
30′	.4772	.8788	.5430	30′
40′	.4797	.8774	.5467	20′
50′	.4823	.8760	.5505	10′
29° 00′	.4848	.8746	.5543	61° 00′
10′	.4874	.8732	.5581	50′
20′	.4899	.8718	.5619	40′
30′	.4924	.8704	.5658	30′
40′	.4950	.8689	.5696	20′
50′	.4975	.8675	.5735	10′
30° 00′	.5000	.8660	.5774	60° 00′
10′	.5025	.8646	.5812	50′
20′	.5050	.8631	.5851	40′
30′	.5075	.8616	.5890	30′
40′	.5100	.8601	.5930	20′
50′	.5125	.8587	.5969	10′
31° 00′	.5150	.8572	.6009	59° 00′
10′	.5175	.8557	.6048	50′
20′	.5200	.8542	.6088	40′
30′	.5225	.8526	.6128	30′
40′	.5250	.8511	.6168	20′
50′	.5275	.8496	.6208	10′
32° 00′	.5299	.8480	.6249	58° 00′
10′	.5324	.8465	.6289	50′
20′	.5348	.8450	.6330	40′
30′	.5373	.8434	.6371	30′
40′	.5398	.8418	.6412	20′
50′	.5422	.8403	.6453	10′
33° 00′	.5446	.8387	.6494	57° 00′
10′	.5471	.8371	.6536	50′
20′	.5495	.8355	.6577	40′
30′	.5519	.8339	.6619	30′
40′	.5544	.8323	.6661	20′
50′	.5568	.8307	.6703	10′
34° 00′	.5592	.8290	.6745	56° 00′
10′	.5616	.8274	.6787	50′
20′	.5640	.8258	.6830	40′
30′	.5664	.8241	.6873	30′
40′	.5688	.8225	.6916	20′
50′	.5712	.8208	.6959	10′
35° 00′	.5736	.8192	.7002	55° 00′
10′	.5760	.8175	.7046	50′
20′	.5783	.8158	.7089	40′
30′	.5807	.8141	.7133	30′
40′	.5831	.8124	.7177	20′
50′	.5854	.8107	.7221	10′
36° 00′	.5878	.8090	.7265	54° 00′
	Cos	Sin		Angle

These examples illustrate the use of the table on page 369.

EXAMPLE 1

Find a, if $\angle A = 32°27'$ and $b = 8$ meters. Refer to the table on page 369.

Solution. $\tan A = \dfrac{a}{b}$

$$a = b \tan A$$

To the nearest $10'$, $\angle A = 32°30'$.
$a = 8 \times \tan 32°30'$
Locate $32°30'$ in the first column of the table and follow across the row to .6371 in the column headed "Tan."
$a = 8 \times .6371$
$a = 5.0968$ meters, or **5.1 meters** (approximately)

EXAMPLE 2

Using the diagram for Example 1, find $\angle A$ if $b = 11$ and $c = 12.9$.

Solution. $\cos A = \dfrac{11}{12.9}$

$\cos A = .8527$ (by division)
Locate the value in the "Cos" column nearest to .8527. This is .8526. Then follow the row to the first column, where you find $32°30'$.
$\angle A =$ **$32°30'$** (approximately)

Round all answers to the closest value in the table on page 369.

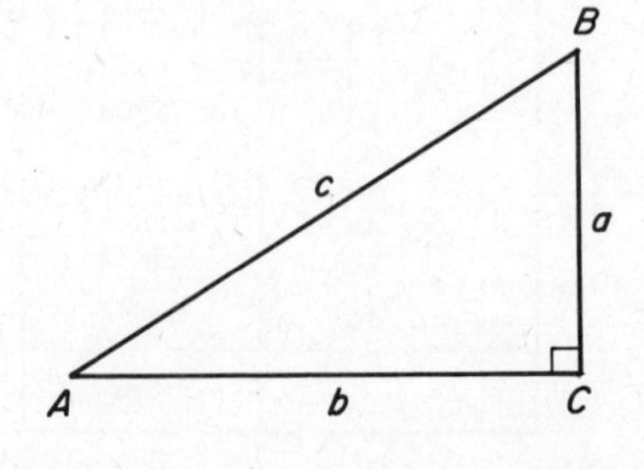

A

1. Find b if $c = 10$ and $\angle A = 27°26'$.
2. Find c if $a = 100$ and $\angle A = 28°18'$.
3. Find $\angle A$ if $a = 5$ and $b = 8$.
4. Find $\angle B$ if $b = 11$ and $c = 20$.

B 5. Find a if $c = 18$ and $\angle A = 57°2'$.
Hint. Find $57°00'$ in the right-hand column, page 369, and follow across to the column having the desired name at the *foot*.

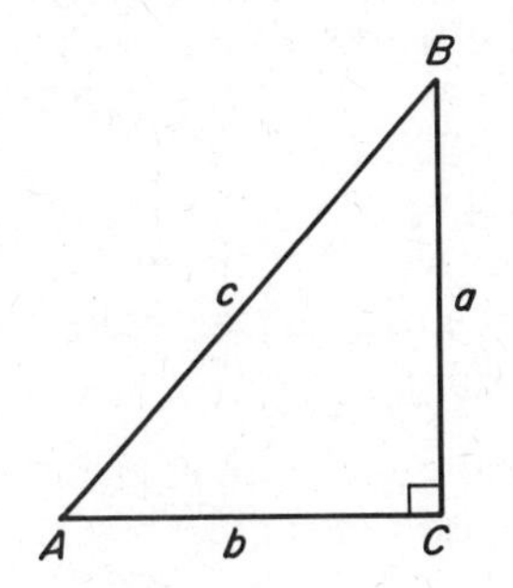

6. Find the pitch angles of the roof of the house.

$\angle x =$ ___?___
$\angle y =$ ___?___

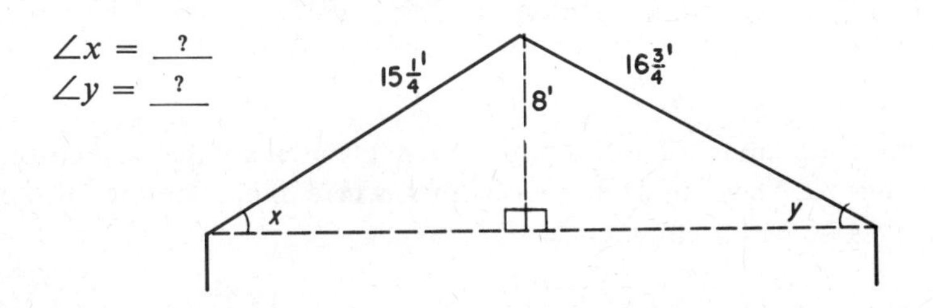

SELF-ANALYSIS TEST IV

Time: 40 minutes

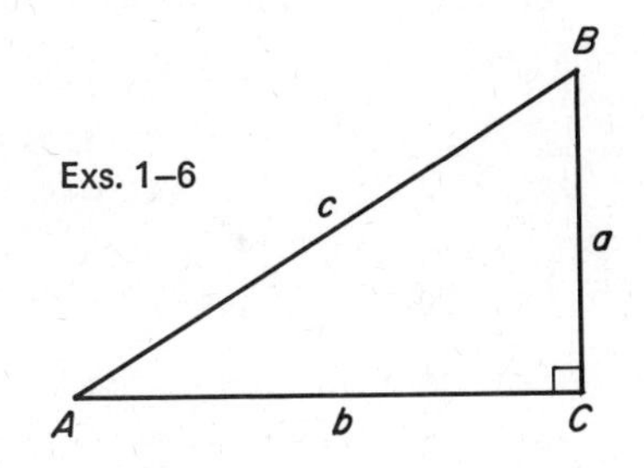

1. Find a if $\angle A = 35°$ and $c = 10$ ft.
2. Find b if $\angle A = 55°$ and $a = 20$ cm.
3. Find c if $\angle A = 80°$ and $a = 30$ mi.
4. Find $\angle A$ if $a = 25$ ft. and $c = 50$ ft.
5. Find $\angle A$ if $a = 4$ in. and $b = 4$ in.
6. Find $\angle A$ if $a = 7$ and $b = 7\sqrt{3}$.
7. Find the height of the building shown below.

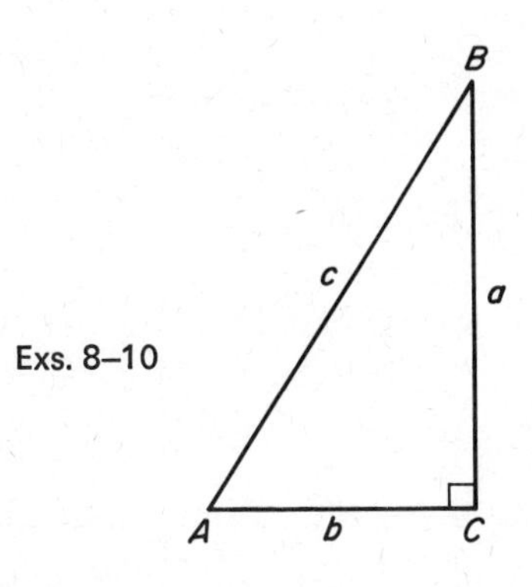

8. Find a if $c = 20$ ft. and $\angle A = 27°4'$.
9. Find c if $a = 1000$ ft. and $\angle A = 62°27'$.
10. Find $\angle A$ if $a = 12$ ft. and $b = 17$ ft.

CHAPTER SUMMARY

1. The Rule of Pythagoras states that the square of the length of the hypotenuse is equal to the sum of the squares of the lengths of the other two sides.

2. The altitude of an equilateral triangle is equal to one half the length of the base times $\sqrt{3}$.

3. In a 30°-60° right triangle,
   a. The measure of the side opposite the 30° angle is equal to one half the measure of the hypotenuse.
   b. The measure of the side opposite the 60° angle is equal to the measure of the side opposite the 30° angle times $\sqrt{3}$.

4. The three trigonometric ratios most commonly used are the sine, cosine, and tangent. They are defined as follows, where a, b, c are the sides of triangle ABC with right angle at C:

$$\sin A = \frac{a}{c}\,;\ \cos A = \frac{b}{c}\,;\ \tan A = \frac{a}{b}$$

5. The use of trigonometric ratios allows us to find measurements indirectly.

CHAPTER TEST

1. Find c.

2. Find b.

3. Find a.

4. Find c.

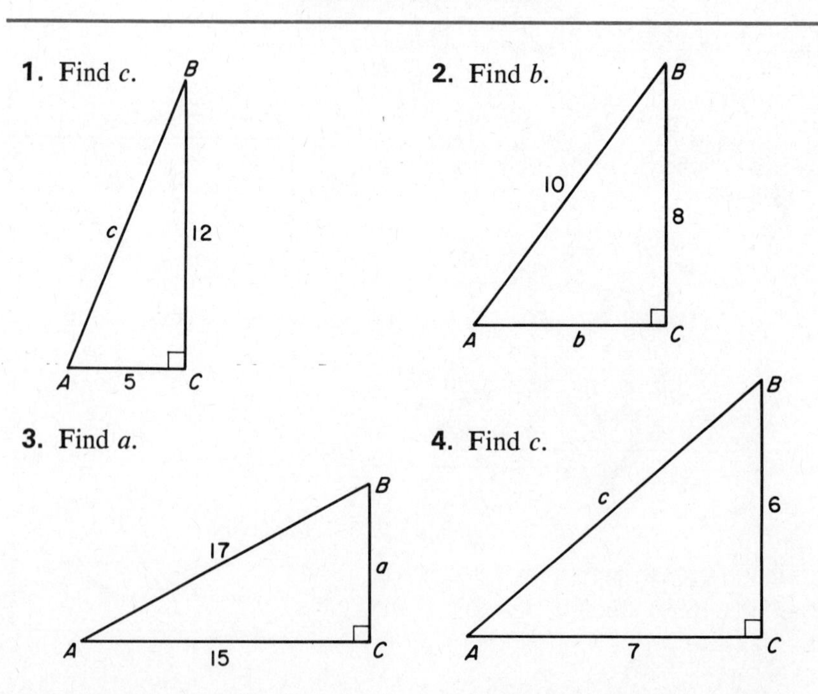

5. Find c.

6. Find d.

7. Find c.

8. Find b.

9. Find a.

10. Find a and c.

11. Find the area of this isosceles trapezoid. $[A = \frac{1}{2}h(b_1 + b_2)]$

12. Find the volume of this rectangular prism. $(V = Bh)$

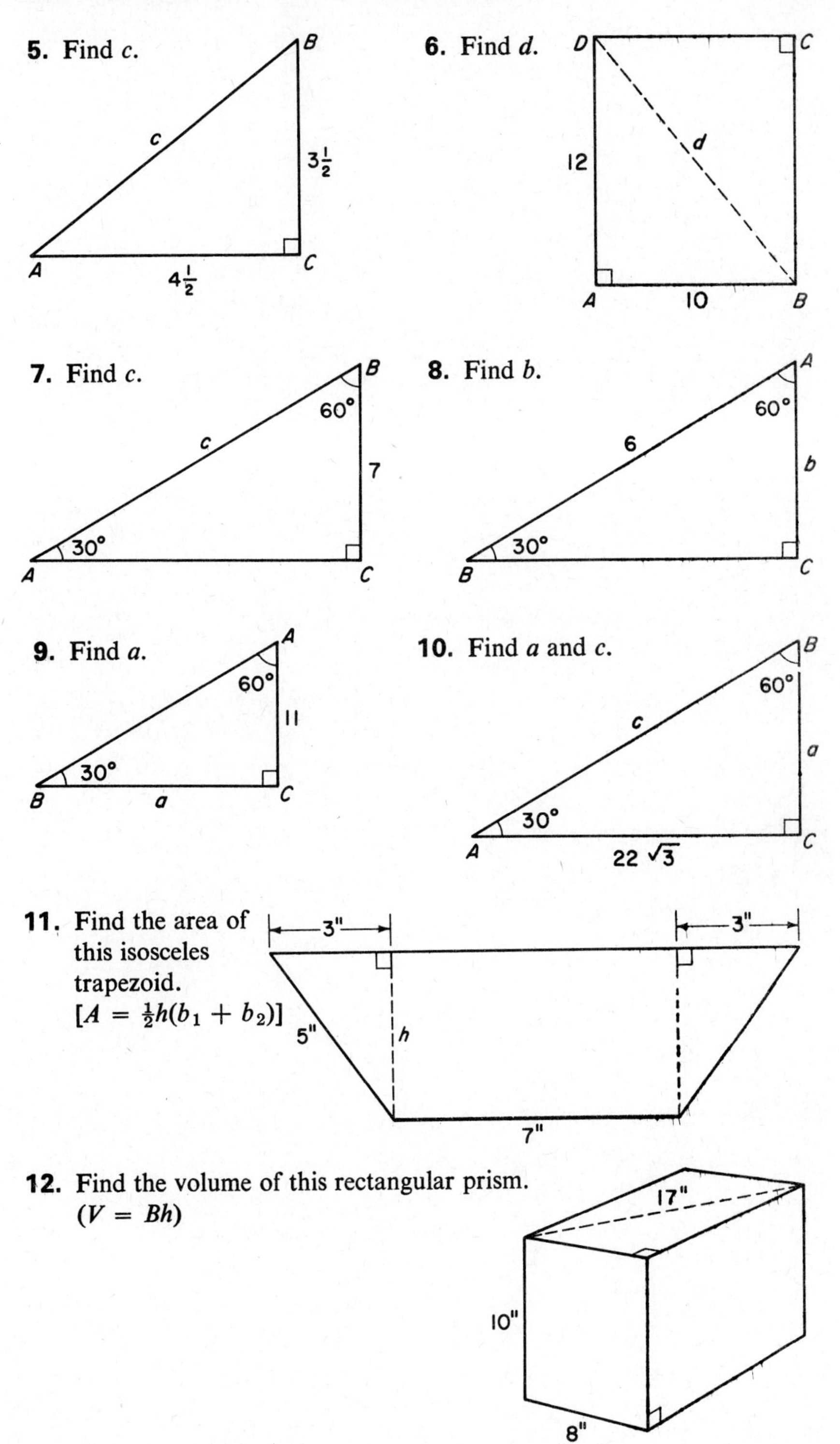

13. Find the total area of the patio described below.
(Area of a rectangle $= lw$)
(Area of a triangle $= \frac{1}{2}bh$)

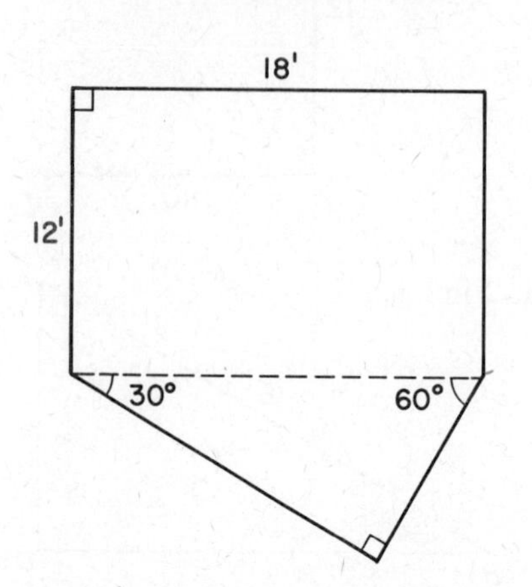

14. Find the volume of the triangular wedge.

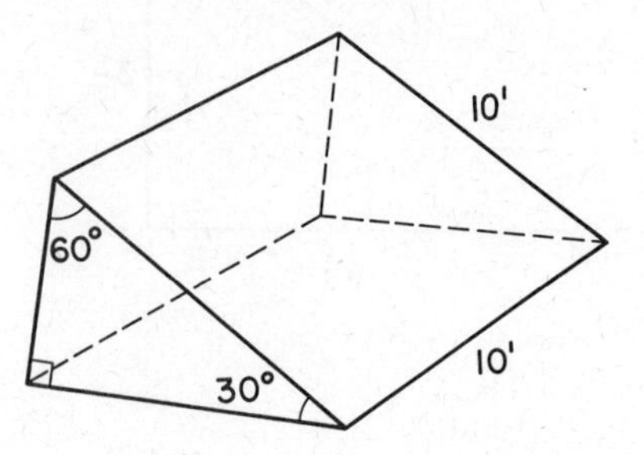

In the following exercises, select the proper formula to solve the problem. Use the tables on pages 363 and 369 as needed.

15. a. $\sin 29° =$ __?__
b. $\tan 35°50' =$ __?__

16. a. $\cos A = .8090$; $\angle A =$ __?__
b. $\tan B = .6009$; $\angle B =$ __?__

17. Find a.

18. Find $\angle A$.

19. Find a if $c = 25$ ft. and $\angle A = 33°23'$.

20. Find $\angle A$, if $a = 500$ ft. and $b = 800$ ft.

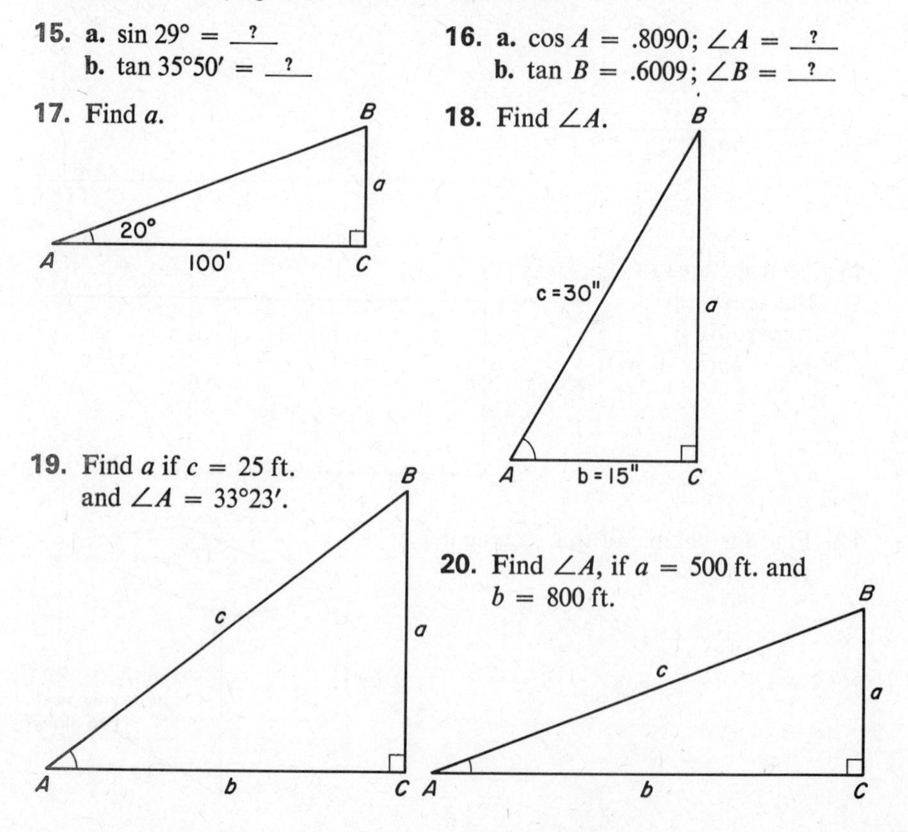

MAINTAINING YOUR SKILLS

Add.

1. $\begin{array}{r} 36 \\ 48 \\ +\ 61 \\ \hline \end{array}$

2. $\begin{array}{r} 91 \\ 78 \\ 56 \\ +\ 34 \\ \hline \end{array}$

3. $\begin{array}{r} 151 \\ 262 \\ +\ 358 \\ \hline \end{array}$

4. $\begin{array}{r} 33{,}425 \\ 6{,}789 \\ 7{,}204 \\ +\ 11{,}703 \\ \hline \end{array}$

5. $42\frac{3}{4} + 61\frac{1}{2} + 33\frac{1}{4}$

6. $843.52 + 768.69$

Subtract.

7. $\begin{array}{r} 74 \\ -\ 47 \\ \hline \end{array}$

8. $\begin{array}{r} 672 \\ -\ 385 \\ \hline \end{array}$

9. $\begin{array}{r} 52.43 \\ -\ 28.75 \\ \hline \end{array}$

10. $\begin{array}{r} 81{,}810 \\ -\ 76{,}769 \\ \hline \end{array}$

11. $\begin{array}{r} 87.52 \\ -\ 59.09 \\ \hline \end{array}$

12. $\begin{array}{r} 33{,}224 \\ -\ 8{,}567 \\ \hline \end{array}$

Multiply.

13. 68×35

14. 324×66

15. 46.05×2.82

16. $.482 \times .313$

17. 606×33.4

18. 62.8×404

Divide.

19. $15\overline{)825}$

20. $25\overline{)19375}$

21. $9.2\overline{)58.512}$

22. $.95\overline{)76.3}$

23. $1\frac{3}{5} \div \frac{3}{4}$

24. $(\frac{7}{8} + \frac{9}{16}) \div \frac{1}{7}$

Simplify.

25. $\sqrt{25}$

26. $\sqrt{81}$

27. $\sqrt{121}$

28. $\sqrt{225}$

29. $\sqrt{11}$

30. $\sqrt{27}$

The graph shows vividly the rise in population of Los Angeles — from about 100 thousand at the turn of the century to about 3 million today. In the background may be seen Dodgers Stadium.

Statistical Tables and Graphs

OBJECTIVES

1. To learn about frequency tables and different kinds of graphs.

2. To learn how to interpret the information presented in tables and graphs.

3. To learn how to draw several kinds of graphs.

Many businesses rely heavily on the use of statistical tables and graphs as a means of recording important information. In this chapter you will learn how to read and interpret frequency tables and statistical graphs like those used in industry. You will also have an opportunity to draw some graphs.

■ Statistical Tables and Pictographs

11–1 Interpreting Tables of Data

Business and industry often use tables of information like the one below.

Accidents among 1000 Employees of the Regal Textiles Company during Last Year

Number of Accidents per Worker	1	2	3	4	5	6	7
Number of Workers	96	44	16	8	1	3	1

To make this table someone had to collect a vast number of individual facts, or **data**, and organize them into sets. Such a table is called a **frequency chart** because it shows how often the two sets of facts are related. What pattern in the frequency of accidents per worker do you notice by glancing at the table? The number of workers involved in subsequent accidents decreases sharply as the number of accidents increases.

Usually when working with frequency charts you are required either to find a specific fact shown in the table, or to interpret the given data by means of ratios and percents. Study the following example.

EXAMPLE

a. How many workers, according to the table, had 6 accidents during the year?

b. What percent of the workers had 6 accidents?

c. What is the ratio of those who had 1 accident to those who had 6 or more accidents?

Solution. **a.** 3 workers had 6 accidents.

b. The total number of workers was 1000. Therefore,

$$\frac{3}{1000} = .003 = \frac{.3}{100}$$

Refer to percent, page 318.

$$= .3 \text{ of } 1\%, \text{ or } \mathbf{.3\%}.$$

c.

$$\frac{\text{Workers having 1 accident}}{\text{Workers having 6 or more accidents}} = \frac{96}{4}$$

$$= \frac{24}{1} \text{ or } \mathbf{24:1}$$

EXERCISES

Use the table on the facing page to answer the following questions.

A

1. How many accidents occurred in the entire year?
2. How many workers had no accidents?
3. What percent of the workers had 1 accident?
4. What percent of the workers had 4 accidents?
5. What percent of the workers had 2 or more accidents?
6. What is the ratio of those who had accidents to the total of all employees?

11–2 Pictographs

One kind of graph often found in newspapers and magazines is the **pictograph**. A pictograph uses pictures or symbols to represent the data in a table. The following pictograph is based on the frequency chart you studied above. What advantages and disadvantages can you see in using the pictograph to show data?

Number of Accidents per Worker

1
2
3
4
5
6
7

Compare this pictograph with the table on page 378. They both represent the same information. Note that, since each symbol represents 5 people, one person is indicated by $\frac{1}{5}$ of a symbol, 2 by $\frac{2}{5}$ of a symbol, and so on.

= 5 Workers

Accidents among 1000 Employees of the Regal Textiles Company during Last Year

EXERCISES

Use the pictograph above to answer the following questions.

A

1. How many workers had an accident during the year?

2. Of the total number of employees, how many workers had 2 accidents or fewer? (Refer to pictograph on page 379.)
3. Of those who had accidents, what percent had 2 accidents or fewer?
4. What is the ratio of those who had 4 or more accidents to the total number of employees?
5. What percent of the total number of employees had at least one accident?

Exercises 6–10 refer to the pictograph below.

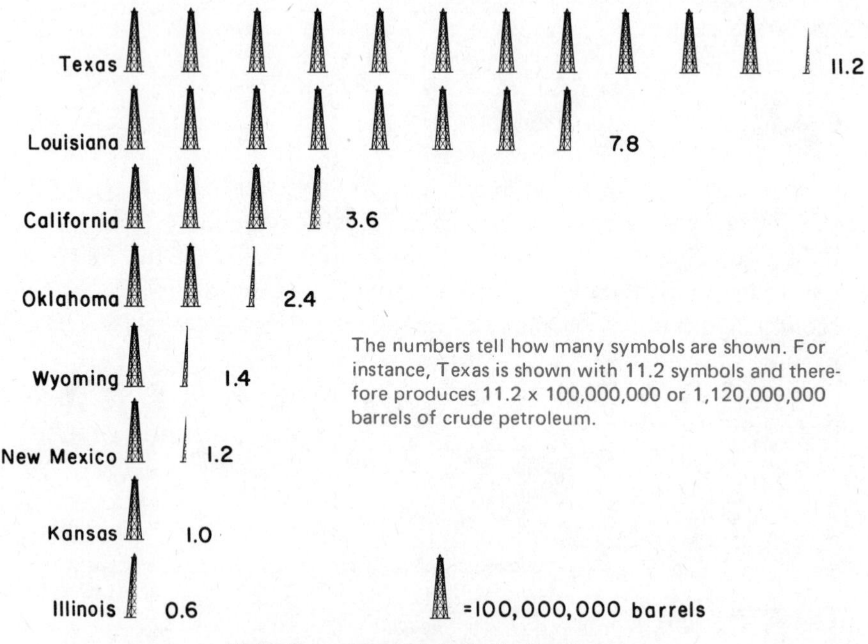

Major States Producing Crude Petroleum

6. How much crude petroleum was produced in Louisiana? in Illinois?
7. How much more petroleum was produced in Oklahoma than in Kansas?
8. What was the combined production of the 3 leading states?
9. What is the ratio of petroleum production in New Mexico to that in California?

B 10. What percent of the crude petroleum produced in the states listed is from Texas?

SELF-ANALYSIS TEST I

Time: 15 minutes

Exercises 1–4 refer to the frequency chart at the top of the next page.

1. How many workers were ill at least one day during the year?
2. How many employees were ill 3 or more days?
3. What percent of the total number of workers were ill 4 days?

Sick Days for 1200 Employees of the Shopcraft Tool Company during Last Year

Sick days	1	2	3	4	6	8	10
Number of Workers	480	270	80	90	12	2	4

4. What is the ratio of those who were absent at least one day to the total number of employees?

In Exercises 5–7, use the pictograph below.

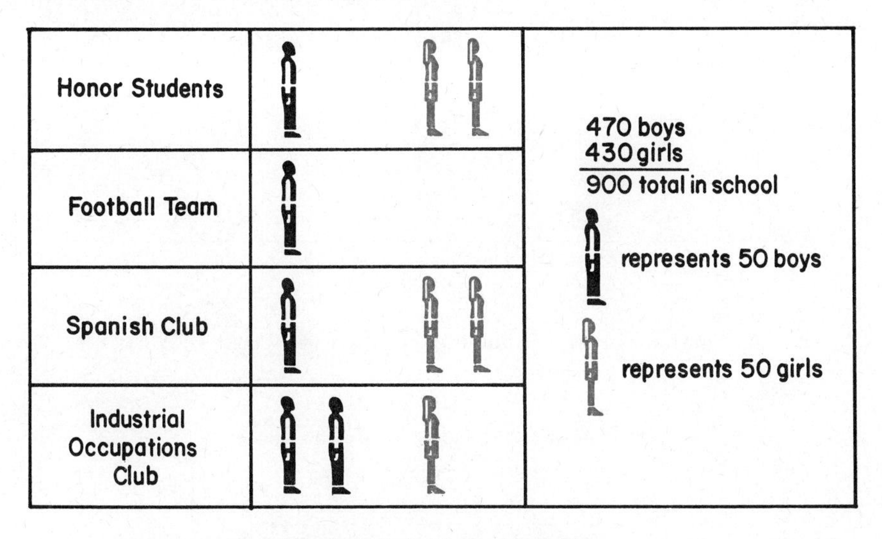

Membership in Student Activities

5. How many students are on the honor roll? How many boys? How many girls?
6. What is the ratio of the number of students in the Industrial Occupations Club to the total enrollment in the school?
7. What is the ratio of the number of students on the football team to the number of students in the Spanish Club?
8. What percent of the total enrollment are members of clubs?

Bar Graphs and Broken-Line Graphs

11–3 Bar Graphs

It is just a short step from a pictograph to a bar graph. Instead of a symbol to represent a number of units, we use a *scale*, beginning at zero and marked off in equal units, as on a ruler. The bar graph which follows is based on the table on page 378. Notice that each division represents 5 workers.

This is a third way to indicate the same information.

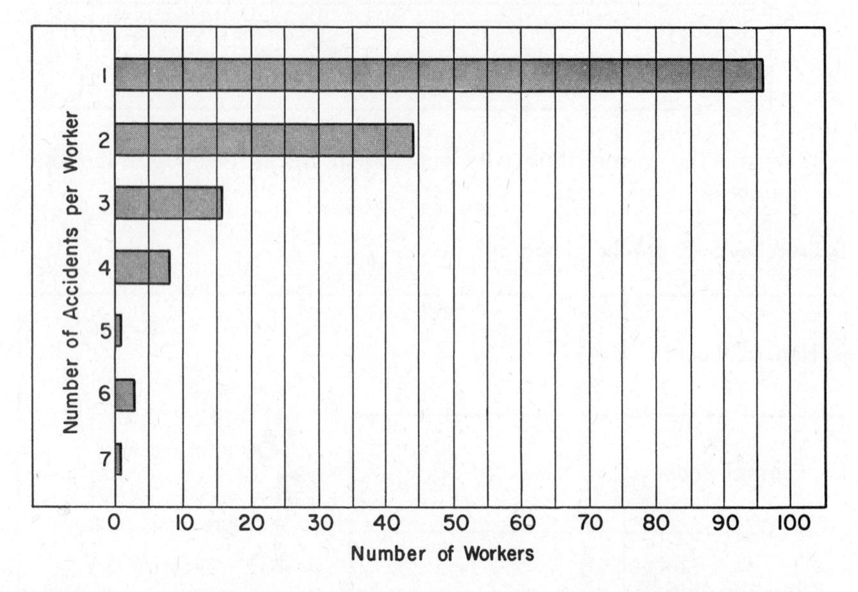

The bars may be drawn either horizontally as above, or vertically as in the graph below. Discuss how the following graph shows two sets of data.

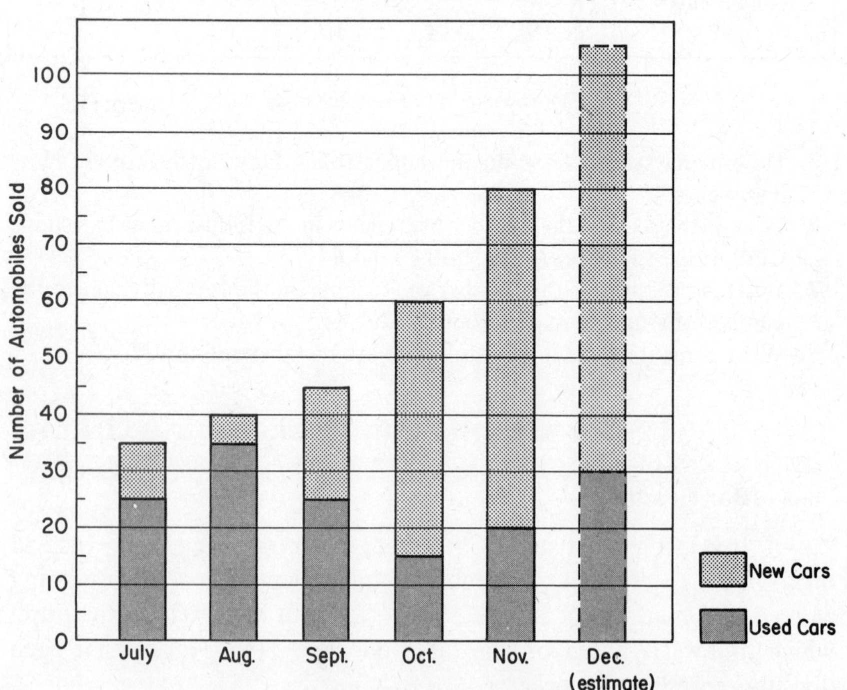

Notice that data concerning both used-car sales and new-car sales can be shown clearly on the same graph. On any bar graph it is important to have the bars begin at zero so that their lengths give a true picture of the data recorded. TM p. 21 , 11-3

EXERCISES

Exercises 1–6 refer to the bar graph at the foot of the facing page.

A

1. In which month did the sale of new cars first exceed the sale of used cars? By how many cars?
2. What percent of the cars sold in August were new cars?
3. What is the ratio of new cars sold to used cars sold in July? In November?
4. What percent of the estimated sales in December will be new cars?
5. What is the ratio of new car sales in August to new car sales in November?
6. If the profit on the sale of a new car averages $450 and on a used car $250, how much profit did the Phillips Agency make in the period from July to November?

Exercises 7–10 refer to the bar graph below.

Stopping Distances for Trucks and Autos

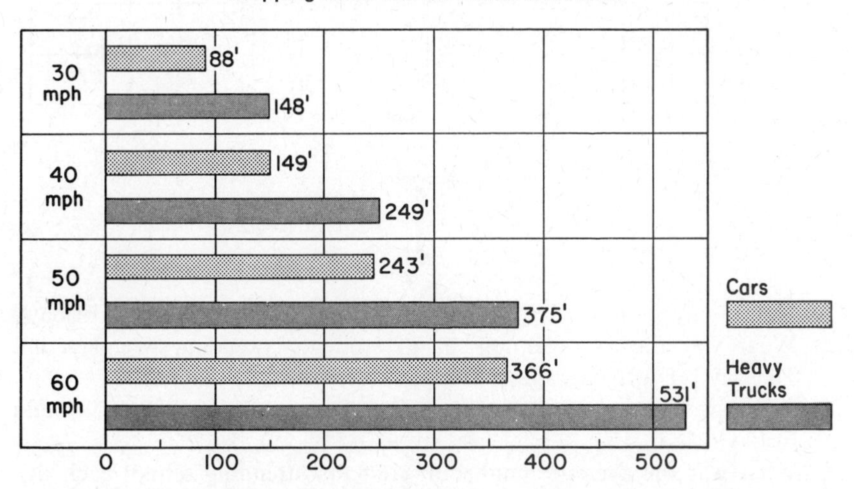

7. How much less distance is needed to stop a car traveling 50 mph than for a heavy truck going 40 mph?
8. At 30 mph what is the ratio of the stopping distance for a truck to that of a car?

9. What percent of the stopping distance for a truck traveling at 50 mph is needed to bring a car to a stop if it is going 50 mph?

10. At 60 mph a vehicle is traveling 88 ft. per second. How many seconds does it take to stop a car traveling at that speed? A truck at that speed?

You may wish to provide interested students with actual data to make this graph.

ACTIVITY: ***Making a Bar Graph of School Attendance.***

Purpose: To picture school attendance by a bar graph.

Plan: On a sheet of paper, copy and complete the bar graph below, using the given data. If you have squared paper available, you may use it.

Data: Number in attendance each day: Monday, 1450; Tuesday, 1500; Wednesday, 1520; Thursday, 1400; and Friday, 1370.

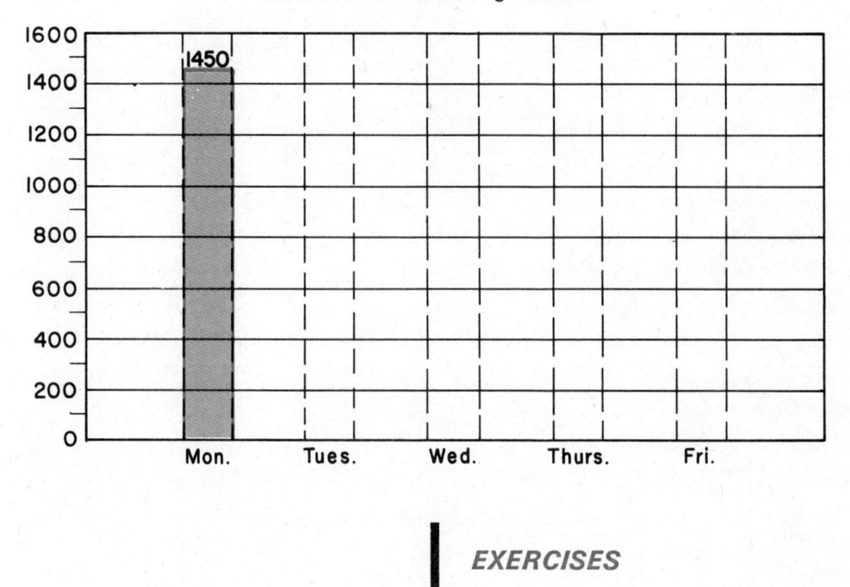

EXERCISES

A

1. How many more students were present on Monday than on Friday?

2. What was the average number of students attending Monday and Tuesday? Hint: Average = no. of students ÷ no. of days.

3. What was the average number of students attending Thursday and Friday?

4. What was the average number of students attending school each day during the week?

5. Look up data on games won by each team in the National League last season and present the figures in a table. Then draw a bar graph based on the table. You may use an almanac to obtain the required information.

11–4 Broken-Line Graphs

If you were to join the tops of the bars in a vertical bar graph by line segments, as suggested below, you would then have drawn a broken-line graph. Of course, you do not ordinarily draw the bars, but simply show their endpoints.

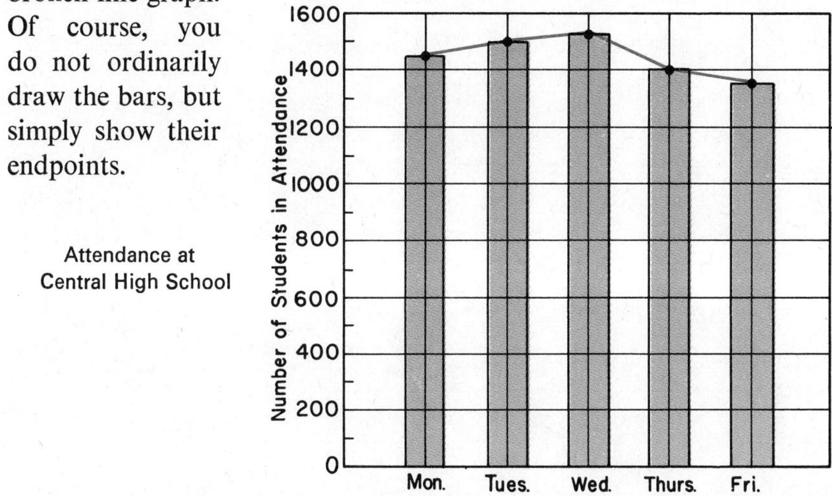

Attendance at Central High School

A broken-line graph is generally used when we want to show the *change* from one point to another. In cases where the change from point to point is very great or very small, it may be difficult to make precise readings from the graph. You may, therefore, wish to revise the scale of the entire graph or of a portion of the graph. In the figure below notice how the break in the scale is indicated by the jagged line.

Point out the advantages of changing the scale in this graph.

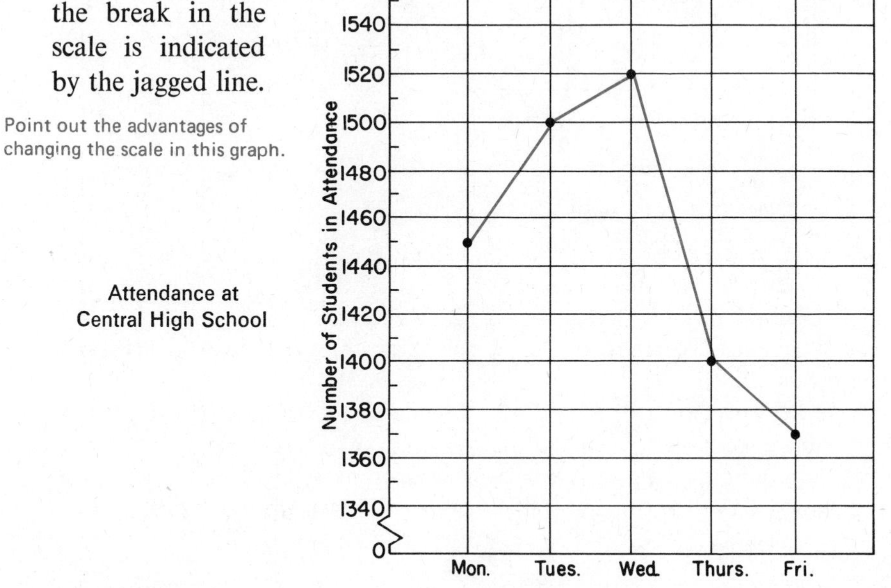

Attendance at Central High School

EXERCISES

For Exercises 1–5 refer to the graph at the foot of the preceding page.

A

1. If the total enrollment at Central High School is 1550 students, what percent were in attendance on Thursday?
2. What is the ratio of those present on Tuesday to those present on Thursday?
3. What percent of the enrollment were absent on Friday?
4. What is the ratio of the number of students present on Tuesday to the number absent?
5. What was the average number of students absent during the week? Recall: Average = total no. absent ÷ no. of days.

For Exercises 6–10 use the graph below.

This graph indicates 3 sets of data.

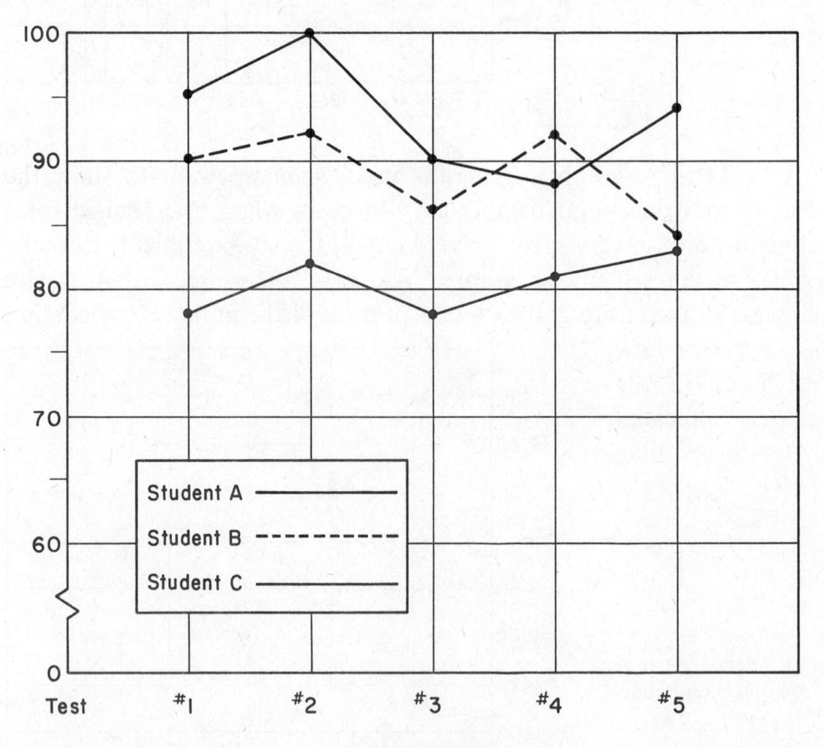

Math Test Scores

6. Which student received the highest score on Test #3?
7. List the 5 scores for Student A.
8. What is the sum of the points scored by Student C on Tests #1, #4, and #5?

9. What was the average score for Student B on Tests #1, #2, and #3?

10. What was the average test score for Students A, B, and C on all five tests?

SELF-ANALYSIS TEST II

Time: 20 minutes

For Exercises 1–3 copy and complete the bar graph from the given data.

Data:

Monday—200 bars sold

1. Tuesday—150 bars sold

2. Wednesday—75 bars sold

3. Thursday—250 bars sold

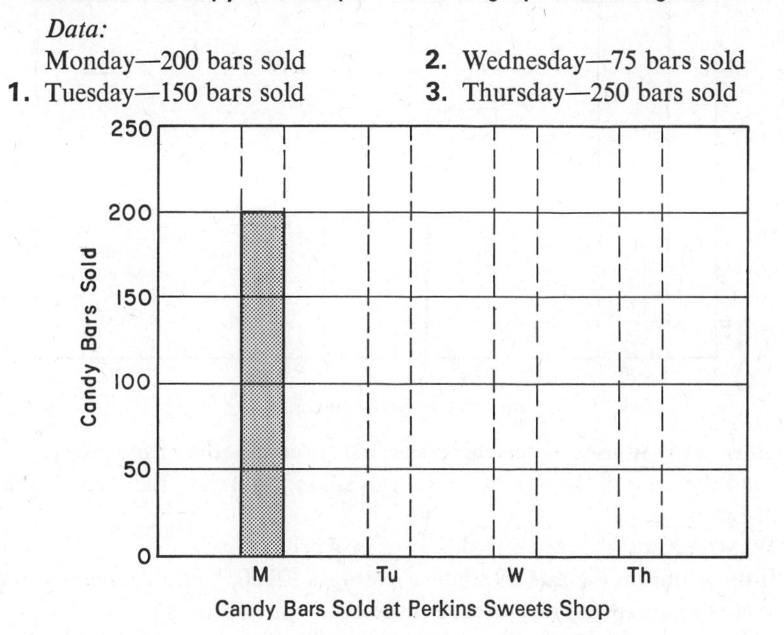

Candy Bars Sold at Perkins Sweets Shop

For Exercises 4–6 copy and complete the line graph from the given data.

Data:

1st week—87°

4. 2d week—78°

5. 3d week—80°

6. 4th week—83°

Temperature Record for August

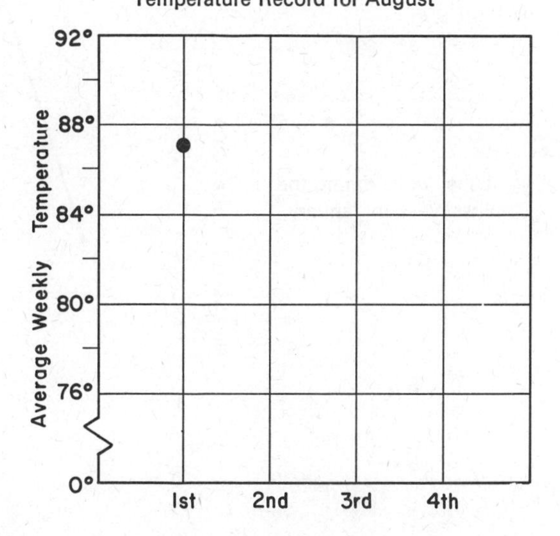

For Exercises 7–10 use the bar graph below.

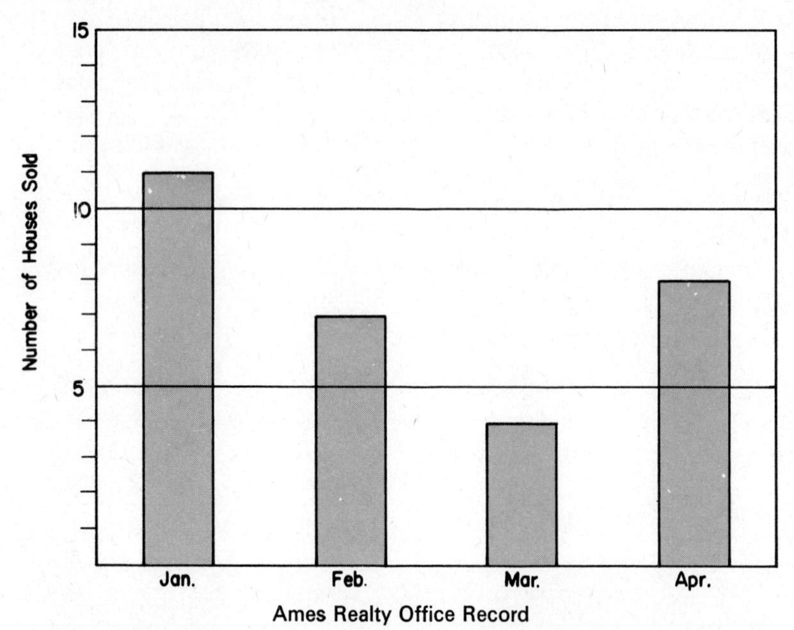

Ames Realty Office Record

7. How many houses were sold in the first three months of the year?

8. Find the ratio of the number of houses sold in March to the number sold in January.

9. What percent of the total sales were in April?

10. If the profit on the sale of a house averages \$2700, by how much did the profits made in January exceed those made in February?

Exercises 11–15 refer to the broken-line graph at the right.

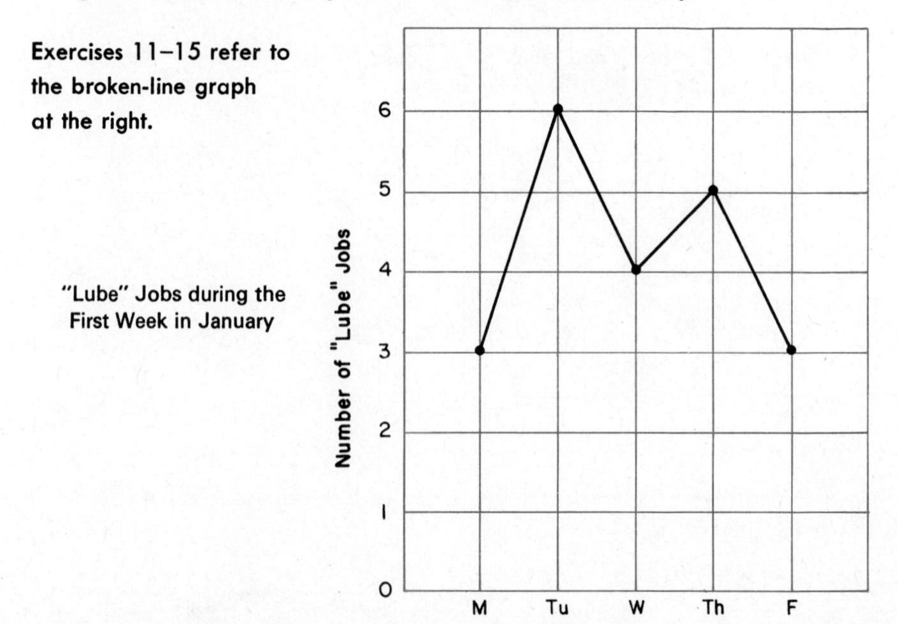

"Lube" Jobs during the First Week in January

11. How many "lube" jobs were done on Wednesday?
12. What was the total number of "lube" jobs done for the week?
13. What percent of the number of "lube" jobs were done on Tuesday?
14. What was the ratio of the number of "lube" jobs done on Friday to the number done on Tuesday?
15. If the charge for a "lube" job is $2.75, how much money did the mechanic take in for "lube" jobs during the week?

Circle Graphs

11–5 Circle Graphs

Here is a different kind of graph, called a **circle graph.** We generally use a circle graph to show a part-by-part breakdown of a whole, as in the figures below.

The percent of the whole allowed for each item is indicated by that fractional portion of the circle.

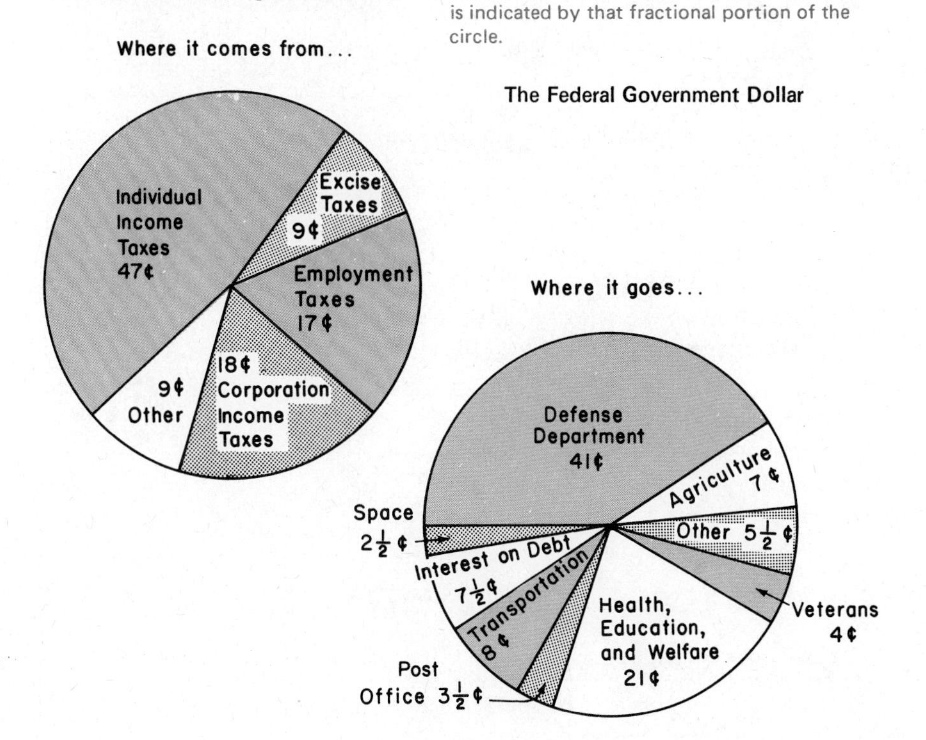

EXAMPLE

What percent of the Federal Government dollar comes from individual income taxes?

Solution. Individual income taxes = 47¢ = .47 or **47%**

EXERCISES

Use the circle graphs on page 389 to solve Exercises 1–6.

A

1. What percent of the government dollar is spent on national defense?
2. What percent of the government dollar comes from corporation income taxes, employment taxes, and excise taxes?
3. What is the ratio of the amount of money spent on agriculture to that spent on health, education, and welfare?
4. What is the ratio of the amount of money received from corporation income taxes to that received from individual income taxes and other sources?
5. What is the ratio of the amount of individual income taxes to the cost for national defense?
6. If the amount spent for transportation is 16 billion dollars, how large is the entire Federal budget? Hint: Use the proportion $\frac{8\%}{\$16 \text{ billion}} = \frac{100\%}{x}$.

A young man found that his yearly car expenses were $1275, divided as shown in the graph below.

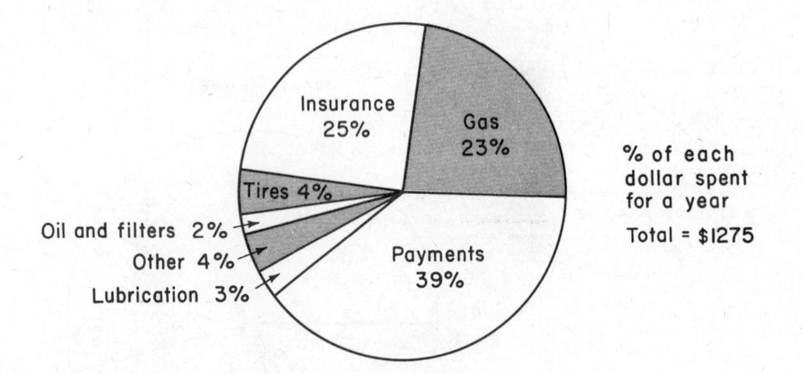

Cost of Operating a Car for One Year

7. What percent of his annual expenses was for insurance?
8. How much money did he spend for insurance for the year?
9. How much did he spend for gas?
10. What is the ratio of the amount of money spent for oil, filters, and lubrication to the amount spent for gas?
11. How much money was spent for tires?
12. What are his monthly payments on the car?

SELF-ANALYSIS TEST III
Time: 7 minutes

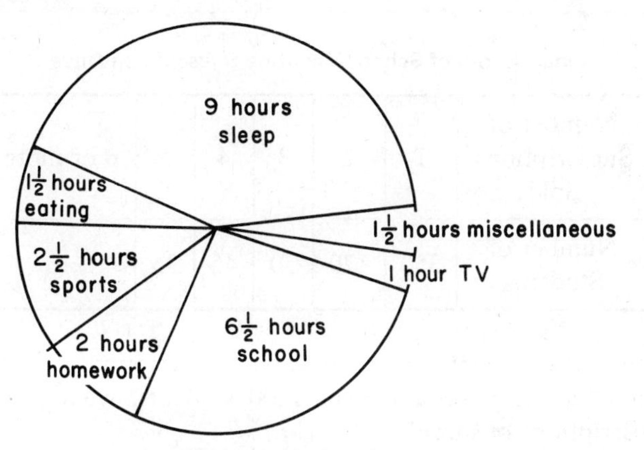

How One Student Spends His Day

Exercises 1–5 refer to the circle graph above.

1. How many hours are spent in school and in doing homework?
2. What is the ratio of the amount of time spent in studying to the amount of time spent in school?
3. What percent of the time is spent in sleeping?
4. What is the ratio of the amount of time spent eating to the amount of time spent for sports and viewing television?
5. What percent of the typical day is spent in school?

CHAPTER SUMMARY

1. A frequency chart is used to show how two sets of facts, or data, are related.

2. A pictograph uses symbols or pictures to represent data.

3. A bar graph presents data by means of a scale, beginning at zero and marked off in equal units. Bar graphs may be drawn either horizontally or vertically.

4. A broken-line graph uses line segments to show the change from one point to another.

5. A circle graph is used to show the breakdown of the parts in a whole.

CHAPTER TEST

Final Record of School Magazine Subscription Drive

Number of Subscriptions Sold	1	2	3	4	5	6 or more
Number of Students	350	170	70	45	35	10

1. **a.** How many students sold at least one subscription?
   b. Out of a total enrollment of 1200 students, what percent sold 4 subscriptions or more?
   c. Of those who sold subscriptions, what percent sold only 1 subscription?
   d. What is the ratio of those who sold 6 or more subscriptions to those selling only 1?

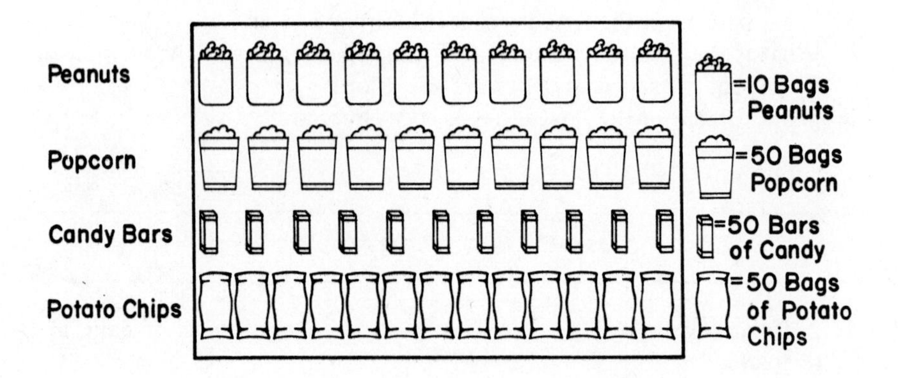

Corner Candy Store Sales for One Month

2. **a.** What is the total number of items sold in the candy store during the month?
   b. What is the ratio of the number of bags of peanuts sold to the number of bags of potato chips sold?
   c. What percent of the total number of items sold were bags of popcorn?
   d. If candy bars are 10¢ each, what was the total amount of their sales for the month?

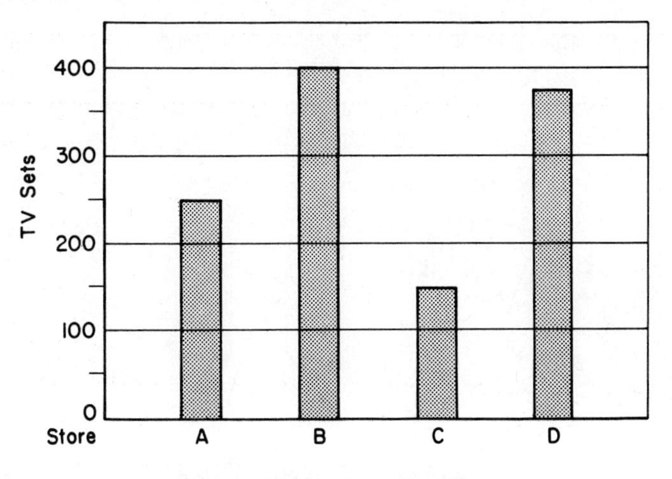

Sales of TV Sets during Last Year

3. **a.** What was the total number of TV sets sold?
   b. What is the ratio of the number of TV sets sold at Store B to the number of those sold at Store C?
   c. What percent of the total number of TV sets sold was sold by Store D?
   d. If the average profit on the sale of a TV set is $130, how much more profit did Store B make than Store A on the sale of TV sets during the year?

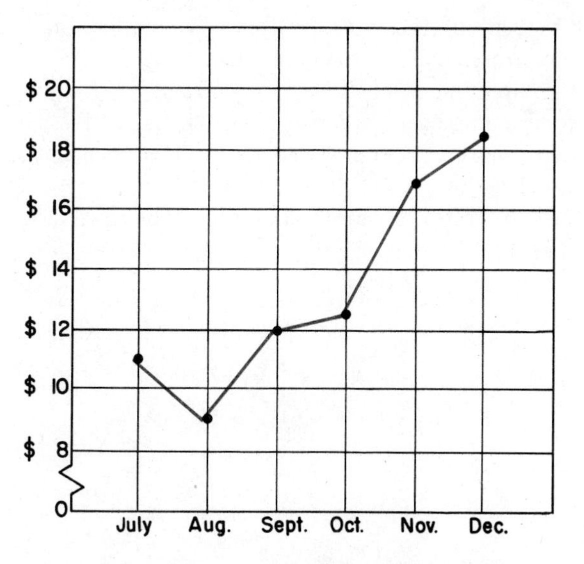

Electric Bills for the Second Half of the Year

4. **a.** How much was spent for electricity during the second half of the year?
   b. What percent of the total bill for the second half of the year was paid for service in September? (continued on next page)

c. What is the ratio of the amount paid for electricity in August to the amount paid in November?

d. What was the average monthly cost for electricity during the second half of the year? Which month's bill is closest to the average monthly cost?

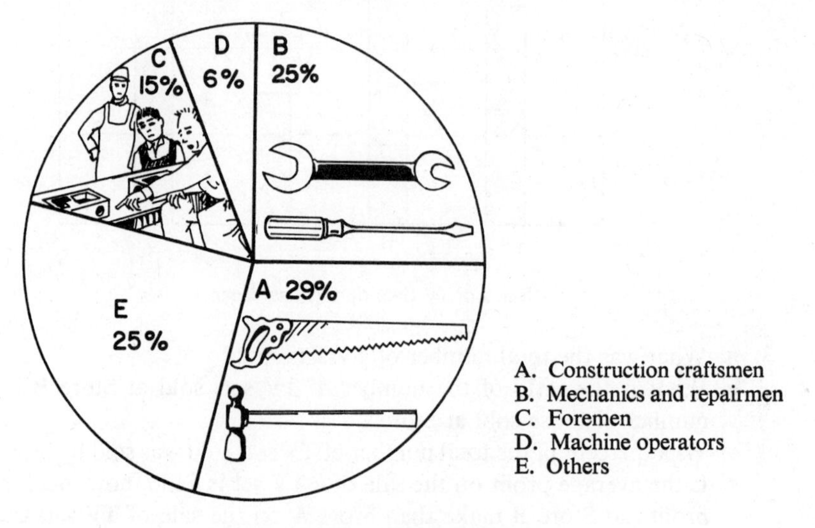

Skilled Workers in the United States

5. a. What percent of the working force is composed of construction craftsmen, foremen, and machine operators?

b. If the total number of skilled workers is 11 million, how many workers are employed as construction craftsmen?

c. How many workers are employed either as foremen and or as machine operators?

d. What is the ratio of mechanics and repairmen to construction craftsmen?

GLOSSARY

ACUTE ANGLE (p. 107): An angle having a measure between 0° and 90°.

ACUTE TRIANGLE (p. 114): A triangle in which each angle is less than 90°.

ALTIMETER (p. 56): An instrument used to measure altitudes.

ALTITUDE OF A CONE (p. 148): The line segment drawn from the vertex perpendicular to the plane of the base.

ALTITUDE OF A CYLINDER (p. 147): A line segment drawn perpendicular to the planes of the bases.

ALTITUDE OF A PARALLELOGRAM (p. 158): A line segment drawn from one side perpendicular to the line containing the opposite side.

ALTITUDE OF A PRISM (p. 124): A line segment drawn perpendicular to the planes of the bases.

ALTITUDE OF A PYRAMID (p. 126): The line segment drawn from the vertex perpendicular to the plane of the base.

ALTITUDE OF A TRIANGLE (p. 115): The line segment drawn from a vertex perpendicular to the line containing the opposite side.

AMPERE (p. 212): A unit used to measure the rate of flow of an electric current.

ANGLE (p. 106): A geometric figure formed by two rays having the same endpoint.

ARC (p. 131): A part of a circle.

AREA OF A PLANE FIGURE (p. 65): The number of square units of measure it contains.

AXIS OF A CONE (p. 147): The line segment from the vertex to the center of the circular base.

AXIS OF A CYLINDER (p. 147): The line segment joining the centers of the circular bases.

BASE OF A PARALLELOGRAM (p. 158): Any side of a parallelogram may be considered as the base.

BASE OF A TRIANGLE (p. 156): Any side of a triangle may be considered as the base.

BASES OF A TRAPEZOID (p. 160): The two parallel sides.

BISECT (p. 256): To divide a line segment or angle into two equal parts.

BOARD FOOT (p. 196): A piece of wood 1 in. thick and 1 ft. square, or its equivalent.

BRAKE HORSEPOWER (p. 207): The horsepower of an engine determined by measuring the force exerted on a friction brake.

CALIBRATE (p. 54): To mark an instrument for measuring according to some unit of measurement.

CAPACITY (p. 233): A measure of the volume of a container.

CENTIGRADE (p. 247): A temperature scale on which the freezing point of water is 0° and the boiling point is 100°.

CENTRAL ANGLE (p. 132): An angle formed by two radii.

CENTROID (p. 272): The point at which the three medians of a triangle intersect.

CHORD OF A CIRCLE (p. 131): A line segment with both endpoints on the circle.

CIRCLE (p. 131): A closed plane curve every point of which is the same distance from a given point.

CIRCUMFERENCE (p. 163): The perimeter of a circle.

COMPASS (p. 51): An instrument used in drawing circles.

COMPLEMENTARY ANGLES (p. 108): Two angles whose measures total 90°.

COMPOUND INTEREST (p. 327): Interest computed each period on the sum of the principal and all previous interest.

CONCENTRIC CIRCLES (p. 131): Two or more circles having the same center.

CONVERSION FACTOR (p. 237): A number used to change from one system of measurement to another.

COSINE OF AN ANGLE (p. 359): In a right triangle, the ratio of the length of the side adjacent to the angle to the length of the hypotenuse.

CUTTING SPEED (p. 218): The speed at which the teeth of a circular saw blade or jointer saw blade are moving.

DATA (p. 378): Statistical facts.

DEGREE (p. 77): The unit of measurement of an angle. One degree is $\frac{1}{360}$ of a complete revolution of a line segment about one of its endpoints.

DENOMINATOR (p. 20): In a fraction, the number named by the numeral below the fraction bar.

DIAMETER (p. 131): A chord which passes through the center of a circle.

DIMENSION LIMITS (p. 63): The maximum and minimum acceptable dimensions.

DISCOUNT (p. 332): A reduction in the marked price of goods.

DIVIDERS (p. 51): An instrument used in checking a length against a scale.

EDGE OF A SOLID (p. 124): A line segment formed by the intersection of two faces.

EFFICIENCY OF A MACHINE (p. 323): The ratio of the power produced (output) to the power used (input).

ELLIPSE (p. 280): A closed plane curve such that the sum of the distances to any point on the curve from two fixed points inside the curve is constant.

ENGINE DISPLACEMENT (p. 209): The product of the displacement of one cylinder and the number of cylinders.

EQUATION (p. 290): A statement of equality.

EQUILATERAL TRIANGLE (p. 113): A triangle with three equal sides.

EXPONENT (p. 39): A number indicating how many times a given number is to be used as a factor.

EXTREMES (p. 289): The first and fourth terms of a proportion.

FACE (p. 124): The part of a plane forming a side of a solid.

FAHRENHEIT (p. 247): A temperature scale on which the freezing point of water is 32° and the boiling point is 212°.

FEELER GAUGE (p. 62): An instrument consisting of several small wires or metal leaves of different thicknesses for measuring small gaps.

FLOW CHART (p. 12): A diagram used to picture the steps in solving a problem.

FOOT-POUND (p. 203): The amount of work done when a force of one pound is applied to an object for a distance of one foot.

FREQUENCY CHART (p. 378): A table showing how often two sets of facts are related.

FULCRUM (p. 290): The pivot point of a lever.

GRAPH (p. 377): A pictorial way of representing data.

HORSEPOWER (p. 204): A unit of power equal to 33,000 foot-pounds per minute.

IDENTITY ELEMENT FOR ADDITION (p. 3): The number 0. 0 added to any number gives the number itself.

IDENTITY ELEMENT FOR MULTIPLICATION (p. 8): The number 1. Any number multiplied by 1 gives the number itself.

IMPROPER FRACTION (p. 20): A fraction in which the numerator is equal to or greater than the denominator.

INSCRIBED ANGLE (p. 134): An angle formed by two chords drawn from the same point on a circle.

INTEREST (p. 324): The amount paid to borrow money for a period of time.

INVOICE (p. 16): An itemized bill.

ISOSCELES TRAPEZOID (p. 121): A trapezoid with its two nonparallel sides equal.

ISOSCELES TRIANGLE (p. 113): A triangle with two sides equal.

LATERAL AREA OF A SOLID (p. 168): The sum of the areas of the lateral faces.

LATERAL FACE OF A SOLID (p. 124): Any side of a solid which is not a base.

LINE (p. 104): A straight line which extends indefinitely.

LINE SEGMENT (p. 105): A part of a line.

LOWEST COMMON DENOMINATOR (LCD) (p. 26): The lowest common multiple of the denominators of two or more fractions.

MASS (p. 245): The amount of matter present in an object.

MEANS (p. 289): The second and third terms of a proportion.

MEDIAN (p. 271): A line segment from a vertex of a triangle to the midpoint of the opposite side.

MICROMETER (p. 58): An instrument which will measure accurately to $\frac{1}{1000}$ of an inch.

MINUTE (p. 79): $\frac{1}{60}$ of one degree.

MIXED NUMBER (p. 20): An improper fraction expressed as a whole number and a proper fraction. $1\frac{1}{4}$ is a mixed number.

NUMERATOR (p. 20): In a fraction, the number named by the numeral above the fraction bar.

OBLIQUE PRISM (p. 124): A prism in which the edges are not perpendicular to the bases.

OBTUSE ANGLE (p. 107): An angle whose measure is between 90° and 180°.

OBTUSE TRIANGLE (p. 114): A triangle containing an obtuse angle.

ODOMETER (p. 54): An instrument used to measure distance.

OHM (p. 212): The unit used to measure the resistance which an electric current meets in flowing through a conductor.

PARALLEL LINES (p. 105): Lines in a plane which do not intersect.

PARALLELOGRAM (p. 120): A quadrilateral whose opposite sides are parallel.

PERCENT (p. 318): A ratio between two numbers, the second of which is always 100.

PERCENTAGE (p. 322): The number which is a certain percent of another number.

PERIMETER OF A PLANE FIGURE (p. 156): The sum of the lengths of the sides.

PERPENDICULAR LINES (p. 107): Lines which meet to form right angles.

PI (π) (p. 163): The quotient of the circumference of a circle divided by its diameter. π equals approximately $\frac{22}{7}$, or 3.14.

PICTOGRAPH (p. 379): A table using pictures to represent data.

PITCH OF A ROOF (p. 202): The rise divided by the span.

PLANE (p. 104): A flat surface which extends indefinitely.

POLYGON (p. 109): A plane figure formed by line segments which meet at their endpoints, do not cross, and completely enclose a part of the plane.

POLYHEDRON (p. 123): A closed, three-dimensional figure formed by planes.

POWER (p. 204): The work done per unit of time; the rate of doing work.

PRINCIPAL (p. 324): The amount of money on which interest is figured.

PRINCIPAL OF 1 (p. 22): Any number multiplied by 1 gives the number itself, and any number divided by 1 gives the number itself.

PRISM (p. 123): A polyhedron whose bases are polygons of the same size and shape situated in parallel planes and whose lateral faces are parallelograms.

PROPER FRACTION (p. 20): A fraction in which the numerator is less than the denominator.

PROPORTION (p. 288): A statement of equality between two ratios.

PROTRACTOR (p. 77): A device used to measure angles.

PYRAMID (p. 125): A polyhedron whose base is a polygon and whose faces are triangles with a common vertex.

QUADRILATERAL (p. 120): A polygon with four sides.

RADIUS (p. 131): A line segment with one endpoint on the circle and the other endpoint at the center.

RATIO (p. 286): The quotient of one number divided by a second number.

RAY (p. 104): A part of a line which has one endpoint and extends in one direction only.

REAR-AXLE RATIO (p. 210): The number of teeth on the ring gear divided by the number of teeth on the pinion gear.

RECIPROCALS (p. 28): Two numbers whose product is 1. $\frac{2}{3}$ and $\frac{3}{2}$ are reciprocals since $\frac{2}{3} \times \frac{3}{2} = 1$.

RECTANGLE (p. 121): A parallelogram with four right angles.

REGULAR POLYGON (p. 111): A polygon with all angles equal and all sides the same length.

REGULAR POLYHEDRON (p. 128): A polyhedron whose faces are regular polygons of the same size and shape.

REGULAR PRISM (p. 124): A prism having regular polygons as bases.

REGULAR PYRAMID (p. 125): A pyramid having all its faces the same size and shape.

RHOMBUS (p. 121): A parallelogram with adjacent sides equal.

RIGHT ANGLE (p. 107): An angle with a measure of 90°.

RIGHT CIRCULAR CONE (p. 147): A closed surface formed by rotating a right triangle about one of the sides of the right angle.

RIGHT CIRCULAR CYLINDER (p. 147): A closed surface formed by rotating a rectangle about one side.

RIGHT PRISM (p. 124): A prism whose edges are perpendicular to the bases.

RIGHT TRIANGLE (p. 114): A triangle containing a right angle.

RISE OF A ROOF (p. 202): The altitude of the right triangle formed by drawing lines from the top plate perpendicular to the line drawn through the center of the ridge pole.

RULE OF PYTHAGORAS (p. 343): For any right triangle, the square of the length of the hypotenuse is equal to the sum of squares of the lengths of the other two sides.

RUN OF A ROOF (p. 202): Half of the span.

SAE HORSEPOWER (p. 208): A method of comparing the power of engines, based on the number of cylinders and their bore.

SCALE (p. 303): The ratio of a length on a drawing to the corresponding length on the object.

SCALENE TRIANGLE (p. 113): A triangle with no two sides equal.

SECANT (p. 131): A line which intersects a circle at two points.

SECOND (p. 79): $\frac{1}{60}$ of one minute.

SECOND DISCOUNT (p. 333): An additional discount computed on the amount remaining after a first discount has been subtracted.

SEGMENT (p. 105): A part of a line.

SIMILAR POLYGONS (p. 299): Polygons with the same shape.

SIMPLE INTEREST (p. 325): Interest computed on the same principal each interest period.

SINE OF AN ANGLE (p. 358): In a right triangle, the ratio of the length of the side opposite the angle to the length of the hypotenuse.

SLANT HEIGHT OF A REGULAR PYRAMID (p. 126): The altitude of a face of the pyramid.

SLANT HEIGHT OF A RIGHT CIRCULAR CONE (p. 148): The length of a line segment joining the vertex and a point on the circular base.

SPAN OF A ROOF (p. 202): The distance over the wall plates.

SPHERE (p. 186): A solid figure all points of which are the same distance from a given point.

SQUARE (p. 121): A rectangle with adjacent sides equal.

SUPPLEMENTARY ANGLES (p. 108): Two angles whose measures total 180°.

TANGENT OF AN ANGLE (p. 359): In a right triangle, the ratio of the length of the side opposite the angle to the length of the side adjacent to the angle.

TANGENT TO A CIRCLE (p. 131): A line which intersects a circle at one and only one point.

TEMPLATE (p. 5): A pattern used as a guide in making something accurately.

TETRAHEDRON (p. 126): A pyramid with a triangular base.

TOLERANCE (p. 63): The difference between the largest and smallest acceptable dimensions.

TOTAL AREA OF A SOLID (p. 169): The sum of the areas of the faces and the base, or bases.

TRANSIT (p. 81): A device used to measure angles in both the vertical and horizontal directions.

TRAPEZOID (p. 121): A quadrilateral with only one pair of opposite sides parallel.

TRIANGLE (p. 110): A polygon having three sides.

TRUE INTEREST RATE (p. 329): The rate of interest on a loan adjusted to allow for the fact that partial repayments must be made during the loan period.

VERTEX OF AN ANGLE (p. 106): The common endpoint of two rays which form an angle.

VERTEX OF A CONE (p. 147): The endpoint of the axis of the cone not lying in the plane of the base.

VERTEX OF A PYRAMID (p. 126): The point at which the faces of the pyramid intersect.

VERTICES OF A POLYGON (p. 110): The vertices of the angles formed by the sides of a polygon.

VERTICES OF A POLYHEDRON (p. 124): The points at which three faces of the polyhedron meet.

VOLT (p. 212): A unit used to measure the amount of pressure pushing an electric current through a conductor.

VOLUME (p. 70): The amount of space occupied by an object.

WATT (p. 214): The unit of power in electricity.

WEIGHT (p. 245): The measure of the force of gravity acting upon an object.

WORK (p. 203): A flow of energy from one body to another.

INDEX

D

E

F

ANSWERS TO SELF-ANALYSIS TESTS

Chapter 1. Arithmetic Review

Page 2. SELF-ANALYSIS TEST I **1.** 12. **2.** 24. **3.** 21. **4.** 24. **5.** 2. **6.** 74. **7.** 19. **8.** 90. **9.** 12. **10.** 210. **11.** 2. **12.** 3. **13.** 11. **14.** 59. **15.** 6. **16.** 12. **17.** 5. **18.** 25. **19.** 3. **20.** 259.

Page 11. SELF-ANALYSIS TEST II **1.** 24. **2.** 10. **3.** 64. **4.** 14. **5.** 35. **6.** 56. **7.** 40. **8.** 22. **9.** 100. **10.** 44. **11.** 144. **12.** 522. **13.** 2,175. **14.** 16,776. **15.** 88. **16.** $40\frac{7}{12}$. **17.** 3. **18.** 9. **19.** 223. **20.** $2 + (5 \times 7) = 37$. **21.** $(3 \times 9) + 4 = 31$. **22.** $7 + (6 \div 3) = 9$. **23.** $24 + (3 \times 2) = 30$. **24.** $(72 \div 8) - 3 = 6$. **25.** $2 \times (8 - 3) = 10$.

Page 14. SELF-ANALYSIS TEST III **1.** \$11.50. **2.** \$19.11. **3.** \$41.01. **4.** \$2.40, \$2.00, \$2.25, \$6.65. **5.** \$.35, \$2.00, \$2.70, \$11.55, \$1.69, \$18.29.

Page 23. SELF-ANALYSIS TEST IV **1.** $\frac{4}{5}$. **2.** $\frac{1}{5}$. **3.** $\frac{1}{2}$. **4.** $\frac{1}{3}$. **5.** $\frac{2}{3}$. **6.** $\frac{3}{5}$. **7.** $\frac{1}{3}$. **8.** $\frac{7}{12}$. **9.** $\frac{7}{8}$. **10.** $1\frac{1}{8}$.

Page 25. SELF-ANALYSIS TEST V **1.** $\frac{12}{20}$. **2.** $\frac{48}{60}$. **3.** $\frac{9}{24}$. **4.** $\frac{9}{12}$. **5.** $\frac{10}{40}$. **6.** $\frac{1}{6}$. **7.** $\frac{3}{8}$. **8.** $\frac{3}{14}$. **9.** $1\frac{11}{42}$. **10.** $1\frac{1}{5}$.

Pages 38–39. SELF-ANALYSIS TEST VI **1.** $\frac{1}{16}$. **2.** $\frac{1}{64}$. **3.** $\frac{1}{8}$. **4.** $\frac{1}{64}$. **5.** $\frac{1}{192}$. **6.** .1875. **7.** .09375. **8.** .09375. **9.** .125. **10.** .390625. **11.** $\frac{1}{2}$. **12.** 2. **13.** $3\frac{1}{3}$. **14.** $1\frac{5}{7}$. **15.** $1\frac{1}{5}$. **16.** .5. **17.** 3. **18.** .8333 . . . **19.** 3. **20.** 3.5.

Page 44. SELF-ANALYSIS TEST VII **1.** 81. **2.** 256. **3.** 529. **4.** 216. **5.** 81. **6.** 11. **7.** 24. **8.** 17. **9.** 11.49. **10.** 20.71.

Chapter 2. Measurement

Page 58. SELF-ANALYSIS TEST I **1.** add. **2.** ruler. **3.** odometer. **4.** altimeter. **5.** 2300 ft. **6.** 5400 ft. **7.** 74,300 ft.

Pages 73–75. SELF-ANALYSIS TEST II **1.** $1\frac{3}{16}''$, $1\frac{5}{8}''$, $1\frac{7}{16}''$; combined length $= 4\frac{1}{4}''$. **2.** distance. **3.** altimeter. **4.** square units. **5.** cubic units. **6.** 20 sq. units. **7.** 12 sq. units. **8. a.** 45 cu. units. **b.** 21 cu. units. **9.** .360″. **10.** .550″. **11.** .340″. **12.** Dimension limits: 4.53″, 4.48″; tolerance: 0.05″.

Pages 85–86. SELF-ANALYSIS TEST III **1.** protractor. **2.** 90°. **3.** minutes; seconds. **4.** National Bureau of Standards. **5.** 90°. **6.** 136°. **7.** 49°. **8.** 20°. **9.** 70°48′5″. **10.** 61°4′19″. **11.** 22°16′56″. **12.** 173.2′ or about 173′.

Pages 96–97. SELF-ANALYSIS TEST IV **1.** sundial. **2.** revolution counter. **3.** thermometer. **4.** kilowatt-hours. **5.** cubic. **6.** 2653 KWH. **7.** 1431 KWH. **8.** 8541 C.C.F. **9.** 4463 C.C.F.

Chapter 3. Geometric Figures

Page 120. SELF-ANALYSIS TEST I **1.** (a); (e). **2.** (d). **3.** (f). **4.** (c). **5.** obtuse. **6.** complementary. **7.** altitude. **8.** acute. **9.** equilateral. **10.** scalene. **11.** right. **12.** 145°. **13.** regular.

Pages 129–130. SELF-ANALYSIS TEST II **1.** parallelogram. **2.** trapezoid. **3.** square or rhombus. **4.** regular pentagon. **5.** planes. **6.** rectangular prism. **7.** pyramid. **8. a.** $\overline{DE}$. **b.** $\overline{DF}$. **c.** $\overline{AD}$; $\overline{BD}$; $\overline{CD}$; $\overline{AB}$; $\overline{BC}$; $\overline{AC}$. **9. a.** triangular. **b.** $\overline{AB}$. **c.** 2. **10.** octahedron.

Pages 138–139. SELF-ANALYSIS TEST III **1.** central. **2.** inscribed. **3.** half the sum of the measures of its intercepted arcs. **4.** 50°. **5.** 60°. **6.** 65°. **7.** 35°. **8.** 60°.

Pages 145–146. SELF-ANALYSIS TEST IV **1.** half the measure of its intercepted arc. **2.** half the difference of the measures of the intercepted arcs. **3.** 160°. **4.** 20°. **5.** $32\frac{1}{2}$°. **6.** 35°. **7.** $27\frac{1}{2}$°. **8.** 80°. **9.** 55°. **10.** $m\angle x = 50°$; $m\angle y = 95°$; $m\angle z = 85°$.

Page 148. SELF-ANALYSIS TEST V **1.** cylinder. **2.** oblique. **3.** bases. **4.** slant. **5.** perpendicular. **6.** altitude. **7.** one; two. **8.** axis.

Chapter 4. Geometric Formulas

Pages 167–168. SELF-ANALYSIS TEST I **1.** 29 in. **2.** 24 in. **3.** 53 in. **4.** 132 in. **5. a.** 42 sq. in. **b.** 18 sq. in. **6. a.** 36 sq. in. **b.** $6\frac{23}{32}$ sq. in. **7. a.** 18 sq. in. **b.** 31 sq. in. **8. a.** $12\frac{4}{7}$ sq. in. **b.** $9\frac{5}{8}$ sq. in. **9. a.** 6 sq. in. **b.** 14 sq. in. **c.** 54 sq. in. **10.** $25\frac{5}{7}$ sq. in.

Pages 179–180. SELF-ANALYSIS TEST II **1.** 72 sq. in. **2.** 32 sq. in. **3.** 44 sq. in. **4.** $113\frac{1}{16}$ sq. in. **5.** 60 cu. in. **6.** 9 cu. in. **7.** 45 sq. in. **8.** 12 sq. in. **9.** 84 sq. in. **10.** $46\frac{2}{3}$ cu. in.

Pages 187–189. SELF-ANALYSIS TEST III **1.** 88 sq. in. **2.** 2112 sq. in. **3.** 140 cu. in. **4.** 41,580 cu. ft. **5.** $47\frac{1}{7}$ sq. in. **6.** $58\frac{13}{14}$ sq. in. **7.** 506 sq. in. **8.** $75\frac{5}{8}$ sq. in. **9.** 154 cu. in. **10.** $1093\frac{5}{7}$ cu. in. **11.** $5028\frac{4}{7}$ sq. ft. **12.** 1386 sq. ft. **13.** $268\frac{4}{21}$ cu. ft. **14.** $65\frac{10}{21}$ cu. in.

Chapter 5. Formulas from Industry

Pages 202–203. SELF-ANALYSIS TEST I **1.** 168 bd. ft. **2.** 315 bd. ft. **3.** $690.00. **4.** 31 bd. ft. **5.** pitch. **6.** span. **7.** run. **8.** rise; ridge. **9.** $\frac{5}{12}$. **10.** 15 ft.

Page 207. SELF-ANALYSIS TEST II **1.** flow. **2.** power. **3.** 550; 33,000. **4.** 62.4. **5.** horsepower. **6.** 6000 ft.-lb. **7.** 25 ft.-lb./sec. **8.** 22,000 ft.-lb./min. **9.** 339. **10.** 140 ft.

Pages 211–212. SELF-ANALYSIS TEST III **1.** $\text{bhp} = \frac{RNW}{5252}$. **2.** $\text{SAE hp} = \frac{D^2 \times N}{2.5}$. **3.** $r = \frac{T}{t}$. **4.** displacement. **5.** no. of cylinders. **6.** 68.5 (approx.). **7.** 28.8. **8.** $265\frac{5}{28}$ or 265 cu. in. **9.** 3.38:1. **10.** 48.

Page 216. SELF-ANALYSIS TEST IV **1.** ampere. **2.** ohms. **3.** volts. **4.** $I = \frac{E}{R}$; $E = IR$; $R = \frac{E}{I}$. **5.** watts. **6.** $2\frac{4}{9}$. **7.** 224. **8.** 1.77 or 1.8. **9.** 2500 mi. **10.** $535\frac{5}{7}$ mph.

Page 219. SELF-ANALYSIS TEST V **1.** $D = \frac{ds}{S}$. **2.** $S = \frac{C \times \text{rpm} \times D}{d \times 12}$. **3.** $S = \frac{C \times \text{rpm}}{12}$. **4.** 7 in. **5.** 700 rpm. **6.** 2750 ft./min. **7.** 2800 ft./min.

Chapter 6. Systems of Measurement

Page 230. SELF-ANALYSIS TEST I **1.** 144 in. **2.** $2\frac{1}{3}$ yd. **3.** 11 ft. **4.** 108 sq. ft. **5.** 400 sq. yd. **6.** 864 sq. in. **7.** 8832 sq. in. **8.** $34\frac{58}{63}$ sq. yd. **9.** $18\frac{6}{7}$ sq. ft. **10.** $14.29.

Page 235. SELF-ANALYSIS TEST II **1.** 243 cu. ft. **2.** 8640 cu. in. **3.** 466,560 cu. in. **4.** 72 qt. **5.** 16 pt. **6.** 432 oz. **7.** 2.62 cu. ft. **8.** 9 sq. in. **9.** 8640 cu. in. **10.** 52 sq. in.

Page 247. SELF-ANALYSIS TEST III **1.** 30.48. **2.** 780. **3.** $\frac{1}{100}$. **4.** 80. **5.** 750. **6.** 1076. **7.** 39. **8.** 0.47. **9.** $4.00. **10.** 10.6 cents.

Page 249. SELF-ANALYSIS TEST IV **1.** 86°. **2.** $93\frac{1}{3}$°. **3.** 100. **4.** 32. **5.** 37°. **6.** 39.2°.

Chapter 7. Geometric Constructions

Page 266. SELF-ANALYSIS TEST I **1.–9.** Check your constructions with a protractor and a ruler.

Page 278. SELF-ANALYSIS TEST II **1.** and **2.** Follow procedure given on page 267 of the text. **3.** and **4.** Follow procedure given on page 268 of the text. **5.** Follow procedure given on pages 116 and 117 of the text. **6.** Follow procedure given on page 269 of the text. **7.** Follow procedure given in exercise 1 on page 271 of the text. **8.** Follow procedure given on page 272 of the text. **9.** Follow procedure given at the top of page 274 of the text. **10.** Follow procedure given at the bottom of page 274 of the text.

Chapter 8. Ratio and Proportion

Pages 293–294. SELF-ANALYSIS TEST I **1. a.** $\frac{1}{3}$. **b.** $\frac{1}{9}$. **c.** $\frac{1}{4}$. **2. a.** true. **b.** false. **c.** true. **d.** false. **3.** 14. **4.** 100. **5.** 37.2. **6.** 38.5. **7.** 0.0433 in. **8.** 0.05 in. **9.** 201 lb. **10.** 67 lb.

Pages 301–303. SELF-ANALYSIS TEST II **1.** equal; proportional. **2.** no. **3.** $\frac{2}{1}$. **4.** A is similar to D; B is similar to C. **5.** $x = 8$; $y = 12$. **6.** $x = 31\frac{1}{2}$. **7.** $a = 9$; $b = 15$; $x = 12$; $y = 6$; $z = 18$. **8.** $x = 1\frac{1}{2}$; $y = 1\frac{1}{4}$; $z = 4$. **9.** 12 in. **10.** $10\frac{1}{9}$ in. **11.** 16 mi.

Pages 310–311. SELF-ANALYSIS TEST III **1.** $4\frac{1}{8}$ ft. **2.** $2\frac{1}{2}$ ft. **3.** length: $43\frac{1}{2}$ in.; height: $19\frac{1}{2}$ in. **4.** length: 30 ft.; height: 24 ft. **5.** $46\frac{7}{8}$ mi. **6.** $37\frac{1}{2}$ mi. **7.** \$2.22. **8.** $168\frac{3}{16}$ sq. ft. **9.** $120\frac{3}{8}$ sq. ft. **10.** $634\frac{1}{2}$ sq. ft.

Chapter 9. Percentage

Page 321. SELF-ANALYSIS TEST I

	Common Fraction	Decimal Fraction	Percent
1.	$\frac{1}{2}$	.50	50%
2.	$\frac{1}{3}$	$.33\frac{1}{3}$	$33\frac{1}{3}\%$
3.	$\frac{1}{4}$	.25	25%
4.	$\frac{1}{5}$	.20	20%
5.	$\frac{1}{6}$	$.16\frac{2}{3}$	$16\frac{2}{3}\%$
6.	$\frac{2}{3}$	$.66\frac{2}{3}$	$66\frac{2}{3}\%$
7.	$\frac{3}{4}$	.75	75%
8.	$\frac{4}{5}$	.80	80%
9.	$\frac{2}{5}$	.40	40%
10.	$\frac{5}{6}$	$.83\frac{1}{3}$	$83\frac{1}{3}\%$

11. $\frac{17}{100}$. **12.** $\frac{9}{10}$. **13.** 30%. **14.** $\frac{1}{4}$. **15.** .55.

Page 326. SELF-ANALYSIS TEST II **1.** 4. **2.** 21. **3.** 30. **4.** 6. **5.** 25%. **6.** 12.00%. **7.** $33\frac{1}{3}\%$. **8.** 80%. **9.** \$300. **10.** 3%.

Page 336. SELF-ANALYSIS TEST III **1. a.** \$5512.50. **b.** \$512.50. **2. a.** \$33,790.00. **b.** \$13,790.

3. a. \$243.80. **b.** \$43.80. **4.** 11.7%. **5.** 6.3%. **6.**

Cost	Net Cost
\$1.75	\$1.40
2.80	2.10
2.30	1.61
9.40	7.52
Total	\$12.63

Chapter 10. Right Triangles and Trigonometry

Page 350. SELF-ANALYSIS TEST I **1.** 5. **2.** 12. **3.** 8. **4.** $\sqrt{117}$. **5.** $\sqrt{21.25}$. **6.** 9.899 cm. **7.** 10. **8.** 3. **9.** 9. **10.** 7.

Pages 356–357. SELF-ANALYSIS TEST II **1.** $5\sqrt{3}$. **2.** $3\frac{1}{2}$. **3.** $a = 2\sqrt{3}$; $c = 4$. **4.** $b = 5$; $a = 5\sqrt{3}$. **5.** $c = 6\frac{1}{4}$; $a = 3\frac{1}{8}\sqrt{3}$. **6.** $a = 4\sqrt{3}$; $\angle A = 60°$; $\angle B = 30°$. **7.** $a = 7\frac{1}{2}\sqrt{3}$; $\angle A = 60°$; $\angle B = 30°$. **8.** $8\sqrt{3} = 13.856$ sq. units. **9.** $32\sqrt{3} = 55.424$ sq. units. **10.** $162\sqrt{3} = 280.584$ cu. in.

Page 365. SELF-ANALYSIS TEST III **1.** $\frac{a}{c}$. **2.** $\frac{b}{c}$. **3.** $\frac{a}{b}$. **4.** $a = 25 \sin 30°$. **5.** $c = \frac{10}{\cos 45°}$. **6.** .4540. **7.** .1392. **8.** 1.3270. **9.** 5°. **10.** 81°.

Page 371. SELF-ANALYSIS TEST IV **1.** 5.736 ft. **2.** 14 cm. **3.** 30.46 mi. **4.** 30°. **5.** 45°. **6.** 30°. **7.** 42.8 ft. **8.** 9.08 ft. **9.** 1127.4 ft. **10.** 35° 10′.

Chapter 11. Statistical Tables and Graphs

Pages 380–381. SELF-ANALYSIS TEST I **1.** 938. **2.** 188. **3.** 7.5%. **4.** 469:600 **5.** 150; 50 boys; 100 girls. **6.** 1:6. **7.** 1:3. **8.** 56%.

Pages 387–389. SELF-ANALYSIS TEST II **1.–3.**

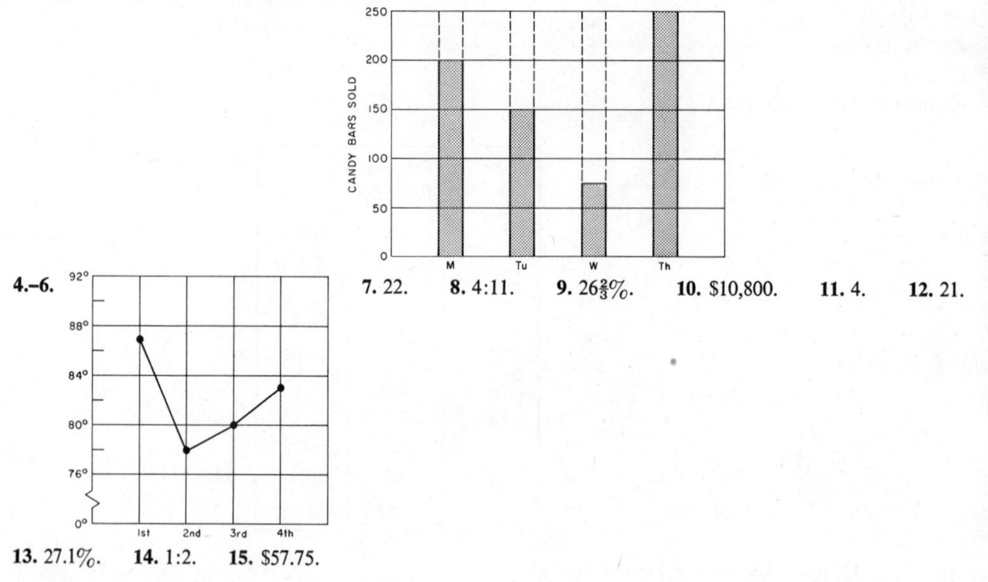

7. 22. **8.** 4:11. **9.** $26\frac{2}{3}$%. **10.** $10,800. **11.** 4. **12.** 21. **13.** 27.1%. **14.** 1:2. **15.** $57.75.

Page 391. SELF-ANALYSIS TEST III **1.** $8\frac{1}{2}$ hr. **2.** 4:13. **3.** $37\frac{1}{2}$%. **4.** 3:7. **5.** 27%.

Answers to
Odd-Numbered Exercises

MODERN APPLIED MATHEMATICS

GOLD/CARLBERG

HOUGHTON MIFFLIN COMPANY

BOSTON New York Atlanta Geneva, Ill. Dallas Palo Alto

ANSWERS TO ODD-NUMBERED EXERCISES

Chapter 1. Arithmetic Review

Page 4. **1.** 106. **3.** 79 **5.** 142. **7.** 763. **9.** 993. **11.** 2790. **13.** 1192. **15.** 2356.

Pages 4–5. **1.** 78. **3.** 15. **5.** 47. **7.** 529. **9.** 545. **11.** 7443. **13.** 968. **15.** 18. **17.** 22. **19.** 1. **21.** 110.

Pages 6–7. **1.** 11″. **3.** 5″. **5.** 7″.

Page 9. **1.** 68. **3.** 504. **5.** 686. **7.** 355. **9.** 87. **11.** 207. **13.** 2128. **15.** 2278. **17.** 1752. **19.** 1764. **21.** 2212. **23.** 13,048. **25.** 174. **27.** 18. **29.** 45. **31.** 0. **33.** 100.

Page 10. **1.** 125. **3.** 24. **5.** 77. **7.** 43. **9.** $11\frac{19}{91}$. **11.** 14.

Page 10. **1.** $(5 \times 4) + 2 = 22$. **3.** $5 \times (4 - 2) = 10$, $(5 \times 4) \div 2 = 10$, or $5 \times (4 \div 2) = 10$. **5.** $5 + 4 + 2 = 11$. **7.** $5 \times (4 + 2) = 30$. **9.** $5 \times 4 \times 2 = 40$.

Page 13. **1.** 32. **3.** 1569. **5.** 154,226.

Page 15. **1.** $1.11. **3.** $32.35. **5.** $216.31. **7.** $10.50, $5.95, $8.72, $3.33, $28.50. **9.** $247.14.

Pages 16–19. **1.** Total for 12CV4: $31.68; total for 4A7GV condenser: $10.44; total for MC4562 coil: $18.96; invoice total: $139.98. **3.** Total for GC-1307B sealed beam: $4.80; total for GC-1308 headlamp door: $7.28; total for GC-8201G side grille: $19.09; total for GC-1667A molding: $8.34; total for GC-73PD4 parking lamp: $6.00; invoice total: $165.34.

Page 20. **1.** 182. **3.** 224 hrs. **5.** 8206 lbs. **7.** 4. **9.** $11.70.

Page 21. **1.** $\frac{2}{4}$, $\frac{4}{8}$. **3.** $\frac{4}{16}$. **5.** $\frac{5}{8}$. **7.** $\frac{2}{4}$, $\frac{1}{2}$. **9.** $\frac{4}{16}$, $\frac{1}{4}$.

Page 22. **1.** $\frac{3}{8}$. **3.** $\frac{6}{13}$. **5.** $\frac{4}{15}$. **7.** $\frac{6}{11}$. **9.** $\frac{8}{15}$.

Page 24. **1.** $\frac{2}{6}$, $\frac{1}{6}$. **3.** $\frac{1}{12}$, $\frac{3}{21}$. **5.** $\frac{1}{61}$, $\frac{6}{61}$. **7.** $\frac{4}{8}$, $\frac{2}{8}$, $\frac{1}{8}$. **9.** $\frac{1}{10}$, $\frac{2}{10}$, $\frac{5}{10}$. **11.** $\frac{2}{3}$. **13.** $\frac{3}{4}$. **15.** $\frac{2}{3}$. **17.** $\frac{2}{3}$. **19.** $\frac{3}{4}$.

Page 25. **1.** $2\frac{1}{4}$. **3.** $\frac{8}{15}$. **5.** $\frac{17}{21}$. **7.** $1\frac{9}{16}$. **9.** $\frac{13}{16}$. **11.** $1\frac{3}{7}$. **13.** $1\frac{101}{120}$. **15.** $\frac{9}{16}$.

Page 26. **1.** 12. **3.** 24. **5.** 40. **7.** 60. **9.** 36. **11.** $1\frac{1}{12}$. **13.** $\frac{5}{8}$. **15.** $\frac{23}{40}$. **17.** $\frac{23}{60}$. **19.** $\frac{25}{36}$.

Pages 27–28. **1.** $\frac{3}{8}$. **3.** $\frac{55}{72}$. **5.** $\frac{18}{35}$. **7.** $\frac{65}{84}$. **9.** $\frac{4}{27}$. **11.** $40\frac{1}{2}$.

Page 29. **1.** 3. **3.** $\frac{1}{3}$. **5.** $\frac{8}{3}$, **7.** $\frac{1}{100}$. **9.** $\frac{4}{3}$. **11.** $1\frac{1}{8}$. **13.** $1\frac{3}{5}$. **15.** $\frac{5}{8}$. **17.** $3\frac{1}{3}$. **19.** $\frac{1}{200}$. **21.** $\frac{14}{15}$. **23.** $3\frac{1}{8}$. **25.** $21\frac{1}{3}$. **27.** $\frac{1}{8}$.

Pages 31–33. **1.** $\frac{7}{12}''$. **3.** $2\frac{27}{32}''$. **5.** $x = \frac{5}{8}''$, $y = \frac{5}{16}''$.

Page 34. **1.** 33.0. **3.** 601.3. **5.** $13.89. **7.** 4.9 miles.

Page 35. **1.** 9.2. **3.** 77.72. **5.** 11.1775. **7.** .1484375. **9.** .0546875.

Page 38. **1.** .375. **3.** .25. **5.** .0625. **7.** .09375. **9.** .015625. **11.** .63. **13.** 5.233. **15.** 1.87. **17.** .406. **19.** .30. **21.** .03. **23.** 6.85. **25.** 3. **27.** .67. **29.** 2.28.

Pages 43–44. **1.** 36. **3.** 144. **5.** 2025. **7.** 16.81. **9.** 12.25. **11.** 2. **13.** 7. **15.** 8. **17.** 12.17. **19.** 5.48. **21.** 60.41. **23.** 8. **25.** 125. **27.** 39.0625. **29.** 9.8596. **31.** 256.

Pages 45–46. **1.** 18. **3.** 42. **5.** 91. **7.** 7. **9.** 250. **11.** $(8 \times 8) \div 8 = 8$. **13.** $(4 \times 11) - 3 = 41$. **15.** $(27 \times 3) \div 9 = 9$. **17.** \$14.00. **19.** \$46.12. **21.** $\frac{8}{8}$. **23.** $\frac{20}{25}$. **25.** 1. **27.** $13\frac{3}{4}$. **29.** $\frac{9}{40}$. **31.** $\frac{5}{176}$. **33.** $\frac{3}{8}$. **35.** 2.5. **37.** 21.21.

Page 47. **1.** 106. **3.** 2115. **5.** 16,698. **7.** 445. **9.** 1134. **11.** 1267. **13.** 1800. **15.** 3151. **17.** 63,837. **19.** 22. **21.** 12. **23.** 16

Chapter 2. Measurement

Page 53. **1.**

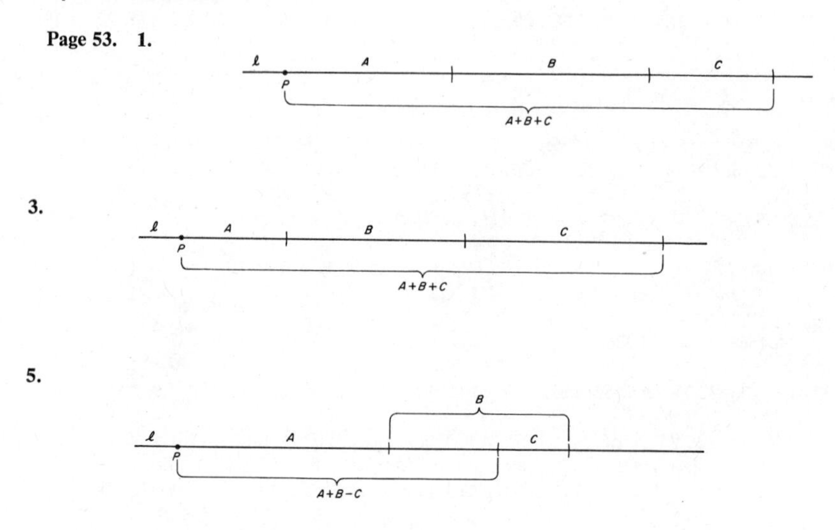

Page 54. **1–9. a.** Answers will vary. **1. b.** $1\frac{3}{4}''$. **3. b.** $1\frac{15}{16}''$. **5. b.** $2\frac{13}{16}''$. **7. b.** $2\frac{3}{16}''$. **9. b.** $1\frac{7}{8}''$.

Page 55. **1–3.** Answers will vary. **5.** 60 ft. 6 in.

Page 57. **1.** 6340 ft. **3.** 1700 ft. **5.** 27,900 ft. **7.** 8800 ft. **9.** 880 ft. **11.** 5400 ft.

Pages 60–61. **1.** .750 in. **3.** .630 in. **5.** .703 in. **7.** .075 in. **9.** .009 in. **11.** .048 in. **13.** .859 in. **15.** .979 in. **17.** .829 in.

Pages 64–65. **1.** Dimension limits: 1.756″, 1.744″; tolerance: 0.012″. **3.** 2.501″, 2.499″. **5.** Dimension limits for $1\frac{1}{2}''$ diameter: 1.503″, 1.498″; tolerance: 0.005″. Dimension limits for $\frac{3}{8}''$ diameter: .377″, .373″; tolerance: .004″.

Pages 66–67. **1.** 12 sq. units. **3.** 13 sq. units. **5.** 15 sq. units. **7.** 19 sq. units. **9.** $18\frac{1}{2}$ sq. units. **11.** 12 sq. units.

Pages 69–70. **1.** 2 sq. in. **3.** $2\frac{1}{4}$ sq. in. **5.** $5\frac{5}{8}$ sq. in. **7.** $2\frac{5}{8}$ sq. in. **9.** $3\frac{3}{32}$ sq. in. **11.** $27\frac{1}{2}$ sq. in. **13.** Answers will vary. **15.** larger

Pages 72–73.

	length $= l$	width $= w$	height $= h$	volume $= V$
1.	3	2	2	12
3.	3	2	6	36
5.	6	4	3	72

Pages 76–77. **1–7.** Answers will vary.

Pages 78–79. **1.** 30°. **3.** 130°. **5.** 51°. **7.** 60°.

Pages 80–81. **1.** 62°56′. **3.** 56°55′59″ **5.** 73°13′5″. **7.** 22°11′23″. **9.** 28°38′4″.

Pages 84–85. **1.** 57.74′ or about 58′. **3.** 12.9636′ or about 13′. **5.** Answers will vary.

Page 89. **1.** 100° centigrade or 212° Fahrenheit. **3.** Answers will vary.

Pages 91–93. **1.** 3564 KWH. **3.** 4735 KWH. **5.** 5633 KWH. **7.** First reading: 3452 KWH; second reading: 3843 KWH; $11.22. **9.** Correct amount is $3.81.

Pages 94–96. **1.** 3664 C.C.F. **3.** 3745 C.C.F. **5.** 8477 C.C.F. **7.** Charge for 28 C.C.F. is $2.40. **9.** Correct amount due is $8.80.

Pages 98–100. **1.** True. **3.** True. **5.** False. An odometer tells the total number of miles a car has been driven. **7.** 24,700 ft. **9.** .245″. **11.** .016″. **13.** 18 sq. units. **15.** 1068 KWH. **17.** 59°7′16″. **19.** 29°43′48″. **21.** $y = 138°$.

Page 101. **1.** 77. **3.** 1052. **5.** 21,409. **7.** 111. **9.** 2205. **11.** 1026. **13.** 1375. **15.** 7825 **17.** 384,625. **19.** 25. **21.** 27. **23.** 190. **25.** $\frac{3}{4}$. **27.** $\frac{4}{5}$ **29.** $\frac{9}{32}$.

Chapter 3. Geometric Figures

Page 109. **7.** $\angle PQR = 45°$; complement $= 45°$. **9.** $\angle GHI = 125°$; supplement $= 55°$. **11.** 47°28′33″. **13.** 42°59′27″.

Pages 112–113. **1.** octagon. **3.** triangle. **5.** quadrilateral. **7.** quadrilateral. **9.** 8. **11.** 6.

	Ex. 13
Name of polygon	pentagon
$m\overline{AB}$ = _?_ inch	1
Are all sides equal?	yes
$m\angle ABC$ = _?_ degrees	110°
Are all angles equal?	yes
Is the polygon regular?	yes

Pages 115–116. **3.** yes. **5.** $\overline{CE} \perp \overline{AB}$. **7.** $\overline{CE}$.

Pages 118–119. **5. a.** $p = 1\frac{11}{16}''$; $q = 1\frac{3}{8}''$; $r = \frac{13}{16}''$ **b.** $p = 1\frac{1}{2}''$; $q = 1\frac{1}{2}''$; $r = \frac{15}{16}''$. **c.** $p = 1\frac{3}{16}''$; $q = 1\frac{13}{16}''$; $r = 1\frac{1}{16}''$. **d.** $p = 1\frac{11}{16}''$; $q = 1\frac{5}{16}''$; $r = 1\frac{1}{16}''$; in every triangle the sum of the lengths of any two sides of a triangle is greater than the length of the third side. **7.** $\angle A = 60°$; $\angle B = 60°$; $\angle C = 60°$; acute triangle. $\angle A = 114°$; $\angle B = 39°$; $\angle C = 27°$; obtuse triangle. $\angle A = 45°$; $\angle B = 45°$; $\angle C = 90°$; right triangle. $\angle A = 58°$; $\angle B = 56°$; $\angle C = 66°$; acute triangle. **9. b.** side opposite 50° angle $= 2\frac{7}{16}''$; side opposite 60° angle $= 2\frac{3}{4}''$; **c.** 70°. **11.** yes.

Page 122. **1.** (a); (c); (d); (e). **3.** (a); (d). **5.** (f). **7.** yes. **9.** All sides are $\frac{7}{8}''$. The square has 4 right angles.

Page 133. **1.** 40°; 40°; 40°. **3.** no. **5.** 55°.

Pages 135–136. **1.** 20°. **3.** 90°. **5.** 216°.

Pages 137–138. **1.** 45°. **3.** 50°.

Pages 140–141. **1.** 44°. **3.** 90°. **5.** $m\widehat{AXB} = 140°$; $m\widehat{AYB} = 220°$. **7.** $m\angle 1 = 40°$; $m\angle 2 = 50°$; $m\angle 3 = 60°$; $m\angle 4 = 30°$; $m\angle 5 = 90°$; $m\angle 6 = 90°$

Page 144. **1.** 60°. **3.** 20°. **5.** 220°.

Page 148. **1.** circles. **3.** oblique. **5.** altitude.

Pages 149–152. **1. a.** $\overline{AO}$. **b.** $\overline{BC}$. **c.** $\overleftrightarrow{GJ}$. **d.** $\overline{HI}$. **e.** $\overleftrightarrow{FE}$. **f.** $\widehat{AB}$. **g.** *D*. **h.** $\widehat{BC}$. **3.** false; An angle greater than 90° but less than 180° is called an obtuse angle. **5.** true. **7.** true. **9.** false; A triangle having an angle of 115° is called an obtuse triangle. **11.** false; A trapezoid whose 2 nonparallel sides are equal is called an isosceles trapezoid. **13.** true. **15.** false; A triangular prism is a prism whose bases are triangles. **17.** false; An angle formed at the center of the circle is called a central angle. **19.** true. **21.** false; An angle formed by two secants is measured by half the difference of its intercepted arcs. **23.** 65°. **25.** 79°. **27.** 30°. **29.** 70°. **31.** 70°. **33.** 160°.

Page 153. **1.** 131. **3.** 2284. **5.** 25,657. **7.** 31. **9.** 1535. **11.** 912. **13.** 525. **15.** 10,625. **17.** 3595.6. **19.** 55. **21.** 165. **23.** 1050. **25.** $\frac{17}{24}$. **27.** $\frac{5}{8}$. **29.** $7\frac{1}{4}$.

Chapter 4. Geometric Formulas

Pages 156–158. **1.** 27 units. **3.** 9 sq. in. **5.** 28 sq. ft. **7.** 12 sq. cm. **9.** 21,600 sq. ft. **11.** $\overline{CB} = 2\frac{1}{16}''$; $\overline{AF} = 2\frac{1}{8}''$; area is approx. $2\frac{3}{16}$ sq. in.

Pages 159–160. **1.** 15 sq. in. **3.** $13\frac{3}{4}$ sq. in. **5.** area of rectangle *ABCD* = 60 sq. in.; area of parallelogram *CDEF* = 60 sq. in.; yes. **7.** 30 in. **9.** perimeter = 152 in.; area = 1008 sq. in.

Pages 161–162. **1.** 7 sq. in. **3.** $16\frac{1}{2}$ sq. in. **5.** $15\frac{5}{12}$ sq. in. **7.** 47 in. **9.** $94\frac{1}{2}$ sq. ft.

Page 164. **1.** $28\frac{2}{7}$ sq. in. **3.** $78\frac{4}{7}$ sq. in. **5.** 88 in. **7.** $62\frac{6}{7}$.

Pages 164–166. **1. a.** 420 sq. ft. **b.** 280 sq. ft. **c.** 1140 sq. ft. **d.** 1840 sq. ft. **3. a.** 12 sq. in. **b.** 16 sq. in. **c.** 4 sq. in. **d.** 32 sq. in. **5.** $12\frac{19}{28}$ sq. in. **7.** 480 sq. in.

Pages 170–171. **1.** 36 sq. in. **3.** 9 sq. in. **5.** 162 sq. in. **7.** 142 sq. in. **9.** 84 sq. in. **11.** 248 sq. in.

Page 173. **1.** 120 cu. in. **3.** $67\frac{1}{2}$ cu. in. **5. a.** 35,700 cu. in. **b.** 4200 sq. in. **c.** 6240 sq. in.

Pages 174–175. **1.** 45 sq. in. **3.** 153 sq. in. **5.** 192 sq. in.

Page 176. **1.** 72 sq. in. **3.** 110.4 sq. in. **5.** 189 sq. in.

Page 178. **1.** 40 cu. in. **3.** $14\frac{7}{24}$ cu. in. **5.** $366\frac{2}{3}$ cu. in.

Page 181. **1.** $94\frac{2}{7}$ sq. in. **3.** $x = 1$(in.). **5.** 572 sq. in.

Page 182. **1.** 572 sq. in. **3.** $421\frac{1}{7}$ sq. in.

Pages 183–184. **1.** 203 cu. in. **3.** 198 cu. in. **5.** 484 cu. in.

Page 186. **1.** 176 sq. in. **3.** 362.34 sq. in. **5.** 115.5 cu. in.

Page 187. **1.** 154 cu. in.; $179\frac{2}{3}$ cu. in. **3.** $314\frac{2}{7}$ sq. in.; $523\frac{17}{21}$ cu. in.

Pages 191–192. **1.** 54 sq. in. **3.** 40 sq. ft. **5. a.** 9 sq. in. **b.** 18 sq. in. **c.** 48 sq. in. **7.** $112\frac{5}{8}$ sq. in. **9.** 192 sq. in. **11.** $\frac{1}{18}$ cu. in. **13.** 176 sq. in. **15.** 2640 sq. in. **17.** $113\frac{1}{7}$ sq. in.

Page 193. **1.** 119. **3.** 2940. **5.** 20,925. **7.** 134. **9.** 1190. **11.** 1287. **13.** 450. **15.** 12,825. **17.** 206.25. **19.** 350. **21.** 125. **23.** 1800. **25.** $1\frac{1}{4}$. **27.** $\frac{3}{40}$. **29.** 2.

Chapter 5. Formulas from Industry

Pages 196–197. **1.** 100 bd. ft. **3.** 35 bd. ft. **5.** $19.25.

7.

	Board feet	Amount
1	288	$25.92
2	48	5.28
3	40	4.80
4	24	2.64
5	64	8.32
6	384	42.24
7	40	6.40
8	324	61.56
9	192	32.64
10	80	21.60
11	48	15.84
12	40	6.80
	Total	$234.04

Pages 199–200. **1.** 165 sq. ft.; $163\frac{5}{9}$ sq. ft. **3.** 49 ft.; $48\frac{7}{12}$ ft. **5.** 24 ft.; $24\frac{1}{6}$ ft. **7. a.** 60 in.; $64\frac{22}{21}$ in. **b.** 300 sq. in.; $335\frac{37}{63}$ sq. in. **9. a.** 240 cu. ft. **b.** $211\frac{1}{9}$ cu. ft.

Page 202. **1.** $\frac{1}{6}$. **3.** $\frac{1}{11}$. **5.** 8 ft. **7.** 4 ft.

Pages 203–204. **1.** 1800 ft.-lb. **3.** 70 ft. **5.** 70,000 ft.-lb.

Page 204. **1.** $\frac{3}{5}$ ft.-lb./sec. **3.** 120 sec.

Page 205. **1.** 9 hp. **3.** $25\frac{25}{33}$.

Page 206. **1.** 2712. **3.** 1,669,473.3. **5.** The waterfall with more water flow.

Page 209. **1.** 514.1 (approx.). **3.** 39.2. **5.** 38.4.

Page 210. **1.** 401 cu. in. (approx.). **3.** 22.5 cu. in. (approx.).

Page 211. **1.** 3.55:1. **3.** 4.09:1. **5.** 63.

Page 213. **1.** 44. **3.** $9\frac{1}{6}$. **5.** 54.

Page 214. **1.** 3.03 or 3. **3.** .68. **5.** 11.8.

Page 215. **1.** 3300 mi. **3.** 650 mph. **5.** 3960 mi.

Page 217. **1.** 12 in. **3.** 420 rpm.

Page 219. **1.** 18,112.5 ft./min. **3.** 8400 ft./min.

Pages 221–222. **1.** $\frac{1}{5}$. **3.** 1600 ft.-lb. **5.** 791. **7.** 29.4 **9.** 4:1. **11.** 5. **13.** 6 hr. **15.** 9 in.

Page 223. **1.** 125. **3.** 20,051. **5.** $1\frac{7}{10}$. **7.** 34. **9.** 3068. **11.** $\frac{7}{8}$. **13.** 945. **15.** 72.54. **17.** $\frac{1}{15}$. **19.** 5. **21.** 20. **23.** 3.37. **25.** 42° 52′. **27.** 71° 33′ 10″. **29.** 51° 57′.

Chapter 6. Systems of Measurement

Pages 226–227. **1.** 216″. **3.** 6 mi. **5.** 63,360 in. **7.** 1800. **9.** 180 yd.

Pages 229–230. **1.** 1872 sq. in. **3.** 11,664 sq. in. **5.** 2 sq. ft. **7. a.** 31,680 sq. in. **b.** 53,856 sq. in. **9.** 44,000 sq. ft.

Pages 232–233. **1.** 81 cu. ft. **3.** 233,280 cu. in. **5.** $13\frac{1}{27}$ cu. yd. **7. a.** 2.5 cu. yd. **b.** $37.50.

Page 235. **1.** 224 qt. **3.** 6 pk. **5.** $\frac{1}{1000}$. **7.** 3.5 gal. **9.** 1 bu. for $5.76.

Page 237. **1.** 2.5 **3.** 100,000,000. **5.** 45. **7.** 3.2. **9.** 1500. **11.** 0.048. **13.** 20. **15.** 1050.

Pages 239–240. **1.** 600. **3.** 32.20 **5.** 2.17. **7.** 3.6 m. **9.** 472.44 in. **11.** 29.53 yd. **13.** 9.1 m. **15.** 218.7 yd. **17.** 28.54 ft. **19.** 9 m.

Page 241. **1.** 300. **3.** 50,000. **5.** 4,000,000. **7.** 807 sq. ft. **9.** 25.9 sq. km.

Page 242. **1.** 2.03 sq. in. **3.** 753.20 sq. ft. **5.** 5.94 sq. m.

Page 243. **1.** 1.62. **3.** 6.5. **5.** 13.86 cu. in.

Page 245. **1.** 1000. **3.** 6.605. **5.** 5.361.

Pages 246–247. **1.** 30,000; 0.020. **3.** 250,000; 0.2. **5.** 2721.6. **7.** 2,310,000. **9.** 75,430,000.

Pages 248–249. **1.** 95. **3.** 104. **5.** 0. **7.** 100. **9.** no.

Pages 250–252. **1.** 96. **3.** 972. **5.** 90. **7.** 1008. **9.** 17,280. **11.** 6. **13.** 2. **15.** 109.4. **17.** 5. **19.** 37.8°. **21.** 50. **23.** 176. **25.** 24,579.55. **27.** 26,460; 28,297.5.

Page 253. **1.** 261. **3.** 22,063. **5.** $12\frac{5}{8}$. **7.** 21. **9.** 17.24. **11.** $10\frac{7}{15}$. **13.** 1012. **15.** 14.1264. **17.** $\frac{5}{22}$. **19.** 42. **21.** 3.75. **23.** 2.62. **25.** 2. **27.** $\frac{9}{14}$. **29.** $1\frac{7}{10}$.

Chapter 7. Geometric Constructions

Page 257. **1–3.** Follow procedure given on page 256 of the text.

Page 259. **1–3.** Follow procedures given on pages 257–259 of the text. **3.** *l* and *m* are parallel lines.

Page 261. . **1–5.** Follow procedure given on page 260 and 261 of the text.

Pages 262–263. **1–5.** Follow procedure given on page 262 of the text.

Page 264. **1.** Follow procedures given on pages 263 and 264 of the text. **3.** See diagram at the top of page 265 of the text. *HJKM* is a square.

Page 266. **1–3.** Follow procedures given on pages 265 and 266 of the text.

Page 269. **1–5.** Follow procedures given on pages 268 and 269 of the text.

Page 270. **1.**

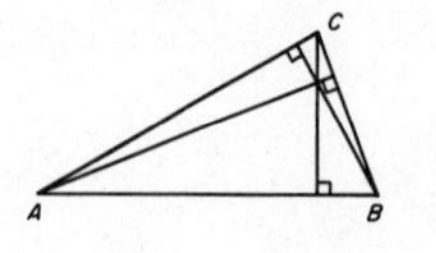

Page 271. **1.** Follow procedure given on page 271 of the text. The medians intersect at one point. **3.** $\overline{AB} = 2\frac{1}{2}''$, $\overline{AC} = 1\frac{13}{16}''$, $\angle A = 34°$.

Page 272. **1.** Triangle should remain level. **3.** Answers will vary.

Page 273. **1.** Follow procedure given on page 272 of the text.

Page 275. (Top) **1.** Follow procedure given on page 273 of the text. **3.** and **5.** Follow procedure given at bottom of page 274 of the text.

Page 275. (Bottom) **1.** Follow procedure given on page 275 of the text.

Page 277. **1–3.** Follow procedure given on page 276 of the text. **5.** Follow procedure given on page 277 of the text.

Page 281. **1.** 8 in.

Page 282. **1.** Follow procedures given on pages 256, 257, and 258 of the text. **3.** Check your construction with a protractor. **5.** Follow procedure given on pages 265 and 266 of the text. **7.** Follo v procedure given on pages 116 and 117 of the text. **9.** Follow procedure given on page 271 of the text.

Page 283. **1.** 115. **3.** 790. **5.** 767.7. **7.** 382. **9.** 543. **11.** 224.14. **13.** 1755. **15.** 3510. **17.** 98.968. **19.** 22. **21.** 0.0225. **23.** $3\frac{1}{3}$. **25.** 3. **27.** 9 ft. 10 in. **29.** 65 ft. 1 in.

Chapter 8. Ratio and Proportion

Pages 286–287. **1.** $\frac{1}{2}$. **3.** $\frac{5}{6}$. **5.** $\frac{3}{4}$. **7.** $\frac{27}{8}$. **9.** $\frac{7}{1}$. **11.** 57:32 or 32:57.

Page 288. **1.** 0.0500 in. **3.** 24.06 threads per in. **5.** 32 threads per in. **7.** 0.0139 in.

Page 290. **1.** 8. **3.** 3. **5.** $2\frac{2}{3}$. **7.** 18. **9.** 25. **11.** 9. **13.** 8. **15.** 7.

Page 293. **1.** 151 lb. **3.** 256 lb. **5.** 4001 lb.

Pages 295–296. **1.** *a* and *c* are similar; *b* and *e* are similar; *d* and *f* are similar.

Pages 297–298. **1.**

BC
9″
$10\frac{1}{2}$″
12″
$13\frac{1}{2}$″
15″

BC increases $1\frac{1}{2}$″ when *AB* increases 3″.

3. $EF = 11\frac{2}{3}$. **5.** $BC = 6\frac{3}{4}$. **7.** 720 yd.

Pages 300–301. **1.** $m = 12$; $n = 15$; $o = 18$. **3.** $r = 2\frac{1}{2}$; $s = 3\frac{1}{2}$; $t = 2$. **5. a.** *A* and *B*. **b.** $\frac{1}{3}$ **c.** $\frac{2}{3}$ and $\frac{5}{7}$; no. **d.** no.

Pages 304–306. **1.** 78 ft. by $37\frac{3}{8}$ ft. **3.** 90 in. **5.** Each door is 16 in. **7.** 10 ft. **9.** 324 in. by 144 in. **11.** $189\frac{1}{16}$ sq. ft. **13.** $206\frac{1}{4}$ sq. ft. **15.** $471\frac{7}{8}$ sq. ft. **17.** $618\frac{3}{4}$ sq. ft.

Pages 307–310. **1. a.** 1875 mi. **b.** $796\frac{7}{8}$ mi. **c.** $1218\frac{3}{4}$ mi. **d.** 750 mi. **3.** 180 mi. **5.** 90 mi. **7.** $82\frac{1}{2}$ mi. **9.** $172\frac{1}{2}$ mi. **11.** $127\frac{1}{2}$ mi. **13.** 285 mi.

Pages 312–314. **1.** $\frac{4}{13}$. **3.** $\frac{9}{16}$. **5.** 0.02165 in. **7.** false. **9.** true. **11.** $3\frac{3}{25}$. **13.** 399 lb. **15.** $X = 15$. **17.** $24\frac{3}{20}$ ft. **19.** $14\frac{1}{2}$ ft. **21.** $468\frac{3}{4}$ mi.; $562\frac{1}{2}$ mi. **23.** 285 mi.

Page 315. **1.** 186. **3.** 2142. **5.** 502.99. **7.** 37. **9.** 8.15. **11.** 10.35. **13.** 2378. **15.** 128.0046. **17.** 1113.75. **19.** 56. **21.** 17. **23.** 22.44. **25.** $7\frac{5}{8}$. **27.** $2\frac{4}{9}$. **29.** $\frac{16}{39}$.

Chapter 9. Percentage

Pages 318–319.

	A Common Fraction	B Decimal Fraction	C Percent
1.	$\frac{1}{2}$	.50	50%
3.	$\frac{2}{3}$	$.66\frac{2}{3}$	$66\frac{2}{3}\%$
5.	$\frac{3}{4}$	.75	75%
7.	$\frac{2}{5}$	.40	40%
9.	$\frac{4}{5}$	.80	80%

13. .80. **15.** .30. **17.** $\frac{1}{4}$. **19.** $\frac{1}{10}$. **21.** $\frac{5}{8}$. **23.** .45. **25.** $.33\frac{1}{3}$. **27.** $\frac{1}{5}$. **29.** $\frac{9}{10}$. **31.** $\frac{2}{3}$.

Page 323. **1.** 10. **3.** 9. **5.** 42. **7.** 10.8. **9.** 100. **11.** 95. **13.** 270. **15.** 110. **17.** 35 sq. in. **19.** 2.548 in.

Page 324. **1.** $33\frac{1}{3}\%$. **3.** 130%. **5. a.** $\frac{9}{10}$. **b.** 90%. **7.** 75%.

Page 326. **1.** $22.00 **3.** 7%. **5.** $3500. **7.** $4\frac{1}{2}\%$. **9.** 6 yr.

Page 329. **1. a.** $486.68. **b.** $86.68. **3. a.** $810.32. **b.** $110.32. **5. a.** $12,562.80. **b.** $6562.80. **7. a.** $31,212.00. **b.** $1212.00. **9. a.** $574,437.50. **b.** $119,437.50. **11. a.** $238.82. **b.** $38.82. **13. a.** $1346.90. **b.** $346.90. **15.** $200 at 6% for 5 years compounded quarterly.

Page 331. **1. a.** $23.33. **b.** $559.92. **c.** $59.92. **d.** 11.13%. **3. a.** $41.67. **b.** $59.96. **c.** $119.84. **d.** $59.88. **5.** 22.2%.

Page 333. **1.** $480. **3.** $12\frac{1}{2}\%$. **5.** $2409.

Pages 334–335. **1.**

Cost	Net Cost
$29.25	$23.40
13.20	9.24
14.10	8.46
11.30	7.91
9.00	6.75

Total	55.76
3% discount	1.67
Net Total	$54.09

Pages 337–338.

	Proper Fraction	Decimal Fraction	Percent
1.	$\frac{1}{4}$	.25	25%
3.	$\frac{2}{3}$	$.66\frac{2}{3}$	$66\frac{2}{3}\%$
5.	$\frac{7}{10}$	.70	70%
7.	$\frac{7}{8}$	.875	$87\frac{1}{2}\%$
9.	$\frac{1}{3}$	$.33\frac{1}{3}$	$33\frac{1}{3}\%$

11. $19,360. **13. a.** 25%. **b.** 150%. **15.** $10,000. **17.** 10.3%.

Page 339. **1.** 168. **3.** 774. **5.** $124\frac{1}{4}$. **7.** 45. **9.** 23.78. **11.** 26.48. **13.** 1425. **15.** 64.0792. **17.** 33,582.5. **19.** $133\frac{4}{7}$. **21.** 269. **23.** $\frac{43}{78}$. **25.** 49. **27.** 121. **29.** 8

Chapter 10. Right Triangles and Trigonometry

Pages 345–347. **1.** 13 ft. **3.** $7\frac{1}{2}$ ft. **5.** $\sqrt{240}$ in. **7.** $\sqrt{45}$ in. **9.** $\sqrt{141.3}$ in. **11.** 14 ft. 2 in. **13.** $\sqrt{8}$ in.

Page 349. **1.** 8 in. **3.** 6 in. **5.** 10 in.

Page 352. **1.** $5\sqrt{3}$ in. **3.** $\frac{\sqrt{3}}{4}$ in. **5.** $AC = 13\frac{1}{2}$ in.; $BC = \frac{27}{2}\sqrt{3}$ in.

Pages 354–356. **1.** 492 sq. ft. **3.** $245\sqrt{3} = 424.34$ cu. in. **5.** $1065\frac{3}{7}$ cu. ft. **7.** $420 + 130\sqrt{3} = 645.16$ sq. in.

Page 360. **1.** $\cos A = \frac{8}{11}$. **3.** $\sin A = \frac{6}{13}$. **5.** $a = 12 \sin 40°$.

Page 364. **1.** .6018. **3.** .6157. **5.** .4540. **7.** .7071. **9.** .5543. **11.** 5°. **13.** 41°. **15.** 33°. **17.** 72°. **19.** 25°.

Pages 367–368. **1.** 13.62 ft. **3.** 11.54 mi. **5.** 74°. **7.** 44.52 ft. **9.** 166.7 ft.

Pages 370–371. **1.** 8.870. **3.** 32° 00′. **5.** $\angle x = 31° 40'$; $\angle y = 28° 30'$.

Pages 372–374. **1.** 13. **3.** 8. **5.** $\sqrt{32\frac{1}{2}} = 5.7$. **7.** 14. **9.** $11\sqrt{3}$. **11.** 40 sq. in. **13.** 286.15 sq. ft. **15. a.** .4848. **b.** .7221. **17.** 36.4 ft. **19.** 13.74 ft.

Page 375. **1.** 145. **3.** 771. **5.** $137\frac{1}{2}$. **7.** 27. **9.** 23.68. **11.** 28.43. **13.** 2380. **15.** 129.8610. **17.** 20,240.4. **19.** 55. **21.** 6.36. **23.** $2\frac{2}{15}$. **25.** 5. **27.** 11. **29.** 3.317.

Chapter 11. Statistical Tables and Graphs

Page 379. **1.** 294. **3.** 9.6%. **5.** 7.3%.

Pages 379–380. **1.** 169. **3.** 82.8%. **5.** 16.9%. **7.** 140,000,000 barrels. **9.** 1:3.

Pages 383–384. **1.** October; 30 cars. **3.** 2:5; 3:1. **5.** 1:12. **7.** 6 ft. **9.** 64.8%.

Page 384. **1.** 80. **3.** 885.

Pages 386 and 387. **1.** 90.3%. **3.** 11.6%. **5.** 102. **7.** 95, 100, 90, 88, 94. **9.** $89\frac{1}{3}$.

Page 390. **1.** 41%. **3.** 1:3. **5.** 47:41. **7.** 25%. **9.** $293.25. **11.** $51.00.

Pages 392–394. **1. a.** 680. **b.** $7\frac{1}{2}$%. **c.** 51.5%. **d.** 1:35. **3. a.** 1175 sets. **b.** 8:3. **c.** 31.9%. **d.** $19,500. **5. a.** 50%. **b.** 3,190,000. **c.** 2,310,000. **d.** 25:29.

BCDEFGHIJ-RM-7987654321

Answers to Exercises

MODERN APPLIED MATHEMATICS

GOLD/CARLBERG

HOUGHTON MIFFLIN COMPANY

BOSTON New York Atlanta Geneva, Ill. Dallas Palo Alto

Library of Congress Catalog Card Number 79-128710

ANSWERS

Chapter 1. Arithmetic Review

Page 3.

+	0	1	2	3	4	5	6	7	8	9
0	0	1	2	3	4	5	6	7	8	9
1	1	2	3	4	5	6	7	8	9	10
2	2	3	4	5	6	7	8	9	10	11
3	3	4	5	6	7	8	9	10	11	12
4	4	5	6	7	8	9	10	11	12	13
5	5	6	7	8	9	10	11	12	13	14
6	6	7	8	9	10	11	12	13	14	15
7	7	8	9	10	11	12	13	14	15	16
8	8	9	10	11	12	13	14	15	16	17
9	9	10	11	12	13	14	15	16	17	18

Page 4. **1.** 106. **2.** 62. **3.** 79. **4.** 61. **5.** 142. **6.** 801. **7.** 763. **8.** 1565. **9.** 993. **10.** 6098. **11.** 2790. **12.** 2841. **13.** 1192. **14.** 15,511. **15.** 2356.

Pages 4–5. **1.** 78. **2.** 9. **3.** 15. **4.** 18. **5.** 47. **6.** 229. **7.** 529. **8.** 7. **9.** 545. **10.** 619. **11.** 7443. **12.** 13,334. **13.** 968. **14.** 18. **15.** 18. **16.** 114. **17.** 22. **18.** 18. **19.** 1. **20.** 9. **21.** 110. **22.** 124.

Pages 6–7. **1.** 11″. **2.** 9″. **3.** 5″. **4.** 1″. **5.** 7″.

Page 8.

×	0	1	2	3	4	5	6	7	8	9	10	11	12
0	0	0	0	0	0	0	0	0	0	0	0	0	0
1	0	1	2	3	4	5	6	7	8	9	10	11	12
2	0	2	4	6	8	10	12	14	16	18	20	22	24
3	0	3	6	9	12	15	18	21	24	27	30	33	36
4	0	4	8	12	16	20	24	28	32	36	40	44	48
5	0	5	10	15	20	25	30	35	40	45	50	55	60
6	0	6	12	18	24	30	36	42	48	54	60	66	72
7	0	7	14	21	28	35	42	49	56	63	70	77	84
8	0	8	16	24	32	40	48	56	64	72	80	88	96
9	0	9	18	27	36	45	54	63	72	81	90	99	108
10	0	10	20	30	40	50	60	70	80	90	100	110	120
11	0	11	22	33	44	55	66	77	88	99	110	121	132
12	0	12	24	36	48	60	72	84	96	108	120	132	144

Page 9. **1.** 68. **2.** 266. **3.** 504. **4.** 165. **5.** 686. **6.** 112. **7.** 355. **8.** 672. **9.** 87. **10.** 282. **11.** 207. **12.** 395. **13.** 2128. **14.** 1768. **15.** 2278. **16.** 3080. **17.** 1752. **18.** 3738. **19.** 1764. **20.** 1350. **21.** 2212. **22.** 37,733. **23.** 13,048. **24.** 34,336. **25.** 174. **26.** 11. **27.** 18. **28.** 12,669. **29.** 45. **30.** 124. **31.** 0. **32.** 771,900. **33.** 100.

Page 10. **1.** 125. **2.** 51. **3.** 24. **4.** 74. **5.** 77. **6.** 197. **7.** 43. **8.** 21. **9.** $11\frac{19}{91}$. **10.** $53\frac{3}{13}$. **11.** 14. **12.** $85\frac{5}{59}$.

Page 10. **1.** $(5 \times 4) + 2 = 22$. **2.** $(5 + 4) \times 2 = 18$, or $(5 \times 4) - 2 = 18$. **3,** $5 \times (4 - 2) = 10$, $(5 \times 4) \div 2 = 10$, or $5 \times (4 \div 2) = 10$. **4.** $(5 - 4) \times 2 = 2$. **5.** $5 + 4 + 2 = 11$. **6.** $5 - (4 \div 2) = 3$, $(5 - 4) + 2 = 3$, or $5 - (4 - 2) = 3$. **7.** $5 \times (4 + 2) = 30$. **8.** $5 + (4 \times 2) = 13$. **9.** $5 \times 4 \times 2 = 40$. **10.** $5 + (4 \div 2) = 7$, $5 + (4 - 2) = 7$, or $(5 + 4) - 2 = 7$.

Page 13. **1.** 32. **2.** 167. **3.** 1569. **4.** 2285. **5.** 154,226. **6.** 22,858.

Page 15. **1.** $1.11. **2.** $5.25. **3.** $32.35. **4.** $52.89. **5.** $216.31. **6.** $3.00, $8.40, $16.20, $27.60. **7.** $10.50, $5.95, $8.72, $3.33, $28.50. **8. a.** $1.23. **b.** $6.15. **c.** $73.80. **9.** $247.14.

Pages 16–19. **1.** Total for 12CV4: $31.68; total for 4A7GV condenser: $10.44; total for MC4562 coil: $18.96; invoice total: $139.98. **2.** Total for wieners: $171.50; total for hamburger buns: $118.80; total for dill pickles: $28.35; total for potatoes: $107.80; invoice total: $882.45. **3.** Total for GC-1307B sealed beam: $4.80; total for GC-1308 headlamp door: $7.28; total for GC-8201G side grille: $19.09; total for GC-1667A molding: $8.34; total for GC-73PD4 parking lamp: $6.00; invoice total: $165.34. **4.** No errors.

Page 20. **1.** 182. **2.** $8750. **3.** 224 hrs. **4.** 7. **5.** 8206 lbs. **6.** 7. **7.** 4. **8.** $32.30. **9.** $11.70. **10.** 33.

Page 21. **1.** $\frac{2}{4}$, $\frac{4}{8}$. **2.** $\frac{3}{4}$. **3.** $\frac{4}{16}$. **4.** $\frac{2}{2}$, $\frac{4}{4}$, $\frac{16}{16}$. **5.** $\frac{5}{8}$. **6.** $\frac{4}{16}$. **7.** $\frac{2}{4}$, $\frac{1}{2}$. **8.** $\frac{3}{8}$. **9.** $\frac{4}{16}$, $\frac{1}{4}$. **10.** $\frac{2}{4}$, $\frac{3}{4}$.

Page 22. **1.** $\frac{3}{8}$. **2.** $\frac{5}{9}$. **3.** $\frac{6}{13}$. **4.** $\frac{4}{7}$. **5.** $\frac{4}{15}$. **6.** $\frac{5}{8}$. **7.** $\frac{6}{11}$. **8.** $\frac{7}{9}$. **9.** $\frac{8}{15}$.

Page 24. **1.** $\frac{2}{6}$, $\frac{1}{6}$. **2.** $\frac{2}{6}$, $\frac{3}{6}$. **3.** $\frac{1}{12}$, $\frac{3}{12}$. **4.** $\frac{3}{4}$, $\frac{2}{4}$. **5.** $\frac{1}{16}$, $\frac{6}{16}$. **6.** $\frac{2}{8}$, $\frac{3}{8}$. **7.** $\frac{4}{8}$, $\frac{2}{8}$, $\frac{1}{8}$. **8.** $\frac{1}{16}$, $\frac{6}{16}$, $\frac{8}{16}$. **9.** $\frac{1}{10}$, $\frac{2}{10}$, $\frac{5}{10}$. **10.** $\frac{2}{3}$. **11.** $\frac{2}{3}$. **12.** $\frac{1}{2}$. **13.** $\frac{3}{4}$. **14.** $\frac{5}{6}$. **15.** $\frac{2}{3}$. **16.** $\frac{8}{9}$. **17.** $\frac{2}{3}$. **18.** $\frac{1}{6}$. **19.** $\frac{3}{4}$.

Page 25. **1.** $2\frac{1}{4}$. **2.** $1\frac{1}{4}$. **3.** $\frac{8}{15}$. **4.** $\frac{5}{6}$. **5.** $\frac{17}{21}$. **6.** $\frac{5}{16}$. **7.** $1\frac{9}{16}$. **8.** $\frac{13}{64}$. **9.** $\frac{18}{16}$. **10.** $\frac{37}{143}$. **11.** $1\frac{3}{7}$. **12.** $1\frac{1}{12}$. **13.** $1\frac{101}{120}$. **14.** $\frac{9}{40}$. **15.** $\frac{9}{16}$.

Page 26. **1.** 12. **2.** 24. **3.** 24. **4.** 24. **5.** 40. **6.** 48. **7.** 60. **8.** 20. **9.** 36. **10.** 42. **11.** $1\frac{1}{12}$. **12.** $\frac{23}{24}$. **13.** $\frac{5}{8}$. **14.** $\frac{17}{24}$. **15.** $\frac{23}{40}$. **16.** $\frac{25}{48}$. **17.** $\frac{23}{60}$. **18.** $\frac{19}{20}$. **19.** $\frac{25}{36}$. **20.** $\frac{23}{42}$.

Pages 27–28. **1.** $\frac{3}{8}$. **2.** $\frac{8}{15}$. **3.** $\frac{55}{72}$. **4.** $3\frac{3}{4}$. **5.** $\frac{18}{35}$. **6.** $\frac{10}{21}$. **7.** $\frac{65}{84}$. **8.** $\frac{6}{35}$. **9.** $\frac{4}{27}$. **10.** $\frac{11}{32}$. **11.** $40\frac{1}{2}$. **12.** $\frac{105}{512}$.

Page 29. **1.** 3. **2.** $\frac{3}{2}$. **3.** $\frac{1}{3}$. **4.** 2. **5.** $\frac{8}{3}$. **6.** $\frac{5}{6}$. **7.** $\frac{1}{100}$. **8.** 10. **9.** $\frac{4}{3}$. **10.** $\frac{3}{4}$. **11.** $1\frac{1}{8}$. **12.** $\frac{4}{21}$. **13.** $1\frac{3}{5}$. **14.** $\frac{7}{8}$. **15.** $\frac{5}{8}$. **16.** $\frac{2}{3}$. **17.** $3\frac{1}{3}$. **18.** $\frac{2}{3}$. **19.** $\frac{1}{200}$. **20.** $\frac{3}{16}$. **21.** $\frac{14}{15}$. **22.** $5\frac{1}{3}$. **23.** $3\frac{1}{8}$. **24.** $1\frac{5}{31}$. **25.** $21\frac{1}{3}$. **26.** 33. **27.** $\frac{1}{8}$. **28.** $\frac{1}{2}$.

Pages 31–33. **1.** $\frac{7}{12}''$. **2.** $3\frac{31}{32}''$. **3.** $2\frac{27}{32}''$. **4.** $\frac{7}{16}''$. **5.** $x = \frac{5}{8}''$, $y = \frac{5}{16}''$.

Page 34. **1.** 33.0. **2.** 49.7. **3.** 601.3. **4.** $109.80. **5.** $13.89. **6.** .747″. **7.** 4.9 miles. **8.** 9.4.

Page 35. **1.** 9.2. **2.** 34.463. **3.** 77.72. **4.** .567.294. **5.** 11.1775. **6.** .05859375. **7.** .1484375. **8.** .140625. **9.** .0546875. **10.** .15625.

Page 38. **1.** .375. **2.** .625. **3.** .25. **4.** .75. **5.** .0625. **6.** .3125. **7.** .09375. **8.** .875. **9.** .015625. **10.** .1875. **11.** .63. **12.** .38. **13.** 5.233. **14.** 12.7. **15.** 1.87. **16.** 3.14. **17.** .406. **18.** 1.141. **19.** .30. **20.** .17. **21.** .03. **22.** 13,090. **23.** 6.85. **24.** 21.14. **25.** 3. **26.** .9. **27.** .67. **28.** 7.33. **29.** 2.28. **30.** .75.

Pages 43–44. **1.** 36. **2.** 64. **3.** 144. **4.** 3721. **5.** 2025. **6.** 15,625. **7.** 16.81. **8.** 1.44. **9.** 12.25.

10. 6400. **11.** 2. **12.** 9. **13.** 7. **14.** 12. **15.** 8. **16.** 15. **17.** 12.17. **18.** 5.39. **19.** 5.48. **20.** 15.81. **21.** 60.41. **22.** 64. **23.** 8. **24.** 512. **25.** 125. **26.** 1000. **27.** 39.0625. **28.** 2.25. **29.** 9.8596. **30.** 16. **31.** 256.

Pages 45–46. **1.** 18. **2.** 14. **3.** 42. **4.** 72. **5.** 91. **6.** 5. **7.** 7. **8.** 7. **9.** 250. **10.** 95. **11.** $(8 \times 8) \div 8 = 8$. **12.** $7 + (6 \times 3) = 25$. **13.** $(4 \times 11) - 3 = 41$. **14.** $(81 \div 9) + 3 = 12$. **15.** $(27 \times 3) \div 9 = 9$. **16.** \$9.00. **17.** \$14.00. **18.** \$16.54. **19.** \$46.12. **20.** \$1.05, \$.72, \$1.43, \$22.10, \$25.30. **21.** $\frac{8}{8}$. **22.** $\frac{5}{5}$. **23.** $\frac{20}{25}$. **24.** 1. **25.** 1. **26.** $\frac{9}{16}$. **27.** $13\frac{3}{4}$. **28.** $4\frac{7}{16}$. **29.** $\frac{9}{40}$. **30.** $\frac{3}{32}$. **31.** $\frac{5}{176}$. **32.** .1875. **33.** $\frac{3}{8}$. **34.** $4\frac{4}{5}$. **35.** 2.5. **36.** $2\frac{5}{8}''$. **37.** 21.21.

Page 47. **1.** 106. **2.** 111. **3.** 2115. **4.** 10,681. **5.** 16,698. **6.** 11,906. **7.** 445. **8.** 178. **9.** 1134. **10.** 3187. **11.** 1267. **12.** 15,575. **13.** 1800. **14.** 266. **15.** 3151. **16.** 16,740. **17.** 63,837. **18.** 272,205. **19.** 22. **20.** 235. **21.** 12. **22.** 17. **23.** 16. **24.** 302.

Chapter 2. Measurement

Page 53. **1.**

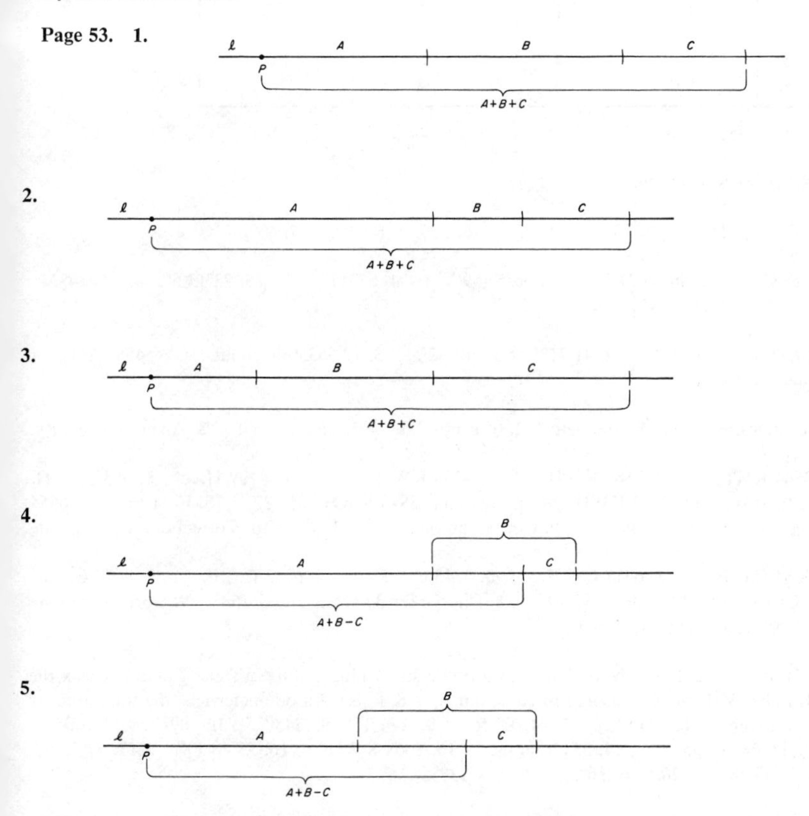

Page 54. **1.–10. a.** Answers will vary. **1. b.** $1\frac{3}{4}''$. **2. b.** $1\frac{11}{16}''$. **3. b.** $1\frac{15}{16}''$. **4. b.** $3\frac{11}{16}''$. **5. b.** $2\frac{13}{16}''$ **6. b.** $2\frac{1}{2}''$. **7. b.** $2\frac{3}{16}''$. **8. b.** $3\frac{7}{16}''$. **9. b.** $1\frac{7}{8}''$. **10. b.** $3\frac{7}{8}''$

Page 55. **1.–3.** Answers will vary. **4.** 90 ft. **5.** 60 ft. 6 in.

Page 57. **1.** 6340 ft. **2.** 3940 ft. **3.** 1700 ft. **4.** 7500 ft. **5.** 27,900 ft. **6.** 71,400 ft. **7.** 8800 ft. **8.** 12,420 ft. **9.** 880 ft. **10.** 3200 ft. **11.** 5400 ft. **12.** 74,320 ft.

Pages 60–61. **1.** .750 in. **2.** .176 in. **3.** .630 in. **4.** .099 in. **5.** .703 in. **6.** .263 in. **7.** .075 in. **8.** .502 in. **9.** .009 in. **10.** .662 in. **11.** .048 in. **12.** .501 in. **13.** .859 in. **14.** .358 in. **15.** .979 in. **16.** .306 in. **17.** .829 in. **18.** .392 in.

Pages 64–65. **1.** Dimension limits: 1.756″, 1.744″; tolerance: 0.012″. **2.** Dimension limits: 3.507″; 3.496″; tolerance: 0.011″. **3.** 2.501″, 2.499″. **4.** 0.005″. **5.** Dimension limits for $1\frac{1}{2}$″ diameter: 1.503″, 1.498″; tolerance: 0.005″. Dimension limits for $\frac{3}{8}$″ diameter: .377″, .373″; tolerance: .004″.

Pages 66–67. **1.** 12 sq. units. **2.** 9 sq. units. **3.** 13 sq. units. **4.** 16 sq. units. **5.** 15 sq. units. **6.** $25\frac{1}{2}$ sq. units. **7.** 19 sq. units. **8.** 17 sq. units. **9.** $18\frac{1}{2}$ sq. units. **10.** $18\frac{1}{2}$ sq. units. **11.** 12 sq. units. **12.** 12 sq. units.

Pages 69–70. **1.** 2 sq. in. **2.** 3 sq. in. **3.** $2\frac{1}{4}$ sq. in. **4.** $1\frac{7}{8}$ sq. in. **5.** $5\frac{5}{8}$ sq. in. **6.** $\frac{3}{8}$ sq. in. **7.** $2\frac{5}{8}$ sq. in. **8.** $\frac{5}{8}$ sq. in. **9.** $3\frac{3}{32}$ sq. in. **10.** $7\frac{35}{64}$ sq. in. **11.** $27\frac{1}{2}$ sq. in. **12.** $23\frac{5}{8}$ sq. in. **13.** Answers will vary. **14.** 144 sq. in. = 1 sq. ft. **15.** larger.

Pages 72–73.

	length = l	width = w	height = h	volume = V
1.	3	2	2	12
2.	4	1	3	12
3.	3	2	6	36
4.	6	4	6	144
5.	6	4	3	72

6. a. 1080 cu. units. **b.** 14,352 cu. units.

Pages 76–77. **1.–8.** Answers will vary.

Pages 78–79. **1.** 30°. **2.** 159°. **3.** 130°. **4.** 17°. **5.** 51°. **6.** 50°. **7.** 60°.

Pages 80–81. **1.** 62°56′. **2.** 46°55′27″. **3.** 56°55′59″. **4.** 67°45′8″. **5.** 73°13′5″. **6.** 14°24′. **7.** 22°11′23″. **8.** 18°48′. **9.** 28°38′4″. **10.** 17°52′48″.

Pages 84–85. **1.** 57.74′ or about 58′. **2.** 41.713′ or about 42′. **3.** 12.9636′ or about 13′. **4.** 17.6211′ or about 18′. **5.** Answers will vary.

Page 89. **1.** 100° centigrade or 212° Fahrenheit. **2.** 0° centigrade or 32° Fahrenheit. **3.** Answers will vary.

Pages 91–93. **1.** 3564 KWH. **2.** 7563 KWH. **3.** 4735 KWH. **4.** 1144 KWH. **5.** 5633 KWH. **6.** 7638 KWH. **7.** First reading: 3452 KWH; second reading: 3843 KWH; $11.22. **8.** First reading: 6554 KWH; second reading: 6836 KWH; $8.49. **9.** Correct amount is $3.81. **10.** Correct amount is $3.45.

Pages 94–96. **1.** 3664 C.C.F. **2.** 6417 C.C.F. **3.** 3745 C.C.F. **4.** 6213 C.C.F. **5.** 8477 C.C.F. **6.** 4661 C.C.F. **7.** Charge for 28 C.C.F. is $2.40. **8.** Charge for 35 C.C.F. is $2.75. **9.** Correct amount due is $14.90. **10.** Correct amount due is $8.90.

Pages 98–100. **1.** True. **2.** False. A mechanic adjusting a spark plug will use a feeler gauge to check the gap. **3.** True. **4.** False. Volume is measured in cubic units. **5.** False. An odometer tells the total number of miles a car has been driven. **6.** 7240 ft. **7.** 24,700 ft. **8.** .136″. **9.** .245″. **10.** .891″. **11.** .016″. **12.** 1.501″, 1.499″. **13.** 18 sq. units. **14.** 28 cu. units. **15.** 1068 KWH. **16.** 55°48′30″. **17.** 59°7′16″. **18.** 13°14′16″. **19.** 29°43′48″. **20.** x = 56°. **21.** y = 138°.

Page 101. **1.** 77. **2.** 119. **3.** 1052. **4.** 11,004. **5.** 21,409. **6.** 21,663. **7.** 111. **8.** 295. **9.** 2205. **10.** 7416. **11.** 1026. **12.** 5376. **13.** 1375. **14.** 3895. **15.** 7825. **16.** 62,075. **17.** 384,625. **18.** 535,941. **19.** 25. **20.** 150. **21.** 27. **22.** 235. **23.** 190. **24.** 106. **25.** $\frac{3}{4}$. **26.** $\frac{7}{8}$. **27.** $\frac{4}{5}$. **28.** $\frac{7}{16}$. **29.** $\frac{9}{32}$. **30.** $\frac{7}{16}$.

Chapter 3. Geometric Figures

Page 109. **6.** $\angle A$ = 25°; complement = 65°. **7.** $\angle PQR$ = 45°; complement = 45°. **8.** $\angle B$ = 75°; supplement = 105°. **9.** $\angle GHI$ = 125°; supplement = 55°. **10.** 62°30′. **11.** 47°28′33″. **12.** 140°17′. **13.** 42°59′27″.

Pages 112–113. **1.** octagon. **2.** pentagon. **3.** triangle. **4.** hexagon. **5.** quadrilateral. **6.** decagon. **7.** quadrilateral. **8.** triangle. **9.** 8. **10.** 10. **11.** 6. **12.** 5. **13.** and **14.**

	Ex. 13	Ex. 14
Name of polygon	pentagon	octagon
$m\overline{AB}$ = ? inch	1	$\frac{3}{4}$
Are all sides equal?	yes	yes
$m\angle ABC$ = ? degrees	110°	135°
Are all angles equal?	yes	yes
Is the polygon regular?	yes	yes

Pages 115–116. **2.** yes. **3.** yes. **4.** $m\angle 1 = 11°$; $m\angle 2 = 9°$; $m\angle 3 = 16°$; $m\angle 4 = 7°$; $m\angle 5 = 7°$; $m\angle 6 = 6°$; $m\angle 7 = 11°$. **5.** $\overline{CE} \perp \overline{AB}$. **6.** $\overline{CE}$. **7.** $\overline{CE}$.

Pages 118–119. **5. a.** $p = 1\frac{11}{16}''$; $q = 1\frac{3}{8}''$; $r = \frac{13}{16}''$ **b.** $p = 1\frac{1}{2}''$; $q = 1\frac{1}{2}''$; $r = \frac{15}{16}''$. **c.** $p = 1\frac{3}{16}''$; $q = 1\frac{13}{16}''$; $r = 1\frac{1}{16}''$. **d.** $p = 1\frac{11}{16}''$; $q = 1\frac{5}{16}''$; $r = 1\frac{1}{16}''$; in every triangle the sum of the lengths of any two sides of a triangle is greater than the length of the third side. **6.** No; see Ex. 5. **7.** $\angle A = 60°$; $\angle B = 60°$; $\angle C = 60°$; acute triangle. $\angle A = 114°$; $\angle B = 39°$; $\angle C = 27°$; obtuse triangle. $\angle A = 45°$; $\angle B = 45°$; $\angle C = 90°$; right triangle. $\angle A = 58°$; $\angle B = 56°$; $\angle C = 66°$; acute triangle. **8.** $\overline{AB} = \frac{11}{16}''$; $\overline{BC} = \frac{11}{16}''$; $\overline{AC} = \frac{11}{16}''$. $\overline{AB} = \frac{9}{16}''$; $\overline{BC} = 1\frac{1}{8}''$; $\overline{AC} = \frac{3}{4}''$. $\overline{AB} = \frac{7}{8}''$; $\overline{BC} = \frac{5}{8}''$; $\overline{AC} = \frac{5}{8}''$. $\overline{AB} = \frac{7}{8}''$; $\overline{BC} = \frac{13}{16}''$; $\overline{AC} = \frac{3}{4}''$. **9. b.** side opposite 50° angle $= 2\frac{7}{16}''$; side opposite 60° angle $= 2\frac{3}{4}''$; **c.** 70°. **11.** yes.

Page 122. **1.** (a); (c); (d); (e). **2.** (d); (e). **3.** (a); (d) **4.** (b); (f). **5.** (f). **6.** yes. **7.** yes. **8.** 90°; yes. **9.** All sides are $\frac{7}{8}''$. The square has 4 right angles. **10.** The square is a regular polygon.

Page 133. **1.** 40°; 40°; 40°. **2.** yes. **3.** no. **5.** 55°. **6.** 305°.

Pages 135–136. **1.** 20°. **2.** 50°. **3.** 90°. **4.** $32\frac{1}{2}°$. **5.** 216°.

Pages 137–138. **1.** 45°. **2.** 65°. **3.** 50°. **4.** $m\widehat{AB} = 90°$; $m\widehat{BC} = 60°$; $m\widehat{CD} = 120°$; $m\widehat{AD} = 90°$; $m\angle BOC = 75°$; $m\angle COD = 105°$; $m\angle BAC = 30°$; $m\angle BAD = 90°$.

Pages 140–141. **1.** 44°. **2.** 100°. **3.** 90°. **4.** 88°. **5.** $m\widehat{AXB} = 140°$; $m\widehat{AYB} = 220°$. **6.** 75°. **7.** $m\angle 1 = 40°$; $m\angle 2 = 50°$; $m\angle 3 = 60°$; $m\angle 4 = 30°$; $m\angle 5 = 90°$; $m\angle 6 = 90°$

Page 144. **1.** 60°. **2.** 80°. **3.** 20°. **4.** $27\frac{1}{2}°$. **5.** 220°. **6.** 65°.

Page 148. **1.** circles. **2.** axis; base. **3.** oblique. **4.** altitude. **5.** altitude.

Pages 149–152. **1. a.** $\overline{AO}$. **b.** $\overline{BC}$. **c.** $\overleftrightarrow{GJ}$. **d.** $\overline{HI}$. **e.** $\overrightarrow{FE}$. **f.** $\widehat{AB}$. **g.** D. **h.** $\widehat{BC}$. **2.** false; A triangle with three equal sides is usually called an equilateral triangle. **3.** false; An angle greater than 90° but less than 180° is called an obtuse angle. **4.** false; The supplement of an angle of 135° is an angle of 45°. **5.** true. **6.** true. **7.** true. **8.** false; A regular polygon is a polygon whose sides are equal and whose angles are equal. **9.** false; A triangle having an angle of 115° is called an obtuse triangle. **10.** false; A quadrilateral is a polygon with four sides. **11.** false; A trapezoid whose 2 nonparallel sides are equal is called an isosceles trapezoid. **12.** true. **13.** true. **14.** false; A polyhedron is a geometric solid bounded by planes. **15.** false; A triangular prism is a prism whose bases are triangles. **16.** true. **17.** false; An angle formed at the center of the circle is called a central angle. **18.** false; An angle formed by two chords drawn from the same point is called an inscribed angle. **19.** true. **20.** false; An angle formed by a tangent and a chord is measured by half the measure of its intercepted arc. **21.** false; An angle formed by two secants is measured by half the difference of its intercepted arcs. **22.** 60°. **23.** 65°. **24.** 40°. **25.** 79°. **26.** 280°. **27.** 30°. **28.** 100°. **29.** 70°. **30.** 25°. **31.** 70°. **32.** 20°. **33.** 160°. **34.** 15°.

Page 153. **1.** 131. **2.** 177. **3.** 2284. **4.** 5160. **5.** 25,657. **6.** 16,310. **7.** 31. **8.** 313. **9.** 1535. **10.** 6780. **11.** 912. **12.** 11,278. **13.** 525. **14.** 1100. **15.** 10,625. **16.** 14,688. **17.** 3595.6. **18.** 34.565. **19.** 55. **20.** 44. **21.** 165. **22.** 115. **23.** 1050. **24.** 5.8. **25.** $\frac{17}{24}$. **26.** $\frac{15}{16}$. **27.** $\frac{5}{8}$. **28.** $\frac{3}{256}$. **29.** $7\frac{1}{4}$. **30.** $2\frac{1}{8}$.

Chapter 4. Geometric Formulas

Pages 156–158. **1.** 27 units. **2.** 36 units. **3.** 9 sq. in. **4.** $24\frac{1}{2}$ sq. in. **5.** 28 sq. ft. **6.** 65 sq. ft. **7.** 12 sq. cm. **8.** 210 sq. in. **9.** 21,600 sq. ft. **10.** $\overline{AB} = 3\frac{5}{8}''$; $\overline{CD} = 1\frac{1}{4}''$; area is approx. $2\frac{1}{4}$ sq. in. **11.** $\overline{CB} = 2\frac{1}{16}''$; $\overline{AF} = 2\frac{1}{8}''$; area is approx. $2\frac{3}{16}$ sq. in. **12.** $\overline{AC} = 2\frac{5}{16}''$; $\overline{BE} = 1\frac{7}{8}''$; area is approx. $2\frac{3}{16}$ sq. in.

Pages 159–160. **1.** 15 sq. in. **2.** 9 sq. in. **3.** $13\frac{3}{4}$ sq. in. **4.** 14 sq. in. **5.** area of rectangle $ABCD = 60$ sq. in.; area of parallelogram $CDEF = 60$ sq. in.; yes. **6.** 32 in. **7.** 30 in. **8.** 28 in. **9.** perimeter = 152 in.; area = 1008 sq. in. **10.** $2\frac{7}{16}$ sq. in.

Pages 161–162. **1.** 7 sq. in. **2.** $16\frac{1}{2}$ sq. in. **3.** $16\frac{1}{2}$ sq. in. **4.** $12\frac{15}{16}$ sq. in. **5.** $15\frac{5}{12}$ sq. in. **6.** 30 in. **7.** 47 in. **8.** 180 sq. ft. **9.** $94\frac{1}{2}$ sq. ft.

Page 164. **1.** $28\frac{2}{7}$ sq. in. **2.** $15\frac{51}{56}$ sq. in. **3.** $78\frac{4}{7}$ sq. in. **4.** $1\frac{25}{63}$ sq. in. **5.** 88 in. **6.** $31\frac{3}{7}$ in. **7.** $62\frac{6}{7}$.

Pages 164–166. **1. a.** 420 sq. ft. **b.** 280 sq. ft. **c.** 1140 sq. ft. **d.** 1840 sq. ft. **2.** $227\frac{1}{2}$ sq. ft. **3. a.** 12 sq. in. **b.** 16 sq. in. **c.** 4 sq. in. **d.** 32 sq. in. **4. a.** 3 sq. in. **b.** 11 sq. in. **c.** 14 sq. in. **d.** 25 sq. in. **e.** 28 sq. in. **5.** $12\frac{19}{28}$ sq. in. **6.** $137\frac{1}{16}$ sq. in. **7.** 480 sq. in.

Pages 170–171. **1.** 36 sq. in. **2.** 144 sq. in. **3.** 9 sq. in. **4.** 90 sq. in. **5.** 162 sq. in. **6.** 40 sq. in. **7.** 142 sq. in. **8.** 17 sq. in. **9.** 84 sq. in. **10.** 6480 sq. in. **11.** 248 sq. in.

Page 173. **1.** 120 cu. in. **2.** 112 cu. in. **3.** $67\frac{1}{2}$ cu. in. **4.** $110\frac{5}{8}$ cu. in. **5. a.** 35,700 cu. in. **b.** 4200 sq. in. **c.** 6240 sq. in. **6.** $37\frac{1}{3}$ truckloads.

Pages 174–175. **1.** 45 sq. in. **2.** $87\frac{1}{2}$ sq. in. **3.** 153 sq. in. **4.** 90 sq. in. **5.** 192 sq. in.

Page 176. **1.** 72 sq. in. **2.** 108 sq. in. **3.** 110.4 sq. in. **4.** 62.4 sq. in. **5.** 189 sq. in. **6.** 299.2 sq. in.

Page 178. **1.** 40 cu. in. **2.** 32 cu. in. **3.** $14\frac{7}{24}$ cu. in. **4.** $7\frac{2}{3}$ cu. in. **5.** $366\frac{2}{3}$ cu. in. **6.** $73\frac{1}{3}$ cu. in.

Page 181. **1.** $94\frac{2}{7}$ sq. in. **2.** 99 sq. in. **3.** $x = 1$(in.). **4.** 132 sq. in. **5.** 572 sq. in. **6.** approx. $20.11.

Page 182. **1.** 572 sq. in. **2.** $226\frac{2}{7}$ sq. in. **3.** $421\frac{1}{7}$ sq. in. **4.** $347\frac{2}{7}$ sq. in.

Pages 183–184. **1.** 203 cu. in. **2.** 1232 cu. in. **3.** 198 cu. in. **4.** 220 cu. in. **5.** 484 cu. in.

Page 186. **1.** 176 sq. in. **2.** 132 sq. in. **3.** 362.34 sq. in. **4.** 550 cu. in. **5.** 115.5 cu. in.

Page 187. **1.** 154 cu. in.; $179\frac{2}{3}$ cu. in. **2.** $28\frac{2}{7}$ sq. in.; $14\frac{1}{7}$ cu. in. **3.** $314\frac{2}{7}$ sq. in.; $523\frac{17}{21}$ cu. in. **4.** $169\frac{5}{7}$ sq. in.; $134\frac{2}{21}$ cu. in.

Pages 191–192. **1.** 54 sq. in. **2.** 36 sq. in. **3.** 40 sq. ft. **4.** 154 sq. in. **5. a.** 9 sq. in. **b.** 18 sq. in. **c.** 48 sq. in. **6.** 48 sq. in. **7.** $112\frac{5}{8}$ sq. in. **8.** 189 cu. in. **9.** 192 sq. in. **10.** 129.6 sq. in. **11.** $\frac{1}{18}$ cu. in. **12.** 506 sq. yd. **13.** 176 sq. in. **14.** 275 cu. in. **15.** 2640 sq. in. **16.** 2464 cu. in. **17.** $113\frac{1}{7}$ sq. in. **18.** $5577\frac{11}{21}$ cu. in.

Page 193. **1.** 119. **2.** 222. **3.** 2940. **4.** 5811. **5.** 20,925. **6.** 21,325. **7.** 134. **9.** 131. **9.** 1190. **10.** 7529. **11.** 1287. **12.** 24,887. **13.** 450. **14.** 1125. **15.** 12,825. **16.** 502,075. **17.** 206.25. **18.** 8.262. **19.** 350. **20.** 15. **21.** 125. **22.** 235. **23.** 1800. **24.** 35.5. **25.** $1\frac{1}{4}$. **26.** $\frac{15}{16}$. **27.** $\frac{3}{40}$. **28.** $\frac{3}{8}$. **29.** 2. **30.** $1\frac{1}{2}$.

Chapter 5. Formulas from Industry

Pages 196–197. **1.** 100 bd. ft. **2.** $6\frac{2}{3}$ bd. ft. **3.** 35 bd. ft. **4.** $366\frac{2}{3}$ bd. ft. **5.** $19.25. **6.** $51.60.

7.

	Board feet	Amount
1	288	$25.92
2	48	5.28
3	40	4.80
4	24	2.64
5	64	8.32
6	384	42.24
7	40	6.40
8	324	61.56
9	192	32.64
10	80	21.60
11	48	15.84
12	40	6.80

Total $234.04

Pages 199–200. **1.** 165 sq. ft.; $163\frac{5}{9}$ sq. ft. **2.** 195 sq. ft.; 187 sq. ft. **3.** 49 ft.; $48\frac{7}{12}$ ft. **4.** 3150 cu. ft.; $3061\frac{35}{64}$ cu. ft. **5.** 24 ft.; $24\frac{1}{6}$ ft. **6.** 71 ft.; $71\frac{17}{24}$ ft. **7. a.** 60 in.; $64\frac{20}{21}$ in. **b.** 300 sq. in.; $335\frac{37}{63}$ sq. in. **8. a.** 50 cu. ft. **b.** $46\frac{373}{512}$ or approx. $46\frac{3}{4}$ cu. ft. **9. a.** 240 cu. ft. **b.** $211\frac{1}{9}$ cu. ft. **10. a.** 128 cu. ft. **b.** $117\frac{9}{64}$ cu. ft.

Page 202. **1.** $\frac{1}{6}$. **2.** $\frac{1}{6}$. **3.** $\frac{1}{11}$. **4.** 5 ft. **5.** 8 ft. **6.** 13 ft. **7.** 4 ft.

Pages 203–204. **1.** 1800 ft.-lb. **2.** 12,500 ft.-lb. **3.** 70 ft. **4.** 40 lb. **5.** 70,000 ft.-lb. **6.** 100 lb.

Page 204. **1.** $\frac{3}{5}$ ft.-lb./sec. **2.** 5 ft.-lb./sec. **3.** 120 sec. **4.** 420 ft.-lb./sec.

Page 205. **1.** 9 hp. **2.** $21\frac{9}{11}$ hp. **3.** $25\frac{25}{33}$. **4.** 30 ft.

Page 206. **1.** 2712. **2.** 2,350,400. **3.** 1,669,473.3. **4.** 45 ft. **5.** The waterfall with more water flow. **6.** The higher waterfall.

Page 209. **1.** 514.1 (approx.). **2.** 296 (approx.). **3.** 39.2. **4.** 28.9. **5.** 38.4.

Page 210. **1.** 401 cu. in. (approx.). **2.** $326\frac{6}{7}$ or 327 cu. in. **3.** 22.5 cu. in. (approx.). **4.** 287 cu. in. (approx.).

Page 211. **1.** 3.55:1. **2.** 3.31:1. **3.** 4.09:1. **4.** 36. **5.** 63.

Page 213. **1.** 44. **2.** 30. **3.** $9\frac{1}{6}$. **4.** $4\frac{7}{12}$. **5.** 54.

Page 214. **1.** 3.03 or 3. **2.** 35.4. **3.** .68. **4.** 4.8. **5.** 11.8.

Page 215. **1.** 3300 mi. **2.** 5 hr. **3.** 650 mph. **4.** 650 mph. **5.** 3960 mi.

Page 217. **1.** 12 in. **2.** $19\frac{1}{5}$ in. **3.** 420 rpm. **4.** 9 in.

Page 219. **1.** 18,112.5 ft./min. **2.** $12,833\frac{1}{3}$ ft./min. **3.** 8400 ft./min. **4.** 4400 ft./min.

Pages 221–222. **1.** $\frac{1}{5}$. **2.** 8 bd. ft. **3.** 1600 ft.-lb. **4.** 7. **5.** 791. **6.** 109.7 (approx.). **7.** 29.4. **8.** $288\frac{3}{4}$ cu. in. **9.** 4:1. **10.** 23. **11.** 5. **12.** .75 (approx.). **13.** 6 hr. **14.** 430 mi. **15.** 9 in. **16.** 2200 ft./min.

Page 223. **1.** 125. **2.** 1545. **3.** 20,051. **4.** $2\frac{7}{8}$. **5.** $1\frac{7}{10}$. **6.** 197.28. **7.** 34. **8.** 13.2. **9.** 3068. **10.** $\frac{1}{8}$. **11.** $\frac{7}{8}$. **12.** 1.21. **13.** 945. **14.** 46.75. **15.** 72.54. **16.** 67.62. **17.** $\frac{1}{15}$. **18.** $\frac{3}{28}$. **19.** 5. **20.** 2053. **21.** 20. **22.** 30,200. **23.** 3.37. **24.** 1.1. **25.** 42° 52′. **26.** 46° 26′ 5″. **27.** 71° 33′ 10″. **28.** 22° 16′ 13″. **29.** 51° 57′. **30.** 14° 44′ 50″.

Chapter 6. Systems of Measurement

Pages 226–227. **1.** 216″. **2.** $12\frac{1}{2}$′. **3.** 6 mi. **4.** $\frac{2}{3}$ yd. **5.** 63,360 in. **6.** 485,760 ft.; 161,920 yd. **7.** 1800. **8.** 104. **9.** 180 yd. **10.** 46 rods.

Pages 229–230. **1.** 1872 sq. in. **2.** 45 sq. ft. **3.** 11,664 sq. in. **4.** 40 sq. yd. **5.** 2 sq. ft. **6.** $114.00. **7. a.** 31,680 sq. in. **b.** 53,856 sq. in. **8.** 594 sq. yd. **9.** 44,000 sq. ft. **10. a.** 770 in. **b.** 25,578 sq. in. **c.** 177.625 sq. ft.

Pages 232–233. **1.** 81 cu. ft. **2.** 4320 cu. in. **3.** 233,280 cu. in. **4.** $\frac{5}{36}$ cu. ft. **5.** $13\frac{1}{27}$ cu. yd. **6. a.** $\frac{77}{216}$ cu. ft. **b.** 27¢ **7. a.** 2.5 cu. yd. **b.** $37.50.

Page 235. **1.** 224 qt. **2.** 64 fl. oz. **3.** 6 pk. **4.** $13\frac{1}{2}$ gal. **5.** $\frac{1}{1000}$. **6.** 3744. **7.** 3.5 gal. **8.** $6.65. **9.** 1 bu. for $5.76. **10.** a 24-ounce can for 87¢.

Page 237. **1.** 2.5. **2.** 500,000. **3.** 100,000,000. **4.** 2000. **5.** 45. **6.** 70,000. **7.** 3.2. **8.** 0.05 **9.** 1500. **10.** 95,000. **11.** 0.048. **12.** 3,250,000. **13.** 20. **14.** 85. **15.** 1050. **16.** .0045.

Pages 239–240. **1.** 600. **2.** 1584. **3.** 32.20. **4.** 3100. **5.** 2.17. **6.** 787.40 in. **7.** 3.6 m. **8.** 38.28 yd. **9.** 472.44 in. **10.** 4.5 m. **11.** 29.53 yd. **12.** 45.93 ft. **13.** 9.1 m. **14.** 32.8 ft. **15.** 218.7 yd. **16.** 2624.67 ft. **17.** 28.54 ft. **18.** 437.44 yd. **19.** 9 m. **20.** 724.65″.

Page 241. **1.** 300. **2.** 10,000. **3.** 50,000. **4.** 1,000,000. **5.** 4,000,000. **6.** 1 sq. in. **7.** 807 sq. ft. **8.** 4.05 sq. m. **9.** 25.9 sq. km. **10.** 117 sq. mi.

Page 242. **1.** 2.03 sq. in. **2.** 6 sq. in. **3.** 753.20 sq. ft. **4.** 18 sq. m. **5.** 5.94 sq. m.

Page 243. **1.** 1.62. **2.** 0.28. **3.** 6.5. **4.** 4.2 cu. m. **5.** 13.86 cu. in.

Page 245. **1.** 1000. **2.** 52.84. **3.** 6.605. **4.** $13.16; 10 cents. **5.** 5.361.

Pages 246–247. **1.** 30,000; 0.020. **2.** 100,000; 3000. **3.** 250,000; 0.2. **4.** 0.625; 5000. **5.** 2721.6. **6.** 45,359.24. **7.** 2,310,000. **8.** 624,000. **9.** 75,430,000.

Pages 248–249. **1.** 95. **2.** 15. **3.** 104. **4.** 35. **5.** 0. **6.** 32. **7.** 100. **8.** 212. **9.** no. **10.** Answers will vary.

Pages 250–252. **1.** 96. **2.** 21. **3.** 972. **4.** 22. **5.** 90. **6.** 300. **7.** 1008. **8.** 135. **9.** 17,280. **10.** 4. **11.** 6. **12.** 10. **13.** 2. **14.** 300. **15.** 109.4. **16.** 4. **17.** 5. **18.** 113°. **19.** 37.8°. **20.** 161. **21.** 50. **22.** 1580. **23.** 176. **24.** 5184. **25.** 24,579.55. **26.** 40′; 39′7″. **27.** 26,460; 28,297.5. **28.** $135; $139.20.

Page 253. **1.** 261. **2.** 1114. **3.** 22,063. **4.** 115.22. **5.** $12\frac{5}{8}$. **6.** $8\frac{3}{16}$. **7.** 21. **8.** 203.3. **9.** 17.24. **10.** $\frac{5}{14}$. **11.** $10\frac{7}{15}$. **12.** $28\frac{5}{8}$. **13.** 1012. **14.** 6820. **15.** 14.1264. **16.** .309168. **17.** $\frac{5}{22}$. **18.** $6\frac{9}{16}$. **19.** 42. **20.** 230. **21.** 3.75. **22.** 4.5. **23.** 2.62. **24.** 99,892. **25.** 2. **26.** $1\frac{1}{2}$. **27.** $\frac{9}{14}$. **28.** $\frac{46}{53}$. **29.** $1\frac{7}{10}$. **30.** $2\frac{9}{22}$.

Chapter 7. Geometric Constructions

Page 257. **1–4.** Follow procedure given on page 256 of the text.

Page 259. **1–3.** Follow procedures given on pages 257–259 of the text. **3.** l and m are parallel lines.

Page 261. **1–5.** Follow procedure given on page 260 and 261 of the text.

Pages 262–263. **1–5.** Follow procedure given on page 262 of the text.

Page 264. **1–2.** Follow procedures given on pages 263 and 264 of the text. **3.** See diagram at the top of page 265 of the text. *HJKM* is a square.

Page 266. **1–3.** Follow procedures given on pages 265 and 266 of the text.

Page 269. **1–6.** Follow procedures given on pages 268 and 269 of the text. **6. a.** right triangle. **b.** 2″.

Page 270. **1.** **2.**

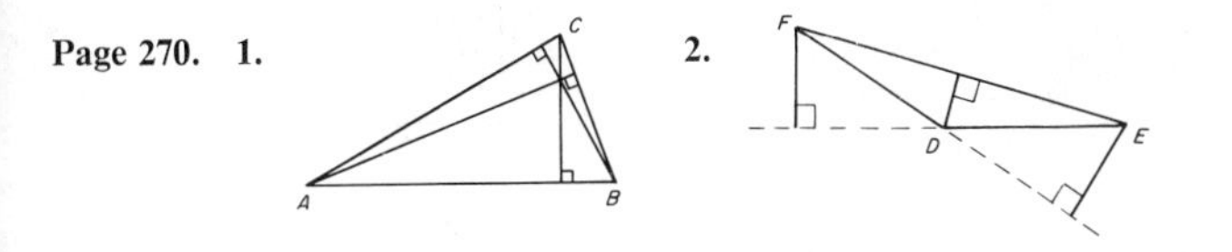

Page 271. **1–4.** Follow procedure given on page 271 of the text. The medians intersect at one point.

Page 272. **1.** Triangle should remain level. **2.** Triangle should remain level. **3.** Answers will vary. **4.** Answers will vary.

Page 273. **1–2.** Follow procedure given on page 272 of the text.

Page 275. (Top) **1.** Follow procedure given on page 273 of the text. **2.** and **4.** Follow procedure given at top of page 274 of the text. **3.** and **5.** Follow procedure given at bottom of page 274 of the text.

Page 275. (Bottom) **1.** and **2.** Follow procedure given on page 275 of the text.

Page 277. **1–4.** Follow procedure given on page 276 of the text. **5.** Follow procedure given on page 277 of the text.

Page 281. **1.** 8 in. **2.** $5\frac{3}{4}$ in.

Page 282. **1.** Follow procedures given on pages 256, 257, and 258 of the text. **2.** Follow procedures given on pages 258 and 259 of the text. **3.** Check your construction with a protractor. **4.** Follow procedure given on page 262 of the text. **5.** Follow procedure given on pages 265 and 266 of the text. **6.** Follow procedure given on page 268 of the text. **7.** Follow procedure given on pages 116 and 117 of the text. **8.** Follow procedure given on page 269 of the text. **9.** Follow procedure given on page 271 of the text.

Page 283. **1.** 115. **2.** 182. **3.** 790. **4.** 40,405. **5.** 767.7. **6.** 1070. **7.** 382. **8.** 278. **9.** 543. **10.** 236,809. **11.** 224.14. **12.** 580.81. **13.** 675. **14.** 2375. **15.** 3510. **16.** 44,213. **17.** 98.968. **18.** 0.768087. **19.** 22. **20.** 53. **21.** 0.0225. **22.** 00. **23.** $3\frac{1}{3}$. **24.** 20. **25.** 3. **26.** 4. **27.** 9 ft. 10 in. **28.** 10 ft. 7 in. **29.** 65 ft. 1 in. **30.** 13 ft. 11 in.

Chapter 8. Ratio and Proportion

Pages 286–287. **1.** $\frac{1}{2}$. **2.** $\frac{1}{3}$. **3.** $\frac{5}{6}$. **4.** $\frac{3}{7}$. **5.** $\frac{3}{4}$. **6.** $\frac{6}{1}$. **7.** $\frac{27}{8}$. **8.** $\frac{22}{3}$. **9.** $\frac{7}{1}$. **10.** $\frac{175}{3}$; $58\frac{1}{3}$ mph. **11.** 57:32 or 32:57. **12. a.** $\frac{8}{7}$. **b.** $\frac{7}{8}$.

Page 288. **1.** 0.0500 in. **2.** 0.0162 in. **3.** 24.06 threads per in. **4.** 11.01 threads per in. **5.** 32 threads per in. **6.** 0.03 in. **7.** 0.0139 in.

Page 290. **1.** 8. **2.** 6. **3.** 3. **4.** $9\frac{1}{3}$. **5.** $2\frac{2}{3}$. **6.** $1\frac{3}{7}$. **7.** 18. **8.** $17\frac{2}{7}$. **9.** 25. **10.** 6. **11.** 9. **12.** 16. **13.** 8. **14.** 1. **15.** 7.

Page 293. **1.** 151 lb. **2.** 5.4 in. **3.** 256 lb. **4.** 57 lb. **5.** 4001 lb. **6.** 1499 lb.

Pages 295–296. **1.** *a* and *c* are similar; *b* and *e* are similar; *d* and *f* are similar.

Pages 297–298. **1.**

BC
9″
$10\frac{1}{2}$″
12″
$13\frac{1}{2}$″
15″

BC increases $1\frac{1}{2}$″ when AB increases 3″. **2.**

AC
23.5″
26.8″
30.2″

3. $EF = 11\frac{2}{3}$. **4.** $AB = 8\frac{1}{3}$. **5.** $BC = 6\frac{3}{4}$. **6.** $20\frac{8}{11}$ ft. **7.** 720 yd.

Pages 300–301. **1.** $m = 12$; $n = 15$; $o = 18$. **2.** $x = 7\frac{1}{2}$; $y = 6$; $z = 7\frac{1}{2}$. **3.** $r = 2\frac{1}{2}$; $s = 3\frac{1}{2}$; $t = 2$. **4.** $x = 6$; $y = 6$; $z = 9$; $w = 2\frac{1}{4}$. **5. a.** A and B. **b.** $\frac{1}{3}$. **c.** $\frac{2}{3}$ and $\frac{5}{7}$; no. **d.** no.

Pages 304–306. **1.** 78 ft. by $37\frac{3}{8}$ ft. **2.** $31\frac{1}{2}$ ft. **3.** 90 in. **4.** 64 in. **5.** Each door is 16 in. **6.** 56 in. **7.** 10 ft. **8.** $52\frac{1}{2}$ ft. **9.** 324 in. by 144 in. **10.** 240 in. by $112\frac{1}{2}$ in. **11.** $189\frac{1}{16}$ sq. ft. **12.** living room: $360\frac{5}{16}$ sq. ft.; patio: $445\frac{5}{16}$ sq. ft. **13.** $206\frac{1}{4}$ sq. ft. **14.** 125 sq. ft. and $140\frac{5}{8}$ sq. ft. **15.** $471\frac{7}{8}$ sq. ft. **16.** $212\frac{1}{2}$ sq. ft. **17.** $618\frac{3}{4}$ sq. ft. **18.** $2718\frac{3}{4}$ sq. ft.

Pages 307–310. **1. a.** 1875 mi. **b.** $796\frac{7}{8}$ mi. **c.** $1218\frac{3}{4}$ mi. **d.** 750 mi. **2. a.** $2015\frac{5}{8}$ mi. **b.** $843\frac{3}{4}$ mi. **c.** $1453\frac{1}{8}$ mi. **d.** 750 mi. **3.** 180 mi. **4.** 30 mi. **5.** 90 mi. **6.** 165 mi. **7.** $82\frac{1}{2}$ mi. **8.** $232\frac{1}{2}$ mi. **9.** $172\frac{1}{2}$ mi. **10.** 120 mi. **11.** $127\frac{1}{2}$ mi. **12.** 120 mi. **13.** 285 mi.

Pages 312–314. **1.** $\frac{4}{13}$. **2.** $\frac{7}{1}$. **3.** $\frac{9}{16}$. **4.** $\frac{19}{8}$. **5.** 0.02165 in. **6.** true. **7.** false. **8.** false. **9.** true. **10.** 6. **11.** $3\frac{3}{25}$. **12.** 4. **13.** 399 lb. **14. a.** AC and D are similar. **b.** A and C—1:2 or 2:1; A and D—1:2 or 2:1; C and D—1:4 or 4:1. **15.** $X = 15$. **16.** $X = 21$; $Y = 9$; $Z = 21$. **17.** $24\frac{3}{20}$ ft. **18.** 20 in. **19.** $14\frac{1}{2}$ ft. **20.** $234\frac{3}{8}$ mi. **21.** $468\frac{3}{4}$ mi.; $562\frac{1}{2}$ mi. **22.** $5.78. **23.** 285 mi. **24.** 90 mi.

Page 315. **1.** 186. **2.** 190. **3.** 2142. **4.** 58,353. **5.** 502.99. **6.** 1374.70. **7.** 37. **8.** 339. **9.** 8.15. **10.** 22,666. **11.** 10.35. **12.** 2175. **13.** 2378. **14.** 8100. **15.** 128.0046. **16.** .335088. **17.** 1113.75. **18.** 18,887. **19.** 56. **20.** 27. **21.** 17. **22.** 35. **23.** 22.44. **24.** $305{,}086\frac{2}{3}$. **25.** $7\frac{5}{8}$. **26.** $9\frac{9}{16}$. **27.** $2\frac{4}{9}$. **28.** $1\frac{9}{16}$. **29.** $\frac{16}{39}$. **30.** 2.

Chapter 9. Percentage

Pages 318–319.

	A Common Fraction	B Decimal Fraction	C Percent
1.	$\frac{1}{2}$	.50	50%
2.	$\frac{1}{3}$	$.33\frac{1}{3}$	$33\frac{1}{3}$%
3.	$\frac{2}{3}$	$.66\frac{2}{3}$	$66\frac{2}{3}$%
4.	$\frac{1}{4}$	.25	25%
5.	$\frac{3}{4}$	.75	75%
6.	$\frac{1}{5}$	.20	20%
7.	$\frac{2}{5}$	.40	40%
8.	$\frac{3}{5}$	.60	60%
9.	$\frac{4}{5}$	.80	80%
10.	$\frac{1}{6}$	$.16\frac{2}{3}$	$16\frac{2}{3}$%

12. .70. **13.** .80. **14.** $.37\frac{1}{2}$. **15.** .30. **16.** .60. **17.** $\frac{1}{4}$. **18.** $\frac{3}{4}$. **19.** $\frac{1}{10}$. **20.** $\frac{4}{5}$. **21.** $\frac{5}{8}$. **22.** .20. **23.** .45. **24.** .70. **25.** $.33\frac{1}{3}$. **26.** $.12\frac{1}{2}$. **27.** $\frac{1}{5}$. **28.** $\frac{17}{100}$. **29.** $\frac{9}{10}$. **30.** $\frac{1}{8}$. **31.** $\frac{2}{3}$.

Page 323. **1.** 10. **2.** 20. **3.** 9. **4.** 7. **5.** 42. **6.** 100. **7.** 10.8. **8.** 360. **9.** 100. **10.** 108. **11.** 95. **12.** 260. **13.** 270. **14.** 336. **15.** 110. **16.** 49 bd. ft. **17.** 35 sq. in. **18.** 3060 rpm. **19.** 2.548 in. **20.** $23.20.

Page 324. **1.** $33\frac{1}{3}\%$. **2.** $83\frac{1}{3}\%$. **3.** 130%. **4.** 250%. **5. a.** $\frac{9}{10}$. **b.** 90%. **6.** 4860 watts. **7.** 75%. **8.** 23%.

Page 326. **1.** $22.00. **2.** $722.50. **3.** 7%. **4.** $7\frac{1}{2}\%$. **5.** $3500. **6.** 8%. **7.** $4\frac{1}{2}\%$. **8.** 7%. **9.** 6 yr. **10.** 3 yr.

Page 329. **1. a.** $486.68. **b.** $86.68. **2. a.** $2272.50. **b.** $472.50. **3. a.** $810.32. **b.** $110.32. **4. a.** $25,468.80. **b.** $1468.80. **5. a.** $12,562.80. **b.** $6562.80. **6. a.** $3116.00. **b.** $1116.00. **7. a.** $31,212.00. **b.** $1212.00. **8. a.** $117,280.80 **b.** $45,280.80. **9. a.** $574,437.50. **b.** $119,437.50. **10. a.** $3,998,700.00. **b.** $2,498,700.00. **11. a.** $238.82. **b.** $38.82. **12. a.** $112.62. **b.** $12.62. **13. a.** $1346.90. **b.** $346.90. **14. a.** $225.30. **b.** $25.30. **15.** $200 at 6% for 5 years compounded quarterly.

Page 331. **1. a.** $23.33. **b.** $559.92. **c.** $59.92. **d.** 11.13%. **2. a.** $93.33. **b.** $2239.92. **c.** $1959.93. **3. a.** $41.67. **b.** $59.96. **c.** $119.84. **d.** $59.88. **4.** 15.38%. **5.** 22.2%. **6.** $6\frac{2}{3}\%$.

Page 333. **1.** $480. **2.** $21.62. **3.** $12\frac{1}{2}\%$. **4.** $70. **5.** $2409. **6.** 28.57%.

Pages 334–335. **1.**

Cost	Net Cost
$29.25	$23.40
13.20	9.24
14.10	8.46
11.30	7.91
9.00	6.75

Total	55.76
3% discount	1.67
Net Total	$54.09

2.

Board feet	Cost	Net Cost
176	$15.84	$14.26
256	28.16	26.75
48	5.28	4.75
80	9.60	8.83
80	8.00	7.20
100	16.00	15.20
96	12.48	70.61

Total	$87.60
5% discount	4.38
Net Total	$83.22

Pages 337–338.

	Proper Fraction	Decimal Fraction	Percent
1.	$\frac{1}{4}$	.25	25%
2.	$\frac{2}{5}$	.40	40%
3.	$\frac{2}{3}$	$.66\frac{2}{3}$	$66\frac{2}{3}\%$
4.	$\frac{53}{100}$	.53	53%
5.	$\frac{7}{10}$	.70	70%
6.	$\frac{1}{8}$	$.12\frac{1}{2}$	$12\frac{1}{2}\%$
7.	$\frac{7}{8}$	$.87\frac{1}{2}$	$87\frac{1}{2}\%$
8.	$\frac{5}{6}$	$.83\frac{1}{3}$	$83\frac{1}{3}\%$
9.	$\frac{1}{3}$	$.33\frac{1}{3}$	$33\frac{1}{3}\%$
10.	$\frac{1}{12}$	$.08\frac{1}{3}$	$8\frac{1}{3}\%$

18.

Cost	Net Cost
$3.75	$3.00
3.30	2.31
9.00	6.75
9.60	8.16
8.75	7.00
6.00	4.20
3.60	2.34
2.70	2.16

Total	$35.92
2% discount	.72
Net Total	$35.20

11. $19,360. **12.** $54. **13. a.** 25%. **b.** 150%. **14.** $1920. **15.** $10,000. **16.** $129.30. **17.** 10.3%.

Page 339. **1.** 168. **2.** 251. **3.** 774. **4.** 34,403. **5.** $124\frac{1}{4}$. **6.** 820.78. **7.** 45. **8.** 244. **9.** 23.78. **10.** 8072. **11.** 26.48. **12.** 12,657. **13.** 1425. **14.** 13,365. **15.** 64.0792. **16.** .610236. **17.** 33,582.5. **18.** 22,967.4. **19.** $133\frac{4}{7}$. **20.** 56. **21.** 269. **22.** .0756. **23.** $\frac{43}{78}$. **24.** $7\frac{1}{2}$. **25.** 49. **26.** 81. **27.** 121. **28.** 2025. **29.** 8. **30.** 125.

Chapter 10. Right Triangles and Trigonometry

Pages 345–347. **1.** 13 ft. **2.** 8 in. **3.** $7\frac{1}{2}$ ft. **4.** 24 in. **5.** $\sqrt{240}$ in. **6.** $\sqrt{26.8}$ in. **7.** $\sqrt{45}$ in. **8.** $\sqrt{148.25}$ in. **9.** $\sqrt{141.3}$ in. **10.** BC = 15 in.; CD = 12 in. **11.** 14 ft. 2 in. **12.** 21 ft. 3 in. **13.** 2.828 in. **14.** CD = 6 in.; $BC = \sqrt{61}$ in.

Page 349. **1.** 8 in. **2.** 5 in. **3.** 6 in. **4.** $4\frac{13}{16}$ in. **5.** 10 in.

Page 352. **1.** $5\sqrt{3}$ in. **2.** $6\sqrt{3}$ in. **3.** $\frac{\sqrt{3}}{4}$ in. **4.** AB = 26 in.; $BC = 13\sqrt{3}$ in. **5.** $AC = 13\frac{1}{2}$ in.; $BC = \frac{27}{2}\sqrt{3}$ in.

Pages 354–356. **1.** 492 sq. ft. **2.** $\sqrt{48.25}$ ft. **3.** $245\sqrt{3}$ = 424.34 cu. in. **4.** 336.2 sq. ft. **5.** $1065\frac{3}{7}$ cu. ft. **6.** $1296\sqrt{3}$ = 2264.672 cu. ft. **7.** $420 + 130\sqrt{3}$ = 645.16 sq. in.

Page 360. **1.** $\cos A = \frac{8}{11}$. **2.** $\tan A = \frac{3}{7}$. **3.** $\sin A = \frac{6}{13}$. **4.** $b = 10 \cos 35°$. **5.** $a = 12 \sin 40°$.

Page 364. **1.** .6018. **2.** .6494. **3.** .6157. **4.** 3.2709. **5.** .4540. **6.** .9205. **7.** .7071. **8.** .6561. **9.** .5543. **10.** .9781. **11.** 5°. **12.** 11°. **13.** 41°. **14.** 39°. **15.** 33°. **16.** 61°. **17.** 72°. **18.** 88°. **19.** 25°. **20.** 3°.

Pages 367–368. **1.** 13.62 ft. **2.** 10 cm. **3.** 11.54 mi. **4.** 30°. **5.** 74°. **6.** 18.8 ft. **7.** 44.52 ft. **8.** 15°. **9.** 166.7 ft. **10.** 14°.

Pages 370–371. **1.** 8.870. **2.** 210.7. **3.** 32° 00′. **4.** 33° 20′. **5.** $\angle x$ = 31° 40′; $\angle y$ = 28° 30′.

Pages 372–374. **1.** 13. **2.** 6. **3.** 8. **4.** $\sqrt{85}$ = 9.22. **5.** $\sqrt{32\frac{1}{2}}$ = 5.7. **6.** $\sqrt{244}$ = 15.620. **7.** 14. **8.** 3. **9.** $11\sqrt{3}$. **10.** a = 22; c = 44. **11.** 40 sq. in. **12.** 1200 cu. in. **13.** 286.15 sq. ft. **14.** 216.5 cu. ft. **15. a.** .4848. **b.** .7221. **16. a.** 36°. **b.** 31°. **17.** 36.4 ft. **18.** 60°. **19.** 13.74 ft. **20.** 32° 00′.

Page 375. **1.** 145. **2.** 259. **3.** 771. **4.** 59,121. **5.** $137\frac{1}{2}$. **6.** 1612.21. **7.** 27. **8.** 287. **9.** 23.68. **10.** 5041. **11.** 28.43. **12.** 24,657. **13.** 2380. **14.** 21,384. **15.** 129.8610. **16.** .150866. **17.** 20,240.4. **18.** 25,371.2. **19.** 55. **20.** 775. **21.** 6.36. **22.** 80.31. **23.** $2\frac{2}{15}$. **24.** $10\frac{1}{16}$. **25.** 5. **26.** 9. **27.** 11. **28.** 15. **29.** 3.317. **30.** 5.196.

Chapter 11. Statistical Tables and Graphs

Page 379. **1.** 294. **2.** 831. **3.** 9.6%. **4.** .8%. **5.** 7.3%. **6.** 169:1000.

Pages 379–380. **1.** 169. **2.** 140. **3.** 82.8%. **4.** 13:1000. **5.** 16.9%. **6.** 780,000,000 barrels; 60,000,000 barrels. **7.** 140,000,000 barrels. **8.** 2,260,000,000 barrels. **9.** 1:3. **10.** 38%.

Pages 383–384. **1.** October; 30 cars. **2.** $12\frac{1}{2}$%. **3.** 2:5; 3:1. **4.** 71.4%. **5.** 1:12. **6.** $93,000. **7.** 6 ft. **8.** 37:22. **9.** 64.8%. **10.** 4.16 sec.; 6.03 sec.

Page 384. **1.** 80. **2.** 1475. **3.** 885. **4.** 1448.

Pages 386 and 387. **1.** 90.3%. **2.** 15:14. **3.** 11.6%. **4.** 30:1. **5.** 102. **6.** A. **7.** 95, 100, 90, 88, 94. **8.** 242. **9.** $89\frac{1}{3}$. **10.** $87\frac{8}{15}$.

Page 390. **1.** 41%. **2.** 44%. **3.** 1:3. **4.** 9:28. **5.** 47:41. **6.** $200 billion. **7.** 25%. **8.** $318.75. **9.** $293.25. **10.** 5:23. **11.** $51.00. **12.** $41.44.

Pages 392–394. **1. a.** 680. **b.** $7\frac{1}{2}$%. **c** 51.5%. **d.** 1:35. **2. a.** 1800 items. **b.** 2:13. **c.** 27.8%. **d.** $55.00. **3. a.** 1175 sets. **b.** 8:3. **c.** 31.9%. **d.** $19,500. **4. a.** $80.00. **b.** 15%. **c.** 9:17. **d.** $13.33; October's. **5. a.** 50%. **b.** 3,190,000. **c.** 2,310,000. **d.** 25:29.